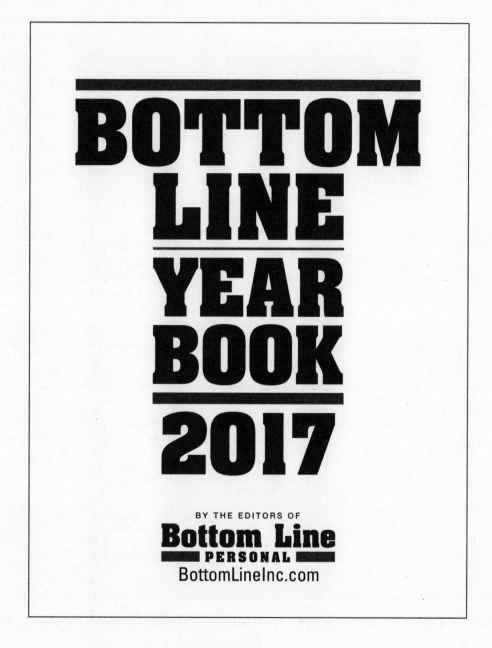

BOTTOM LINE YEAR BOOK 2017

BY THE EDITORS OF

Bottom Line
PERSONAL

BottomLineInc.com

Contents

PART TWO: YOUR MONEY

7 • MONEYWISE

14 • HAVING SOME FUN

PART FIVE: YOUR LIFE

15 • ON THE ROAD

16 • FAMILY TIME

17 • AROUND THE HOUSE

Preface

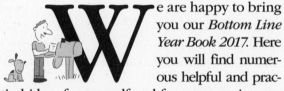**W**e are happy to bring you our *Bottom Line Year Book 2017*. Here you will find numerous helpful and practical ideas for yourself and for everyone in your family.

At Bottom Line Books, it is our mission to provide all of our readers with the best information to help them gain better health, greater wealth, more wisdom, extra time and increased happiness.

The *Year Book 2017* represents the very best and the most useful Bottom Line articles from the past year. Whether you are looking for ways to get the most from your money or how to get your business noticed…boost your heart health naturally or avoid misdiagnosis at the doctor…have a better relationship with your adult children or deal with those difficult people in your life, you'll find it all in this book…and a whole lot more.

Over the past 36 years, we have built a network of thousands of expert sources.

When you consult the *2017 Year Book*, you are accessing a stellar group of authorities in fields that range from natural and conventional medicine…to shopping, investing, taxes and insurance…to cars, travel, security and self-improvement. Our advisers are affiliated with the premier universities, financial institutions, law firms and hospitals. These experts are truly among the most knowledgeable people in the country.

As a reader of a Bottom Line book, you can be assured that you are receiving reliable, well-researched and up-to-date information from a trusted source.

We are very confident that the *Bottom Line Year Book 2017* can help you and your family have a healthier, wealthier, wiser life. Enjoy!

The Editors, *Bottom Line Personal*
Stamford, CT

1

Health News

Stop a Heart Attack *Before* It Happens: These Subtle Signs Could Save Your Life

Chest pain…feeling faint…shortness of breath…discomfort in your arm—or even in your neck, jaw or back. If you are overcome by such symptoms and perhaps even have an intense and sudden "sense of doom," you're likely to suspect a heart attack and rush to a hospital.

But wouldn't it be better to get a heads-up *beforehand* that a heart attack is on the way?

What most people don't realize: For about 60% of heart attack victims, warning symptoms *do* occur days or even weeks before the actual heart attack. But all too often, these signs are missed or shrugged off as something trivial.

What's behind this early-warning system? The blockage that creates a heart attack often develops over time and its symptoms, though they may be mild and elusive, should *not* be ignored.

Knowing the early red flags—including those you might not immediately connect to a heart problem—can allow you to see a doctor before a life-threatening heart attack occurs. Women, especially, can have symptoms that do not immediately bring heart disease to mind.

Important: If these symptoms are extreme and last for more than a few minutes—especially if they are accompanied by any of the more typical symptoms such as those described above—call 911. You could be having an actual heart attack. Even if these symptoms

John A. Elefteriades, MD, the William W.L. Glenn Professor of Surgery and director of the Aortic Institute at Yale University and Yale–New Haven Hospital. He serves on the editorial boards of *The American Journal of Cardiology, Journal of Cardiac Surgery, Cardiology* and *The Journal of Thoracic and Cardiovascular Surgery* and is author of several books, including *Your Heart: An Owner's Guide.* HeartAuthorMD.com are mild to moderate but seem unexplained, call your doctor. If he/she cannot be reached but you're still concerned, go to the emergency room.

The following are examples of the subtle symptoms that can precede a heart attack—sometimes by days or weeks...

•**Fatigue.** If you feel more tired than usual, it's easy to tell yourself you're just growing older or getting out of shape. But pay attention! It could be the early-warning sign of heart trouble.

If your usual daily activities, whether it's walking the dog or cleaning the house, leave you feeling more tired than normal, talk to your doctor.

•**Flulike symptoms.** If you get hit with extreme fatigue, as well as weakness and/or feelings of light-headedness, you may think you're coming down with the flu. But people report having these same symptoms prior to a heart attack.

Call your doctor if you experience flulike symptoms but no fever (a telltale flu symptom).

Another clue: The flu generally comes on quickly, while flulike symptoms associated with heart disease may develop gradually.

•**Nausea and/or indigestion.** These are among the most overlooked symptoms of a heart attack—perhaps because they are typically due to gastrointestinal problems.

But if you are feeling sick to your stomach and throwing up, it could be a heart attack rather than food poisoning or some other stomach problem—especially if you're also sweating and your skin has turned an ashen color. If indigestion comes and goes, does *not* occur after a meal or doesn't improve within a day or so—especially if you're using antacids or antinausea medication—this could also mean heart problems. See a doctor.

•**Excessive perspiration.** If you are sweating more than usual—especially during times when you're not exerting yourself—it could mean that there are blockages. This can cause your heart to work harder, which may lead to excessive sweating. See your doctor. Clammy skin and night sweats also can be warning signs. This is likely to be a cold sweat, instead of the heat experienced in menopausal hot flashes. If sweating occurs with any of the classic heart attack symptoms described above, don't think twice—call 911.

•**Shortness of breath.** If you notice that you are beginning to feel more winded than normal, see your doctor. Shortness of breath can be a precursor to heart attack. If shortness of breath becomes stronger or lasts longer than usual, call 911. Shortness of breath may be your only symptom of a heart attack and may occur while you are resting or doing only minor physical activity.

•**Sexual dysfunction.** Men with heart problems that can lead to heart attack often have trouble achieving and/or keeping an erection. Because poor blood flow to the penis can be a sign of possible blockages elsewhere in the body, including the heart, erectile dysfunction can be an early-warning sign to get checked for cardiovascular disease. Men should absolutely discuss this symptom with their doctors.

WOMEN, PAY ATTENTION!

After a woman goes through menopause—when the body's production of heart-protective estrogen declines—her risk for a heart attack dramatically increases.

Important facts for women: More women die of heart disease each year than men. Nearly two-thirds of women who died from heart attacks had no history of chest pain. The higher death rate for women is likely due to the fact that women don't seek medical attention as promptly as men because they are afraid of being embarrassed if the symptoms turn out to be nothing serious. Don't let this fear stop you from seeking immediate care. If the symptoms turn out to be nothing serious, the emergency medical team will be happy!

Some women don't call 911 when they are having a heart attack because they don't recognize the symptoms.

What to watch for: While most (but not all) men experience crushing or squeezing chest pain (usually under the breastbone), women are more likely to have no chest pain (or simply a feeling of "fullness" in the chest). Also, women are more likely than men to suffer dizziness, shortness of breath and/or nausea as the main symptoms of heart attack. Most women (71%) experience sudden onset of extreme weakness that feels like the flu.

4 Must-Have Heart Tests: They Are Truly Lifesaving

Joel K. Kahn, MD, a clinical professor of medicine at Wayne State University School of Medicine in Detroit and founder of the Kahn Center for Cardiac Longevity in Bloomfield Hills, Michigan. He is also an associate professor at Oakland University William Beaumont School of Medicine in Rochester, Michigan, and author of *The Whole Heart Solution*. DrJoelKahn.com

Heart disease is tricky. Like other "silent" conditions, such as high blood pressure and kidney disease, you may not know that you have it until you're doubled over from a heart attack.

That's because traditional methods of assessing patients for heart disease, such as cholesterol tests and blood pressure measurements, along with questions about smoking and other lifestyle factors, don't always tell a patient's whole story.

Shocking finding: In a recent study, doctors followed nearly 6,000 men and women (ages 55 to 88) who had been deemed healthy by standard heart tests for three years and then gave them basic imaging tests.

Result: 60% were found to have atherosclerosis. These study participants were eight times more likely to suffer a heart attack or stroke, compared with subjects without this fatty buildup (plaque) in the arteries.

THE MUST-HAVE TESTS

Below are four simple tests that can catch arterial damage at the earliest possible stage—when it can still be reversed and before it has a chance to cause a heart attack or stroke.

My advice: Even though doctors don't routinely order these tests, everyone over age 50 should have them at least once—and sometimes more often, depending on the findings. Smokers and people with diabetes, very high

cholesterol levels (more than 300 mg/dL) and/or a family history of heart disease should have these tests before age 50. *Having these tests can literally save your life…*

•**Coronary calcium computed tomography (CT) scan.** This imaging test checks for calcium deposits in the arteries—a telltale sign of atherosclerosis. People who have little or no calcium in the arteries (a score of zero) have less than a 5% risk of having a heart attack over the next three to five years. The risk is twice as high in people with a score of one to 10…and *more than nine times higher* in those with scores above 400.

While the American College of Cardiology recommends this test for people who haven't been diagnosed with heart disease but have known risk factors, such as high blood pressure and/or a family history of heart disease, I advise everyone to have this test at about age 50.* The test takes only 10 to 15 minutes and doesn't require the injection of a contrast agent.

Cost: $99 and up, which may be covered by insurance.

I use the calcium score as a onetime test. Unless they abandon their healthy habits, people who have a score of zero are unlikely to develop *arterial calcification* later in life. Those who do have deposits will know what they have to do—exercise, eat a more health-

*People already diagnosed with heart disease and/or who have had a stent or bypass surgery do not need the coronary calcium CT.

ful diet, manage cholesterol and blood pressure, etc.

One drawback, however, is radiation exposure. Even though the dose is low (much less than you'd get during cardiac catheterization, for example), you should always limit your exposure.

My advice: Choose an imaging center with the fastest CT machine. A faster machine (a 256-slice CT, for example) gives less radiation exposure than, say, a 64-slice machine.

• **Carotid intima-media thickness (CIMT).** The *intima* and *media* are the innermost linings of blood vessels. Their combined thickness in the carotid arteries in the neck is affected by how much plaque is present. Thickening of these arteries can indicate increased risk for stroke and heart attack.

The beauty of this test is that it's performed with ultrasound. There's no radiation, it's fast (10 minutes) and it's painless. I often recommend it as a follow-up to the coronary calcium test or as an alternative for people who want to avoid the radiation of the coronary calcium CT.

The good news is that you can decrease CIMT—with a more healthful diet, increased exercise and the use of statin medications. Pomegranate—the whole fruit, juice or a supplement—can reduce carotid plaque, too. In addition, research has found Kyolic "aged" garlic (the product brand studied) and vitamin K-2 to also be effective.

Cost: $250 to $350. It may not be covered by insurance.

• **Advanced lipid test.** Traditional cholesterol tests are less helpful than experts once thought—particularly because more than 50% of heart attacks occur in patients with normal LDL "bad" cholesterol levels.

Experts have now identified a number of cholesterol subtypes that aren't measured by standard tests. The *advanced lipid test* (also known as an expanded test) still measures total cholesterol and LDL but also looks at the amounts and sizes of different types of cholesterol.

Suppose that you have a normal LDL reading of 100 mg/dL. You still might have an elevated risk for a heart attack if you happen to have a high number of small, dense LDL particles (found in an advanced LDL particle test), since they can more easily enter the arterial wall.

My advice: Get the advanced lipid test at least once after age 50. It usually costs $39 and up and may be covered by insurance.

If your readings look good, you can switch to a standard cholesterol test every few years. If the numbers are less than ideal, talk to your doctor about treatment options, which might include statins or niacin, along with lifestyle changes. Helpful supplements include omega-3 fatty acids, vitamin E and plant sterols.

• **High-sensitivity C-reactive protein (hs-CRP).** This simple blood test has been available for years, but it's not used as often as it should be. Elevated C-reactive protein indicates inflammation in the body, including in the blood vessels. Data from the Physicians' Health Study found that people with elevated CRP were about three times more likely to have a heart attack than those with normal levels.

If you test low (less than 1 mg/L) or average (1 mg/L to 3 mg/L), you can repeat the test every few years. If your CRP is high (above 3 mg/L), I recommend repeating the test at least once a year. It's a good way to measure any progress you may be making from taking medications (such as statins, which reduce inflammation), improving your diet and getting more exercise.

Cost: About $50. It is usually covered by insurance.

Why Donating Blood Is Good for Your Health

People with type A, B or AB blood are at a higher risk for heart attacks and strokes because individuals with these blood types have higher levels of coagulation proteins that increase the risk for blood clots. Regular blood donation may decrease these protein levels and possibly the risk for vascular disease. People with thicker blood (higher red-blood-cell counts)—typically men—could see improvements in their circulation with frequent blood donation at safe intervals.

Phillip J. DeChristopher, MD, PhD, a professor of pathology and medicine at Loyola University Health System, Maywood, Illinois.

Are Your Blood Pressure Readings Fooling You?

Samuel J. Mann, MD, a hypertension specialist and professor of clinical medicine at New York-Presbyterian Hospital/Weill-Cornell Medical College in New York City. Dr. Mann has written more than 50 scientific articles and book chapters about hypertension. He is also author of *Hypertension and You: Old Drugs, New Drugs and the Right Drugs for Your High Blood Pressure.*

When your blood pressure is taken at the doctor's office, it is very good news when it's normal. But a growing body of scientific evidence now shows that these readings may be giving you only part of the picture.

Recent finding: Studies have reported that about 10% to 20% of people who have normal blood pressure in a doctor's office actually have elevated blood pressure when outside the doctor's office—a condition known as *masked hypertension.*

Why this is important: Like traditional hypertension (140/90 mmHg or higher), masked hypertension increases risk for coronary artery disease and stroke. In fact, people with masked hypertension may face even more risk because they don't know they have it—leaving them without a diagnosis or the necessary treatment. *What you need to know...*

HYPERTENSION AT HOME

Many people have heard of *white-coat hypertension,* the surge in blood pressure that occurs at medical offices when otherwise healthy people see a doctor and get their pressure tested. The theory behind this is that blood pressure rises because you're anxious about having it measured.

Masked hypertension poses a different challenge. Because there's no evidence of high blood pressure at the doctor's office, blood pressure can remain elevated and untreated if it is not checked at home in those who have this condition.

How then can you tell if you have masked hypertension and need to be treated? Should everyone check his/her blood pressure at home, even if it was normal at the doctor's office?

Watching for the danger zone: If your office systolic (top number) blood pressure reading is less than 120, you're not likely to develop hypertension in the near future, since studies show that few people in this range have elevated pressure at home.

But if it is in the 130s, particularly in people under the age of 60, it would be considered borderline hypertension (also called prehypertension) and needs to be followed—both at home and in the doctor's office. Most masked hypertension is actually borderline hypertension, a warning sign that you may need to improve your diet, get more exercise, lose weight and reduce excessive sodium intake.

The risk: Research has found that patients with masked hypertension have more than twice the cardiovascular risk—including risk for heart attack and atherosclerosis—as patients with normal blood pressure. Meanwhile, a recent study presented at an annual meeting of the American Society of Hypertension found that the risk for cognitive dysfunction in people with untreated masked hypertension was twice as high as for those who had controlled hypertension.

Of course, everyone's blood pressure does naturally vary, depending on age, activity levels, stress and other factors. That's why doctors should take at least two or three office readings, during separate appointments, before diagnosing traditional hypertension.

For a more complete picture, your physician might ask you to also take home readings (see below for details) to better assess your blood pressure and check for masked hypertension.

DO YOU NEED HOME-TESTING?

If your systolic readings are in the 130s in the doctor's office, talk to your doctor about at-home blood pressure monitoring.

The main options for home blood pressure testing are either ambulatory or self-monitoring. Ambulatory monitoring, in which you wear a blood pressure monitor for 24 hours, provides a more reliable picture of your blood pressure and is considered a better predictor of cardiovascular risk than office measurements.

Self-monitoring allows you to check your blood pressure over time. *To get the most accurate readings when self-monitoring, be sure to follow these tips…*

• **Don't check every day.** I tell patients *not* to check their blood pressure every day. It can become an obsession that can even affect your blood pressure readings. Your doctor can guide you on how often to check, depending on your readings and overall health. People with severe hypertension (frequent systolic readings of 160 or higher) or who have recently changed medications and/or doses may need to check their pressure more often until it is stable.

• **Use an arm cuff.** It's more reliable than a wrist or finger device. I recommend Omron automated blood pressure monitors, which hypertension specialists consider to be reliable. Depending on the device, the cost can range from about $50 to $110.

What to do: Put the cuff in place with the bottom of the cuff about one-half to one inch above the elbow crease, then sit and relax for five minutes.

Next, take three readings a minute or so apart to obtain your resting blood pressure. Because the first reading can be unreliable, I recommend averaging the other two. As long as your doctor has found that your blood pressure is about the same in both arms, you need to check only one arm.

• **Test at different times of day.** It will help you get a sense of what your usual blood pressure is. However, you don't want to test immediately upon awakening. Blood pressure is commonly elevated when you first wake up, so wait half an hour or so.

Also important: Keep a written or digital record of your readings, and share them with your doctor. If your systolic blood pressure average is 135 or higher, your doctor may want to begin treatment with medication…and should also talk to you about better diet and exercise habits.

BLOOD PRESSURE ALERT...

Bad Sign: Big Swings in Blood Pressure

Big variations in blood pressure increase risk for cardiovascular disease.

Recent finding: People whose systolic pressure (top number) varies by more than 14 mm Hg between one doctor visit and the next are 46% more likely to have a stroke and 30% more likely to have a heart attack or fatal coronary artery disease.

Theory: Big swings may indicate stiff arteries.

Paul Muntner, PhD, vice chair and professor of epidemiology at University of Alabama at Birmingham and leader of a study of 25,814 patients, published in *Annals of Internal Medicine*.

Beta-Blocker Warning

People taking beta-blockers for high blood pressure are more likely to have complications such as heart attack or stroke within 30 days after noncardiac surgery. If you are scheduled for noncardiac surgery, ask your doctor if you should switch to a different blood pressure drug or temporarily stop taking medication before surgery. Never stop taking a blood pressure drug on your own. Beta-blockers include drugs such as *metoprolol* (Lopressor), *nadolol* (Corgard) and *propranolol* (Inderal).

Mads Emil Jørgensen, MB, a researcher at Copenhagen University Hospital Gentofte, Hellebæk, Denmark, and leader of a study published in *JAMA Internal Medicine*.

The Ugly Truth About Statins: What the Research Now Says

Barbara H. Roberts, MD, director of the Women's Cardiac Center at The Miriam Hospital and a clinical associate professor of medicine at Alpert Medical School of Brown University, both in Providence. She is author of *The Truth About Statins: Risks and Alternatives to Cholesterol-Lowering Drugs.*

Under recent controversial guidelines from the American Heart Association, nearly half of all American adults between the ages of 40 and 75 would be advised to take a cholesterol-lowering statin drug. This class of drugs includes *simvastatin* (Zocor), *atorvastatin* (Lipitor), *rosuvastatin* (Crestor) and others. About 25% of adults are taking a statin now.

Statins do an impressive job of lowering LDL "bad" cholesterol—by up to 50% in some cases. How well do they achieve the real goal of reducing the risk for heart attacks? That evidence isn't impressive. And statins can have serious side effects.

IS LDL REALLY THE ENEMY?

For decades, the public-health message has not changed. High cholesterol—particularly high levels of LDL cholesterol—leads to atherosclerosis, blood clots and heart attacks.

Yet many important studies, including the Framingham Heart Study, have shown that most patients who have had a heart attack have cholesterol levels that are nearly identical to those who haven't. Further, many experts believe that HDL "good" cholesterol is a more important predictor of heart disease than LDL.

Statins can lower the risk for recurrent heart attack by a small amount in people who already have had one. But most studies of statins have not shown a reduction in mortality. And way too often, they're used for primary prevention—to lower LDL in those who haven't been diagnosed with heart disease.

In people who haven't been diagnosed with cardiovascular disease, the use of statins reduced the risk for heart attacks and other cardiovascular events by a paltry 1% to 2%.

SERIOUS SIDE EFFECTS

Statins are not the benign drugs that they're made out to be. About 20% to 25% of patients experience side effects, some of which are serious. For example, statins reduce blood levels of CoQ10, which is involved in energy production inside cells. Low CoQ10 has been linked to heart failure, hypertension, fatigue and "mental fog."

The most common side effect of statin therapy is *myalgia,* or muscle pain. The pain usually is mild, but the risk—and severity—increases at higher doses. *Rhabdomyolysis* is a severe form of statin-related muscle damage that can lead to kidney failure, which can be fatal.

Side effects are an acceptable trade-off when drugs truly save lives. This isn't the case for the vast majority of patients who take statins.

Two exceptions: If you have high LDL and have had a heart attack…or if you've been diagnosed with cardiovascular disease (or diabetes if you are a man), a statin can make sense. I also recommend statins to patients who have *familial hypercholesterolemia,* sky-high cholesterol caused by a genetic abnormality.

A BETTER APPROACH

I advise most patients to work on their diets before resorting to statins. *Dietary changes can increase HDL and reduce triglycerides, which is more important than reducing LDL…*

• **Mediterranean diet.** The Lyon Diet Heart Study showed conclusively that heart attack patients who followed a Mediterranean-type diet (more whole grains, vegetables, fruit and fish, and less beef, lamb and pork, among other factors) greatly improve their odds of never having another heart attack. Compared with those who followed a "prudent" Western diet, they were 56% less likely to die from any cause…65% less likely to suffer cardiac death… and 70% less likely to have a heart attack.

You might assume patients in the Mediterranean diet group had lower LDL. Not so. Their LDL was roughly the same as that of people in the control group—further proof that you don't need to reduce LDL to improve cardiovascular risks. For more on the Mediterranean diet, read my book or the book *Low-Fat Lies, High-Fat Frauds and the Healthiest Diet in the World* by Kevin Vigilante, MD, MPH, and Mary Flynn, PhD.

Why was the Mediterranean diet so effective? Some credit goes to olive oil and fish (see below) and antioxidant-rich fruits and vegetables, which reduce inflammation and blood clots. The diet also is low in *pro-inflammatory* omega-6 fatty acids (from corn and other vegetable-based oils) and high in fiber.

• **More olive oil.** Extra-virgin olive oil is rich in phytochemicals, many of which inhibit oxidation. Oxidized cholesterol increases atherosclerosis and the "stiffening" of arteries that leads to higher blood pressure. Olive oil also has been shown to increase HDL.

I advise patients with low HDL to have three to four tablespoons of olive oil daily in addition to the small amounts that are used in cooking. Use it in salad dressings, or drizzle it on fish or poultry.

• **Don't worry about saturated fat.** Patients with high cholesterol usually are advised to consume less saturated fat. It's true that saturated fat raises LDL—but only the "fluffy" LDL particles that are largely benign. Saturated fat, such as dairy fat, is an effective way to increase HDL. There's some evidence that the saturated fat found in milk and other dairy foods reduces diabetes risk.

• **Seafood a few times a week.** In parts of the world where people eat a lot of fatty fish (such as salmon and tuna), the risk for cardiovascular disease tends to be lower. The omega-3 fatty acids in fish reduce triglycerides and inflammation.

• **Enjoy your wine.** Moderate drinking (no more than two drinks a day for men and one for women) has been shown to reduce the risk for heart disease. Red wine may be particularly helpful because it is high in antioxidants.

• **Be wary of "white" foods**—simple carbohydrates such as white bread, white rice, white pasta and some breakfast cereals. These are essentially sugar and cause a surge of insulin, which increases the risk for cardiovascular disease. Insulin also increases fat storage, particularly in the abdomen. Abdominal fat is a leading risk factor for heart disease.

BETTER WAY...

How to Avoid "Statin Brain"

Statins can cause memory loss in some patients, despite a recent study that found they don't have cognitive side effects. The study was a generalized statistical study—not a personalized look at vulnerable patients. Some people who are susceptible do have "statin brain." Symptoms stop when the drug is stopped. These patients should talk to their doctors. Anyone considering starting a statin should ask about every-other-day rather than daily dosing.

Linda L. Restifo, MD, PhD, professor in the department of neurology at University of Arizona, Tucson.

• **Do not forget to exercise.** You already know the importance of regular exercise, but it is worth repeating. Everyone should get at least 150 minutes of moderate-intensity exercise a week with brisk walking, biking, swimming, etc. It is among the best ways to lower the risk for diabetes, hypertension and heart disease.

What to Do Before You Take Statins...

Consider having a heart scan before starting to take statins. A *coronary artery calcium* test looks for signs of plaque in the heart—a significant risk factor for heart attack. Patients with a zero calcium score may choose to forgo statins and instead control cardiac risk through lifestyle changes.

The coronary artery test uses low-dose radiation—about as much as a mammogram—and typically costs about $100. It generally is not covered by insurance.

Khurram Nasir, MD, MPH, director of Healthcare Advancements & Outcomes at Baptist Health South Florida, Miami Beach, and lead author of a study published in *Journal of the American College of Cardiology*.

The Aspirin Question: Too Many People Are Making the *Wrong* Choice

Randall S. Stafford, MD, PhD, a professor of medicine at the Stanford Prevention Research Center and the director of the Program on Prevention Outcomes and Practices, both at the Stanford School of Medicine in Palo Alto, California. Dr. Stafford is a member of the Council on Aspirin for Health and Prevention and a leading developer of the content for The Aspirin Project, its educational program (AspirinProject.org). He also is author or coauthor of more than 170 scientific publications.

It seems harmless enough…popping an aspirin from that familiar little bottle tucked away in your medicine cabinet.

In fact, millions of Americans take an aspirin every day as a blood thinner to help prevent the artery-clogging blood clots that cause most heart attacks and strokes. But for many of these people, aspirin is doing more harm than good.

Recent finding: In a study of 68,800 adults taking daily aspirin therapy for heart attack and/or stroke prevention, nearly 12% were doing so unnecessarily based on their limited chances of actually suffering from one of these conditions over the next decade. In doing so, these individuals were found to be *increasing* their risk for potentially dangerous side effects, such as internal bleeding, for no good reason.

A tragic toll: Among the more than 16,000 deaths each year linked to bleeding associated with use of nonsteroidal anti-inflammatory drugs (NSAIDs), about one-third of these deaths occur in those who take low-dose (81-milligram) aspirin.

IS ASPIRIN RIGHT FOR YOU?

You may assume from these frightening statistics that aspirin is *never* worth the risk, but that would be a mistake. Whether you're trying to prevent a heart attack, stroke or cancer, to make the best decision about using aspirin, you and your doctor need to weigh *your* potential benefits against *your* potential harms and then make a choice based on your preferences. *When aspirin use may help…*

HEART ATTACK OR STROKE

If you've already had coronary bypass surgery, a heart attack or ischemic stroke (caused by a blood clot), taking aspirin and/or another blood-thinning drug, such as *clopidogrel* (Plavix) or *warfarin* (Coumadin), is wise. That's because study after study shows that aspirin significantly reduces the risk for a *second* heart attack or stroke. (A person whose risk for bleeding is extremely high may be an exception.)

If your goal is to prevent a *first* heart attack or stroke, the decision is a bit more complicated. Guidelines from the American Heart Association (AHA) and the US Preventive Services Task Force recommend aspirin for primary prevention in people at high risk for cardiovascular disease. In 2014, the FDA weighed in, releasing a statement that warned against widespread use in people of average risk.

My advice: I advise some—but not all—of my male patients who are over age 45 to take aspirin for primary prevention. For women, I recommend aspirin for most who are age 65 and older. There are exceptions, especially for those who are at high risk for bleeding. Meanwhile, men and women younger than these ages sometimes have enough risk factors for heart attack and stroke that they will benefit from aspirin.

Scientific evidence: An analysis of multiple studies published in *The Journal of the American Medical Association* that involved nearly 100,000 people showed that daily aspirin can decrease heart attacks in men age 45 and older by 32%. In women, research has found that the greatest benefit—for reduction in ischemic stroke and heart attack—occurs for those age 65 and older.

What's my criteria for recommending aspirin? If the patient's chance of having a heart attack or stroke in the next 10 years is higher than 5% to 10%.

To determine your heart attack and stroke risk: Use the cardiovascular disease (CVD) "risk calculator" created by the American College of Cardiology and the AHA. To download the calculator onto your computer or an app onto your smartphone, go to My.AmericanHeart. org (under "Guidelines & Statements," click on "Prevention Guidelines").

If your risk is above 5% to 10%, talk to your doctor about whether you should be taking aspirin.

Important: Once you have your result from the risk calculator, you must balance your potential benefit from taking aspirin to prevent a heart attack or stroke against possible harm. Have you had gastrointestinal (GI) bleeding in the past? Are you regularly taking another anti-inflammatory medicine such as *ibuprofen* (Motrin), which also increases your risk for GI bleeding?

Are you age 80 or over? Aspirin might help you, but there's no solid evidence to guide your decision. Nonetheless, older adults have the most to gain from aspirin, but need to be particularly careful to avoid bleeding problems.

PREVENTING CANCER

In weighing your decision to take aspirin for heart attack and stroke, you also may want to take into account recent research showing that aspirin may help prevent cancer—and perhaps even extend the lives of people who have had a malignancy.

Landmark findings: When researchers at the University of Oxford analyzed dozens of studies on aspirin, they found that regular use of the medicine may help prevent cancer—with a 38% reduction in the risk for colon cancer and similar reductions in breast, esophageal and stomach cancers.

Note: There is some debate about whether low-dose aspirin is always enough, and it appears to take years of aspirin use to see a reduction in risk.

According to a study published in 2014 in *Anticancer Research*, regular aspirin takers who had colon cancer were 60% less likely to have a recurrence or to die from the disease than colon cancer patients who weren't taking aspirin. Researchers theorize that cancer cells may spread throughout the body behind a protective shield of platelets—and aspirin may disrupt that process.

What this means for you: If you're a man over age 45 or a woman over age 65…and con-

sidering taking aspirin for primary prevention of a heart attack or stroke…and your risk for cardiovascular disease is "borderline" (around a 5% chance of having a heart attack or stroke in the next 10 years, according to the calculator)—your desire to prevent cancer (particularly colon cancer) may tip the scales in favor of regular use of low-dose aspirin.

With this level of evidence, however, no one should take daily, low-dose aspirin *solely* for the purpose of preventing cancer.

Stroke: You Can Do *Much More* to Protect Yourself

Ralph L. Sacco, MD, chairman of neurology, the Olemberg Family Chair in Neurological Disorders and the Miller Professor of Neurology, Epidemiology and Public Health, Human Genetics and Neurosurgery at the Miller School of Medicine at the University of Miami, where he is the executive director of the Evelyn McKnight Brain Institute. He is also the chief of the Neurology Service at Jackson Memorial Hospital and the 2014 recipient of the American Heart Association's Cor Vitae Stroke Award.

No one likes to think about having a stroke. But maybe you should. *The grim reality:* Stroke strikes about 800,000 Americans each year and is the leading cause of disability.

Now for the remarkable part: About 80% of strokes can be prevented. You may think that you've heard it all when it comes to preventing strokes—it's about controlling your blood pressure, eating a good diet and getting some exercise, right? Actually, that's only part of what you can be doing to protect yourself. *Surprising recent findings on stroke—and the latest advice on how to avoid it…*

• **Even "low" high blood pressure is a red flag.** High blood pressure—a reading of 140/90 mmHg or higher—is widely known to increase one's odds of having a stroke. But even *slight* elevations in blood pressure may also be a problem.

An important recent study that looked at data from more than half a million patients found that those with blood pressure readings that were just slightly higher than a normal reading of 120/80 mmHg were more likely to have a stroke.

Any increase in blood pressure is worrisome. In fact, the risk for a stroke or heart attack doubles for each 20-point rise in systolic (the top number) pressure above 115/75 mmHg—and for each 10-point rise in diastolic (the bottom number) pressure.

My advice: Don't wait for your doctor to advise treatment if your blood pressure is even a few points higher than normal. Be sure to *tell* him/her that you are concerned. Lifestyle changes—such as getting adequate exercise, avoiding too much alcohol and maintaining a healthful diet—often reverse slightly elevated blood pressure. However, blood pressure that's consistently above 140/90 mmHg generally requires medication.

•**Sleep can be dangerous.** People who are sleep deprived—generally defined as getting less than six hours of sleep per night—are at increased risk for stroke.

What most people don't realize is that getting *too much* sleep is also a problem. When researchers at the University of Cambridge tracked the sleep habits of nearly 10,000 people over a 10-year period, they found that those who slept more than eight hours a night were 46% more likely to have a stroke than those who slept six to eight hours.

It is possible that people who spend less/more time sleeping have other, unrecognized conditions that affect both sleep and stroke risk.

Example: Sleep apnea, a breathing disorder that interferes with sleep, causes an increase in blood pressure that can lead to stroke. Meanwhile, sleeping too much can be a symptom of depression—another stroke risk factor.

My advice: See a doctor if you tend to wake up unrefreshed...are a loud snorer...or often snort or thrash while you sleep. You may have sleep apnea. If you sleep too much, also talk to your doctor to see if you are suffering from depression or some other condition that may increase your stroke risk.

What's the sweet spot for nightly shut-eye? When it comes to stroke risk, it's six to eight hours per night.

•**What you drink matters, too.** A Mediterranean-style diet—plenty of whole grains, legumes, nuts, fish, produce and olive oil—is perhaps the best diet going when it comes to minimizing stroke risk. A recent study concluded that about 30% of strokes could be prevented if people simply switched to this diet.

But there's more you can do. Research has found that people who drank six cups of green or black tea a day were 42% less likely to have strokes than people who did not drink tea. With three daily cups, risk dropped by 21%. The antioxidant *epigallocatechin gallate* or the amino acid *L-theanine* may be responsible.

•**Emotional stress shouldn't be pooh-poohed.** If you're prone to angry outbursts, don't assume it's no big deal. Emotional stress triggers the release of cortisol, adrenaline and other so-called stress hormones that can increase blood pressure and heart rate, leading to stroke.

In one study, about 30% of stroke patients had heightened negative emotions (such as anger) in the two hours preceding the stroke.

My advice: Don't ignore your mental health —especially anger (it is frequently a sign of depression, a potent stroke risk factor). If you are suffering from "negative" emotions, exercise regularly, try relaxation strategies (such as meditation) and don't hesitate to get professional help.

•**Be alert for subtle signs of stroke.** The acronym "FAST" helps people identify signs of stroke. "F" stands for *facial drooping*—does one side of the face droop or is it numb? Is the person's smile uneven? "A" stands for *arm weakness*—ask the person to raise both arms. Does one arm drift downward? "S" stands for *speech difficulty*—is speech slurred? Is the person unable to speak or hard to understand? Can he/she repeat a simple sentence such as, "The sky is blue" correctly? "T" stands for *time*—if a person shows any of these symptoms (even if they go away), call 911 immediately. Note the time so that you know when symptoms first appeared.

But stroke can also cause one symptom that isn't widely known—a loss of touch sensation. This can occur if a stroke causes injury to the parts of the brain that detect touch. If you suddenly can't "feel" your fingers or toes—or have trouble with simple tasks such as buttoning a shirt—you could be having a stroke. You might notice that you can't feel temperatures or that you can't feel it when your feet touch the floor.

It's *never* normal to lose your sense of touch for an unknown reason—or to have unexpected difficulty seeing, hearing and/or speaking. Get to an emergency room!

Also important: If you think you're having a stroke, don't waste time calling your regular doctor. Call an ambulance, and ask to be taken to the nearest hospital with a *primary stroke center.* You'll get much better care than you would at a regular hospital emergency room.

A meta-analysis found that there were 21% fewer deaths among patients treated at stroke centers, and the surviving patients had faster recoveries and fewer stroke-related complications.

My advice: If you have any stroke risk factors, including high blood pressure, diabetes or elevated cholesterol, find out now which hospitals in your area have stroke centers. To find one near you, go to Hospitalmaps.heart.org.

How to Survive the Worst Type of Stroke

Edward C. Jauch, MD, director of the division of emergency medicine at the Medical University of South Carolina in Charleston, where he is also a professor in the department of neurosciences, the associate vice-chair for research in the department of medicine and director of Acute Stroke Trials, ongoing clinical research into the optimal treatment approaches for stroke.

If someone asked you for a quick definition of a stroke, you would probably say that it is caused by a blood clot...and requires quick treatment with a clot-dissolving drug. These points *are* true for the most common strokes, called *ischemic* strokes, but there's another type of stroke that doesn't get nearly as much attention.

The "other" stroke: A *hemorrhagic,* or bleeding, stroke is entirely different from an ischemic stroke—and usually more devastating. Fortunately, new research has uncovered potentially lifesaving advice for people who suffer this type of stroke. *The facts you (and your loved ones) need...*

THE GRIM STATISTICS

Up to 20% of the nearly 800,000 new or recurrent strokes that occur each year in the US are hemorrhagic strokes, but they account for 40% of stroke deaths.

What makes these strokes so dangerous? Hemorrhagic strokes result from bleeding into or around the brain, a catastrophic event that damages brain tissue. In addition, as the pooled blood degrades, it releases iron from red blood cells. Iron is toxic for brain tissue.

WORST HEADACHE OF YOUR LIFE

While most people can identify the main symptoms of an ischemic stroke (for example, facial drooping...numbness or weakness on one side of the body...and/or trouble speaking), the red flags for hemorrhagic stroke are not as well known.

With hemorrhagic strokes, a sudden, intense headache is usually the main symptom. Sometimes mild headaches can be a warning sign a few days or weeks before this type of stroke.

Important: Headache sometimes happens with an ischemic stroke, but it is usually accompanied by other symptoms, such as those described above. With a hemorrhagic stroke, additional symptoms may include nausea, vomiting and/or loss of consciousness. Symptoms can overlap, however, with both types of stroke, and only an imaging test can tell the difference.

If you have a severe headache that's unusual for you: Call 911. This is particularly true if you have stroke risk factors such as smoking, high blood pressure or diabetes.

A lifesaving new finding: For people suffering a *subarachnoid* hemorrhage (a type of hemorrhagic stroke described below), treatment at a comprehensive stroke center was associated with a 27% reduced risk for death, compared with care at a hospital that did not provide specialized stroke care. Comprehensive stroke centers have specialists who are trained to deal with these strokes and 24-hour access to a neurosurgeon (if needed).

For the nearest comprehensive stroke center: Go to the National Stroke Association website, Stroke.org/emergency-stroke-center-locations. A family member can ask the ambulance driver to take you there.

HOW BLEEDING STROKES OCCUR

There are two main types of hemorrhagic stroke…

• **Subarachnoid hemorrhage.** About half of hemorrhagic strokes occur in the *subarachnoid space,* between the inner and middle layers of tissue that cover the brain.

What happens: Most subarachnoid hemorrhages are caused by a ruptured *aneurysm,* a bulge in an artery wall that tends to develop after age 40, due to years of high blood pressure. It can also be congenital (present at birth). An aneurysm that doesn't bleed isn't necessarily a problem—you can have one for decades and not know it unless it shows up during an imaging test for some other condition.

But once an aneurysm "bursts" and bleeds, you will likely have a "thunderclap" headache that gets progressively worse—and may be followed by a brief loss of consciousness. You may also have blurred vision or loss of vision and/or pain behind and above one eye. Permanent brain damage or death can occur within hours or even minutes. *Get to an ER.*

Next steps: This type of stroke can be quickly identified with a CT scan or an MRI, and with magnetic resonance angiography (MRA) and/or cerebral angiography (a catheter is used to inject a dye, which illuminates blood vessels in the brain). *Once the damaged artery is identified, there are two main choices…*

• Clipping, the traditional approach, is done under general anesthesia. A surgeon creates an opening in the skull (craniotomy), locates the aneurysm and seals it off with a titanium clip that remains on the artery permanently.

• Endovascular coiling is a newer approach. With this minimally invasive technique, there is no incision in the skull. A tiny catheter is inserted into an artery in the groin, then threaded through the vascular system (with the aid of a special type of X-ray) until it's inside the aneurysm. Then, a flexible platinum coil is placed within the aneurysm to stop the bleeding.

Which technique is better? It depends on the location and size of the aneurysm, as well as the overall health of the patient. One large study found that the risk for disability or death in patients who were treated with coils was almost 27% lower than in those who were clipped. However, the study found a greater risk for the brain to bleed again with coils versus clipping.

• **Intracerebral hemorrhage.** Intracerebral hemorrhages cause bleeding within the brain. They're often caused by decades of high blood pressure, which can damage small blood vessels. They can also be caused by excessive doses of blood thinners taken for cardiovascular disease…or bleeding disorders (such as hemophilia).

Along with a severe headache, symptoms might include weakness, paralysis, a loss of speech or vision and sometimes mental confusion. Headache and high blood pressure are more common with this type of stroke than with ischemic stroke, but only a CT scan or MRI can provide an accurate diagnosis.

In some cases, surgery or endoscopic drainage may be helpful to remove blood that's causing excess pressure. *Next steps…*

• Lower systolic (top number) blood pressure to below 140. This will reduce brain bleeding.

• Reverse the medication's effects in patients with strokes that are caused by blood thinners. This can be done, for example, by giving an intravenous solution that contains clotting factors, platelets or other products that help blood clot.

Survivors of hemorrhagic stroke should receive rehabilitation care to aid their recovery.

Better Stroke Treatment

Stroke patients who underwent *thrombectomy,* a minimally invasive procedure that removes the blood clot responsible for a stroke, and received the clot-dissolving drug *tissue plasminogen activator* (tPA) within six hours of the onset of symptoms were far less likely to experience disabilities, such as difficulty walking and/or speaking, 90 days later than stroke patients who received just tPA. Blood flow to the brain was restored within 27 hours for about 83% of those who had thrombectomy versus 40% of those who had only tPA.

Demetrius Lopes, MD, chief of cerebrovascular surgery, Rush University Medical Center, Chicago.

News on Stroke Recovery

When hospitalized after an ischemic stroke (the most common type, caused by a blood clot), patients should lie as flat as possible to keep blood flowing to the brain.

Recent research: The head of the bed should be raised if brain swelling is suspected, to improve blood drainage and reduce intracranial pressure.

If a loved one suffers a stroke: Talk to the doctor about the most beneficial positioning of the patient's bed.

Murray Flaster, MD, PhD, associate professor of neurology, Stritch School of Medicine, Loyola University Chicago.

Better Glucose Monitoring

The FDA recently approved the first set of mobile medical apps that allow people with diabetes to automatically and securely share data from a *continuous glucose monitor* (CGM) with other people in real time using iPhones or other Apple devices.

With Dexcom Share Direct Secondary Displays, a sensor is implanted beneath the skin to track glucose levels. An alert is sent when levels are dangerously high or low.

Helpful: CGM data can be shared with up to five people, such as family members, caregivers and doctors.

Eric Pahon, spokesman, FDA, Silver Spring, Maryland.

GOOD TO KNOW...
Cut Your Diabetes Risk 57%!

Taking blood pressure medication at bedtime (versus in the morning) cut the risk of developing diabetes by 57%, according to a recent study.

Why: ACE inhibitors, some beta-blockers and other such drugs block the effects of a hormone that narrows blood vessels, which can lead to increased blood pressure and decreased insulin sensitivity.

Important: Consult your doctor before changing the timing of your medication.

Ramon Hermida, PhD, professor of medicine, University of Vigo, Spain.

Diabetes Drug Danger

Diabetes drugs may raise congestive heart failure risk. Overall, *thiazolidinediones* (TZDs), including *rosiglitazone* (Avandia) and *pioglitazone* (Actos), increase heart-failure risk by 42%. Overall, *dipeptidyl peptidase-4 (DPP-4) inhibitors*, including *saxagliptin* and *alogliptin*, raise heart-failure risk by about 25%.

Good news: If you are overweight, losing weight to control blood sugar reduces the risk.

Jacob A. Udell, MD, MPH, a cardiologist at Women's College Hospital, Peter Munk Cardiac Centre, Toronto General Hospital and University of Toronto, all in Toronto, Canada. He was principal investigator in a study published in *The Lancet Diabetes & Endocrinology*.

Itching After a Shower... and Other Surprising Cancer Symptoms

Eugene Ahn, MD, hematologist and oncologist at Cancer Treatment Centers of America (CTCA) and medical director for clinical research in integrative oncology at CTCA at Midwestern Regional Medical Center in Zion, Illinois. CancerCenter.com

Certain cancer symptoms almost always prompt a visit to the doctor. A breast lump. A mole that changes in size, shape or color. Blood in the stool.

But there are other symptoms that most people ignore.

Startling recent finding: In a study published in *British Journal of General Practice*, nearly half of people with a warning sign of cancer decided not to see a doctor about it, often because they thought the symptom was insignificant.

For the following symptoms, your first step is to visit your primary care physician who can perform the appropriate tests and/or refer you to a specialist.

If you have any one of these symptoms in isolation, the likelihood of you having cancer is less than 1%. That doesn't mean you should dismiss the symptom. But it does mean that you shouldn't panic if it shows up.

HEARTBURN

Most likely cause: Gastroesophageal reflux disease (GERD).

But it could be a sign of: Esophagus or stomach cancer. The symptoms of heartburn can include burning pain or discomfort in the stomach, upper abdomen, chest and/or throat…and/or excessive burping, bloating or nausea after eating. If those symptoms are chronic, it's time to see a doctor for a workup. You might have Barrett's esophagus—this is a precancerous condition that is triggered by chronic inflammation and increases the risk for esophageal cancer. Or you might have *H. pylori,* a bacterial infection of the stomach that increases your risk for stomach cancer (and ulcers)—but is easily treatable with a two-week treatment that includes antibiotics and possibly a proton-pump inhibitor.

What to do: Ask your doctor if you need an *esophagogastroduodenoscopy* (EGD), in which an endoscope is used to explore your esophagus, stomach and duodenum (the first section of the small intestine). A biopsy can be taken during the procedure if there is suspicious-looking tissue.

ITCHING AFTER A HOT SHOWER

Most likely cause: Dry skin or a contact allergy to a cleansing product.

But it could be a sign of: Polycythemia vera, a common myeloproliferative disorder, a type of blood cancer. In the early stages of this cancer, histamine-containing mast cells (cells behind allergic reactions) become hypersensitive, causing the skin to react to hot water.

What to do: If you're over age 40 (when this cancer most commonly occurs), ask your doctor for a complete blood count (CBC), which will detect an elevation of red blood cells, a feature of polycythemia vera.

EATING ICE

Likely cause: Iron deficiency.

But it could be a sign of: Gastrointestinal cancers, bladder cancer or any cancer that leads to blood loss. Called *pica,* this phenomenon—a compulsion to eat ice, sand, soil, clay, paper or chalk or to chew on something metallic—usually occurs during pregnancy and can be a sign of iron deficiency. But iron deficiency also can signal chronic internal blood loss, sometimes from cancer.

What to do: Ask your doctor about a blood test for iron deficiency. If you have an iron deficiency, work with your doctor to determine the cause.

UNBEARABLE PAIN IN A BONE WHEN TOUCHED

Most likely causes: Trauma, rheumatological disease or infection.

But it could be a sign of: Bone metastases (the spread of an original, primary tumor into the bone). This symptom is a hallmark of bone cancer.

What to do: If you have unexplained pain that tends to increase over a month—particularly if it's sensitive to the touch—talk to your doctor about imaging studies, such as a CT scan, a bone scan, an X-ray or an MRI.

DIARRHEA PLUS FACIAL FLUSHING

Likely cause: Irritable bowel syndrome (IBS).

But it could be a sign of: Neuroendocrine tumor, metastasized to the liver. Diarrhea alone rarely leads to a diagnosis of cancer, but diarrhea and flushing of the face are a unique pair of symptoms that could indicate a neuroendocrine tumor—a type of cancer arising from the hormone-producing cells in the body.

What to do: Talk to your doctor about possible imaging (CT, PET or MRI) to potentially detect liver metastases and primary tumor.

REDDENED SKIN ON THE BREAST

Likely cause: Skin infection.

But it could be a sign of: Breast cancer. A lump is not the only warning sign of breast cancer. Redness of the breast—particularly if the skin also is thickened, with the texture of an orange peel—is a sign of inflammatory breast cancer, a rare and aggressive form of the disease that can be missed by a mammogram, an ultrasound or an MRI.

What to do: Ask your doctor about a breast biopsy, the best way to detect this type of cancer.

Important: If the doctor diagnoses the redness as an infection and treats it with antibiotics, and the redness doesn't resolve or worsens, return quickly for a follow-up examination.

BLOOD CLOT

Likely causes: Leg or arm injury, such as a sprained ankle...recent hospitalization or surgery...a long period of inactivity, such as a plane ride.

But it could be a sign of: Breast, pancreatic, ovarian and many other cancers. A blood clot (a symptom of *deep vein thrombosis,* or DVT) is a common problem, affecting 900,000 Americans yearly. But DVT is not commonly understood as a potential early warning sign of cancer and so is often overlooked as a cancer symptom, even though as many as one in 10 patients with an unexplained blood clot may have some type of cancer.

What to do: If you have a blood clot (typically signaled by a sudden, painful swelling of an arm or a leg) without any of the common triggers (see common causes above), talk to your doctor about a workup for cancer. This is an early warning sign that often is missed.

BLOATING

Likely cause: Eating too much or too fast.

But it could be a sign of: Ovarian cancer. Bloating is a common symptom that is rarely a sign of cancer. But *persistent* bloating can be a sign of cancer in the peritoneal cavity, a common feature of advanced ovarian cancer, particularly if accompanied by a *persistent,* dull ache in the abdomen and unexplained weight loss (a symptom of advanced cancer).

What to do: Your doctor may recommend a CT scan or a transvaginal ultrasound. If the results are negative, ask about getting a laparoscopy, in which a thin, lighted tube is put through an incision in the belly to look at the abdominal and reproductive organs. A CT scan or a transvaginal ultrasound can easily miss ovarian cancer.

QUITTING SMOKING EASILY

Likely cause: You decided to quit, and you succeeded.

But it could be a sign of: Lung cancer. A chronic smoker who suddenly finds it unusually easy to quit may be experiencing a strange physiological symptom of lung cancer—inexplicably losing the desire to smoke. Usually, non-small-cell lung cancer is diagnosed three to four years after a chronic smoker easily quits, and small-cell lung cancer (a more aggressive type) is diagnosed about six months after quitting.

What to do: If you have been a lifelong smoker who suddenly finds it easy to quit, talk to your doctor about having a chest CT scan for lung cancer. You also would benefit from routine annual surveillance even if the scan is negative.

Breakthrough Cancer Treatment: A Radical New Approach That's Saving Lives

Louis Weiner, MD, director, Lombardi Comprehensive Cancer Center, Georgetown University, Washington, DC. He is an internationally recognized medical oncologist specializing in the treatment of gastrointestinal cancers. His lab researches novel immunotherapy treatments.

It seems like every week there's a promising new cancer treatment—that never happens. Too often we read about a new theoretical approach that saves lives in one or two studies…only to wait and wait for the treatment to materialize in the practice of cancer medicine. This time is different.

Now the powerful cancer-fighting drugs are not theoretical or another case of overhyping, overpromising and underdelivering. These medications really do work. This new way of fighting cancer uses the body's own immune system to wage war on cancer cells. Many leading cancer experts believe this approach, known as cancer immunotherapy, could revolutionize how we treat many forms of cancer.

When it comes to certain cancers, the revolution has already begun. In fact, former President Jimmy Carter, 91, is now said to be "cancer free" (based on MRI scans) after using one of these drugs for the melanoma that spread to his brain.

The new treatments aren't about enhancing immunity in general. Instead, this is an intriguing approach that can prevent cancerous tumors from hijacking our own immune defenses—so that our amazing immune system can do its job.

6 THINGS YOU NEED TO KNOW

Here are the details on this latest form of cancer immunotherapy…

1. It treats the body's immune system so the immune system can fight the cancer. *T cells* are the immune system's main line of defense, but they're not always effective against cancer cells. In the 1990s, cancer researchers identified a class of molecules in the body that are known as *immune checkpoints*. These molecules keep T cells from attacking normal cells, but cancer cells can hijack them for their own purposes. Cancer cells employ *immune "checkpoints"* to turn off killer T cells that would otherwise recognize and destroy a cancer that was growing in a person's body. Drugs that block these checkpoints so T cells can do their job are game changers called *immune checkpoint inhibitors*.

2. It still has side effects, but early results suggest a less toxic experience. All of us would love to see a day when very toxic chemotherapy agents that cause hair loss, low blood counts, fatigue, etc., are no longer the backbone of therapy for cancer. With check-point inhibitors, there will potentially be fewer side effects and certainly different ones. So far, the most common side effects caused by checkpoint inhibitors already in use include fatigue, cough, nausea, skin rash and itching. But more serious side effects including severe diarrhea, colitis and intestinal inflammation (even perforation) have also been reported.

3. It can be very effective as wel as long-lasting. Consider the effects of checkpoint inhibitors against end-stage Hodgkin's disease, where the patients had already received every imaginable therapy and were running out of hope. More than 90% of these patients went into remissions, many of them complete. When checkpoint inhibitors are combined against *metastatic melanoma*—the most deadly form of skin cancer—more than half of those cancers are eliminated or controlled, with benefits that have lasted for many years in some cases.

4. It works against many forms of cancer. In a viewpoint recently published in *JAMA,* James Allison, PhD, who pioneered the use of immune checkpoint inhibitors against cancer, wrote: "The therapy does not target the tumor cell but rather engages a target on the patient's immune system. Thus, there is no inherent reason that it would not be successful against a wide variety of tumors."

At this time, checkpoint inhibitors are FDA approved for treating only certain types of melanoma and lung cancer. But studies show that they also work against no fewer than 20 different cancers, including certain forms of kidney cancer, triple negative breast cancer, stomach cancer, Hodgkin's disease, bladder cancer and head and neck cancer.

5. It is very expensive. It can cost tens of thousands of dollars or more to have a course of therapy with these drugs, especially if you start combining them with other expensive cancer therapies. (See next page for more details on insurance coverage.)

6. It is still evolving. One promising innovation in cancer immunotherapy that is currently being researched is *chimeric antigen receptor (CAR) T-cell therapy.* In this case, a patient's T cells are genetically engineered to produce antibodies against a specific type of cancer. When these T cells proliferate, they pass their cancer-killing modifications along.

So far, this experimental treatment has had outstanding results against a hard-to-treat and deadly form of leukemia called acute lymphocytic leukemia.

WHAT'S AVAILABLE NOW

While many checkpoint inhibitors are in development, currently only three have been approved by the FDA…

• **Opdivo (*nivolumab*) and Keytruda (*pembrolizumab*)** are approved for advanced-stage non-small cell lung cancer that has spread and that is not responding to conventional platinum-based chemotherapy…and for advanced melanoma.

• **Yervoy *(ipilimumab)*** is approved for melanoma that has spread within the body (metastasized) or that cannot be removed by surgery.

Until new drugs for different cancers make it through the FDA approval process—or the existing approved ones get future approvals for different cancers—these are the only three of this type of cancer treatment that insurance companies or Medicare are likely to cover. If you have the financial wherewithal, you may be able to have your doctor prescribe the approved drugs off-label and pay for them yourself.

For everyone else, however, there is another potential option. If there is an immunotherapy cancer drug in development for a cancer that you are being treated for, ask your oncologist whether there is a clinical trial that you can join. You can also check the website Clinical Trials.gov.

Protect Your Kidneys— Before It's Too Late

Mildred Lam, MD, a professor of medicine at Case Western Reserve University School of Medicine and a nephrologist at MetroHealth Medical Center, both in Cleveland. Dr. Lam's clinical interests include acute and chronic kidney disease, hypertension and dialysis.

I*magine this:* You have just had a routine checkup, and your doctor gives you some surprising news. Blood and urine tests indicate that you've got *chronic kidney disease* (CKD). How could that be? You feel fine.

What most people don't realize: Kidney disease can be "silent" and often sneaks up on you. Nine out of 10 people who already have early-stage CKD don't realize it, and as a result, they aren't taking the necessary steps to protect their kidneys.

ARE YOU AT RISK?

Our kidneys naturally lose some function as we age. If you are 60 or older, there's a one-in-four chance that you already have CKD— though you may not know it.

You're also at increased risk for this disease if you have high blood pressure, diabetes or a family history of CKD (in a first-degree relative such as a parent or sibling).

With the right tests (see below), it's relatively easy to find out if you have CKD. But once your kidneys are damaged, you won't be able to reverse the damage. The goal is to not develop the disease or slow its progression.

PROTECT YOUR KIDNEYS

Whether you're trying to avoid CKD or prevent it from worsening, the best way to protect your kidney function is to control your blood sugar (crucial if you have diabetes), blood pressure and cholesterol levels, and to avoid smoking. *Other promising new approaches…*

• **Watch out for sleep apnea.** Researchers have found that sleep apnea is associated with

---

BREAKTHROUGH…

Antibiotics for Appendicitis?

Antibiotics—not surgery—may be enough to treat appendicitis in many cases. Three-fourths of patients treated with antibiotics recovered easily, and no patient who had surgery after a course of antibiotics was worse off because of waiting. *Note:* Antibiotics are appropriate *only in uncomplicated appendicitis*, not in cases where people have a perforated appendix, a blockage or another additional issue.

Study of 530 people, ages 18 to 60, by researchers at Turku University Hospital, Turku, Finland, published in *JAMA*.

increased protein levels in the urine (an indicator of CKD). For this reason, sleep apnea is now considered an independent risk factor for CKD—and it may cause the disease to progress in people who already have it.

My advice: If you have sleep apnea, be sure to get your kidney function tested. Similarly, if you know you have CKD, you may also have sleep apnea, especially if you snore or sleep restlessly. Get tested.

If you're diagnosed with sleep apnea, be vigilant about wearing your continuous positive airway pressure (CPAP) mask—the preferred treatment for this condition—while sleeping. Getting the proper amount of oxygen at night will help maintain your kidney function.

• **Keep an eye on your diet.** At one time, salt was the only potential dietary danger for anyone concerned about kidney health. People with CKD, especially those who also have high blood pressure, are still urged to follow a "no-salt-added" diet—that is, avoiding salty foods, such as canned soups, chips and lunch meats, and not adding salt to food when cooking or eating. *Other dietary advice…*

• Eat more vegetable protein (instead of animal protein). Eating large amounts of any kind of protein can tax the kidneys. But when you do eat protein, vegetable protein—found in such foods as soybeans, legumes, nuts and quinoa—is healthier because it generally contains fewer calories, less saturated fat, less sodium and less acid than meat protein.

• Avoid soft drinks. High amounts of sugar (glucose) in your blood—a given with sugary soft drinks—will stress your kidneys. According to a recent Japanese study, consuming at least two soft drinks per day may increase protein levels in the urine and, in turn, one's risk for CKD. If you're at increased risk or already have CKD, it's safest to drink water and avoid sugary soft drinks, especially if you have diabetes.

• **Use caution with painkillers.** Long-term use (more than 10 consecutive days) of nonsteroidal anti-inflammatory drugs (NSAIDs), such as *ibuprofen* (Motrin) or *naproxen* (Aleve), can harm the kidneys. If you're a frequent NSAID user, be sure that your doctor tests your kidney function routinely.

If you know that you have CKD, take an NSAID only if pain is severe and for no more than three to five consecutive days…or talk to your doctor about pain relievers that may be safer to take such as *acetaminophen* (Tylenol). Additionally, recent research has found that when an NSAID is combined with blood pressure drugs—an ACE inhibitor or *angiotensin receptor blocker* (ARB) and a diuretic ("water pill")—it may create a "triple threat" that can cause acute kidney injury, further damaging the kidneys.

My advice: People who are concerned about their kidney health or who already have CKD should *always ask* a doctor before taking any new drug—even if it's over-the-counter.

Also: Many supplements (such as potassium) and herbs (including periwinkle and aloe) can cause harm in people with kidney disease. Before taking any dietary supplement, consult your doctor—especially if you have CKD.

THE TESTS YOU NEED

If you are over age 40, you should have annual urine and blood tests to monitor your kidneys. People with diabetes or other chronic conditions should start sooner, and may need to be tested more often. *What needs to be checked…*

• **Albumin.** If this protein appears in your urine, it can be a sign of early kidney disease. Urine microalbumin/creatinine ratio (a very sensitive indicator of early kidney damage) should be less than 30 mg/g. Urine protein/creatinine ratio should be less than 150 mg/g.

• **Creatinine.** If your blood level of creatinine (a waste product filtered by the kidneys) is higher than 1.2 for women or 1.4 for men, you may have chronic kidney disease (CKD).

Your doctor may refer you to a nephrologist (kidney specialist) for more blood and urine tests and a renal ultrasound to check for kidney scarring or other conditions, such as kidney stones or a tumor.

• **Estimated glomerular filtration rate (eGFR).** Your creatinine result can also be calculated in a formula that includes your age, weight, race and sex to determine your eGFR, which indicates how well your kidneys are filtering blood and getting rid of waste. A normal reading for eGFR ranges from 90 ml/min to 130 ml/min, with no protein in the urine. A reading of 60 to 89 may indicate a mild decrease in kidney function. Many people are diagnosed with CKD at stage 3 (an eGFR of 30 to 59), which is considered "moderate."

Iced Tea Danger

Drinking too much iced tea can damage kidneys. A 56-year-old man suffered kidney damage because he drank 16 eight-ounce glasses of iced tea a day. Black tea is high in *oxalate*. Consuming 16 cups meant that the man consumed more than 1,500 milligrams (mg) of oxalate—as much as 30 times more than the Academy of Nutrition and Dietetics recommends. High oxalate levels increase risk for kidney stones and damage.

Letter by Fahd Syed, MD, Central Arkansas Veterans Healthcare System, and Alejandra Mena-Gutierrez, MD, and Umbar Ghaffar, MD, University of Arkansas for Medical Sciences, both in Little Rock.

OTC Painkillers That Can Be Deadly

Lynn R. Webster, MD, vice president of scientific affairs with PRA Health Sciences, a research organization, Salt Lake City, and past president of the American Academy of Pain Medicine. He is author of *The Painful Truth*. ThePainfulTruthBook.com

The Food and Drug Administration recently strengthened an existing label warning that non-aspirin nonsteroidal anti-inflammatory drugs (NSAIDs) increase the risk for heart attack and stroke. Popular over-the-counter medications including *ibuprofen* (Advil and Motrin) and *naproxen* (Aleve) are among the products affected. Taking these regularly for as little as a few weeks can put people's lives at risk…as could exceeding recommended dosages.

What to do: If you take an NSAID, keep your dose as low as possible and your duration of use as short as possible. People who have a history of heart disease, kidney disease or stroke should be especially careful to limit NSAID use.

Hidden danger: When you take a cold medication or sore throat medication, check the ingredients on the label for NSAIDs. If you see these, avoid extended use and do not take these medications if you also are taking a painkiller that contains any NSAID—the combined dose could put you in danger.

If you must take a painkiller for more than a week or so or if you have a history of stroke, heart problems or kidney issues, speak with your doctor about options other than NSAIDs. *Acetaminophen* could be a safer choice in certain circumstances, for example. Also, acupuncture and mindfulness meditation can help.

Diabetes Drugs and Joint Pain

Certain diabetes drugs may cause debilitating arthritis that results in joint pain. The four medications—*alogliptin* (Nesina), *linagliptin* (Tradjenta), *saxagliptin* (Onglyza) and *sitagliptin* (Januvia)—belong to a relatively new class of medications called *dipeptidyl peptidase-4 (DPP-4) inhibitors.* If you experience severe, persistent joint pain, consult your physician. He/she may switch you to another medication. Do not stop taking the drug on your own.

Osama Hamdy, MD, PhD, director of the inpatient diabetes program at Joslin Diabetes Center, Harvard Medical School, Boston.

DID YOU KNOW THAT…

Most Doctors Overprescribe Opioids

The government wants opioid prescriptions limited to three days—but 99% of physicians who prescribe the narcotic painkillers, such as OxyContin, Percocet and Vicodin, prescribe them for much longer. Opioids account for more overdose deaths than heroin and cocaine combined.

Survey of 200 doctors by the National Safety Council, published in *Insurance Journal*.

Got Knee Pain? How to Choose the Right Treatment

Jordan Metzl, MD, a sports medicine physician at the Hospital for Special Surgery in New York City. He is coauthor of *The Exercise Cure: A Doctor's All-Natural, No-Pill Prescription for Better Health & Longer Life*. Dr. Metzl maintains practices in New York City and Stamford, Connecticut. He has run in 33 marathons and finished 12 Ironman competitions. DrJordanMetzl.com

Why live with a bum knee when you can have less pain and more mobility with a new one? With such great promises and the relative ease of knee-replacement surgery, it's no surprise that this is now one of the most popular procedures in the US.

It's true that the procedure can be a blessing for those with severe arthritis (the main reason for surgery) that impairs their ability to live an active, pain-free life. But the decision to have surgery should *not* be made casually—and if you do end up getting a knee replacement, there are facts you should know before choosing between the tried-and-true approach and the newer, less invasive surgical procedure.

TO AVOID SURGERY

If you have mild-to-moderate knee pain, but you're still able to work and do normal activities, chances are you can greatly improve *without* surgery by following these steps…

• **Stretch and strengthen the muscles.** Studies have shown that simply strengthening the muscles that support the knees (the quadriceps in the front of the thighs and the hamstrings in the backs) can reduce damage, pain and disability.

My advice: Work those muscles three or four times a week for at least six to eight weeks before making a decision about surgery.

Examples: Leg extensions, hamstring curls and clamshells.

Even if your knee is hurting you, it's worth taking an over-the-counter painkiller, such as *ibuprofen* (Advil) or *acetaminophen* (Tylenol), about 30 minutes before your workout so that you can do the exercises. Curcumin supple-

ments have also been shown to decrease inflammation and arthritis pain. A physical therapist or personal trainer can help design a workout that includes targeted stretches and strengthening exercises that are right for you.

• **Drop some excess weight.** Every single pound of body weight equals several pounds of "loading force." This means if you are 10 pounds overweight, for example, your knees get an extra 40 pounds of pressure. That's enough to increase pain and limit mobility—and accelerate arthritis-related damage.

My advice: If you're overweight—even by a few pounds—it's affecting your knees. Get serious about losing those extra pounds!

• **Try hyaluronic acid.** This naturally occurring substance acts as a lubricant to the joints and may work as well as painkillers and steroids (without the side effects) for some people. It's usually injected into the affected joints once a week for three to five weeks.

My advice: There's no way to predict who will benefit from these injections. Consider them if exercise and weight loss haven't given you adequate relief. Insurance typically covers the cost.

WHAT NEXT?

If you've given the strategies described earlier your best shot and still have serious knee pain, surgery is usually the next step. *What to consider…*

• **Partial knee replacement.** This approach, also known as *unicompartmental knee replacement*, is newer than total knee replacement and gets a lot of attention because it is less invasive. The advantages include an incision that is roughly half the size (about three to 3.5 inches) of that used for total knee replacement. Patients also are hospitalized for just a day or two rather than three to five days for a total knee replacement. With the partial approach, the knee may feel more "natural"— for example, it may have less "creakiness" and better range of motion—than it would after a more extensive procedure.

But a partial knee replacement isn't for everyone. To be a candidate for this procedure, the damage is generally isolated to only one part of the knee. Also, the research is not yet clear, but patients who have partial procedures may be more likely to require subsequent "revision" surgery—because of continuing arthritis, for example, or because the first procedure didn't improve pain and/or mobility. For many patients, the risks from repeat surgery could outweigh the benefits of a less traumatic initial procedure.

•**Total knee replacement.** This procedure is called a "total" replacement because the damaged surfaces of the knee bones are replaced—the *tibia* (shinbone)…*femur* (thighbone)…and sometimes the *patella* (kneecap). The surgery requires a large incision (usually seven to eight inches) and typically takes about two hours.

The majority of patients who opt for knee surgery require a total replacement. Surgeons have a lot of experience with the procedure—and there's strong evidence that it works. More than 90% of total knee-replacement patients report that they have a lot less pain…and about 85% of these artificial knees are still going strong after 20 years. While patients who receive total replacements have somewhat less flexibility than those who go the partial route, most are able to do light hiking, ballroom dancing and biking.

THE BOTTOM LINE

No matter which approach your surgeon suggests, make sure you're comfortable with the plan. Some patients will feel best about the decision if they get a second opinion.

Until more is known about the long-term benefits and risks of partial knee replacement, most surgeons advise their patients with severe arthritis to get it over with and have a total replacement.

Patients with osteoarthritis in all areas of the knee and those with inflammatory arthritis (such as rheumatoid arthritis), which tends to affect the entire knee, are not candidates for a partial approach and require a total knee replacement.

Consider a partial procedure only if you mainly have damage in just one part of the knee, you haven't improved after physical therapy, weight loss and the other suggestions described above, and your pain prevents you

from sleeping through the night and/or performing your normal daily activities.

Celiac Tied to Bone Fractures

People with celiac disease (an autoimmune condition linked to the consumption of gluten protein found in wheat, rye and barley) have nearly twice the risk for bone fractures as those without the condition, a recent study finds. It's possible that fracture risk is higher even for celiac patients who consume a gluten-free diet.

If you have celiac disease: Follow a gluten-free diet, but also be sure to do regular weight-bearing exercise to help protect your bones and eat a balanced diet with plenty of calcium and vitamin D.

Katriina Heikkilä, PhD, researcher at University of Tampere School of Medicine, Finland.

Medications That Can Hurt Your Eyes

Jeffrey R. Anshel, OD, optometrist and founder of Corporate Vision Consulting, which addresses visual demands in the workplace. He has written six books on computer vision concerns and nutritional influences on vision, the latest being *The Ocular Nutrition Handbook.* He is a Fellow of the American Academy of Optometry and founder and past president of the Ocular Nutrition Society. He maintains a private practice in Carlsbad, California.

Are your eyes dry or sensitive to light? Do you have blurred vision or "floaters"? These and other eye problems could be side effects of common medications.

Few people make the connection between changes in their eyes and medications they take—yet the truth is that many prescription and over-the-counter drugs cause ocular side effects. *Here are common symptoms and the drugs that could be causing them…*

Osteoporosis May Harm Your Hearing

In a recent 10-year analysis of almost 43,000 adults, those with osteoporosis were nearly twice as likely to develop sudden, unexplained deafness in one ear than adults who did not have the bone condition.

Possible explanation: Osteoporosis can damage tiny bones in the ear.

If you have osteoporosis: Get tested for hearing loss every three years, especially if you are age 50 or older.

Kai-Jen Tien, MD, attending physician, Chi Mei Medical Center, Tainan City, Taiwan.

Important: Contact your physician (eye doctor or primary care) if you have any of these symptoms. Most are not dangerous, and minor eye problems may be a reasonable trade-off for a potentially lifesaving drug. Always bring with you to the doctor a complete list of the medications you take—prescription and over-the-counter—as well as the doses. Stopping the medications can reverse the symptoms in many cases.

●**Abnormalities in pupil size.** Discrepancies in how your pupils react to light (called *aniscoria*) can be caused by a variety of medications, including Catapres (for hypertension), Donnatal (irritable bowel syndrome/ulcers), Humulin (diabetes) and Tavist (allergies).

If your pupils aren't always the same size—especially if only one pupil is abnormally enlarged—it's important to go to the emergency room immediately. The brain controls pupil size, so a disturbance there can cause pupils to be different sizes.

●**Cataracts.** If you live long enough, you eventually will develop cataracts (lenses that have clouded over, making it more difficult to see). Certain drugs may speed the process, including Coumadin (for heart disease), Plaquenil (malaria, rheumatoid arthritis and lupus) and most steroids.

●**Difficulty focusing.** The medical term for this condition is "accommodative insufficien-cy." It grows more common with age and also is a side effect of some medications. These include Adipex (for obesity), Enduron (hypertension), Norpramin (depression) and Xanax (anxiety).

●**Double or blurred vision.** There are many potential causes for seeing double or for vision that suddenly blurs. Medications that can cause this include Adipex (for obesity), Celebrex (inflammation), Lamictal (seizures), Mevacor (elevated cholesterol), Tylenol (pain relief) and Zantac (ulcers).

If your blurred or double vision is sudden, severe and unrelenting, go to the emergency room immediately. This visual impairment is not only unsafe (for instance, when you are driving), but it could be a sign of a serious medical problem such as a stroke or brain lesion.

●**Dry eyes.** Many factors (including computer use, wearing contact lenses and allergies) can reduce tear production and cause dry eyes—and so can certain medications, such as Actifed (for allergies), Catapres (hypertension), Detrol (bladder control) and Paxil (depression).

Until you see your doctor, self-treatment options for dry eyes include blinking as often as possible...use of artificial tear solutions (available in drugstores and chain stores)...avoiding irritants, including eye makeup and air pollution...and wearing sunglasses. Or try an oral gamma-linolenic acid (GLA) product such as BioTears.

●**Eye irritation.** Redness in the whites of your eyes or irritations on your eyelids can be caused by medications such as Aricept (taken to improve cognitive loss), Cardizem (heart disease), Enduron (heart disease) and Voltaren (rheumatoid arthritis, osteoporosis).

●**Floaters and other visual disturbances.** Flashes of light or color, floaters and other visual disturbances can occur for a host of reasons, including as a side effect of a drug. Medications linked to visual disturbances include Benadryl (for allergies), Cardizem (heart disease), Elavil (depression) and Xanax (anxiety).

The causes of visual disturbances can range from inconsequential to potentially serious, so they should be checked out by your eye doctor as quickly as possible. This is especially true if you suddenly see flashes of light or if numerous new floaters appear—that could be a sign of a retinal detachment.

•**Light sensitivity.** Though there are other possible causes, light sensitivity may be a side effect of drugs (including cocaine and amphetamines). Drugs linked with light sensitivity include Diabinese (for diabetes), Dilantin (epilepsy), Lipitor (high cholesterol/heart disease), Pepcid (gastric ulcers) and Viagra (erectile dysfunction). If light sensitivity is severe and your pupils are enlarged—especially if only one pupil is enlarged—go to the ER. It could be a sign of stroke or a brain tumor.

•**Yellowed eyes.** There are several conditions that can cause the white parts of the eye to turn yellow, including illness, sun exposure and drugs such as Diabinese (for diabetes), Elavil (depression) and Librium (anxiety). Yellowing may be a sign of cirrhosis or hepatitis. It is important to see your doctor quickly to have this checked out.

Recent Study Reveals Calcium Caution

Calcium supplements may be linked to *age-related macular degeneration* (AMD). In a recent study, adults (age 68 and older) who took more than 800 milligrams (mg) of calcium a day were twice as likely to have AMD, a leading cause of blindness in people age 50 and older, as those who didn't take calcium.

Possible explanation: Drusen, fatty yellow deposits beneath the retina that can be a sign of AMD, may accumulate around tiny specks of calcium.

If you have risk factors for AMD, such as family history, smoking or age (60 or older), talk to your doctor about the risks and benefits of using calcium supplements.

Shan Lin, MD, professor of ophthalmology, University of California, San Francisco.

Shocking Danger for Contact Lens Wearers

Jennifer Cope, MD, MPH, a medical epidemiologist with the Centers for Disease Control and Prevention's Division of Foodborne, Waterborne and Environmental Diseases in Atlanta. CDC.gov

There has been an increase in recent years in the number of eye infections caused by the rare but dangerous *Acanthamoeba* parasite. These infections can be very difficult to treat and sometimes lead to blindness.

Contact lens wearers usually are the victims, because Acanthamoeba can attach itself to the surface of a contact lens and then enter the eye through tiny cuts in the cornea. Contact lenses can cause some of these tiny cuts (microtrauma).

Three things contact lens wearers can do to stay safe…

•**Remove your lenses before showering, bathing and swimming.** Acanthamoeba can live in tap water…swimming pool water…hot tub water…and even in natural bodies of water, both fresh and salt. This danger exists even if the water has been treated by a local water district and is perfectly safe to drink… and even if swimming pool water has been chlorinated. Acanthamoeba can survive these treatments, and infections have been increasing since 2004. Previously there were one to two cases per million American contact lens wearers. Now there are about 15 cases per

---

ON THE HORIZON…

Promising New Treatment for Alzheimer's

Ultrasound may someday treat Alzheimer's. Scientists used high-frequency sound waves to clear *amyloid beta*—a plaque seen in people with Alzheimer's disease—from the brains of mice. The treatment cleared plaque and restored memory in 75% of the mice within several weeks.

Study by researchers at Clem Jones Centre for Ageing Dementia Research, University of Queensland, Brisbane, Australia, published in *Science Translational Medicine*.

million. It is not apparent what is causing the increase.

• **Remove and thoroughly disinfect your lenses as soon as possible if they are exposed to water.** Peroxide cleaning systems are the only type that have been shown to kill Acanthamoeba.

•**Never use tap water to rinse off lenses or lens cases.**

Dementia-Drug Danger Escalates

Doctors have been warned against using antipsychotic drugs to reduce delusions and agitation in patients with Alzheimer's disease and other forms of dementia.

Now: A review of the medical records of nearly 91,000 veterans age 65 and older with dementia found that the harms were worse than previously thought. Those taking antipsychotics, such as *olanzapine* (Zyprexa), or the mood stabilizer *valproic acid* (Depakote) had a significantly higher risk for death over an 11-year period than those who took antidepressants or no medication.

Nondrug approaches, such as reducing triggers for behavioral problems, are preferred.

Donovan Maust, MD, assistant professor of psychiatry, University of Michigan, Ann Arbor.

Better Parkinson's Treatment

In a recent finding, Parkinson's patients who received *low-frequency (60 Hz) deep-brain stimulation* (DBS), in which an implanted "brain pacemaker" sends electrical impulses to the brain, had significant improvements in swallowing difficulty and in their walking gait—problems that were not resolved with standard treatment, including high-frequency

(130 Hz) DBS or medication, such as *carbidopa* and *levodopa*. The patients in the study received daily low-frequency treatments for six weeks.

Tao Xie, MD, PhD, assistant professor of neurology, The University of Chicago.

How Safe Are Antidepressants?

Erick Turner, MD, associate professor in the department of psychiatry and the department of pharmacology at Oregon Health & Science University (OHSU) School of Medicine in Portland. He is also a senior scholar with OHSU's Center for Ethics in Health Care. He has published numerous papers on publication bias in drug research in medical journals.

In 2001, a major study funded by the manufacturer of the antidepressant *paroxetine* (Paxil) found that the drug was safe and effective for adolescents suffering from depression. Since that time, doctors have written millions of prescriptions for depressed teens to take this drug.

Now: A re-analysis of that study conducted by an independent research group has come to a strikingly different conclusion—Paroxetine was *not* helpful in treating depression in teens and, in fact, increased their risk for suicide.

How could such a disparity exist in the interpretation of the evidence—and what does it mean for people of all ages who may be taking an antidepressant?

To find out, we spoke with Erick Turner, MD, a psychiatrist who has extensively studied scientific reporting methods within the psychiatric literature.

•**How can an independent analysis of the drug manufacturer's research come to such a different conclusion from the earlier findings?** One problem that affects the findings is a way that the data is interpreted if someone drops out of the study. It could be that 20% to 30% of patients don't make it to the end of the study, and there are various methods for handling that. One method—a misleading one—is to analyze data only from patients who make it to the end of the study. That way, you wind up with a skewed sample because people may have dropped out because the drug wasn't working for them or they were experiencing side effects. If those people are excluded from the overall analysis, then it makes the drug look more effective for depressed patients than it actually is, which makes the drug look better to doctors.

Also, regarding the issue of suicidal thinking and behavior, it's all about the coding. Suppose there's a patient who was angry one moment, crying the next and then thinking about jumping off a building. If the researchers code that as "emotional lability" (the opposite of "emotional stability"), but don't code the suicidal behavior, then it gets brushed aside and doesn't get counted the way it should. Coding differences of this sort led to different findings in the new report. This basic level of research can be subjective, so different parties can arrive at different conclusions.

• **Should adults who take Paxil or another antidepressant now be concerned about the safety and effectiveness of these drugs?** This is just one study among many. The totality of the evidence may tell a different story. The real message with this new study is this—if an independent party gets access to the raw data at the granular level, they can reach very different conclusions and it can depend on whether the researcher has a vested interest in the study's results.

• **In general, then, how effective and safe are antidepressants for depression?** You can't count on these drugs to be a magic bullet. You may have an excellent response, or you may not. You'll likely need some persistence—you might need to try a second or third type of antidepressant or consider a combination of drugs. You can also start treatment with psychotherapy and consider medication later.

And in terms of safety, the FDA has found that the risk regarding suicidal tendencies seems to decrease with age. The risk is highest with people under age 18 and somewhat less among those ages 18 to 25. For people 25 and older, the risk seems to be neutral—the drugs are even protective after age 65.

• **What are the possible side effects of antidepressants?** Selective serotonin reuptake inhibitors (SSRIs), which include not only paroxetine but also *fluoxetine* (Prozac), *citalopram* (Celexa), *escitalopram* (Lexapro) and *sertraline* (Zoloft), are the ones most commonly prescribed, and they're usually pretty well tolerated. But one common side effect is sexual dysfunction. For some patients, that makes these drugs a no-go… but for other patients, it's a nonissue.

Other types of antidepressants have different side effects. For example, *mirtazapine* (Remeron) tends to be sedating, which can be good for people who have trouble sleeping, but the potential downside is that it can cause increased appetite and weight gain. However, weight gain can be a welcome side effect for patients who aren't eating enough.

The dosage of an antidepressant should be gradually increased. With Zoloft, for instance, the FDA-recommended dosage for depression ranges from 50 milligrams (mg) to 200 mg once daily. I generally start people at 25 mg daily and continue that for a week or two…then go to 50 mg daily for a week or two…then 75 mg and then 100 mg. After a few months, the patient might need to go up to 150 mg or to the 200-mg maximum daily dose. It depends on the balance between therapeutic benefits and side effects.

Tapering off antidepressants should be done gradually, as well. If you run out of pills or stop suddenly, you could have discontinuation syndrome with side effects including nausea, dizziness and feeling teary and emotionally unstable.

So you should consult your doctor—an internist or a mental-health practitioner—whenever starting or going off antidepressants.

• **In general, when do the benefits of antidepressants outweigh the risks?** A number of studies have shown that you get more bang for your buck in terms of effectiveness when the depression is more severe. So if a person is severely depressed—if he/she can't get out of bed or has suicidal thinking—then it's certainly worth pulling out all the stops to help that person.

You and your doctor should be sure to review your progress after six to 12 months of treatment. It's important to remember not to stop treatment once you begin to feel better. And never stop taking antidepressants without first consulting your doctor.

But if you have mild depression, you're less likely to see a substantial benefit from taking an antidepressant. You might consider other ways to treat your depression—decreasing isolation, getting more exercise and seeking psychotherapy.

A recent study found that light therapy—sitting in front of a light box daily—helped ease depression symptoms. But check with your doctor first before considering light therapy, especially if you have bipolar disorder or certain other health conditions. Your doctor can guide you on the optimal amount of time to use a light box.

Surprising Dangers of Air Pollution: It Can Hurt Much More Than Your Lungs

Neil Schachter, MD, medical director of the respiratory care department at Mount Sinai Hospital and the Maurice Hexter Professor of Pulmonary Medicine at the Icahn School of Medicine at Mount Sinai, both in New York City. He is author of *The Good Doctor's Guide to Colds and Flu* and serves on the American Lung Association's Northeast Board of Directors.

You may assume that air pollution problems in the US are a thing of the past, since environmental laws have reduced the haze that once blanketed our big cities. But that's not true. Air pollution still ranks high on the list of health threats—and not just for city dwellers.

Wake-up call: More than 40% of Americans—nearly 140 million of us—breathe unhealthy air, according to a recent report by the American Lung Association.

Even when the sky appears crystal clear, you're inhaling exhaust fumes, ground-level ozone and microscopic particles—common pollutants that can increase your risk for health problems ranging from heart disease to asthma.

Small-town living helps but not completely. Even in the wide-open spaces of the American West, drought and high summer temperatures increase levels of dust and other airborne particles that can worsen conditions such as asthma and chronic obstructive pulmonary disease (COPD).

THE BIGGEST DANGERS

You would expect bad air to threaten your lung health, but there's increasing evidence showing that the risk is far more pervasive. *Examples…*

•**Heart disease.** Air pollution is ranked ninth among the most important cardiovascular risk factors—making it more harmful than lack of exercise or elevated cholesterol, according to a report in the *European Heart Journal*.

What makes air pollution so hard on the heart? Airborne particles trigger inflammation in the lungs and blood vessels that can increase atherosclerosis and the risk for clots. Even brief exposures to *PM2.5*—common airborne particles that are about one-fifth the size of a speck of dust—may increase cardiovascular risks. You are likely inhaling these particles if you drive to work with your car windows open, walk past a construction site or light a fire in your fireplace. In areas where particle concentrations are persistently high, such as near busy roads, there's an 11% average increased risk of dying from heart attack, heart failure or stroke.

•**Stroke.** Even if you live in a rural, "wholesome" area, you will occasionally breathe high levels of carbon monoxide and other gaseous pollutants—when you're behind a truck, for example. Such limited exposures may seem harmless, but an analysis of more than 100 studies found that intermittent spikes in air pollution caused a corresponding increase in hospitalizations and deaths from stroke.

•**Heart-rate changes.** The varying intervals between heartbeats, known as *heart-rate variability*, are a sign of cardiovascular health. Bad air—even *inside* the home—can have a harmful effect. People who frequently use air fresheners are more likely to have reduced heart-rate variability, research has found. Many air fresheners contain terpenes, chemicals that can smell like pine or citrus. They interact with other chemicals in the air and form heart-damaging compounds.

WHAT CAN YOU DO?

To help protect your health...

• **Track the Air Quality Index (AQI).** The AQI is a rating based on daily levels of major pollutants—carbon monoxide, sulfur dioxide, particle pollution, etc. When the number rises above 100, it's wise to avoid outdoor activities—particularly if you have already been diagnosed with lung or heart disease or diabetes. For an up-to-date AQI, go to AirNow.gov.

• **Exercise away from major roads.** Levels of PM2.5 particles tend to be much higher in areas with heavy traffic. If you like to walk, jog or bike, do it as close to nature as possible—and away from busy streets. Pollution is usually highest within 50 feet of roads.

Also helpful: Avoid rush-hour traffic if you can...and drive with the windows closed (see below).

• **Use the AC.** It is nice to conserve power (and save money), but don't skimp on air-conditioning. It filters incoming air and traps large particles. In fact, a study in Taiwan found that people who used home air conditioners showed none of the "cardiovascular endpoints"—such as inflammation and heart rhythm disturbances—that were apparent when they kept windows open.

In the car: Be sure to use the "recirculate" setting. Research has found that recirculating air will keep out 80% of outside air pollution.

• **Filter the air.** Dust is a major irritant for people with asthma, COPD or other lung diseases, as well as for those with cardiovascular disease. And even if it's cleaned often, the average home has a lot of dust.

My advice: If you have any of the health issues mentioned above, invest in a HEPA air purifier for any room you spend a lot of time in. Many brands are available—most of which will remove up to 99% of suspended particles in a given room. They work more effectively than electrostatic air purifiers, and they don't produce the ozone (another lung irritant) that can result from electrostatic units. HEPA filtration is also available in central ventilation systems.

Also: To keep indoor air cleaner, install solid floors (such as wood or tile)—not wall-to-wall carpet...and avoid floor-to-ceiling curtains.

• **Use natural scents.** Commercial air fresheners may smell nice, but they all contain chemical compounds. Why take chances? Natural scents smell better—and cost less.

Examples: Spritz rosewater in the air...or simmer lemon or orange peels on the stove.

CHECK YOUR AIR QUALITY

In the American Lung Association's recent report *State of the Air 2015*, six cities were ranked as having the cleanest air in the nation. They had no days when the air quality reached unhealthy levels for ozone or short-term particle pollution and had the best records for year-round particle pollution. The cities, listed in alphabetical order, are Bismarck, North Dakota...Cape Coral-Fort Myers-Naples, Florida...Elmira-Corning, New York...Fargo-Wahpeton, North Dakota...Rapid City-Spearfish, South Dakota...and Salinas, California.

To check your county, go to StateoftheAir.org and enter your zip code.

There Could Be Lead in Your Water!

Robert D. Morris, MD, PhD, an environmental epidemiologist based in Seattle and former professor at Tufts University School of Medicine, Boston. He is author of *The Blue Death*. EHTrust.org

A water utility does not officially have a lead problem unless at least 10% of homes tested have problems. That means thousands of households could be exposed to lead poisoning even in areas where the water is "safe." Lead poisoning can cause behavioral and developmental issues in children, as well as high blood pressure and kidney disease in adults.

Lead is not easy for water utilities to monitor and control because it is not present when water leaves treatment facilities. It gets into water from the pipes in homes and under yards. Older homes face the greatest risks.

Prior to 1920, when local municipalities began to prohibit the use of lead pipes, they were routinely used to connect homes to the water main under the street. The EPA did not ban their use nationally until 1986. A private well installed before 1986 also may have pipes and fixtures that contain lead.

If you are uncertain whether your home is connected to the water main by a lead pipe, check the home inspector's report conducted when you bought the property—if there's a lead pipe, this should be noted. Or find where your water supply enters your home—if this pipe is dull gray and can be easily scratched with a sharp knife, it's probably lead. Or have a licensed plumber check for you ($45 to $150).

What to do: Install a water filter on your kitchen faucet or below your sink. Expect to pay $200 to $400 for an under-sink unit, plus a few hundred more to have it professionally installed. Faucet-mounted filters cost less than $100 and are easy to install but tend to slow water flow and don't fit every faucet. If you do not have a filter, run your tap for one to two minutes in the morning before using it (lead leaches into water as it sits in the pipes), and do not drink hot water from the tap (hot water absorbs more lead).

Not all water filters remove lead, so check the packaging or the manufacturer's website. Or use the independent-testing company NSF's online search tool to find lead-reduction filters (Info.NSF.org/certified/dwtu).

Nail-Salon Health Dangers

The late Mitchell Gaynor, MD, founder and president of Gaynor Integrative Oncology in New York City and board-certified oncologist, internist and hematologist. He was also clinical assistant professor of medicine at Weill Cornell Medical College and is author of *The Gene Therapy Plan: Taking Control of Your Genetic Destiny with Diet and Lifestyle.*

There has been a lot of media coverage about toxins in nail salons and the effect that these chemicals can have on the people working at the salons.

But weekly salon goers also should take precautions to reduce their exposure to the toxic trio—*toluene, formaldehyde* and *dibutyl phthalate*—often found in typical nail products used at salons. These toxins have been linked to serious health conditions including kidney problems, asthma-like attacks, breast and prostate cancers, and abnormal fetal development. The thing to remember is that when it comes to toxins, it's not just about what you inhale but also about what touches your skin.

When you get that weekly mani/pedi, your skin—an absorbent surface—comes into contact with these chemicals. And while no one has studied toxin levels in people who frequent salons, the levels could be high.

But there are ways to help protect yourself. Choose a salon with a good exhaust system to reduce the amount of toxins you inhale during your visit. Read the labels of the products that the salon uses, and if toxin-free versions of polishes, hardeners and removers are not available, consider bringing your own. This helps you and your manicurist.

Finally, consider skipping the salon and polishing your nails at home with toxin-free products, such as those from Scotch Naturals, Zoya and Acquarella.

Mercury and MS

Mercury may cause autoimmune diseases. Mercury found in swordfish, king mackerel, tilefish and other seafood can impair the immune system, especially among women of childbearing age. The higher the level of exposure to mercury, the more proteins, called "autoantibodies," which can be an indicator of autoimmune disease. Autoimmune disease causes the immune system to attack healthy cells, which then leads to such diseases as lupus, rheumatoid arthritis and multiple sclerosis.

Study of government data from the National Health and Nutrition Examination Survey of women ages 16 to 49 by researchers at University of Michigan, Ann Arbor, published in *Environmental Health Perspectives*.

Many Food Cans Still Contain BPA

The chemical *bisphenol A* (BPA) often is used to line the inside of metal food cans to prevent food from touching the metal. It has been linked to health problems that affect the brain and the nervous system. While used less often than in the past, BPA still appears in about one-third of cans studied. Manufacturers are not required to identify cans with or without BPA. Among brands found to be BPA-free are Amy's, Earth's Best Organic, Health Valley, Seneca, Sprouts Farmers Market and Tyson. For more information on brands using BPA and those that are BPA-free, go to EWG.org/research/bpa-cannedfood.

Study of 252 brands made by 119 companies between January and August 2014 by researchers at Environmental Working Group, an advocacy organization in Washington, DC.

Junk Food Strikes... Again!

A laboratory study found that animals given marshmallows, chocolate bars and cookies in place of a healthier diet developed the same type of kidney damage that occurs with diabetes.

Experimental Physiology.

Bird Flu Tied to Eating Poultry and Eggs?

You cannot get avian flu from eating poultry or eggs. Bird flu is transferred through respiratory secretions or bird droppings, so to contract the virus, you typically need to have come in close contact with live poultry infected with avian flu.

William Schaffner, MD, professor of preventive medicine in the department of health policy, and professor of medicine, Division of Infectious Diseases at Vanderbilt University School of Medicine, Nashville.

Why Your Salad Needs Some Eggs

The fats in whole eggs boost absorption of beneficial *carotenoids* in raw vegetables. In a recent study, carotenoid absorption was up to nine times higher when adults ate a salad with three eggs versus those whose salads had no eggs.

Why: Carotenoids such as *beta-carotene* (found in carrots)...*lutein* (in spinach)...and *lycopene* (in tomatoes) require some fat for proper absorption, and eggs are a healthful option.

Wayne W. Campbell, PhD, professor of nutrition science, Purdue University, West Lafayette, Indiana.

2

Your Medical Advocate

How to Get In to See Your Busy Doctor

Not too long ago, I was concerned about what I thought was a suspicious lesion on my back, so I called my dermatologist's office for an appointment. The receptionist told me that the earliest available appointment was two months away. Before I hung up, though, I got scheduled for an appointment just two days away! Below, I'll tell you how I did it.

But first, let me explain what's happening all over the country. Over the past few years, more and more patients have been complaining about how long it takes to get appointments with their doctors—even doctors they have been seeing for years. While the problem tends to occur more often with specialists, who are harder to come by than primary care doctors in some locales, the declining number of primary care doctors is creating a backlog for some practices, too. But with the help of the following secrets, you'll greatly increase your chances of getting a medical appointment sooner.

What works best…

• **Talk to the *right* person.** The receptionist answering the phone at a medical practice usually has little discretion over scheduling. She'll book you into an opening on the calendar, often weeks or months away. If you need a quicker appointment, ask to speak to the nurse who works with your doctor. That's what I did to get my appointment with the dermatologist so much quicker. Even if you have never been to the practice before, this usually works.

Charles B. Inlander, a consumer advocate and health-care consultant based in Fogelsville, Pennsylvania. He was founding president of the nonprofit People's Medical Society, a consumer advocacy organization credited with key improvements in the quality of US health care, and is author or coauthor of more than 20 consumer-health books.

Insider secret: Don't cry wolf. When you talk to the nurse, give a legitimate medical reason (such as a recurrence of a previously treated condition) for the expedited appointment.

●**Do *not* ask about a "waiting list."** If you can't get through to the nurse, you'll probably assume that you should ask to be put on a waiting list (so you'll be called if there's a cancellation). Don't do that!

Insider secret: Instead of mentioning a waiting list, ask the receptionist if you can be put on the "quick call" list. This is the term that most medical practices use when referring to the list for people who get priority appointments when a cancellation or opening occurs. Asking for the quick call list tells the receptionist that you are something of an insider, which will help you get priority status.

●**Consider an urgent-care center.** If you are having a nonemergency problem (such as flulike symptoms or pain due to a minor injury) but cannot get a timely appointment with your primary care doctor or a specialist, head to your nearest hospital-affiliated or freestanding urgent-care center or even one at your local drugstore or supermarket. These walk-in practices can quickly determine if you need to see a specialist (or need hospital care)…and, if needed, usually can get you a quick appointment with an affiliated specialist (sometimes on the same day). If you're trying to see a specialist for an initial appointment, a call from your primary care doctor may help you get in sooner.

Important: For serious problems, such as chest pains, high fever, breathing difficulties or burns, go to an emergency room!

●**Get a new doctor.** If one of your current doctors regularly makes you wait several weeks or longer for an appointment, don't hesitate to find a new doctor. While he/she may be busy, your time is valuable too, and it's reasonable to expect to be seen within a month for a routine appointment or within a few days for a special need.

When to Think Twice About Medical Advice

H. Gilbert Welch, MD, MPH, an internist at White River Junction VA Medical Center, Vermont, and a professor of medicine at The Dartmouth Institute for Health Policy & Clinical Practice, where he specializes in the effects of medical testing. He is also author of *Less Medicine, More Health: 7 Assumptions That Drive Too Much Medical Care.*

It's natural to assume that more health care is better than less—that checkups, tests and treatments make people healthier. But that isn't always the case.

Obviously, people who are sick need to see doctors and get the necessary tests. Those who are healthy may benefit from preventive medicine. But many of the assumed benefits of medicine don't always pan out.

Here are four common but false assumptions about medical care…

FALSE: It never hurts to obtain more information. It would seem that getting as much medical information as possible would be a good thing. Not necessarily.

Example: A colleague's father was 85 years old and in good health when his doctor noticed an abdominal bulge during a checkup. He ordered an ultrasound, which showed that the bulge wasn't a problem—but the test did reveal a possible problem with the pancreas.

To check it out, the doctor ordered a CT scan. The pancreas was normal, but the test showed a possible nodule on the liver. A biopsy showed that the liver was healthy, but the biopsy caused serious bleeding and other complications, necessitating a week in the hospital.

More data can produce more problems, which require more tests, which can create problems of their own. And all this can cost you real money—yet not improve your health.

More data also can distract your doctor. Minor laboratory abnormalities identified during a routine visit—such as slightly elevated cholesterol or slightly depressed thyroid function—often draw physicians away from the problems you want to talk about.

My advice: Expect more and more opportunities to get tested for a variety of conditions. Know that while all these tests may serve the financial interests of their manufacturers, they may not serve your interests. Before agreeing to any test, ask your doctor what he/she is looking for. Is there a specific problem you are likely to have? Or is it a fishing expedition? Avoid the latter—it's too easy to catch trash fish (meaningless abnormalities). Also, ask your doctor whether more information will change what you should do. If not, don't seek more information.

FALSE: It's always better to fix the problem. All medical treatments are a bit of a gamble. You might improve when a problem is "fixed." Or things could go wrong and you could get worse. It's often better to *manage* a problem than to bring out the big guns.

Consider coronary artery disease. It's potentially life-threatening, so it needs to be treated. Many doctors recommend balloon angioplasty, a procedure to expand the arterial opening and restore normal blood flow. It can eliminate symptoms almost immediately, but it also carries significant risks to the patient.

With medical management, on the other hand, your doctor will treat the problem with medications and advice for a healthier lifestyle. You'll still have the underlying problem, but you'll learn to live with it.

How do the approaches compare? One large study found that patients with stable angina who had balloon angioplasty were no less likely to die or have a heart attack than those who depended on lower-risk medical management.

My advice: When you're faced with a medical decision—scheduling a test, having surgery, starting medications—tell your doctor that you want to take a *stepwise* approach. Start with the easiest, safest treatments first. You can always add more aggressive treatments later.

Think about upper-respiratory infections. Sure, you could get pneumonia, and you might eventually need antibiotics. But most people can just wait it out. Do not get tests or treatments unless your doctor convinces you, with good evidence, that you need them.

FALSE: It's always better to find it sooner. The argument for cancer screening seems obvious. If you had cancer, wouldn't you want to know as soon as possible? Screening (looking for disease in large populations) does turn up a lot of cancers. Does this save lives? Less often than you might think.

Take mammography. It's been used for widespread screening for 30 years, yet the number of women who are diagnosed with metastatic breast cancer is about the same now as it was before. For every 1,000 women who get the screenings, at most three (likely closer to less than one) will avoid dying from breast cancer as a result. The numbers are roughly the same for men who are screened for prostate cancer.

The benefits are huge if you happen to be in one of these small groups, but what about the rest? They're faced with the cost and inconvenience of the initial test. Many will be advised to get biopsies or other follow-up tests. Some will have surgery or radiation for cancers that probably would have done *nothing*.

I'm not saying that screening tests are all bad—just that they aren't all good.

My advice: Ask your doctor if he/she is confident that you, as an individual, will benefit from screening tests.

FALSE: Newer treatments are always better. There's a saying in medicine, "When you have a new hammer, everything looks like a nail." When doctors discover a new treatment, such as a drug or a particular surgery, they tend to want to use it again and again.

Some new drugs really are superior to old ones—but not that often. Vioxx is a good example. It's an aspirin-like arthritis drug that got a lot of attention because it was somewhat less likely than similar drugs to cause stomach bleeding. But a few years after it was approved by the FDA, it was removed from the market because it was found to increase the risk for heart attack and stroke.

New drugs are tested in relatively small numbers of people. It can take many years before their benefits and risks become fully apparent.

My advice: Unless you have to take a new, breakthrough drug, tell your doctor that you would prefer something tried and true—preferably a drug that's been on the market for seven years or more.

Don't Let Your Doctor Get It Wrong

Helen Haskell, MA, president of Mothers Against Medical Error, a nonprofit patient-safety organization, MAME momsonline.org. She serves on the board of directors of the National Patient Safety Foundation and is a board member of the Institute for Healthcare Improvement and the International Society for Rapid Response Systems. In 2015, she was named one of the top 50 patient-safety experts in the country by *Becker's Hospital Review.*

Fifteen years ago, my teenage son Lewis went to the hospital for an elective surgical procedure. After the operation, his doctors failed to notice that he was suffering from an undetected infection and blood loss from an ulcer caused by pain medication. They believed his symptoms were an indication of constipation from other pain medications he was taking. This mistake cost my son his life—he died four days after entering the hospital.

Now: I teach patients skills that can help them avoid a similar tragedy.

A "BLIND SPOT" IN MEDICINE

A groundbreaking new report from the prestigious Institute of Medicine (IOM) concluded that most Americans will experience at least one diagnostic error—that is, an inaccurate, missed or delayed diagnosis, as determined by later definitive testing—at some point in their lives.

The IOM report called diagnostic errors a "blind spot" in the delivery of quality health care. Each year, about one in 20 patients who seek outpatient care will suffer from a wrong or delayed diagnosis. According to autopsy studies, diagnostic mistakes contribute to about 10% of patient deaths. Unfortunately, diagnostic errors haven't gotten as much attention as treatment and surgical errors—for example, operating on the wrong body part—partially because the latter are easier and quicker to identify. Now patient-safety experts are taking steps to better understand why diagnostic errors occur. *Key reasons…*

•**Tests help—and hurt.** Patients may be given a staggering number of tests—X-rays, blood tests, biopsies and more. The process of ordering, conducting and conveying the results of a test, however, can be complex and poorly organized.

•**Poor communication.** Can you count on the internist to talk to the nurse? Will the radiologist convey all of the pertinent information to the surgeon? Don't count on it. Patients also play a role. They should tell their doctors about *all* the symptoms they're having and whether they're getting better or worse after starting a new treatment.

•**Snap judgments.** Doctors often develop a working diagnosis within the first few minutes of hearing the patient's reported symptoms. The danger is that doctors can develop a so-called *anchoring bias* that leads them to cling to their initial diagnosis and prevents them from fully considering new information or looking for other possibilities.

HOW TO MAKE SURE YOUR DOCTOR GETS IT RIGHT

Major medical groups, including the Society to Improve Diagnosis in Medicine, have identified a number of institutional factors—such as stronger teamwork—to reduce errors. But no one has more at stake in these situations than the patients themselves. *Four steps you can take to avoid a misdiagnosis…*

STEP 1: Organize your thoughts. Most of the time, doctors have only 15 minutes with each patient, so you need to make the most of your time together.

Plan ahead: Your medical history—including a description of symptoms and when the problem started—is the most important part of an exam. Describe the nature and context of your symptoms in as much detail as you can. When do you feel them? What makes them worse or better? Why are you worried? Keep it concise and on topic, but include your own thoughts so the doctor can address the issues that concern you.

My advice: If possible, *before* you see the doctor, use the Internet to investigate your symptoms and the likely causes. Your findings should not be used to challenge your doctor, but rather as a way to have a more informed conversation. If you don't have confidence in your own abilities to do research, take advantage of a service like Expert HealthSearch (Improve Diagnosis.org/?page=ExpertHealthSearch), a free service that puts you in touch with a medical librarian who can search the literature for you.

STEP 2: Don't be afraid to question test results. They are more prone to error than most people imagine. In one study, experts who reviewed biopsies of more than 6,000 cancer patients concluded that 86 had been given a wrong diagnosis. Samples can be too small or even contaminated…technicians can make mistakes…and there can be false-negatives or false-positives. Results can be misinterpreted, or even more often, they can go unreported to the patient.

My advice: If a test result seems to fly in the face of the symptoms you are experiencing, consider asking to repeat the test or have a second doctor review it. And *never* assume that no news is good news. Follow up to be sure that your test results have been received and reviewed and that you know what they are.

STEP 3: Ask about alternatives. Many common symptoms—such as fatigue, muscle aches and abdominal pain—are known as

nonspecific symptoms. They can be caused by dozens of conditions.

My advice: To help understand your doctor's thinking, ask him/her this question: *Could you please explain your differential diagnoses?* This is a list of possible diagnoses ranked in order of likelihood. It's a thought process that helps a diagnostician avoid overlooking any likely possibilities. The most serious conditions on the list should be ruled out before settling on a less serious diagnosis, and the doctor should be looking for causes and not just treating symptoms.

What to ask: If there is any question about a diagnosis, patients can help assess the "fit" by asking three important questions: *Does this diagnosis match all my symptoms? What else could it be? Could there be more than one thing going on?*

STEP 4: Don't skip the second opinion. I cannot stress this enough. In the study of cancer patients cited earlier, Johns Hopkins University researchers found that one to two of every 100 who got a second opinion with definitive testing after a tumor biopsy had gotten a wrong diagnosis the first time.

My advice: It's not always possible to get a second opinion—sometimes in medicine you have to move fast. But if you can, a second (or even a third) opinion is smart when symptoms seem severe…if your doctor is recommending surgery…or if you are told that you have a rare or fatal condition. Check first, but usually insurance will pay for a second opinion. Outside of emergencies, most of the time a brief delay in treatment while you get a second opinion will not affect your outcome.

Danger After Doctor Visits

The bacteria *Clostridium difficile* (C. difficile), which can cause deadly diarrhea, used to be a problem primarily in hospitals, but now patients are becoming infected after visiting doctor and dentist offices. Antibiotic exposure is a risk factor for the bacteria because antibiotics suppress the normal bacteria in the colon, allowing C. difficile to flourish.

Self-defense: Take antibiotics only when needed. Wash hands with soap and water—do not rely on alcohol-based gels, which are not effective against C. difficile.

L. Clifford McDonald, MD, a medical epidemiologist in the division of Healthcare Quality Promotion, Centers for Disease Control and Prevention, Atlanta, and coauthor of a study published in *The New England Journal of Medicine.*

If Your Doctor Dumps You...

Trisha Torrey, founder and director, Alliance of Professional Health Advocates, Baldwinsville, New York. EveryPatientsAdvocate.com

What do you do if you get a letter in the mail from your doctor saying that he's "culling" his patient list?

It may be difficult not to take it personally, especially if you've been a patient for many years, but your doctor's decision may have nothing to do with you as a patient. He may no longer accept your insurance or could be cutting back on his practice for personal reasons.

Under federal law, doctors cannot discriminate based on race, religion or sexual orientation or refuse to see patients in the midst of ongoing treatments, such as chemotherapy. But they may certainly dismiss patients who fail to follow treatment recommendations, don't show up for appointments, are rude or refuse to pay their portions of medical bills. In most states, doctors are not obligated to give patients a reason for ending their relationship.

If you really want to go back to that doctor, you can politely ask him to reconsider. But it may be better to request copies of your medical records and find another doctor.

How to Get into a Cancer Clinical Trial...

Toni Kay Mangskau, a social worker and clinical trials referral coordinator at the Mayo Clinic Cancer Center in Rochester, Minnesota. She counsels cancer patients, helps determine their eligibility for clinical studies and provides logistical support for study participants.

About 20% of newly diagnosed adult cancer patients in the US are eligible for clinical trials, studies for which people volunteer to test new drugs or other treatments. Yet only about 3% to 5% actually participate.

Why? Most people assume that clinical studies are an option for only the sickest patients for whom there are no effective treatments. Not true! The only requirement for many studies is having a specific type of cancer or being in a certain age group or other demographic category. Also, many people assume that one group in a study receives a placebo. The fact is that a placebo is not used in the vast majority of studies. In treatment studies, some patients are given the drug/procedure under investigation...others are given the best available standard treatment.

Here's what else you need to know about clinical trials...

WHAT'S AVAILABLE?

At any given time, thousands of clinical trials are under way. The National Cancer Institute website alone lists more than 12,000 trials that are looking for participants. The studies that get the most attention are those that look at breakthrough cancer treatments, but that's just the tip of the iceberg. Other trials compare single drugs with combination treatments... find new uses for old drugs...study new surgical techniques or radiation treatments, etc.

DID YOU KNOW THAT...

Misdiagnosis Is *Very* Common

Most Americans will be diagnosed incorrectly at least once during their lives. A mistaken diagnosis can result in missed or unnecessary treatments and traumatize patients.

Report by the Institute of Medicine (IOM), Washington, DC.

For some studies, all you have to do is give researchers permission to review your medical records.

Example: Researchers at the Mayo Clinic Cancer Center learned from chart review studies that patients with chronic lymphocytic leukemia responded better to treatments when they had normal blood levels of vitamin D.

RANDOM SELECTION

Typically, a computer will assign a participant to a group in a clinical trial. One group will be given the new drug/treatment. The control group will be given a standard treatment.

If you're randomly assigned to the control group, you'll still get the same treatment that you likely would have gotten if you hadn't joined the study. Those in the "active" group will get something that's expected to be at least as good—and possibly better.

THE RISKS

New drugs/procedures can have side effects or other complications that the researchers didn't anticipate. Should you take the risk?

It's a valid concern, particularly if it's an early-phase study, with a lot of unknowns. But most treatment studies already have a long history. Cancer drugs typically have been studied for at least six years in the laboratory before they make it to clinical trials with humans. It may take another eight years before drugs are approved—or not—by the FDA.

Researchers may not know everything about the drug/treatment, but they know a lot by the time these studies begin. It's always possible that the therapy being researched in the clinical trial is going to be less effective than the standard treatment. But typically study data is reviewed while the study is under way—and a study could be stopped because of side effects or because a treatment is not showing effectiveness.

My advice: If you are considering joining a particular study, ask the researchers how familiar they are with the treatment being researched. Some treatments have been used for other purposes for decades—they're unlikely to bring too many surprises. The diabetes drug *metformin*, for example, now is being studied as a treatment for breast and ovarian cancers. Doctors are knowledgeable about the drug and the probable side effects.

HOW TO PARTICIPATE

• **Talk to your oncologist.** In one poll, patients reported that 70% of their doctors never mentioned a clinical trial as an option. So ask. Even if your doctor isn't personally involved in a clinical trial, he/she can talk you through the issues—the pros and cons of participating...where to look for studies that involve your type of cancer...and what the studies are likely to involve.

Helpful: For a list of cancer clinical trials, go to Cancer.gov/clinicaltrials.

• **Make the decision early.** One of the first things you should ask your oncologist is how quickly you must make a decision about treatment options. Some studies accept only patients who haven't started other treatments.

Important: If you decide to participate in a study, you can change your mind later. Patients can quit a study at any time.

• **Is it practical?** Even if you would like to participate, you may find that it's not a good fit.

Example: A study might require weekly tests at a medical center hundreds of miles away. That's not practical for most people. But other studies may involve monthly visits at a site closer to home. Or there may be times when routine blood work or imaging may be done at your local doctor's office and results sent to the study team.

Study participants typically get more face time with doctors—along with additional checkups, tests, etc.—than patients who don't participate in studies. One study found that 95% of those who participated in one clinical study said that they would consider doing so again.

• **Check the costs.** Many tests and treatments will be paid for by the study sponsor—but that doesn't mean all of your care is free. In most cases, you (or your insurer) still will be responsible for "routine" care costs—for example, routine blood work or scans. Travel expenses are rarely covered.

Under the Affordable Care Act, some health plans are required to cover the routine costs of study participants. Check with your insurance company, or contact your state's Health Insurance Commission.

THE 4 PHASES OF A STUDY

Before joining a clinical trial, ask about the *study phase*. This will give you some idea of how much is known about the treatment.

•**Phase 0 is the earliest stage.** Small doses of a drug are tested in just a few people to find out if it reaches the tumor, how it's metabolized, etc. A participant won't benefit from a phase 0 study, but future patients might.

•**Phase 1 studies are used to determine the highest drug dose** that can be given safely and identify possible side effects. Sometimes, these are referred to as "dosing" studies. Researchers also may make sure that the treatment has some benefit, such as slowing tumor growth.

•**Phase 2 trials involve slightly larger numbers of patients.** The goal is to see if the treatment actually works—for example, if it causes a tumor to shrink. If enough patients benefit and side effects aren't too much of a problem, the drug then may go on to the final stage.

•**Phase 3 studies look at anywhere from hundreds to thousands of patients.** These are the treatment studies that most cancer patients join. If the drug is clearly effective, an application for approval is submitted to the FDA.

The New Support Group: How Today's Groups Can Help You Heal

Trisha Torrey, a Baldwinsville, New York–based patient advocacy consultant, also known as "Every Patient's Advocate," and author of *You Bet Your Life! The 10 Mistakes Every Patient Makes.* Torrey is also founder and director of the Alliance of Professional Health Advocates and lectures across the country on the best ways to navigate the healthcare system. EveryPatientsAdvocate.com

---

Support groups have come a long way from church basement meetings. In fact, these groups can be a great way to access the latest treatment options for a specific medical condition…and some can even change the course of your disease. *What today's support groups can offer you…*

•**Online options.** Although many support groups still meet in-person, numerous groups now take place online, either through national organizations such as the Alzheimer's Association and American Cancer Society or on social media sites such as Twitter or Facebook, where a niche topic might be covered.

Some of these groups are scheduled at a particular time…with other groups, people can join in the conversation at their convenience.

Some examples of online groups that may be helpful: The groups on Inspire.com and the online quit-smoking group from the American Lung Association. Also, every Monday evening at 9 pm EST, a breast cancer group called @BCSM meets on Twitter, where experts answer questions and provide support through real-time chats.

•**A way to stay up-to-date on the latest treatment alternatives and research.** New treatments and research are often discussed in support groups. Participants talk about their firsthand experiences of what seems to be working and what's not working for them. (*Note:* See below for a caveat on following medical advice heard in a group.)

If you're interested in finding out more about your disease or condition, you should at the very least monitor online support groups (by reading through threads of conversation) to learn what's going on with others who have the same condition as you. Once you have gathered information from a support group and done your own research, you can go to your doctor with informed questions.

Some support groups have even been instrumental in starting new research studies and have influenced standards of care for particular diseases.

•**Emotional support.** It's easy to underestimate the support that these groups offer. Illness and radical life changes are often isolating, and a support group is a place where you can vent your frustrations and share your victories with others who understand exactly what you're going through because they are going through it as well.

In a study published in the *Journal of the American Geriatrics Society*, patients who attended a six-session diabetes-education program and 18 meetings of a self-help group had less stress and depression and better blood sugar control than those who did not participate in these programs.

IS IT RIGHT FOR YOU?

After you have identified a group that addresses your need (see below), plan to visit it two or three times before deciding if it's right for you. During the first few visits, just listen (or read, in the case of online groups) and observe to see if the tone of the group and topics discussed appeal to you. If the group is online, you can scroll through past discussion threads to get a good sense of the group's dynamic.

You should also assess the group leader if there is one. A good moderator doesn't have to have a particular degree, but he/she should have been diagnosed and treated for the same disease (or a similar disease) as those in the group. The moderator shouldn't dominate the conversation or focus on his agenda, but instead set the stage for solid, informative discussions. He should also be able to effectively handle members who try to monopolize the discussion. And you need to feel comfortable enough with the leader to reach out to him if something about the group bothers you.

HOW TO PROTECT YOURSELF

• **Medical advice heard in a group should be carefully vetted by your doctor.** It's easy to get carried away by another member's enthusiasm for a particular treatment, but what works for one person may not be right for you. And if you're online, never assume someone is a medical professional just because he says so. Always check with your doctor before trying anything new to avoid harm.

• **Remain anonymous online to keep your health information private.** To protect your privacy, set up an e-mail address that you use only for health-related research and online support groups, and don't use your real name or location.

Also, read the terms of use on the site so that you understand how your data may be shared. The risks of revealing too much about yourself and your condition can range from getting targeted by marketers to being stalked.

Important: Be sure to check the "About" section on websites and/or any fine print to determine who sponsors a support group you are thinking of trying. If the group is underwritten by a pharmaceutical or medical-device company, the group may be no more than a marketing vehicle for the company's drugs or therapies.

Guard Against Radiation: What to Do Before Getting Imaging Tests

Leo Galland, MD, director of the Foundation for Integrated Medicine in New York City. He has held faculty positions at Rockefeller University, Albert Einstein College of Medicine of Yeshiva University and Stony Brook University. He specializes in the medicinal use of supplements and is the developer of the website PillAdvised. com, which discusses how to avoid dangerous interactions when combining medications with supplements.

Let's say your doctor has advised you to get an X-ray or a CT scan. You're likely to book the appointment without giving it much thought. But before you do so, it's worth asking whether you *really* need the test.

A growing threat: In the 1980s, about 15% of a typical person's lifetime exposure to radiation came from medical tests. Now these tests account for about *half* of one's lifetime exposure. Why the increase? Doctors are now prescribing more imaging tests, and newer tests, such as computed tomography (CT) scans, produce more radiation than those available in the past.* This is true even though some CT scans now have lower radiation levels than when they were first introduced.

A DOUBLE-EDGED SWORD

There's no question that imaging tests save lives. They can reveal hidden problems and have greatly improved doctors' ability to diagnose and treat serious diseases. But the use of CT scans, to give just one example, has increased *20-fold* in the last 25 years. Fortunately, the cancer risk from a single scan—or even a few scans—is negligible.

The real risk: Research shows that repeated CT scans over a lifetime could increase one's risk of developing cancer by 2.7% to 12%. Cancers that have been linked to medical radiation include leukemia and malignancies of the breast, thyroid and bladder.

SHOULD YOU WORRY?

Everyone is exposed to small amounts of radiation. Cosmic rays, radon gas and radioactive minerals in the soil are among the most common sources. Typically, the amount of radiation from these "background" sources adds up to only about 3 millisieverts (mSv), a standard unit of measurement, a year—not enough to worry about.

However, imaging tests *exponentially* add to your lifetime exposure.

Examples: Approximately 1.5 mSv from a spinal X-ray…6 mSv from a pelvic CT scan…and about 20 mSv from a whole-body positron emission tomography (PET)/CT scan to detect cancer.

*X-rays, computed tomography (CT) and positron emission tomography (PET) scans produce damaging radiation…ultrasounds and magnetic resonance imaging (MRI) scans do not.

QUESTIONS TO ASK

Before agreeing to a test, ask your doctor why it's needed and if the results will possibly change your diagnosis or treatment (if not, you don't need the test). If an imaging test is crucial, you can ask whether there's a radiation-free alternative, such as ultrasound, or whether a lower-radiation test is available— say, an X-ray instead of a CT scan. Also be sure that the medical facility where you will receive the imaging test has been accredited by the American College of Radiology (ACR). To check a facility's accreditation status, go to the ACR website, ACR.org.

Also helpful: Keep a log of any radiation-based tests that you get. You can refer to your radiation history whenever you and your doctor are considering a medical test that will expose you to radiation.

SUPPLEMENTS TO CONSIDER

Emerging evidence suggests that *radioprotective* supplements can help reduce the risks of radiation exposure. The research isn't conclusive (and is primarily extrapolated from findings related to radiation from nuclear accidents), but lab studies have found that some supplements may help protect you from the dangers of radiation exposure, including that from medical tests. *Examples…*

• **Ginkgo extract.** After the nuclear meltdown at Chernobyl, scientists studied a number of natural products to see what could help reduce radiation damage in first responders. They found that a ginkgo extract, known as *Egb 761*, reduced the damaging effects of radiation on chromosomes—and the benefits persisted for several months after workers stopped taking it. Other studies have found similar results.

My advice: Take Egb 761 for a week after having a CT scan or other imaging tests. It's available at health-food stores and from online retailers such as Amazon.com.

Typical dose: 120 milligrams (mg) daily.

Good product: Tebonin.

Possible side effect: Egb 761 can increase bleeding when it's combined with aspirin or other blood-thinning drugs, such as *warfarin*

(Coumadin). Ask your doctor if it's safe for you to use.

• **Hesperidin.** This flavonoid (a type of antioxidant) is found in fruits, especially citrus. It is also available as a dietary supplement.

An animal study published in *The British Journal of Radiology* found that hesperidin taken before radiation exposure decreased blood-cell damage. In human testing, results were similar—it reduced radiation-induced damage by about one-third.

My advice: Take 250 mg of hesperidin about one hour before testing. It's unlikely to cause side effects.

RADIATION DOSES

Depending on the type of imaging test you receive, the radiation dose can vary widely. *According to the Radiological Society of North America...*

• **Bone densitometry (or DEXA)** requires an approximate radiation dose of 0.001 millisieverts (mSv).

• **Mammography** requires an approximate radiation dose of 0.4 mSv.

• **X-ray of the spine** requires an approximate radiation dose of 1.5 mSv.

• **Computed tomography (CT)** of the head requires an approximate radiation dose of 2 mSv.

• **CT of the chest** requires an approximate radiation dose of 7 mSv.

• **X-ray of the lower gastrointestinal tract** requires an approximate radiation dose of 8 mSv.

• **CT of the abdomen** and pelvis requires an approximate radiation dose of 10 mSv.

• **Coronary CT angiography (CTA)** requires an approximate radiation dose of 12 mSv.

The Truth About Biopsies

Biopsies do *not* cause cancer to spread. Patients with pancreatic cancer who had fine-needle biopsies lived longer and had better outcomes than patients who were not biopsied. This dispels the myth that biopsies spread cancer. The fine-needle technique is safe for other cancers as well.

Study of more than 2,000 pancreatic cancer patients by researchers at Mayo Clinic, Jacksonville, Florida, published in Gut.

Blood Work Follow-Up

Trisha Torrey, founder and director, Alliance of Professional Health Advocates, Baldwinsville, New York. EveryPatientsAdvocate.com

In the past, doctors' offices usually called if there was a problem with a patient's blood work. But more doctors seem to be requesting a follow-up visit to go over results. Is this really necessary?

It may be necessary in some cases. If your test reveals a problem or something that will require new treatment, then your doctor needs to tell you in person. But test results that are normal for you should not require a follow-up office visit.

In any case, do not ever assume the doctor will call you with your results. Let the office know how you would prefer to receive your results—phone, e-mail or postal mail—and ask when they will be ready. If your doctor still insists on an office visit, contact your insurer to see if it's covered. You can also arrange for blood work to be done before your appointment, so your doctor can go over it when you meet.

The Overdose Danger: How to Be Sure You Get the Right Dose

Jack E. Fincham, PhD, RPh, a professor of pharmacy administration at Presbyterian College School of Pharmacy in Clinton, South Carolina. He is also a former panel member of the FDA Nonprescription Drugs Advisory Committee and currently serves on grant review panels for the Canadian Institutes of Health Research Drug Safety and Effectiveness Network.

When you get a new prescription, the first thing your doctor does (after choosing the drug) is decide on the appropriate dose.

What most people don't think about: Your doctor's dosing decision is crucial—getting even slightly more of a medication than you need can *greatly* increase your risk for side effects. Correct dosing, however, can lessen (or even eliminate) side effects.

Each year in the US, drug side effects are estimated to cause more than one million hospitalizations and more than 100,000 deaths. Yet many doctors reflexively prescribe "average" doses without checking recommendations for optimal dosing based on such factors as age, sex and body weight.

For example, a 100-pound woman might be given the same dose as a 200-pound man… and a 75-year-old may be given the same dose as a healthy college student. It's not hard to guess who is more likely to have preventable side effects. While many people know that taking a blood thinner in a dose that's too high can have devastating consequences, recent research is focusing on *other* drugs that can also have dangerous side effects.

Important recent finding: With blood pressure drugs and diabetes medication, in particular, excessive doses can increase risk for dizzy spells, confusion, falls and even death—especially among adults age 70 and older, according to recent research in *JAMA Internal Medicine*.

DOSING DANGERS*

Common drugs to watch out for…

*Never change a medication dose without consulting your doctor.

• **Blood pressure drugs.** About 25% of patients who take one or more of these medications stop using them within six months because of side effects, and up to half quit taking them within a year. The majority of people who take blood pressure drugs will initially suffer from dizziness, unsteadiness, falls or other side effects. Alert your physician if you experience any of these side effects. Even though the discomfort typically wanes over time, it can often be prevented altogether by starting with a lower dose of medication.

Beta-blockers, such as *metoprolol* (Lopressor) and *propranolol* (Inderal), are particularly dose-sensitive. So are alpha-blockers, such as *prazosin* (Minipress). Women who take these drugs tend to have a greater drop in blood pressure/heart rate than men, so they typically need a lower dose. The same may be true of patients who have both high blood pressure and lung disease, who often suffer shortness of breath when they take excessive doses. People who take multiple blood pressure medications are also more likely to have side effects.

My advice: Tell your doctor that you would like to start with one drug. Emphasize that you'd like to take the lowest possible dose—and that you're willing to be retested (or check your own blood pressure at home with an automated blood pressure monitor) to make sure that the treatment is working.

• **Diabetes medications.** The risks for diabetes complications—such as nerve damage, blindness, stroke and heart attack—are so great that doctors tend to treat it aggressively. But oral diabetes drugs given in high doses can easily cause blood sugar to fall too low.

Example: Patients who take *glyburide* (Micronase) or *repaglinide* (Prandin) often develop hypoglycemia, excessively low blood sugar that can cause dizziness, confusion and other symptoms. Even if the initial dose was correct, physiological changes as you age and/ or changes in your lifestyle could make that starting dose too potent. For example, suppose that you start exercising more and eating a healthier diet. You'll probably need a lower drug dose than you did before, but your doctor might not think (or know) to change the prescription.

My advice: Tell your doctor right away about any lifestyle changes that could affect your blood sugar levels, such as exercise frequency (or intensity), changes in meal timing, etc. Keep careful tabs on your blood sugar with home tests. If your blood sugar is consistently testing at the lower end of the recommended range (or below it), call your doctor and ask whether you should switch to a lower drug dose.

•**Painkillers.** Nonsteroidal anti-inflammatory drugs (NSAIDs), such as aspirin and *ibuprofen* (Motrin), are widely available and effective. But they're also dangerous at high doses. One study found that more than 70% of people who take these drugs daily on a regular basis suffer at least some damage to the small intestine. Like the blood thinner *warfarin* (Coumadin), they're a common cause of excessive bleeding.

My advice: Take the lowest possible dose… use painkillers as rarely as possible…and always take them with food. People assume that over-the-counter drugs are safe, but none of these medications are meant to be used long term (more than four weeks).

If you can, switch to one of the many brands of *acetaminophen* (such as Tylenol). It has about the same pain-relieving effects, but even with its increased risk for liver damage, acetaminophen (taken at the recommended dosage) is less likely than an NSAID to cause side effects.

•**Sedatives.** Valium and related medications, known as *benzodiazepines*, are commonly prescribed sedatives in the US, but the standard doses can be much too high for women as well as older adults.

Medications such as *diazepam* (Valium), *triazolam* (Halcion) and *zolpidem* (Ambien) accumulate in fatty tissue. Since women have a higher percentage of body fat than men, the drug effects can linger, causing next-day drowsiness or a decline in alertness and concentration. In older adults, the drugs are metabolized (broken down) more slowly, causing unacceptably high levels to accumulate in the body.

My advice: Women who are given a prescription for one of these drugs should always ask if the dose is *sex-specific*. They can ask something like, "Do I need a lower dose because I'm a woman?"

Also, in my opinion, people age 65 or older should avoid these drugs altogether unless they have to take them for a serious problem, such as a seizure disorder. If your doctor says that you need a sedative, ask if you can use a shorter-acting drug such as *lorazepam* (Ativan)…if you can take it for a short period of time (less than a month)…or if you can get by with a lower dose.

Important: These drugs should never be combined with alcohol. The combination increases the sedative effects.

To read more about a drug you're taking: Go to Drugs.com.

Surprising Drug Side Effects

Robert Steven Gold, RPh, a hospital pharmacist and affiliate instructor of clinical pharmacy at Purdue University in West Lafayette, Indiana. He is author of *Are Your Meds Making You Sick?*—a book that examines several adverse drug reactions.

We all know that drugs can have side effects, but we don't always make the connection between the drug and the adverse reaction. That's because some drug side effects are surprisingly hard to recognize. That can be dangerous. A recent Harvard study found that adverse drug reactions accounted for more than 4 million annual visits to ERs and outpatient clinics. *Troubling symptoms that could actually be caused by a drug you're taking…**

SYMPTOM: A dry, hacking cough that gets worse when you lie down at night—and that you don't think is caused by a cold, allergies or smoking.

POSSIBLE CAUSE: An angiotensin converting enzyme (ACE) inhibitor, such as *lisinopril* (Zestril, Prinivil), *captopril* (Capoten) or *enalapril* (Vasotec). Patients are usually told that this class of blood pressure–lowering drugs can sometimes cause dizziness. But doctors don't always mention that a nagging cough will plague up to 20% of patients.

More clues: An ACE-related cough usually develops several months after starting the drug (although it may begin immediately)…is more common in women and the elderly…and usually will go away after a few days of stopping the drug (but this can sometimes take up to four weeks).

My advice: You might be able to switch to a different ACE inhibitor, but the "class effect" means that similar drugs often have similar side effects. You will probably need to discontinue the drug and switch to an angiotensin receptor blocker (ARB), such as *losartan* (Cozaar) or *valsartan* (Diovan). These drugs work in much the same way as ACE inhibitors but don't cause coughing.

SYMPTOM: Irregular heartbeat (arrhythmia) that often occurs when you stand up after sitting or lying down—and feels as though your heart is pounding or racing as if you just exercised heavily.

POSSIBLE CAUSE: A broad-spectrum antibiotic, such as *levofloxacin* (Levaquin) or *ciprofloxacin* (Cipro). Drugs in this class, known as quinolone antibiotics, can trigger *torsades de pointes*, a dangerous type of arrhythmia. Macrolide antibiotics, such as *azithromycin* (Zithromax), can also have this effect.

The risk for arrhythmias is particularly high in patients who take a quinolone antibiotic plus

*Never stop taking a prescribed drug or change your dose without consulting your doctor.

a thiazide diuretic, such as *hydrochlorothiazide* (Microzide), typically used for high blood pressure. Some diuretics can lower levels of potassium and change the heart's normal rhythm, which can magnify the arrhythmia caused by the antibiotic.

Lengthy episodes (10 seconds or more) of torsades de pointes can cause seizures, a loss of consciousness or even death.

My advice: Get to an ER immediately if you develop a rapid heartbeat. Tell the doctor that you're taking a quinolone or macrolide antibiotic. He/she will probably prescribe a different drug (assuming that you still need the antibiotic). In most cases, the heart will "reset" itself fairly quickly after treatment. This type of arrhythmia won't come back once the drug is discontinued.

SYMPTOM: Sudden psychosis, a change in mental status that affects you emotionally and physically, causing severe confusion, nervousness, slurred speech and/or poor coordination.

POSSIBLE CAUSE: *Phenytoin* (Dilantin), commonly used to treat epileptic seizures and, in some cases, an irregular heartbeat. It's a tricky drug to use because there's a fine line between a *therapeutic dose* and a *toxic dose*. Most people who develop psychosis have been given a dose that's too high.

My advice: Don't neglect to get laboratory tests recommended by your doctor. Patients who take phenytoin require regular tests—every three months or monthly if the drug dose changes or adverse drug effects are suspected—to measure drug levels in the blood. Routine tests also measure albumin, a protein that binds to the drug. Phenytoin is more likely to cause problems in patients with low albumin levels (less than 3.4 g/dL).

Patients who experience a change in mental status will recover quickly once the drug is discontinued for a few days, then restarted at a lower dose. If toxic levels of phenytoin occur regularly despite decreasing the dosage, a different medication should be considered.

SYMPTOM: Sudden hearing loss. You might notice that you're having trouble hearing high frequencies (high music notes, women's voices, etc.) or that everything sounds a little "muddy."

POSSIBLE CAUSE: *Furosemide* **(Lasix),** a diuretic that's often used to treat high blood pressure and swelling in the feet and/or legs. At high doses, it can cause a loss of potassium, which can impair the hair cells in the inner ear and the nerves that transmit sounds to the brain.

Most cases of *ototoxicity* (damage to the inner ear) occur in patients who take the drug intravenously. But it can also occur with standard oral doses, particularly when furosemide is paired with other drugs (such as the painkillers Celebrex and Advil) that also have hearing loss as a side effect.

My advice: If you're taking furosemide and notice any degree of hearing loss—or you suddenly develop tinnitus (ringing sounds in the ears)—see your doctor right away. Hearing loss is a rare side effect, but the damage can be permanent if the drug isn't stopped quickly enough. Careful monitoring is crucial, especially when using a high dose.

TAKE NOTE...

Too Many Pills All at Once?

If you take many supplements and prescription drugs with your coffee every morning, you might need to rethink this routine.

Some drugs interact with certain nutrients, and some nutrients can interact with other nutrients. These interactions can interfere in some cases with the benefits of your prescription drugs and/or nutrients in your supplements. The interactions may even increase adverse side effects of the medications.

Caffeine and some other compounds in coffee can interact with various prescription drugs, so it's best not to take them with coffee unless your doctor says it's OK. Whether or not what you are doing is safe depends on the drugs and nutrients you are taking.

You should list all your supplements and medications and then consult your doctor, pharmacist or another knowledgeable health-care practitioner on the best way to take them.

Alan R. Gaby, MD, author of Nutritional Medicine. DoctorGaby.com

---

SYMPTOM: Intense abdominal pain that isn't accompanied by fever or other signs of illness.

POSSIBLE CAUSE: Codeine or other narcotic painkillers. Many people know that these drugs can cause constipation, which occurs in up to 90% of those who take them. What they don't realize is that constipation that lasts for more than one or two weeks can lead to fecal impaction, an intestinal blockage that completely stops the passage of stools, causing intense pain.

My advice: Ask your doctor to prescribe the lowest possible dose. It won't completely prevent constipation, but it will reduce the risk for impaction. Be sure to drink a glass of water every few hours and get regular exercise. Fluids and exercise moisten stools and increase the frequency of bowel movements.

Also helpful: Take a daily dose of a stool-softening medication, such as *docusate* (Colace) or use stimulant laxatives such as *bisacodyl* (Dulcolax) when you have not had a bowel movement for several days.

Another option: Ask your doctor if you can use nonopiate forms of pain control, such as lidocaine patches.

When It's Best to "Split Fill" a Prescription

Fill only part of a prescription for a new drug. "Split filling" a prescription lets you find out if the drug has undesirable side effects before you pay for a full prescription. Ask your doctor to write the prescription so that you can fill only part of it at first, then fill the rest later...or talk to your pharmacist about dispensing only some of what is prescribed. Most insurance plans allow split fills—but check with your insurer.

Charles B. Inlander, a consumer advocate and health-care consultant, based in Fogelsville, Pennsylvania.

4 Mistakes to Avoid During an Emergency

Leslie D. Michelson, founder and CEO of Los Angeles–based Private Health Management, a consultancy that partners with physicians to develop state-of-the-art treatment plans for clients dealing with medical emergencies and complex conditions and coordinates all medical and logistical aspects of their care. He also is author of *The Patient's Playbook: How to Save Your Life and the Lives of Those You Love.*

There are no two ways about it—medical emergencies fill us with fright, confusion and sometimes panic. While you may think that you can't prepare for an unexpected health crisis, the truth is that you can—and *should*.

Whether you're dealing with a stroke, heart attack or even a relatively minor injury such as a broken ankle, the consequences of not being prepared can be quite serious. In the most extreme cases, it can result in a preventable medical error, which studies show is a leading cause of death in the US.

Below are four common mistakes that patients make during the first 24 hours—and simple steps you can take to avoid them…

MISTAKE #1: Not calling 911. In the first moments of a health crisis, it's hard to know what to do. Simply render aid? Call 911? Or load the patient in the car and take him/her to the hospital yourself? *What to consider…*

•**What's the nature of the problem?** If it's a minor injury to a limb (arm or leg) or an extremity (hand or foot), it's generally less urgent than an injury to the head or torso, where vital organs are located. (*Note:* If bleeding from a limb or extremity won't stop even when pressure is applied or there is a very long or deep cut, the situation may be serious and warrants a 911 call.)

If there's no visible injury but the person is experiencing troubling symptoms, be sure to pay close attention. Does he have unexplained shortness of breath? Is he clammy and cold or faint and dizzy? (All are potential heart attack signs.) Is the pain getting worse? Does he appear to be having an acute allergic reaction or asthma attack? Any of these scenarios could become life-threatening and should prompt an immediate call to 911.

If the patient is stable, talking coherently and none of the above symptoms are present, it's helpful to call the patient's primary care physician and ask if the situation can be handled in an office visit. If you can't reach the doctor or you have any doubts, call 911.

•**What's the age and health status of the patient?** If you're dealing with someone who's in his 70s or older and/or has a chronic condition such as diabetes, heart disease or cancer, it's best to err on the side of caution and call 911 if there is any question whether the person requires emergency treatment.

MISTAKE #2: Heading to the wrong hospital. When a patient realizes that he is at a hospital that simply doesn't have the expertise and resources to properly render care, it can require dozens of phone calls over days and pushback from the insurance company to get a transfer to another hospital. Instead, get to the right hospital the first time. *Here's how…*

•**Before there's ever an emergency, check to see if you have a designated "trauma center" in your area.** An emergency room is considered a trauma center when it has the manpower and technology to handle the worst physical injuries—such as those from car crashes, high falls, etc. There are five different levels of trauma centers—a Level I center has the most resources while a Level V center would provide basic trauma care. To find out if you have a trauma center near you, go to FACS.org/search/trauma-centers.

If your condition is not life-threatening, you can ask the ambulance driver to take you to your preferred hospital. If he resists, request that the driver contact his supervisor for permission. However, if it's a true emergency, such as a heart attack, you should be taken to the closest ER available.

Important: When you reach an emergency department (or even while in transit, if possible), call your doctor. This will enable the medical staff to more accurately place your diagnosis in the context of your medical history.

Note: If you have the choice of going to a trauma center (not all locations will have one) or the hospital where your doctor has privileges (meaning he has been cleared to use the hospital's facilities), you need to consider the specific situation. For example, if it's a chronic problem that might require a lengthy stay, having your primary care physician present becomes more important. If you've been in a car accident, a trauma center is likely better.

MISTAKE #3: Not communicating clearly. Once you're at the emergency room, you (or your loved one) will need to convey a lot of information *fast*. And that might not be so easy. *What helps…*

• **Don't assume that electronic medical records will be in place.** In this age of electronic medical records, that advice to carry an up-to-date medical information card in your wallet is no longer valid, right? Oh yes, it is! The electronic medical record systems of many hospitals and doctors' offices are *not* compatible at this point, so it's still wise to have that card with you at all times. Be sure to include any allergies, chronic conditions such as asthma or diabetes, medications (and dosages) and phone numbers for emergency contacts.

• **Make sure you are heard.** Studies show that the average ER patient gets interrupted after 12 seconds of explaining his symptoms. For the best care, it's crucial to give the medical staff your full range of symptoms and medical history, so be clear and detailed. Also, be assertive if you are interrupted and let your needs be known.

MISTAKE #4: Giving up your power. When illness strikes you or a family member, it's easy to believe that if you simply obey the doctors and nurses, all will be well. Not so. The patient is ultimately in charge of his own health destiny. *What helps…*

• **Find out who is treating you.** If you're at a teaching hospital, it can be difficult to tell whether it's an attending physician, a resident or an intern who might be working in the emergency room. It's perfectly reasonable to ask, "Could you tell me what your title is?" If your health issue is complex, politely request to be examined by the *attending physician*. This way, you'll be sure to have a doctor who

has completed his training (and is actually supervising the others) caring for you.

• **Don't forget your records.** By federal law, all your medical records belong to you. Before you're discharged after an ER visit, ask for copies of all of your medical records in case you have a complication later and the doctors treating you need to know your medical history. The cost for these copies varies by state.

Don't Skip Your Follow-Up After an ER Visit

If you go to the ER for chest pain, treatment guidelines urge you to see a physician for further evaluation within 72 hours of being released. But a recent study of nearly 57,000 such patients showed that 25% of them *didn't* get this follow-up—increasing their risk for future problems such as heart attack.

Dennis Ko, MD, senior scientist, Sunnybrook Research Institute, University of Toronto, Canada.

Time for a New Hospital?

Charles B. Inlander, a consumer advocate and healthcare consultant based in Fogelsville, Pennsylvania. He was founding president of the nonprofit People's Medical Society, a consumer advocacy organization credited with key improvements in the quality of US health care.

Until recently, if you were hospitalized, odds are you would end up in a room with other patients. When you left, you might—or might not—get a discharge plan for the care you needed at home. And the only follow-up you got was a bill!

Now all that is changing. These days, one-third of doctors are employed by hospitals, which are aggressively marketing their physicians and upgraded medical facilities directly to patients. Hospitals are also focusing more on getting people well while they are hospitalized—and keeping them well after discharge—due to financial incentives and penalties associated with insurance reimbursement. *To take advantage of these changes…*

•**Ask for a private room.** Most hospitals are now either building new facilities with only single-bed rooms or converting many of their existing rooms to single beds. In a private room, you'll have a lower risk for infection and you'll get peace and quiet. However, private rooms may cost you extra—at least $100 more per night. Private rooms are covered by all insurance plans, including Medicare and Medicaid, if there are no multi-bed rooms available or your doctor deems a single-bed room "medically necessary" (which means your recovery or care is at risk in a multi-bed room).

Action step: Check the hospital(s) where your doctor has privileges to see if it charges extra for private rooms. If that hospital does charge extra, then ask your doctor whether he/she considers a private room medically necessary for you.

•**Get thorough discharge plans.** Health insurers are now reducing hospital payments if you are readmitted within 30 days after your discharge. As a result, most hospitals are trying to provide patients with more and better information about what they need to do to stay well when they get home.

Action steps: Check with your assigned discharge planner (usually a nurse or social worker) to make sure you get a list of the medications you need to take once you're home, and ask the hospital to call your pharmacy to order those drugs before you leave. Also, ask for a list of phone numbers where you can reach hospital personnel 24 hours a day if you have a problem once you're home. If you need at-home care, make sure the hospital orders it—and any equipment you may need such as oxygen or a walker—before you are discharged. And insist that you be given instruction on any special care you may need to administer yourself, such as injections, bandages or insulin pumps.

•**Use follow-up services.** Besides buying up private doctors' practices, hospitals are also buying up many formerly independent medical services, such as agencies that provide home care and physical therapy and occupational therapy. Some hospitals even have contractual arrangements with in-store drugstore-owned clinics such as those found at CVS, Walgreens or Rite Aid stores for routine posthospital monitoring of incision sites, blood pressure, etc. While you should choose the service providers you prefer, it's often wise to consider using ones that are affiliated with your hospital to help ensure the continuity of your care (they typically have access to all your records and easy communication with the hospital).

Action step: If possible, find out before your hospital stay what follow-up services you will need and what providers are affiliated with the hospital so you can check them out in advance and request a particular provider(s) you may like and/or find convenient.

BETTER WAY...

The Healing Power of Music

Surgical patients have less anxiety when they listen to music before and after surgery. They also are more satisfied with their care and require less pain medicine than patients who do not listen to music or choose what is played.

Catherine Meads, MB ChB, PhD, a Reader in Health Technology Assessment at Health Economics Research Group, Brunel University London, Uxbridge, UK, and leader of a review of data from 72 studies including nearly 7,000 patients, published in *The Lancet*.

Common Meds That *Slow* Surgery Recovery

Patients sometimes take antianxiety drugs to calm themselves prior to surgery. But people who took *lorazepam* (Ativan) before a surgical procedure requiring general anesthesia needed ventilation tubes longer, had poorer-quality postsurgical sleep, had more postsurgery amnesia and took longer to recover cognitive abilities than people who took a placebo or nothing.

Study led by researchers at Timone Hospital, Marseille, France, of 1,062 patients admitted to French hospitals, published in *JAMA*.

3

Quick Cures

Surprising Food Cures: How to Use the Natural Pharmacy in Your Kitchen

"Let food be your medicine," Hippocrates once advised. And judging from the thousands of letters and e-mails we've gotten over the years from people who have relieved common ailments with items most people have in their homes, the ancient Greek physician was really on to something.

Some food remedies are backed up by science, while others are simply anecdotal, but there's no denying that specific foods can help many common health problems…

RAISINS FOR REDUCING NIGHTTIME BATHROOM VISITS

Getting out of bed multiple times a night to urinate is not just annoying, it is actually a proven predictor of mortality. That's because sleep disruption predisposes you to a number of chronic illnesses, such as hypertension and heart disease.

As far as we know, there's no scientific research to support this remedy, but we've heard many times that it works…

One woman informed us that two spoonfuls of raisins before bed helped her reduce bathroom visits from once every hour or two to about once a night. And another individual claimed that consuming 10 raisins three times a day allowed him to stop taking bladder medication!

Joe Graedon, MS, a pharmacologist, and Terry Graedon, PhD, a medical anthropologist. The Graedons are coauthors of *The People's Pharmacy Quick & Handy Home Remedies* and cohosts of *The People's Pharmacy* public radio program. Joe Graedon is an adjunct assistant professor in the division of practice advancement and clinical education at the University of North Carolina Eshelman School of Pharmacy at Chapel Hill, and Terry Graedon is a founding member of Duke University Health System's Patient Advocacy Council, Durham. PeoplesPharmacy.com

Important: Never stop taking a prescription medication without consulting your doctor first.

What to do: Try eating a tablespoon of raisins before you brush and floss your teeth at night.

TART CHERRY JUICE
FOR MUSCLE PAIN

Tart cherry juice has gained popularity as an effective remedy for painful gout. This pleasant-tasting beverage seems to lower the level of uric acid circulating in the body. The Arthritis Foundation reports that tart cherry juice may also improve symptoms of osteoarthritis.

What you may not know: Tart cherry juice can also alleviate muscle pain after running and other workouts, according to a study published in the *Journal of the International Society of Sports Nutrition.* When runners drank the anti-inflammatory juice twice a day for a week prior to a race, they reported up to 67% less pain afterward compared with those taking a placebo.

What to do: Drink one cup of tart cherry juice two times a day.

Note: Be sure to choose juice made from tart or Montmorency cherries—the varieties shown in studies to provide benefits.

SOY SAUCE FOR BURNS

One woman told us that when she burned her hand on a hot frying pan, she tried an old wives' tale—she filled a rubber glove with soy sauce and put her hand in.

Result: The pain disappeared quickly, and there was no blistering the next day.

Scientific evidence: We're not exactly sure why the salty liquid worked, but she's not the first person to experience success with soy for burns. A 2015 Israeli animal study showed that incorporating soy protein into bandage materials for burn wounds led to quicker healing than traditional dressing material.

While serious burns demand immediate medical attention, milder burns may benefit from a dose of soy. (It's probably a minor burn if only the outer layer of skin seems to be affected with some redness, splotchiness or small blisters.)

What to do: If you want to try soy for burns, we hear that regular soy sauce is more effective for some reason than the low-sodium kind. You can soak the burned skin in soy sauce or apply gauze soaked in soy sauce to the burn.

Caution: You may have been told that butter helps burns, but it should not be used for this purpose—the greasy spread seals in heat.

CHEWING GUM FOR HEARTBURN

In a study published in the *Journal of Dental Research,* acid reflux patients were fed lunches that included whole milk, lots of cheese, chips and salad with mayonnaise—fare that would give almost anyone heartburn. Some subjects were then given sugar-free gum to chew for 30 minutes.

Result: Two hours later, the gum chewers had significantly lower acid levels than people who hadn't chewed gum.

Explanation: Chewing gum stimulates saliva production, which helps rinse the esophagus of acid.

What to do: If you frequently suffer from heartburn, try chewing gum after meals. Be sure to choose sugar-free gum to keep cavities at bay.

Note: Mint gum or gum with sorbitol can cause digestive upset in some people.

Grow Medicine for Common Ailments in Your Garden!

Jamison Starbuck, ND, a naturopathic physician in family practice and a guest lecturer at the University of Montana, both in Missoula. She is also a past president of the American Association of Naturopathic Physicians and a contributing editor to *The Alternative Advisor: The Complete Guide to Natural Therapies and Alternative Treatments.* DrJamisonStarbuck.com

Anyone who is health savvy knows that gardening is good exercise. But when I recommend this activity for my patients, I encourage them to get even greater benefits by growing *medicinal* plants. As a naturopathic physician and an avid gardener myself, I'm convinced that gardening is especially well suited for people suffering from depression or anxiety or a condition such as stroke that can lead to mobility difficulties or chronic lung problems that may interfere with biking, hiking or doing other outdoor activities. And if you're going to do some gardening, it makes perfect sense to cultivate plants that can be used to treat everyday health problems.

You might assume that you need a yard to plant a garden, but that's not true. Pots and window boxes work just fine. In most areas of the US, spring is the preferred time to get started. It's best to purchase small plants early in the growing season in order to ensure abundant leaves for harvest all summer. To dry your plants for use in tea (see below), cut the plant at the base of the stem, then hang your harvest to dry indoors or under cover outdoors for two to three weeks. Strip the leaves or flowers from the stem, and store in an airtight container.

My favorite plants to include in a medicinal garden…

• **Lemon balm.** This remedy calms the nervous system (to help fight sleeplessness and stress) and reduces discomfort from indigestion.

What to do: For tea, use two teaspoons of dried lemon balm leaves or five fresh leaves per cup of boiling water. Steep, covered, for 10 minutes. Discard herbs. Lemon balm is stronger than other sedative herbs such as chamomile, so limit your intake to 16 ounces of tea in a 24-hour period.

Note: Since lemon balm may slow thyroid function, people with hypothyroidism (low thyroid) should avoid it. Do not use lemon balm if you take a sedative—it may interact with the drug.

• **Calendula.** This herb acts as a skin antiseptic to help heal cuts, burns, boils and insect bites.

What to do: Use one-quarter cup of dried calendula flowers per 20 ounces of boiling water to make a strong tea. Let steep for 10 minutes. Use the tea topically on cuts, burns or insect bites. Add fresh calendula flowers, a rich source of beta-carotene, to summer salads. People who are allergic to ragweed may also have an allergic reaction to calendula.

• **Catnip.** You might think of catnip only as that potent little plant that cats love so much. Well, the flowering tops of this plant also act as medicine for humans.

What to do: Use two teaspoons of crumbled, dried catnip leaves per eight ounces of boiling water. Steep for 10 minutes. Discard herbs. Drink one to four cups per 24 hours as needed for stress headaches or indigestion.

Caution: Avoid catnip if you take lithium or a sedative—it may interact with these medications.

• **Thyme.** This herb can be used as an antimicrobial.

What to do: Grow thyme from seeds or small seedlings. For a cold or flu, use dried thyme leaves to make a tea (one teaspoon dried leaves per 10 ounces of boiling water). Add other herbs—such as echinacea or ginger—if you like. Discard herbs before drinking. To reduce congestion, put two teaspoons of dried thyme leaves in 16 ounces of simmering water and carefully breathe the steam for up to 10 minutes twice daily as long as congestion lasts.

GOOD TO KNOW…

Simple Way to Stop a Cold

After tracking the sleep patterns of 164 healthy adults for seven days, researchers then exposed them to a common cold virus. Those who slept six hours or less a night were four times more likely to get sick within five days than those who slept seven hours or more.

Why: Adequate sleep is essential for a healthy immune system.

Aric A. Prather, PhD, assistant professor of psychiatry, University of California, San Francisco School of Medicine.

The Average Sneeze...

One sneeze can contaminate an entire room in minutes. Researchers analyzed videos of two people sneezing about 50 times over several days and found that the average sneeze spread germs throughout a room in minutes and reached as high as the ventilation ducts in the ceiling.

Study by researchers at Massachusetts Institute of Technology, reported at WebMD.com.

Cocktail to Unclog Sinuses

In a pot, combine one cup tomato juice, one teaspoon minced garlic, one-quarter teaspoon cayenne pepper and one teaspoon lemon juice. Heat until warm, and drink!

Joan Wilen and Lydia Wilen, authors of *Bottom Line's Treasury of Home Remedies & Natural Cures*. Subscribe to their free e-letter, *Household Magic Daily Tips*, at BottomLineInc.com.

Beat the Flu...Naturally

Jamison Starbuck, ND, a naturopathic physician in family practice and a guest lecturer at the University of Montana, both in Missoula. She is also a past president of the American Association of Naturopathic Physicians and a contributing editor to *The Alternative Advisor: The Complete Guide to Natural Therapies and Alternative Treatments*. DrJamisonStarbuck.com

You got a flu shot, wash your hands frequently and eat a nutritious diet. There's no way you'll get the flu, right? Despite your best efforts, it still can happen. You'll know soon enough when you're overcome with those all-too-familiar body aches and are beset with fever or chills...a runny nose...headache...tickly cough...and fatigue. As soon as these symptoms strike, it's time to try my "accelerated flu recovery" protocol,

---

EASY-TO-DO...

One-Minute Immunity Boost

Take a one-minute cold shower to ward off illness. Research at the Thrombosis Research Institute in London has found that cold water stimulates immune cell production.

Theory: The body tries to warm itself during and after a cold shower, which speeds up the metabolic rate, activating the immune system.

DailyMail.co.uk

---

which can also be used if you're taking a conventional flu medication such as Tamiflu. *My advice...*

• **Use an antiviral tincture.** Research shows that botanical medicines with antiviral properties stimulate our immune defenses, in part by increasing white blood cell activity. I like herbs in tincture form because they are easily absorbed by the body.

My favorite antiflu formula: Mix equal parts echinacea, osha, lomatium and Oregon grape root (or find a product that contains at least two of these herbs).

Typical adult dose: For three to five days, take 60 drops every four waking hours in two ounces of water 30 minutes before or after eating. (Check with your doctor first if you take medication or are allergic to plants in the daisy family, since some of the herbs could cause a reaction.)

• **Use a face pack.** To speed your flu recovery, it helps to use a "face pack" to get rid of virus-laden mucus from your nose and sinuses.

What to do: Apply one drop of an essential oil—eucalyptus, lavender, sage or thyme, for example, work well for flu—directly to your face at six sinus points (blend with a little baby oil if your skin is sensitive). The sinus points are located on each side of the middle of your nose, about one inch away from the edge...and about one-quarter inch under the inside curve of each eyebrow and above the center of each eyebrow. When you have congestion or the flu, these points may be tender to the touch. Gently rub the essential oil into each spot for 30 seconds (be careful not to get the oil in your eye). Then cover the top of your nose and forehead with a hot, moist towel. Place a dry towel on top of the moist one and lie down with your head slightly elevated for 15 minutes. Breathe deeply, and blow your nose from time to time as needed.

• **Take an Epsom salts bath.** Epsom salts help relieve the body aches that accompany acute flu.

What to do: Put two cups of Epsom salts directly into a hot bath and soak for about 20 minutes once daily. Drink plenty of water before you get into the bath to avoid getting dehydrated and feeling light-headed from the heat. After soaking, drain the water while you remain seated in the tub. Immerse a facecloth in cool water, wring it out and briskly rub the cool, moist cloth all over your arms, legs and trunk before leaving the tub. Take about 45 seconds to do this cooldown—it stimulates blood flow, which promotes healing. Then towel off and lie down, well covered, for at least an hour's rest.

• **Avoid "immunity busters."** When you have the flu, you need to avoid anything that taxes your immune system—for example, exercise, work, stress and technology (computers and cell phones). Your body will heal most quickly if you get a jump-start on healing during the first three days of the flu—before your immune system gets overwhelmed.

Important: See your doctor if you have a fever for more than two days, chest pain, difficulty breathing and/or severe pain—these symptoms could signal a serious condition such as pneumonia.

Flu Facts

Most adults will get the flu two times in 10 years. Children and young adults are more susceptible to the virus—children get it an average of once every other year. After age 30, most adults have built up immunity to the infection and susceptibility decreases. Fre-quency of infection will vary depending on exposure and vaccination history.

Study by researchers at Imperial College of London, UK, published in *PLOS Biology*.

Natural Relief from Asthma

Jamison Starbuck, ND, a naturopathic physician in family practice and a guest lecturer at the University of Montana, both in Missoula. She is also a past president of the American Association of Naturopathic Physicians and a contributing editor to *The Alternative Advisor: The Complete Guide to Natural Therapies and Alternative Treatments.* DrJamisonStarbuck.com

Asthma is a disease that begins in childhood, right? Well, not always. Though many adult asthma sufferers have struggled with the condition since childhood, research shows that up to 40% of new asthma patients are over age 40 when they have their first asthma attack. Some of my patients are surprised when I explain to them the role that a naturopathic physician can play in helping them prevent and control mild-to-moderate asthma. While patients with severe or unresponsive moderate asthma need conventional medical attention, natural medicine has a lot to offer.

First, it's important to recognize which adults are at increased risk of developing asthma. This includes people who suffer from frequent and recurrent upper respiratory infections, such as colds, sinusitis and the flu. When these illnesses occur too frequently (once a month or more often), inflammation can damage the respiratory tract—a perfect setup for asthma. Asthma is also closely linked to allergies (due, for example, to certain food preservatives, such as sodium bisulfate, and inhaled irritants, such as pollen and mold) as well as exposure to pollutants and toxins, including cigarette smoke. Research now shows that severe stress can also trigger an asthma attack.

There's no one-size-fits-all approach to treating asthma. In general, I recommend approaches for my patients that will reduce inflammation and enhance their lung and immune health.

GOOD TO KNOW...

Natural Heartburn Remedy

Chew one to two teaspoons of uncooked oat flakes before swallowing. Oatmeal may help absorb the stomach acid that contributes to heartburn.

David Foley, medical herbalist, TheNaturalWayBlog. blogspot.com.

Asthma-fighting supplements that I frequently recommend (all can be used with asthma medication, if needed)...*

• **Fish oil.** Research has found that these oils reduce bronchial inflammation that often accompanies asthma.

Typical dose: 2,000 milligrams (mg) daily.

• **Antioxidants.** Vitamin C—2,000 mg per day—and vitamin E—400 international units (IU) daily. Both improve immune health and reduce the allergic response that so often triggers an asthma attack.

• **Magnesium.** Use of this mineral (300 mg to 500 mg daily) can reduce *bronchospasm* (a tightening of the airways that makes breathing more difficult).

• **Botanicals.** One of my favorites is astragalus. It supports both lung and immune health.

Typical dose: Use one-quarter teaspoon of tincture in two ounces of water, daily until asthma symptoms improve. Repeat when needed.

Also helpful: Deep-breathing exercises and/or yoga help prevent asthma attacks by calming the nervous system and increasing lung capacity.

Because all asthma patients have different needs, I recommend seeing a naturopathic doctor (ND) to help create a personalized natural regimen. To find an ND near you, consult The American Association of Naturopathic Physicians, Naturopathic.org. But remember, not all asthma can be well controlled with natural medicine. If you have more than mild-to-moderate asthma, you should also be under the care of an allergist or pulmonologist

*Consult your doctor to find out if this asthma-fighting protocol is right for you.

and not shirk any prescription drugs, such as inhalers, that he/she has prescribed for you.

Combining natural medicine with prescription medication (when needed) gives you the best chance of keeping your asthma well controlled!

Powerful Probiotics

Probiotics do more than help digestion. These helpful bacteria also may help prevent a cold, treat high cholesterol, ease anxiety and alleviate allergies. Probiotics must be taken for about five straight days to build up to a useful level and then continue to be consumed regularly. They alter gastrointestinal balance in ways that can fight diarrhea and constipation...prevent release of toxins by harmful bacteria...and improve the strength of the gastrointestinal barrier that allows nutrients through and repels pathogens. Probiotics have few side effects—although people with digestive disorders should talk with a doctor before taking them.

Daniel J. Merenstein, MD, probiotics expert and associate professor of family medicine at Georgetown University in Washington, DC, quoted in *Good Housekeeping.*

Shapewear Warning

Shapewear and restrictive compression athletic tops and pants, worn to enhance the figure or improve athletic performance, put pressure on the abdomen. This can compress your stomach, intestines and colon—making acid reflux and heartburn worse. Shapewear also can worsen symptoms of irritable bowel syndrome and stress incontinence. And sweating in tight clothing can cause skin irritation and yeast infections.

John Kuemmerle, MD, professor and chair, division of gastroenterology, hepatology and nutrition at Virginia Commonwealth University, Richmond.

Better Treatment for Rosacea

The topical cream *ivermectin* has proved to be more effective in treating *papulopustular rosacea*—the type that causes bumps and pus pimples in addition to redness and flushing—than previous medications. In a recent study, 40% of patients who used ivermectin cream once daily over the course of 12 weeks were completely clear or almost clear of lesions associated with this type of rosacea.

Linda Stein Gold, MD, director of clinical research in the department of dermatology at Henry Ford Hospital, Detroit.

Little-Known Dangers to Teeth

Chlorine from swimming pool water can cause dental abrasion—so swim in saltwater whenever possible. *Acidic beverages* such as lemonade and sports drinks can weaken tooth enamel, so drink water instead—or at least have a glass of water after consuming one of these acidic drinks. *White wine* is more acidic than red wine and can erode tooth enamel, so drink water or eat bread between sips of wine. *Berry juices and smoothies* can discolor teeth—drink them with a straw to help liquid pass to the back of your mouth, avoiding your teeth.

EveryDayHealth.com

The Joint That Causes Many Health Issues

The *temporomandibular joint* (TMJ) is a hinge connecting the jaw to the skull near the ear. According to Traditional Chinese Medicine, the joint is connected with the small intestine meridian—a line of energy based on the body's acupuncture points.

Result: TMJ problems can cause digestive disorders. They also can be responsible for trouble chewing, ringing in the ears, headaches, earaches, vertigo and neck and back pain.

Among the treatments for TMJ disorders: Jaw exercises…facial massage…stress management…and/or a nighttime mouth guard.

Victor Zeines, DDS, a holistic dentist in New York City and author of *Healthy Mouth, Healthy Body: The Natural Dental Program for Total Wellness.* NatDent.com

Voice Problems with Age

Susan A. Eicher, MD, associate professor of otolaryngology, Baylor College of Medicine, Houston.

As we age, our muscles and other soft tissues atrophy to some degree, including those in our vocal cords and throat. Older adults may experience a reduction in vocal pitch, volume and endurance. In addition, mucous membranes in the throat thin and dry out during the aging process, which can result in hoarseness.

Talk to your doctor about ways to ease these age-related changes, such as drinking plenty of water (half your body weight in fluid ounces) each day and avoiding alcohol and caffeine. Many medications, such as some blood pressure drugs and antihistamines, can also cause dehydration.

What helps: You can strengthen your voice by reading or singing out loud for 10 or 15 minutes two or three times a day. You may also want to consult a speech-language pathologist, who can devise a program of vocal exercises to specifically address your concerns.

But keep in mind that changes in your voice can also be caused by many medical conditions, such as *gastroesophageal reflux disease* (GERD), allergies, upper-respiratory infection, and in some cases, cancer or Parkinson's disease. If your vocal changes are accompanied

55

by other symptoms, such as pain, coughing up blood, difficulty swallowing, a lump in the neck or hoarseness (possible signs of cancer or other conditions) lasting longer than three weeks, consult an otolaryngologist.

Real Help for Hiccups

Anil Minocha, MD, professor of medicine and chief of gastroenterology, Overton Brooks VA Medical Center, Shreveport, Louisiana, and author of *Dr. M's Seven-X Plan for Digestive Health*.

Hiccups, those annoying chest spasms, are usually caused by gulping air… drinking carbonated or alcoholic beverages…or stress.

What happens: The diaphragm muscle that separates the chest from the abdomen involuntarily contracts, which causes the vocal cords to close suddenly, triggering the "hic" sound. Most episodes of hiccups are brief and don't require medical follow-up.

Folk wisdom abounds, but certain remedies do cure hiccups.

Examples: Close your ears with your fingers while drinking water through a straw. Biting on a lemon also works!

But if your hiccups are persistent and painful, you need to see your doctor. Hiccups can be a sign of many conditions, including *gastroesophageal reflux disease* (GERD), kidney disease or a brain or esophageal tumor.

Hiccups, accompanied by chest pain, can also be a little-known early symptom of stroke in women. Other symptoms of stroke that are unique to women may include shortness of breath and whole-body numbness. If your hiccups are painful and unrelenting and you are also experiencing traditional stroke symptoms—such as blurred vision, severe headache, arm weakness, facial drooping, confusion and/or speech difficulty—call 911.

No More Gout Pain: 5 Easy Steps

Kenneth Saag, MD, a rheumatologist and professor of medicine at The University of Alabama at Birmingham. Dr. Saag is an outcomes researcher with expertise in the safety of drugs used for musculoskeletal disorders and has a clinical focus on bone health. He is the only rheumatologist on the board of directors of the National Osteoporosis Foundation. NOF.org

Julia, age 65, woke with a start at 2 am with excruciating pain in her big toe (it felt like nothing she had experienced before). Even the light touch of the sheet was unbearable. The toe was not only extremely painful but red, swollen and stiff.

Her diagnosis the next day at the doctor: Gout.

If you've ever had an attack of gout, you'd certainly remember it and want to do everything you can to dodge a future attack. On the other hand, if you've never experienced it, you will want to do what you can to avoid going down that painful road.

Caused by a buildup of uric acid, a first attack of gout tends to strike in the middle of the night, usually in the joint of the big toe. And risk for follow-up attacks is very high.

The dangers: While the initial flare-up may subside in about three to 10 days without treatment, long-term complications from repeated attacks can be serious. Gout can damage and deform your joints and bones…interfere with walking, driving and other day-to-day activities…and seriously harm your quality of life. It's also been associated with greater risk for stroke, high blood pressure, heart attack and kidney stones.

Gout is on the rise, now affecting about 8.3 million Americans—most likely due to the increase of chronic disease and obesity in the US. It tends to run in families, occurs more often in people who suffer from chronic illness such as those mentioned above and is affecting more women than ever before.

But there are actions you can take that have been proven to reduce the likelihood of having one of these painful episodes—whether you're looking to ward off recurrent gout flare-ups or a first attack…*

• **Lose weight.** Extra weight reduces the ability of the kidneys to flush out uric acid, resulting in a greater possibility of a gout flare-up. One study in women found that obesity increased the risk for gout by 2.4 times. That number jumped to 2.8 for those who became obese in early or mid-adulthood.

What to do: Talk with your doctor about losing weight gradually through diet and exercise. Ironically, crash dieting (eating very little in order to lose weight quickly) and low-carb diets can *increase* the odds of a flare-up, as both cause uric acid levels to rise.

• **Avoid high-purine foods.** Purines are chemicals in food that lead to the production of uric acid.

The list of foods with purine is very long. You don't need to avoid all of these foods, but if you're prone to gout it's best to moderate your consumption of purine-rich red meat, organ meats and seafood (particularly anchovies, herring, mackerel, sardines, tuna, haddock and scallops).

Foods that may offer protection against gout flare-ups: Low-fat dairy products and cherries. Vitamin C (from food or a supplement) may also help.

• **Re-evaluate aspirin and diuretics.** Daily low-dose aspirin can trigger gout by increasing levels of uric acid in the blood. And diuretics, which are commonly used to treat high blood pressure and heart disease, may limit the kidneys' ability to remove uric acid.

If you take one of these drugs and develop gout, ask your doctor if there are other medications (or dosages) that can be considered.

Caution: Never stop taking a medication without your doctor's approval.

• **Stay well hydrated.** If you're predisposed to gout, drinking too little liquid can increase the concentration of uric acid in the blood, resulting in an attack.

Best: Drink eight eight-ounce glasses of water a day (excess uric acid will then be ex-

*If your gout flares up more than twice a year, it is important to see a doctor for treatment.

creted via urination). Also, avoid regular soda and many other sweetened drinks that contain high-fructose corn syrup, which has been shown to increase uric acid levels.

• **Limit alcohol use.** Overindulging in alcohol results in a damaging one-two punch to the body. It not only increases uric acid levels in the bloodstream and kidneys but also blocks the kidneys from excreting uric acid. While some studies have suggested that beer and hard liquor are worse than wine, the jury's still out.

What to do: If you have gout or are looking to prevent it, play it safe—avoid beer and hard liquor and limit consumption of wine.

A MEDICATION THAT STEMS FLARE-UPS

Most patients will have a significant reduction, if not complete resolution, of gout attacks with the prescription drug *allopurinol*, which can be taken indefinitely, unless there is a change in health that lowers uric acid levels in the body naturally.

It may take a few dosage adjustments to achieve the target uric acid level of 6 mg/dL or lower. Also, especially in the first two weeks of taking this drug, some patients experience a gout flare-up, so doctors often prescribe anti-inflammatory medications with this drug.

Allopurinol is generally very well tolerated, but in rare cases, it can cause a severe rash. If this happens, contact your doctor.

TAKE NOTE…

About Gout

Gout, one of the most painful forms of arthritis, is caused by a buildup of uric acid, which is normally eliminated through urination. If the kidneys aren't able to process uric acid correctly or if the body ups the amount it's producing, uric acid morphs into sharp crystal deposits. These crystals tend to collect in the joints (most commonly in the joint of the big toe, but deposits can also collect in the ankle or knee joint and even under the skin), causing swelling, heat, stiffness and excruciating pain.

A Plan for Plantar Fasciitis

A common condition in middle-aged adults, plantar fasciitis happens when the ligament that connects the heel bone to the toes becomes inflamed. Wearing a splint at night should help ease pain by gently stretching the ligament. Another way to stretch is to place a rolled towel on the ball of your foot, then hold both ends of the towel and gently pull with your knee straight. You should do this several times a day. Rolling the foot on a frozen plastic bottle of water and taking a nonsteroidal anti-inflammatory drug such as *ibuprofen* (Motrin) or *naproxen* (Aleve) will help with pain and inflammation. It is also important to wear shoes with good arch support and a cushioned sole, and use orthotic inserts if needed. Avoid wearing flip-flops.

If these measures don't help, consult a board-certified podiatrist, who may recommend custom orthotics, corticosteroid injections or, in some cases, surgery.

Neil A. Campbell, DPM, staff podiatrist, Cuero Community Hospital, Texas.

EASY-TO-DO...

Prevent an Ingrown Toenail

An ingrown toenail is painful and hard to get rid of—but British researchers offer a physics-based solution. Ingrown toenails are caused by disparities in force (rate of growth plus the nail's attachment to the skin) in different parts of the nail bed. Solve this by cutting nails with an ever-so-slight curve at the corners and arcing up toward the center rather than straight across. This helps balance the forces so that the nail will grow up without pushing back into the skin at the corners of the nail bed.

Study conducted by physicists Cyril Rauch and Mohammed Cherkaoui-Rbati of University of Nottingham, UK, published in *Physical Biology*.

How to Get Your Balance Back: 5 Strategies to Help You Stay Active

Jack J. Wazen, MD, an otology and neurotology surgeon and a partner at the Silverstein Institute and Florida Ear and Sinus Center in Sarasota. He specializes in the treatment of acoustic neuromas, ear-bone degeneration and other conditions that affect hearing/balance. He is coauthor of *Dizzy: What You Need to Know About Managing and Treating Balance Disorders*.

Anyone who has ever suffered from dizziness and/or that wobbly feeling of being unsteady on your feet knows how miserable it can be.

Literally *hundreds* of conditions can cause dizziness and related balance problems. This topsy-turvy feeling usually doesn't last more than a week or two and can generally be treated with medication or simply waited out—but not always.

Good news: For the estimated 10 million Americans who suffer from chronic dizziness and/or balance problems, many therapies can help.

WHAT GOES WRONG

Most people with long-term dizziness and balance problems have some sort of damage to the *vestibular system*, a complex structure of nerves and fluid-filled tubes and chambers in the inner ear that detect motion and send signals to the brain to help maintain equilibrium.

As we grow older, the number of vestibular nerve cells naturally decreases and blood circulation declines, including to the inner ear. These changes—along with conditions such as diabetes (blood vessels in the body may narrow, impeding blood circulation)...viral infections of the vestibular nerve...benign tumors (such as acoustic neuromas, which grow on the nerve leading from the inner ear to the brain)...or Ménière's disease (fluid buildup in the inner ear)—can cause a permanent dizzy and/or unsteady feeling.

WHERE TO START

If you have suffered from dizziness and/or a balance problem, specifically a spinning sensation, see an ENT (ear, nose and throat specialist), who can determine if your vestibular system may be affected. Some problems can be treated with a simple head maneuver in a doctor's office, while others may require further testing, medications or even the help of a physical therapist trained in vestibular rehabilitation.

This form of therapy, which involves gait training, head movements and positioning exercises, will strengthen the vestibular system, reduce symptoms and improve your sense of balance. To find a local therapist, consult the Vestibular Disorders Association website, Vestibular.org. Most insurers cover this therapy if an ENT orders it.

HOW TO HELP YOURSELF

In addition to working with a physical therapist, self-care approaches can be a tremendous help...

SECRET #1: Try tai chi and/or yoga. Both tai chi and yoga can improve gait, posture and other measures of physical performance in people with vestibular disorders. If you feel a little unsteady, these gentle workouts tend to be more enjoyable—and safer—than most other forms of exercise. Either exercise can be done weekly or even daily for an hour at a time.

Caution: For certain vestibular disorders, such as a treatable inner ear problem known as *benign positional vertigo*, your vertigo may worsen with these exercises, so see an ENT first. If your dizziness/balance problem is due to some other condition, your symptoms may also initially worsen because the exercises are stressing a system that's somewhat damaged. The dizziness/balance problems should start to improve within a few weeks.

SECRET #2: Take off your shoes. Your feet are more than just a platform for standing. They're part of the *proprioceptive system*, which integrates nerve signals from the feet, ankles, eyes and other parts of the body to provide spatial orientation. Walking barefoot makes it easier to "feel" that you're in the right space.

Try walking barefoot when you're active at home or doing exercises such as tai chi or yoga. When it's not practical to take off your shoes, wear shoes with thin soles or thick, protective, slip-proof socks if you're worried about foot injuries in the house. Most people feel steadier—and less dizzy—when their feet can feel what's under them.

Helpful: Practice standing and walking on various floor surfaces—such as a hard floor, a thin carpet and a thick rug—to improve your dizziness/balance problems. Doing this can challenge and "re-educate" the proprioceptive system.

SECRET #3: Cope with "busy" spaces. Our balance largely depends on our vision to identify points of reference (such as an object in the distance) that tell us if we are moving in a straight line or heading off course. In places with a lot of activity and "clutter," such as shopping malls and supermarkets, it's hard to get a visual fix.

Helpful: Keep your eyes focused on what's right in front of you. Don't let your eyes wander until you need to look at something new—for example, when you're reaching for a product on a shelf.

SECRET #4: Learn your visual weaknesses. Some people with dizziness/balance problems avoid escalators because they can't handle the movement of the steps...or feel unsteady when they walk, say, on checkered tiles. Even though you're working to retrain the vestibular system and be comfortable in the world, you may simply need to avoid certain environments, such as busy restaurants, sporting events and crowded shopping malls.

SECRET #5: Change positions slowly. *Orthostatic hypotension* is a common trigger for dizziness and balance problems. It's caused by low blood pressure that usually occurs when you're changing positions—when you get out of bed, for example, or when you stand up from a seated position. You probably don't need treatment if it's mild—and your doctor has ruled out a more serious problem, such as heart disease or hypoglycemia. But you must be careful!

My advice: Take your time when changing positions. In the morning, sit up in bed for a minute or two so that your blood pressure can stabilize before you stand up. Then carefully stand up. Stand still for a moment, then walk when you're sure that you're steady.

A Vitamin That Prevents Falls!

You can help prevent falls with vitamin D. When 68 homebound people over age 65 received either a monthly vitamin D supplement (100,000 international units) or a placebo, those who took vitamin D fell about half as often as the placebo group over a five-month period.

Why: Those who took vitamin D corrected deficiencies. Adequate levels of this vitamin are needed for muscle strength and balance.

Denise Houston, PhD, RD, associate professor of internal medicine, Wake Forest School of Medicine, Winston-Salem, North Carolina.

How to Fall Safely

Marilyn Moffat, DPT, PhD, a professor of physical therapy at New York University in New York City, reported by Rebecca Shannonhouse, editor, *Bottom Line Health.*

I knew it was going to be bad. I had caught the heel of my boot on my pants leg and felt myself hurtling down the final few steps of a marble staircase. Somehow, I surprised myself and managed to land on my feet. But not everyone is so lucky.

We've all read plenty of articles about the best ways to prevent falls, but few of them describe how to fall.

BETTER WAY...

Quick Pain Relief

Fill a sock with uncooked rice, and tie a knot at the end. To soothe aches and pains, microwave the sock 20 seconds at a time until warm and use it as a heat pack—or freeze it for a cold pack.

Blisstree.com

Sooner or later, we all encounter one of the many fall hazards—uneven sidewalks, curb grates, an unexpected step or simply tangled feet. What do you do when you know you're going down?

Try these pointers...

If you fall forward: Don't stick out your arms to "break" the fall. The only thing that will get broken is your arm or wrist.

Instead, keep your head up and let your knees hit the ground first. If you can, briefly slap your palms on the ground to slow the fall.

If you fall sideways: Try to grab the opposite hip and roll sideways as you fall.

For a backward fall: Fold your hips and knees at the same time...land on your buttocks...and roll backward.

But how do you remember all this when you're going down? "Individuals may practice falling," says Marilyn Moffat, DPT, PhD, a professor of physical therapy at New York University in New York City. You can use soft mats to absorb any impact—but only if your bones and joints are healthy, she adds. For appropriate guidance, consult a physical therapist, since strength and balance may need to be developed first.

For practical videos that show fall techniques, go to TWU.edu/health-safety/Falling Safely.asp.

No More Neck Pain! 4 Simple Stretches

Robert Turner, PT, OCS, a board-certified orthopedic clinical specialist and clinical supervisor at the Hospital for Special Surgery's Spine Therapy Center in New York City. Turner is also a licensed acupuncturist and certified Pilates instructor.

Neck pain can be agonizing. But there's more at stake than the discomfort itself. This common complaint also can lead to collateral damage that you'd never expect—by contributing to anxiety or depression.

Problem: Far too many people live with this painful condition for *years* because they don't really get to the root of the problem.

What's the cause of all this pain? Much of it boils down to poor posture—we sit at computers or in cars for hours at a time…our heads leaning forward to help us see the screen or the road. With our arms extended in front of us, we naturally round forward and our chests tighten, weakening the back muscles—a significant but under-appreciated cause of neck pain.

If you hold a phone between your ear and shoulder or carry a heavy bag over one shoulder, you're only making matters worse. Or you may awaken with a "crick" in your neck from sleeping in an awkward position. And if you lie on the couch for hours at a time, you're speeding the muscle atrophy and inflexibility that will keep you in misery.

But there is hope! Doing the right type of stretching is incredibly effective at relieving neck pain.

What gets overlooked: While you might be tempted to target only the neck itself in these stretches, it's crucial to also do chest and back stretches to help correct musculoskeletal system imbalances and restore flexibility.

Here are four great stretches for neck pain—the entire routine can be performed in about 10 minutes.* (If you're short on time, just do the first two stretches when you start to feel

*These exercises are safe for most people. If you experience pain, numbness or tingling in the hand or arm that does not go away after exercise or becomes worse, don't do the exercise again and tell your doctor.

neck discomfort or after you've been sitting for 90 minutes.)

• **Chicken wings.** This move opens the chest and strengthens the shoulder blades, which helps relieve pressure on the neck.

What to do: While sitting up straight on a chair, extend your arms out to the sides and touch your fingertips to your shoulders. Roll both shoulders back and down. You should feel the muscles between your blades contract. The key is not working too hard—give it 50% of your effort, not 100%—or you'll end up straining your neck. Hold for one breath in and one breath out, then relax. Repeat 10 times. Perform this series twice a day.

• **Triple neck stretch.** These exercises stretch the larger muscles that attach the head and neck to the shoulders.

What to do: While sitting on the edge of a chair, lightly press the back of your right hand against the middle of your lower back, with your right elbow pointing directly out to the side. While looking straight ahead, tilt your head to the left, being careful not to rotate your neck. (You can use your left hand to gently pull your head down, intensifying the stretch.) Hold for five to 10 breaths.

For the second step, with your right hand still on your back and your head still tilted to the left, rotate your chin down so that your nose is pointing toward your left armpit. You'll start to feel a deeper stretch in the back of your neck and chest. (Keep sitting tall, and don't let your right shoulder hunch forward.) Hold for five to 10 breaths.

Lastly, with your nose still pointing toward your armpit, place the palm of your right hand behind your neck, keeping your shoulder blades down, and hold for five to 10 breaths. Repeat the three-step series on the other side of your body, and you have just completed one round. Try to do one or two more rounds throughout the day...or whenever pain crops up.

• **Prone extension.** This move strengthens your back muscles so that your neck does not have to work so hard to maintain proper posture. *Note:* If you have low-back pain, put a pillow under your hips when doing this stretch and the next one to avoid straining this part of your back.

What to do: Lie on your stomach on a padded mat or carpet with your hands stacked beneath your forehead, legs straight and your knees and ankles together.

Pull your navel in toward your spine to help support your lower back, and push both shoulder blades down toward your feet as you in-

hale and arch your upper back at least two to three inches off the floor (your hands and arms should rise with your upper body). Exhale on the way back down. Repeat for a total of 10 lifts. Take a brief break, then repeat two more sets, eventually progressing to three sets of 15.

• **Shoulder blade lift.** This stretch will strengthen the back and shoulder muscles that help maintain correct head and neck alignment.

What to do: Lie on your stomach on a padded mat or carpet with a rolled-up towel placed beneath your forehead, nose point-

ing toward the floor to keep your neck in a straight line and your arms pointed forward in a Y formation.

While keeping your head down and neck relaxed, inhale as you lift your arms, hands and upper chest a few inches off the floor... hold for a beat, and exhale as your arms lower back down. Repeat 10 times. You will feel the muscles around the shoulder blades and middle back engage to lift the arms.

Caution: If you experience shoulder pain, modify the stretch by bending your elbows

into a wide goalpost position. People who have had rotator cuff surgery or a shoulder injury can try this move while lying facedown on a bed, raising the arms off the edge of the bed toward the ceiling.

6 Health Mistakes You're Making Before 10 am...and Easy Fixes

Reza Yavari, MD, founder of Beyond Care, a life-style-management center based in Madison, Connecticut, that focuses on endocrine and metabolic disorders. He is adjunct faculty member at Yale University School of Medicine and author of *It Must Be My Metabolism!*. BeyondCare.net

You had plenty of sleep, a good breakfast and maybe even got in some exercise. That's a good start on the day, right? Not necessarily. You may be surprised to learn that you are making several health mistakes before you even walk out the door in the morning. *Here are six common health mistakes many people make every morning— and quick, easy fixes...*

1. Your supposedly healthful breakfast leaves you hungry and tired by midmorning. We all know that eating breakfast is a must. After a long night without food, your blood sugar is low and you won't have the mental and physical energy to function well if you don't fuel up.

Common mistake: Eating only carbohydrates—such as a whole-wheat English muffin with jam. By eating an all-carb morning meal, you are setting yourself up for all-day food cravings. The carbs cause a spike in insulin followed by a plummet in your blood sugar, which in turn makes you hungry and leaves you craving more carbs in an hour or two.

The fix: For breakfast, go ahead and have your whole-wheat or whole-grain English muffin or toast, if you like, but add protein (an egg or two) and perhaps even some fat— cheese on the egg, for instance, or peanut butter on toast. Doing this releases your satiety hormones and maintains steady blood sugar so that you won't be hungry and fatigued by midmorning.

2. You're stuck in an exercise routine. Research shows that exercise in the morning helps you feel more alert because it boosts your circulation. It also revs up your metabolism for about six hours afterward.

Common mistake: Doing the same workout every morning. Limiting yourself to one type of exercise is certainly better than being sedentary, but it shortchanges you of important fitness benefits. Switching among a variety of workouts challenges different body parts. Optimal health requires a mix of both heart-healthy cardio and strength-building resistance-training.

The fix: Mix up your workout routine to incorporate variety. For instance, you might take an early-morning walk on Monday and Wednesday…visit the gym Tuesday, Thursday and Friday mornings (doing different activities at each visit)…and then, on weekends, go for a bike ride, swim or hike.

3. You are making your coffee wrong. If you love the caffeine jolt from a cup of coffee, the news is good. Though coffee used to be considered unhealthy, medical research shows that most people can safely drink several cups a day, and it even may bring health benefits. Drinking coffee has been linked with lower risk for depression, Parkinson's disease, diabetes and other illnesses.

Common mistake: Though it may seem fiscally and environmentally responsible to purchase a reusable metallic filter, doing so may cause a rise in your cholesterol. Why? Paper filters absorb—and therefore block—a substance called *cafestol* that is found in the oil contained in coffee beans. Cafestol stimulates the production of LDL (bad) cholesterol, the kind you're better off keeping low.

The fix: Use paper coffee filters if you have high cholesterol or want to prevent it. In addition to avoiding metal filters, don't use a French press or K-cups.

4. You hit the snooze button on your alarm clock. It's true that you probably could use more sleep. Though adults need between seven and eight hours of sleep a night, nearly 30% of us get less than six hours, according to the Centers for Disease Control and Prevention. Insufficient sleep is linked to a wide range of health and medical problems, including cancer, heart disease, obesity and premature death.

Common mistake: Hitting the snooze button and closing your eyes for just a few more minutes. You may justify this by telling yourself that a bit more rest will improve your day, but actually it won't. You're allowing yourself to drift back to sleep just when your body is beginning to wake up. You'll probably feel more out of it, even though you actually spent extra time in bed.

The fix: It's best to establish a sleep schedule that allows your body to rest when you are tired and wake up refreshed when it is time to start the day. Try to fall asleep and wake up at the same times each day. If you can't wake up naturally, it's OK to use an alarm, but get up when it first wakes you—don't hit the snooze button. If possible, choose an alarm with a sound that's gentle, not jarring (many smartphones offer a variety of tones for this purpose). Or look for an alarm clock with sounds that gradually increase in intensity or one that wakes you up with a light that grows brighter by the minute.

5. You're not opening the shades. Whether for privacy or because a partner needs to sleep longer, many people don't get morning light.

Common mistake: Keeping the curtains/ blinds closed as you get up and get dressed. The morning light is a signal to your brain and body that the day has begun. It also triggers your body to switch off the production of *melatonin*, the hormone that helps your body keep track of time and also regulates the need to sleep. Darkness after awakening prolongs your sleepiness.

The fix: If possible, open your shades or curtains to bring in the morning light. If that's not possible or it's dark outside when you get up, turn on the lights. If your partner needs to sleep longer, try getting dressed in another room.

6. You don't listen to your partner's complaints that you snore. Many couples, even happy ones, stop listening to each other even when they have legitimate complaints.

Common mistake: Ignoring your significant other's complaints about your snoring. That's bad for two reasons—your snoring could ruin his/her sleep…and it could be affecting your own health. The research that links snoring and sleep apnea to serious medical problems continues to pile up. Just recently, researchers at NYU Langone Medical Center in New York City found that loud snorers developed symptoms of dementia 10 years earlier, on average, than people who don't snore—and that getting treatment for snoring helped delay the onset of dementia.

The fix: Talk to your doctor about getting tested for sleep apnea. Treatment (ranging from losing weight to the use of a breathing machine, among other options) can reduce dementia risk.

When to Have Your First Cup of Coffee…

Wait to have your first cup of coffee until between 9:30 am and 11:30 am.

Reason: For most people, the body naturally produces cortisol—a hormone that makes us feel alert, between 8:00 am and 9:00 am, so you don't need caffeine that early to help you wake up.

And: Drinking caffeine too early can lead to too much cortisol, and that can disturb your body's circadian rhythms.

Psychology Today. PsychologyToday.com

Mouth-and-Tongue Exercises to Reduce Snoring

Among people who snore, including those who have a mild form of obstructive sleep apnea, mouth-and-tongue exercises decreased the frequency of snoring by 36% and intensity of sound by 59%.

Exercises included pushing the tip of the tongue against the roof of the mouth and sliding the tongue backward…sucking the tongue upward against the roof of the mouth and pressing the entire tongue against the roof of the mouth…forcing the back of the tongue against the floor of the mouth while keeping the tip of the tongue in contact with the bottom front teeth…and while eating, biting down, then lifting your tongue to the roof of your mouth as you swallow, without tightening your cheek muscles.

Study led by researchers at University of São Paulo Medical School, São Paulo, Brazil, published in the journal *Chest.*

TAKE NOTE…

Foods That Help You Sleep

Try having one of these snacks one hour before bedtime. Kiwis are rich in *serotonin*, a hormone and neurotransmitter that promotes sleep. Cheese and whole-wheat crackers contain 80% carbohydrates and 20% protein, the best ratio for boosting serotonin. But skip aged cheeses, such as Parmesan—they have an amino acid that can raise levels of stimulating chemicals. Tart cherry juice contains high levels of the hormone *melatonin*, which may help you sleep longer and more soundly.

Michael Breus, PhD, sleep specialist in private practice in Los Angeles and author of *The Power of When: Discover Your Chronotype*, writing in *Shape.* TheSleepDoctor.com

Benefits of Sleeping in the Buff...

There are numerous health benefits to sleeping naked (but it is inadvisable with small children around or pets in the bed). Recent research has found that sleeping in a chilly room (or staying cool by sleeping naked) increases brown fat, a healthy type of fat that burns calories to make heat. For the best night's sleep, aim for a bedroom temperature of about 65°F and keep your hands and feet warm.

Men (and women) who sleep in their underwear or tight pajamas are more likely to get genital infections due to trapped heat and moisture. But the best benefit of sleeping in the nude may be skin-to-skin contact between bed partners, which triggers the release of the feel-good hormone *oxytocin*. Studies have shown that oxytocin increases a feeling of connection between partners, relieves stress and lowers blood pressure.

Michael Breus, PhD, sleep specialist in private practice in Los Angeles and author of *The Power of When: Discover Your Chronotype*. TheSleepDoctor.com

4 Healthful Snacks When You're in a Hurry

Dawn Jackson Blatner, RDN, a registered dietitian nutritionist in private practice in Chicago. She is also author of *The Flexitarian Diet: The Mostly Vegetarian Way to Lose Weight, Be Healthier, Prevent Disease, and Add Years to Your Life* and the nutrition consultant for the Chicago Cubs.

Is it just wishful thinking that snacks can be healthful, tasty and satisfying? Absolutely not!

One cup of grape tomatoes plus a stick of string cheese is a great option for pizza lovers. Got a sweet and salty craving? A green apple plus 10 lightly salted almonds will do the trick. And if you are a "crunchaholic," try three celery stalks, each topped with a half tablespoon of peanut butter.

BETTER WAY...

The Coffee Nap

A 20-minute coffee nap can make you more alert.

What to do: Drink a cup of caffeinated coffee—it takes about 20 minutes for caffeine to affect your brain. Then immediately take a nap or rest calmly if you cannot fall fully asleep. The combination of brief rest and the caffeine in coffee makes you more alert when you get up.

Vox.com, a general-interest news site.

But if it's true convenience that you're looking for—something that requires no prep time, can be grabbed on your way out the door and even left in your bag for a day or two—you'll need to look further.

A good solution: More and more companies are now introducing prepackaged creative snacking solutions that are packed with vitamins and minerals as well as satisfying combinations of protein and fiber.

If you're watching your weight: Thoughtful snacking can help you bridge meals so you can get from lunch to dinner without becoming so ravenous that you go overboard when you get home. The snacks below have 100 to 200 calories per serving.

Four healthful snack choices...

•**Ocean's Halo Seaweed Chips.** A single serving (26 chips) of this hearty, crunchy snack contains 200% of your daily iodine requirement (great for thyroid health)...and 130% of your daily requirement for vitamin B-12 (a nutrient commonly found in animal protein and often lacking in vegetarians and adults over the age of 50, whose bodies are less able to absorb it).

These chips are also relatively high in protein (6 grams [g] per serving) and fiber (4 g per serving), so they'll keep you full far longer than potato chips. And they come in fun flavors such as Chili Lime and Korean BBQ.

Cost: $3.99/bag.* The chips are available at Safeway, Vons and Whole Foods Market. Or online at OceansHalo.com.

*Prices subject to change.

Quick Memory Trick

For an easy trick to help you remember, close your eyes.

Recent research: Adults who closed their eyes after watching videos of crime reenactments had 23% better recall of what they'd seen and heard than those who kept their eyes open.

Explanation: Closing your eyes helps block distractions, improves focus and helps you visualize what you're trying to remember about past events and experiences.

Robert A. Nash, PhD, lecturer in psychology, Aston University, Birmingham, UK.

•**SuperSeedz Gourmet Pumpkin Seeds.** This delicious snack is a protein powerhouse—depending on the flavor, each one-quarter cup serving contains as much as 9 g (as much protein as you will find in a jumbo egg).

Unlike nuts, seeds are allergen-friendly, and each serving of pumpkin seeds provides 15% of your daily needs for both zinc (good for prostate health) and iron (a nutrient that boosts energy). Additionally, each serving has up to 2 g of fiber.

The mouth-watering flavors are also great to spice up meals: Curious Curry, for example, would be tasty in a veggie stir-fry...Maple Sugar & Sea Salt would liven up oatmeal...and Tomato Italiano could be sprinkled over a salad for a savory crunch. You could even grind up the latter and use them to coat chicken or fish.

Cost: $3.99 to $4.99/bag. Available at King Kullen, Sprouts Farmers Market and Whole Foods Market. Or online at SuperSeedz.com.

•**i heart keenwah Quinoa Clusters.** These crunchy little squares are made with organic quinoa and nuts. They are a respectable option when it comes to protein and fiber—3 g and 2 g per serving respectively. And with sweet flavor options such as Chocolate Sea Salt and Peanut Ginger, they are a smarter way to satisfy a sugar craving than, say, a cookie. Still, they do contain a fair amount of sugar (about

7 g per serving), so be sure to portion each four-ounce bag into four separate servings.

Cost: $4.99/bag. Available at Safeway, The Fresh Market and Whole Foods Market. Or online at iheartkeenwah.com.

•**Epic Bars.** Remember those hard-to-gnaw Slim Jim–style meat snacks sold at the gas station? Well, there's now a more natural jerky option. Epic Bars are tender, protein-rich treats (11 g per bar) that are made with interesting cuts of meats (Bison Bacon Cranberry...Lamb Currant Mint...and Pulled Pork Pineapple) and are fairly low in sodium (about 220 mg per serving). Because the animals are grass-fed, the meat is high in omega-3 fatty acids for cardiovascular health, and conjugated linoleic acid, a naturally occurring fatty acid that may reduce body fat.

Cost: $2.69 to $2.99 each. These bars are vailable at REI, Sprouts Farmers Market and Whole Foods Market. Or online at Bottom LineStore.com (type "Epic Bars" in the search box) or at EpicBar.com.

Easy Energy Boost

During an afternoon slump, brush your teeth. This gets you up for a few minutes and gives your mind a break...and the rush of mint perks you up. No time to brush? Try mint gum.

GovLoop.com

Happier in 30 Seconds

A recent study found that people reported feeling happier, more energetic and less stressed after watching a cat video. To find a video, go to YouTube.com and search "cat" or "Lil Bub" (an Internet favorite).

Study of nearly 7,000 people conducted by Jessica Gall Myrick, PhD, assistant professor at Indiana University, Bloomington, published in *Computers in Human Behavior.*

4

Easy Fitness and Diet

5 Reasons You Can't Lose Weight...

Most people can't lose weight and keep it off simply by focusing on calories and exercise. Millions of Americans who exercise and diet still cannot drop all of the pounds they really want to—or keep off the pounds that they manage to lose initially. Why not?

It's because weight loss (or the tendency to gain weight) depends on thousands of biochemical reactions that are not affected just by exercise and calories. Most people need a multilevel approach to get their weight where they want it.

Here's what to do...

PREVENT INSULIN SURGES

Research has shown that high insulin triggers food cravings, particularly cravings for high-carbohydrate (and calorie-laden) foods.

And elevated insulin stimulates the liver to convert blood sugar into fat.

One cause of elevated insulin is a low-fiber diet—most Americans consume only about 15 grams (g) a day, far less than the 30 g to 50 g grams that many experts recommend.

People who increase their fiber intake by eating more fruits, vegetables, legumes and other plant foods feel less hungry. They're less likely to load up on fattening, sugar-rich foods. More of their blood sugar is burned as energy—and less is stored as fat.

Bonus: Fiber can help reduce cholesterol and reduce the risk for heart disease, high blood pressure and diabetes.

Pamela Wartian Smith, MD, MPH, MS, codirector, Master's Program in Medical Sciences with a concentration in metabolic and nutritional medicine, Morsani College of Medicine, University of South Florida, Tampa. She is also founding partner of the Center for Personalized Medicine with offices in Michigan and Florida and author of *Why You Can't Lose Weight: Why It's So Hard to Shed Pounds and What You Can Do About It.* CFHLL.com

My advice: Look for foods that contain at least 5 g of fiber per serving. A single cup of lentils, for example, has about 15 g of fiber. A large apple has about 5 g, and a sweet potato has about 6 g.

Many of my patients take advantage of high-fiber powders or drinks. These products typically contain 10 g or more of fiber per serving—some contain as much as 30 grams. Supplementing with fiber can help if you're not getting enough from "real" foods. Make sure you choose a fiber supplement that does not have a lot of sugar added.

Important: Drink at least a few extra glasses of water a day when you're increasing fiber. Fiber absorbs water in the intestine and can lead to constipation if you don't stay hydrated.

BEWARE OF SLEEP-DEPRIVATION CRAVINGS

It's estimated that about 60 million American adults don't get a good night's sleep. Sleep deprivation causes the body to produce more *ghrelin* (an appetite-stimulating hormone) and less *leptin* (a hormone that suppresses hunger).

Research has shown that sleep loss tends to trigger cravings for "quick energy" foods such as sodas and snacks. Paradoxically, these are the same foods that ultimately can increase your overall fatigue.

My advice: In addition to better sleep hygiene—such as keeping regular hours, not watching TV or using a computer in bed and avoiding late-day caffeine—sip a cup of chamomile tea about an hour before going to bed. It's a natural tranquilizer that will help you fall asleep more quickly. Lemon balm tea has a similar effect.

Also helpful: Talk to your doctor about taking 100 milligrams (mg) to 200 mg of a magnesium supplement daily at bedtime. It's a "calming" mineral that helps the brain shut down at the end of the day.

REDUCE CORTISOL

Cortisol is a hormone that slows metabolism and causes more calories to be stored as fat. Cortisol also stimulates appetite and increases levels of *neuropeptide Y*, a substance that triggers carb cravings.

Chronic stress increases cortisol. People have gotten so accustomed to living in a high-stress world that they don't even notice they are stressed. But your body notices.

Warning: Elevated cortisol causes more of the body's fat to be stored in the abdomen. Abdominal fat increases the risk for heart disease and other serious conditions—and is harder to lose than other types of fat.

My advice: Ask your doctor for a saliva test for cortisol. It will indicate how much (or how little) stress you really have. I have found that people who test high get really motivated about taking life down a notch—with exercise, meditation, fun hobbies, etc. The test typically costs between $50 and $150 or more and may be covered by insurance.

Lifestyle changes will help most people cope with stress more efficiently, but they don't work for everyone. You may need a nutritional supplement to reduce cortisol. I recommend combination products because they tend to work better than single-ingredient supplements. The active ingredients should include magnesium and the herbs ginseng, ashwaghanda and rhodiola. Ask at your pharmacy or health-food store for recommendations. Take the dose listed on the label.

REDUCE INFLAMMATION

If you're overweight, you can assume that you have ongoing inflammation in your body. Unlike the acute inflammation that accompanies wounds and infections, such chronic inflammation occurs when the body continues to produce inflammatory substances (such as *cytokines*) even in the absence of injuries or infections.

The body's *adipose* (fatty) tissue produces *C-reactive protein* and other chemicals that fuel inflammation. Chronic inflammation makes the body resistant to the appetite-suppressing effects of leptin. It also interferes with the breakdown of fat and causes fat cells to get larger.

Inflammation also has indirect effects on your weight. Suppose that you have rheumatoid arthritis, asthma or another inflammatory condition. You'll naturally be less active and more likely to gain weight.

My advice: Ask your doctor to test you for indicators of chronic inflammation. The tests might include CRP (C-reactive protein), ESR (*erythrocyte sedimentation rate*) or an inflammatory cytokine profile.

Also, eat less meat, fat and processed foods (which tend to be inflammatory) and more plant foods. A Mediterranean-type diet is probably ideal because it's high in anti-inflammatory compounds—from fish, vegetables, olive oil, etc.

DEAL WITH MENOPAUSE

The average woman gains 12 to 15 pounds or more during menopause. This is partly due to an age-related drop in metabolism. In addition, the menopausal decline in estrogen causes the body to seek this hormone elsewhere—and fat cells are the primary source. The result is that your body works harder to convert calories into fat. The increase in fat slows your metabolism even more, which promotes even more weight gain.

My advice: Hormone therapy is an effective way to prevent menopause-associated weight gain. See a doctor who specializes in *bioidentical natural hormone replacement*. Bioidentical hormones don't appear to have the same health risks that have been linked to synthetic hormones.

Also important: Exercise for at least 30 minutes three to four days of the week—more if you can. A combination of aerobic exercise and strength training is ideal. Regular exercise helps counteract the drop in metabolism

caused by menopause-related fluctuations of estrogen, progesterone and other hormones.

Want to Lose Weight? Stop Dieting!

John M. Kennedy, MD, a clinical associate professor of cardiology at Harbor-UCLA Medical Center in Los Angeles, director of preventive cardiology and wellness at Marina Del Rey Hospital and founder of Encardia Wellness, a health, wellness and fitness consultancy in San Francisco. He is author of *The Heart Health Bible: The 5-Step Plan to Prevent and Reverse Heart Disease.*

People will go on a diet (or watch their weight) for a variety of reasons—to keep their hearts healthy...to avoid diabetes and other chronic diseases...or simply to look better.

But clearly something isn't working. More than two-thirds of American adults are overweight or obese. The average American dieter makes up to five weight-loss attempts a year—but within a year, two-thirds of dieters regain *all* of the weight that they lost...and more than 95% gain it back within five years.

Why are so many people losing the battle of the bulge?

AVOIDING THE NOT-SO-OBVIOUS TRAPS

The truth is, if we all stuck to healthful, whole foods—such as vegetables, fruits, lean meats and fish and nuts—far fewer people would ever have to go on a "diet." Have you ever seen anyone eat too much broccoli? But sticking to this principle of eating whole (not processed) foods isn't always easy. *So here are the other steps I recommend to prevent out-of-control eating...*

• **Downsize your dishes.** Have you noticed that serving dishes have gotten larger? A generation ago, the standard dinner plate was 10 inches...now it's 12 inches, and it's human nature to fill that extra real estate with bigger portions.

Even nutrition experts, who know all about these dangers, can be fooled by the so-called *Delboeuf illusion*, in which a food portion can seem large or small, depending on the empty space that surrounds it.

Fascinating study: Nutrition experts were given either a small bowl or a large one, along with an ice cream scoop. Those given the larger bowls took 31% more ice cream than those with the smaller ones. The big bowl made the large serving appear "normal"—even to those who should know better.

What to do: To avoid the Delboeuf illusion, use smaller plates and bowls. Not worth the effort?

Consider this: Research shows that going from 12-inch plates to 10-inch plates reduces caloric intake by 22%.

Where to find 10-inch dinner plates: Bed Bath & Beyond…and Walmart. For fun colors in plates this size, go to Zak.com or CB2.com.

Also helpful: Some people notice that they also eat less if they start using chopsticks…or hold utensils with their nondominant hand.

•**Go with single-serves.** A study published in the journal *Appetite* found that men ate up to 37% more (women 18% more) when food came in bigger bags.

Single-serve bags typically contain one to two ounces. Admittedly, that's not very much. But if you're going to indulge now and then by having, say, potato chips, a single-serve portion has about 150 calories. Think how much more you'd get by dipping your hand repeatedly into an oversized bag!

Also helpful: If you decide to save money with bigger packages, pour the amount that you want to eat into a bowl…and don't go back for refills. To cut the compulsion to go back for another serving, take a few sips of lemon water to break the cycle of wanting to eat more.

•**Slow down.** It takes roughly 20 minutes for chemical signals of fullness to reach the brain. People who eat quickly tend to get more calories than they need—or even want.

Scientific evidence: When researchers instructed participants to either rush through a meal or take their time, the slow eaters (who took small bites, chewed their food well and put down their forks between bites) consumed 88 fewer calories. They also reported

that they felt less hungry than when they ate more quickly.

What helps: When eating a meal, set a timer (or an alarm on your cell phone) for 20 minutes and pace your eating so that it takes that much time to finish.

•**Watch what you're watching!** You may know that television leads to "mindless eating"—one study found that adults who ate pizza while watching TV consumed 36% more calories than those listening to music. The reason? They were too distracted to notice what they were doing—or when they were full. But new research shows that some types of viewing are worse than others. Action movies and sad movies are more likely to trigger distracted and/or emotional eating than more sedate viewing choices.

What helps: To avoid excessive eating when watching a movie or TV, especially an action movie or a tearjerker, sit down with some crunchy veggies instead of a bowl of popcorn or other snacks.

Find the Diet That's Best for *You*

No one weight-loss diet is right for everyone. Each person's body responds differently to identical foods. This means Atkins, Paleo, Dukan and other diets won't work for all those who try them.

Examples: Bread and rice cause blood sugar increases in some people but not in others. A regimen such as the Mediterranean diet—which includes tomatoes—may be a poor choice for some people because tomatoes cause blood sugar levels to surge in certain individuals.

Study of 800 people's response to 46,898 meals by researchers at Weizmann Institute, Rehovot, Israel, published in *Cell*.

The "Gut-Bug" Diet Really Works: Lose Weight by Balancing Your Intestinal Flora

Gerard E. Mullin, MD, a gastroenterologist and associate professor of medicine at The Johns Hopkins University School of Medicine and director of Integrative GI Nutrition Services at The Johns Hopkins Hospital, both in Baltimore. Dr. Mullin's latest book is *The Gut Balance Revolution*.

By now, virtually everyone has heard of probiotics, the beneficial bacteria that you can get from yogurt and other fermented foods—or from the many probiotic supplements that are now widely available.

Probiotics can, of course, ease the diarrhea that may occur when taking antibiotics, which kill both "bad" *and* "good" bacteria. They can also help digestive problems unrelated to antibiotics, such as bloating, gas and constipation. But that doesn't scratch the surface of what probiotics can do.

What's new: Researchers are now finding that the bacterial populations in the intestine, known as *gut microbiome* or *intestinal flora*, can profoundly affect weight gain. *Here's what you need to know about gut bacteria and weight gain...*

BUGS OUT OF BALANCE

Ideally, the bacteria that inhabit the intestine are in equilibrium—with a preponderance of beneficial organisms that keep the harmful bugs in check. But if you're overweight, there is a good chance that you have a bacterial imbalance of the digestive tract, known as *dysbiosis*.

This is caused in part by the overuse of antibiotics, both from the medicine we take and from the drugs that are given to farm animals and later end up in our food supply. On top of that, about 13% of calories in the average diet now come from added sugar (including refined cane sugar and honey)—and harmful bacteria love sugar.

Important recent finding: People who are overweight or obese tend to have larger populations of *Firmicutes*, organisms known as

"fat bugs" because they are involved in weight gain. Lean people, on the other hand, have larger populations of *Bifidobacteria*, beneficial organisms that fight the inflammatory intestinal environment that triggers weight gain.

FOODS THAT HELP

The traditional American diet—heavy on inflammation-promoting processed foods with not nearly enough anti-inflammatory plant foods—seems to promote the production of fat-forming Firmicutes.

Research shows that adopting a Mediterranean-style diet (see below for more on this) is the best way to maintain a healthier bacterial balance. But other steps can also be taken to achieve a better balance of bacteria.

There's only preliminary evidence that probiotic supplements prevent weight gain or help with weight loss. What you need are *probiotic fermented foods* that have live bacteria and *prebiotic foods* that supply the raw ingredients that feed the beneficial bacteria.

Research from Belgium shows that people who get as little as 16 grams (g) (less than one ounce) of prebiotic foods daily can shift their microbial balance...reduce their appetite...experience greater degrees of fullness after eating...and have a reduced body mass. Even if you are not concerned about weight gain, prebiotic foods feed the intestinal flora. This helps strengthen gut health, which can increase immunity.

Gut-balancing foods worth trying...

• **Fermented milk.** Fermented milk products (such as yogurt, kefir and buttermilk) create an intestinal environment that promotes the production of beneficial bacteria. Plus, these foods are rich in *Lactobacillus gasseri*, a microbe that reduces subcutaneous (under the skin) and visceral (around the organs) fat.

Studies have shown that people who eat at least three servings of yogurt a week tend to have decreased hunger and a lower waist-to-hip circumference as well as improvements in blood lipids and better preservation of muscle mass.

Helpful: I recommend White Mountain Bulgarian yogurt, available at WhiteMountain Foods.com. It contains up to 90 billion organisms per serving (much more than a typical supermarket brand).

- **Kimchi,** a Korean side dish that's a potent prebiotic. It's made of pickled cabbage and spices and also contains *kochukaru*, crushed red chili pepper, which has fat-burning effects. It's best to have kimchi (available in Asian markets and online) at least three to four times a week.

- **Berries.** All types of berries, including blueberries, strawberries and raspberries, have been linked to weight loss. Why? Because beneficial bacteria love them. People who eat berries tend to accumulate less fat and have an improved insulin response—important in preventing diabetes. I recommend having two ounces of berries three or more times a week.

- **Green tea.** Two to three cups of green tea daily are enough to support the growth of fat-burning bacteria. When researchers analyzed the results of 15 previous studies, they concluded that green tea with caffeine is associated with weight loss, reduced waist circumference and a lower body mass index.

- **Cinnamon.** This all-around great spice lowers blood sugar after meals and delays the time that it takes the stomach to empty—crucial for feeling full after eating.

It's best to use Ceylon cinnamon, which can be found in specialty stores, rather than the more common cassia cinnamon found in supermarkets. Ceylon cinnamon is more potent. Sprinkle about one-quarter teaspoon in your morning coffee or on cereal or yogurt daily.

- **Asparagus.** It contains the prebiotic *inulin*, which increases populations of Bifidobacteria, Lactobacillus and other beneficial bacteria. Asparagus is one of the few foods (beside cruciferous vegetables) that provides a lot of *glutathione*, an antioxidant that reduces inflammation-related weight gain. Eat asparagus once or twice weekly.

SMART DIET SECRET

A Mediterranean-style diet has been shown to greatly reduce the risk for heart disease, diabetes and other chronic diseases.

More recently, scientists have discovered that the same style of eating—lots of fish, olive oil, whole grains, fresh fruits and vegetables and modest amounts of wine—is probably ideal for the microbiome, the bacterial populations in the body.

Recent finding: A study of overweight and obese men and women found that those who ate a Mediterranean-type diet for just two weeks had an increase in microbial diversity, along with impressive 13% average reductions in triglycerides and LDL "bad" cholesterol.

A Vitamin for Weight Loss?

Vitamin D supplements will not cause you to lose weight, but people who are vitamin D–deficient may experience muscle weakness, fatigue and joint pain, which could result in weight gain. Adults should take 1,500 international units (IU) to 2,000 IU of vitamin D a day. If you're obese, you may need more.

Michael F. Holick, PhD, MD, professor of medicine, physiology and biophysics at Boston University School of Medicine.

A More Filling Breakfast

Want to eat less at lunch? Choose oatmeal for breakfast.

Recent study: Volunteers who ate a bowl of hot instant oatmeal with skim milk reported feeling fuller longer and ate significantly less at lunch than on the days that they ate a breakfast of cold, oat-based cereal and skim milk.

Explanation: Although both the oatmeal and cold cereal consumed in the study had the same number of calories, oatmeal has more fiber, which increases satiety.

Candida Rebello, MS, RD, researcher, Louisiana State University School of Nutrition & Food Sciences in Baton Rouge.

5 Ways to Get Rid of Stubborn Belly Fat

Timothy McCall, MD, an internist and medical editor of *Yoga Journal*. He is author of *Yoga as Medicine: The Yogic Prescription for Health and Healing*, in which he reports on the connection between stress and weight gain. Along with his wife, Eliana, he codirects The Simply Yoga Institute in Summit, New Jersey, and teaches yoga-therapy seminars worldwide. His articles have appeared in *The New England Journal of Medicine* and *JAMA*. DrMcCall.com

Don't count on the latest diet to shrink an expanding waistline. Belly fat is stubborn. Unlike fat around the thighs, buttocks and hips, which visibly diminishes when you cut calories, belly fat tends to stick around. Even strenuous exercise might not make a dent.

The persistence of a belly bulge isn't merely cosmetic. Beneath the *subcutaneous fat* that you can pinch with your fingers, fat deep in the abdomen is metabolically different from "normal" fat. Known as *visceral fat*, it secretes inflammatory substances that increase the risk for heart attack, type 2 diabetes and some cancers. Even if you're not overweight, a larger-than-average waistline increases health risks.

Surprisingly, even thin people can have a high percentage of visceral fat. It might not be visible, but the risks are the same.

Weight-loss diets can certainly help you drop pounds—and some of that weight will come from the deep abdominal area. But unless you take a broader approach than the standard diet and exercise advice, it's very difficult to maintain visceral fat reductions over the long haul. *Here are better approaches to shrink your belly…*

• **Don't stress over losing weight.** Everyone knows about "stress eating." After a fight with your spouse or a hard day at work, food can be a welcome distraction. What people don't realize is that the struggle to lose weight may itself be highly stressful and that it can cause your belly fat to stick around.

How this happens: Cortisol, one of the main stress-related hormones, increases appetite and makes you less mindful of what you eat. It causes the body to store more fat, particularly visceral fat. People who worry a lot about their weight actually may find themselves eating more.

Take action to reduce stress by practicing yoga, meditation or tai chi for even just a few minutes a day. One study found that there was little or no obesity among more than 200 women over age 45 who had practiced yoga for many years. The key is regular practice—it's better to do 10 minutes of yoga a day than a 90-minute class once a week.

Also helpful: Belly breathing. Sit up straight in a chair or lie down on your back, close your eyes, and tune into your breathing. Breathe in and out through your nose slowly and deeply but without straining. You'll feel your belly gently moving out as you inhale and then in as you exhale.

This type of breathing is an effective form of stress control. Try it for one to five minutes once or twice a day…or anytime you're feeling stressed.

• **Cultivate mindfulness in your everyday life.** According to yoga and Ayurvedic medicine (a system of healing that originated in India), an overly busy mind can play as big a role in weight gain as diet or exercise. We all need to step back from the chaos of life and give our nervous system a chance to unwind. Take it one step at a time. Do less multitasking. Try to move a little more slowly and deliberately. Spend less time on the Internet and watching television—especially when you're eating. Although these activities may seem relaxing, they can stimulate the mind and the nervous system and lead to overeating.

Bonus: When you eat mindfully, you will enjoy your food more and need less to feel satisfied.

•**Exercise, but don't go crazy.** Exercise, particularly aerobic exercise, can obviously be good for weight loss. But for many people, the intensity at which they exercise becomes yet another source of stress.

Example: One of my medical colleagues described a "Type A" patient who was an exercise fanatic. Despite her strenuous fitness program, she had a stubborn 10 pounds that she couldn't get rid of. He suggested that she might have more luck if she'd simply relax a bit. She ignored his advice—until she broke a leg and had to take a break. The 10 pounds melted away.

My advice: Get plenty of exercise, but enjoy it. Don't let it be stressful—make it a soothing part of your day. Go for a bike ride…swim in a lake…take a hike in nature. Exercise that is relaxing may burn just as many calories as a do-or-die gym workout but without the stress-related rise in cortisol.

Tip: If you've practiced belly breathing (see page 73), try to bring that kind of breath focus to your exercise. It's even possible to slowly train yourself to breathe through your nose while you exercise, potentially lowering cortisol levels and the rebound hunger that is so common after a workout.

•**Eat more fresh, unprocessed food.** What really matters for health and healthy weight is the quality of your food. Many diets that have been shown to be effective—such as the low-fat vegetarian Ornish program…the Mediterranean diet…and some high-protein plans—disagree with one another, but they all emphasize old-fashioned unprocessed food.

My advice: Worry less about micro-nutrients such as specific vitamins, minerals and types of fat or your protein/carbohydrate balance, and instead focus on eating more fresh

---

TAKE NOTE...

Breakthrough Drug for Obesity

A breakthrough obesity drug is now available. *Liraglutide* (Saxenda) is a high-dose version of the diabetes drug Victoza. Like other weight-loss drugs, liraglutide curbs appetite—but it also acts like a natural hormone to slow stomach emptying. Gastrointestinal upsets are the most common side effect. Liraglutide, which is injected daily, is used in combination with exercise and a weight-loss diet.

Whom it may help: Overweight people who have diabetes, prediabetes or another weight-related health condition.

Angela Fitch, MD, director of medical weight management and associate professor of medicine, University of Cincinnati College of Medicine.

---

vegetables, legumes, whole grains, fruit, nuts and seeds. If you eat animal foods, choose free-range and pasture-raised meat and dairy products, organic if possible.

•**Cut back on refined sugar.** If you follow the advice above and avoid processed foods, you'll naturally consume less sugar, refined grains (such as white bread) and other "simple" carbohydrates. This will help prevent insulin surges that can lead to more visceral fat.

As always, balance is important. I don't advise anyone to give up all sources of sugar or all carbohydrates. After all, a plum is loaded with the sugar fructose—and fruits are good for you! It's the added sugar in junk and fast food that's the problem. Just be aware that any processed food—including many snacks that are marketed as healthier alternatives—will make it harder to control your weight.

Supplement Warning

Beware of certain weight-loss and brain-enhancing supplements. Labels on the supplements, which also include some sports supplements, state that they contain the plant substance *Acacia rigidula*, but instead they actually contain the chemical *beta-methyl-phenylethylamine* (BMPEA), a synthetic cousin of amphetamines that can cause stroke, heart attack or even death.

Pieter Cohen, MD, an assistant professor at Harvard Medical School, Boston, and an internist at Cambridge Health Alliance, Somerville, Massachusetts. He led a study published in *Drug Testing and Analysis*.

The One-Minute Workout Miracle: Short Bursts of Activity Beat Nonstop Exercise

Jonathan Little, PhD, exercise physiologist and assistant professor in the School of Health and Exercise Sciences at University of British Columbia-Okanagan, Kelowna, where he studies exercise metabolism and the effects of exercise on inflammation, obesity, insulin resistance and diabetes.

Even if you enjoy aerobic workouts, you probably wish that they took less time. *Good news:* New research shows that you can get all of the metabolic and cardiovascular benefits of aerobic exercise in about 60 minutes a week.

The secret is *high-intensity interval training* (HIIT) where you exercise intensely for one minute and leisurely for another minute, working up to a total of 20 minutes three times a week. *How it works…*

NEW THINKING

For years, the American College of Sports Medicine has advised Americans to walk, bike or get other forms of moderate-intensity aerobic exercise for at least 30 minutes, five days a week. That's two-and-a-half hours—minimum.

HIIT can be a refreshing change. You do the same activities (walking, biking, stair-climbing, etc.), but you do them hard—ideally at 80% to 90% of your *estimated maximal heart rate*. On a 1-to-10 scale, you'll rate the exertion between 7 and 8 (compared with about 5 for conventional aerobic workouts).

Here's the good part. After just 30 to 60 seconds of pushing yourself, you take a break. During the *recovery phase*, you keep moving, but at a leisurely pace—a slow walk, slow pedaling on the bike, etc. You rest for the same length of time that you exercised—between 30 and 60 seconds. Then you push yourself again. Each on-off cycle is one *interval*.

Exercise scientists used to think that HIIT was helpful mainly for athletes or very fit adults who wanted to take their fitness to an even higher level. But new studies suggest that this technique can be equally effective—and, in most cases, equally safe—for just about everyone who is in reasonably good health.

IMPORTANT BENEFITS

For our recent study, we recruited 41 "regular" people who typically engaged in aerobic activities only two or fewer times a week. After they completed preliminary tests and questionnaires, they completed a single workout that involved HIIT (one minute on, one minute off, for a total of 20 minutes), conventional high-intensity aerobic exercise (20 minutes)… or conventional moderate-intensity aerobic exercise (40 minutes). Each participant did all three workouts, in a randomized order, separated by about one week.

At the end of the study, 24 of the participants said that they preferred HIIT, compared with just 13 who preferred conventional, moderate-intensity aerobic workouts. The remaining four people preferred the conventional high-intensity aerobic workout.

This is an important finding because people who *enjoy* exercise are more likely to keep doing it. Just as important, the study showed that nonathletes are *able* to do HIIT. Mixing the high-intensity "challenges" with frequent rest breaks boosted their confidence.

Other benefits…

•**Higher metabolism.** You actually burn fewer calories during an HIIT session than you would during a standard aerobic workout. But HIIT elevates your basal metabolic rate for up to 24 hours after the workout. You burn more calories *post-exercise* than you normally would.

Researchers at McMaster University in Hamilton, Canada, studied participants who followed a 20-week program of conventional aerobics and others who followed a 15-week HIIT program. The first group burned 48% more calories per session than the HIIT group, but the HIIT group burned 900% more fat over the 15 weeks than the first group burned in 20 weeks.

•**Cardiovascular health.** A number of studies have looked at the effects of HIIT in patients with heart disease. They found that participants had better outcomes—improved blood lipids, less insulin resistance, more elastic blood vessels, etc.—than those who did traditional workouts.

•**Improved fitness.** The body's ability to use oxygen is among the best measures of cardiovascular health and longevity. People who do these workouts have improved peak *oxygen uptake* after as little as two weeks.

Important warning: There's some evidence that the resting component makes HIIT safer than traditional aerobic workouts for people with heart disease or other chronic conditions. But any form of vigorous exercise can be risky for those with health problems. Get the OK from your doctor before trying it.

A TYPICAL WORKOUT

To do an HIIT workout, you first need to pick your activity. It could be walking, biking, swimming, jogging, stair-climbing or any other form of aerobic exercise. *After that…*

•**Warm up.** Take three to five minutes just to get ready—with slow walking, easy pedaling, etc.

•**Do a "speed" session.** If you're new to HIIT, I recommend limiting your initial speed sessions to 30 seconds each. You can increase the time each time you work out. Your goal will be 60 seconds.

As discussed above, you want an exertion level that you would rate as a 7 or 8 out of 10. If you're not sure if you're pushing hard enough, use the talk test—you should have just enough wind to blurt out a short word or two. If you can speak an entire sentence, increase the exertion.

•**Now take a break.** The recovery phase will last just as long as the exertion phase. If you exercised for 30 seconds, rest for 30 seconds. As noted above, "rest" doesn't mean do-

ing nothing. You'll keep doing the activity, but at an easy pace—say, between 15% and 20% of your maximum ability (1 or 2 on a 0-to-10 scale).

•**Immediately start the next interval.** After resting, repeat the speed part of the exercise. Do it for 30 seconds…recover for 30 seconds…and so on.

•**Increase the intervals.** I advise people who are new to HIIT to complete a total of four intervals. If that feels like too much, you can do just one or two, increasing the number when you feel ready. In our studies with non-athletes, we started with four intervals during the first session. We added one interval during each subsequent session until they reached a total of 10. We found that most people adjusted quickly.

•**Three times a week.** Because these workouts are more intense than a conventional, moderate-intensity workout, you don't want to do them every day. Your muscles need time to recover. Every other day is optimal.

•**Be flexible.** The typical HIIT workout involves a 1:1 ratio—one minute of exertion followed by one minute of rest. But there's nothing magical about this ratio. For someone who has been sedentary for a long time, I might recommend a 30-to-60-second exertion phase followed by a two-minute or even a four-minute break. In general, the more in-

---

EASY-TO-DO…

Cut Workout Time in Half!

In a recent 10-week study, adults who completed a 25-minute high-intensity workout that included cycling sprints three times a week showed similar health benefits, such as improved insulin sensitivity and cholesterol levels, as those who did a moderate-intensity cycling workout for 45 minutes five days a week.

Bonus: 80% of the high-intensity group versus 60% of the moderate-intensity group had stuck to their workouts three months later—most likely due to the shorter time commitment.

Christopher S. Shaw, PhD, senior lecturer in exercise physiology, Deakin University, Geelong, Australia.

tensely you exercise, the more rest you'll need. Your body will tell you what you need.

Get Powered Up with Medicine Ball Workouts

Daniel Taylor, MS, a performance enhancement specialist (PES) and a certified strength and conditioning specialist (CSCS). Taylor is a conditioning coach at Siena College in Loudonville, New York, and coauthor of *Conditioning to the Core*.

You probably don't think of yourself as an "athlete," but adopting a secret from the pros will help you stay as strong and fit as possible. More and more professional athletes, including football and soccer players, are now adding medicine ball workouts to their exercise regimens—and you can, too.

You've probably heard of medicine balls. Originally made out of animal hide, they date back to ancient times and were used for the same reason we use them today—to increase strength and cardiovascular fitness. Modern medicine balls, typically made out of rubber, leather or nylon, come in a variety of sizes and weights, ranging from one pound to 50 pounds and costing as little as $12 to about $100.

What can a medicine ball do for you? Plenty! Throwing and catching a medicine ball is a *plyometric* exercise—that is, it combines stretching and contracting movements to build strength, speed and endurance. Medicine ball workouts are particularly effective for people who have chronic conditions that improve with consistent strength training (such as osteoporosis, back pain, diabetes or high blood pressure)…and/or those who don't have much gym experience. Barbells, machines, kettlebells (heavy weights with handles) and other gym equipment can be intimidating if you are new to them—balls are not. Medicine balls are comfortable and fun to use!

YOUR CORE CURRICULUM

Medicine ball training primarily addresses the core—all those muscles in your abdomen and lower back. Strengthening these muscles is particularly important to help prevent back pain, improve posture and make everyday movement easier.

There's no one-size-fits-all weight for the ball. You want one that you can throw…but if it doesn't require much effort to do so, then you should go a bit heavier. Most beginners start with six- to eight-pound medicine balls. People with an intermediate level of fitness can use a 10- to 12-pound ball…and those who consider themselves very physically fit may use a ball that is 15 pounds or heavier.

The following workout is a great complement to a regular exercise regimen that might include aerobic activity, such as regular walking or running, and stretching exercises. Adults at various fitness levels can perform the exercises below. Do them two to four times per week on nonconsecutive days.*

• **Push-up.** The purpose of the push-up is to strengthen the chest, shoulders and abdomen, which improves strength for carrying heavy items.

What to do: While lying facedown on the floor, position your prone body next to a relatively solid medicine ball. Place your right hand on the ball and your  left hand on the floor. Lift your body so that your left hand and toes are the only parts of your body touching the floor while your right hand is on the ball. The ball may feel a bit unstable—if you can't control it, prop the ball against a wall. Then simply do a push-up with one hand on the ball and the other hand on the floor. Repeat eight to 12 times. If this is too difficult, do the push-up with your knees on the floor.

• **The overhead slam.** This move strengthens the shoulders, back and abdominals for core fitness.

What to do: Stand with your feet parallel and hip-width apart. Slightly bend your knees. While holding the ball, extend your arms in

---

*Check with your doctor before beginning medicine ball workouts—or any new exercise program. This is especially important if you have osteoarthritis, heart disease and/or diminished hand-eye coordination.

front of you, then raise the ball overhead. Next, throw the ball as hard as you can at the floor, then catch the rebound. Repeat eight times.

•**Side throw.** This exercise strengthens the shoulders, back, side abdominals and hips for better turning movements (such as golf swings) and to help prevent falls.

What to do: Kneel on a gym mat parallel to a wall (about your body length away). Your right knee should be on the mat while your left leg is bent at a 90-degree angle with your foot flat on the floor. Tighten your glutes (buttocks) and abdomen to create stability. Throughout the exercise, maintain a completely straight body alignment for maximum effectiveness. Using both hands, hold the medicine ball to the side of your waist about a hand span away. Rotating through your shoulders (not your lower back), throw the ball as hard as possible in a baseball-swing fashion against the wall. Perform eight repetitions. Repeat on the opposite side.

Medicine ball photos provided by Human Kinetics.

The Wall Workout: 5 Exercises to Improve Strength, Flexibility and Posture

Joel Harper, a personal trainer in New York City who designs workouts for Olympic athletes, celebrities, musicians and business executives. Harper created the workout chapters for the best-selling YOU series of books by Michael Roizen, MD, and Mehmet Oz, MD. He is also author of *Mind Your Body: 10 Core Concepts for an Optimally Balanced You*. JoelHarperFitness.com

Forget crowded gyms, clunky dumbbells and complicated exercise machines. If you have access to a wall, you can get a great strength workout using nothing more than the weight of your own body. Body-weight exercises are a simple, no-frills way to improve strength, flexibility and posture. Because you use a wall for balance, you can hold the positions longer—important for improving endurance as well as strength.

Wall workouts are particularly helpful for those who aren't accustomed to exercise…for people with physical limitations (such as back pain or knee arthritis)…or when you're recovering from surgery or other physical problems.*

The workout below is designed to use every major muscle. To further improve your balance and foot strength, you can also do the routine barefoot. Aim to do these exercises every other day for two weeks…and if you feel the benefits, continue at the same frequency thereafter…

•**Imaginary chair.** It's a great exercise for increasing thigh and gluteal (buttock) strength, which is needed to support your spine. Unlike traditional squats, which involve lowering your body and rising back up, in this exercise you hold one position—helpful  for those who have knee pain or limited knee strength.

What to do: Stand with your back against a wall. While keeping your back in contact with the wall, slowly slide your back down the wall while simultaneously walking your feet forward until your legs are in right angles. Go only as far as it feels comfortable for your knees. If your knees start to ache, stop moving forward…a "higher" position is easier for beginners. Once you're "sitting," count for as long as you can comfortably hold the position. Each day, try for 10 more seconds. To help improve your posture, keep your stomach taut, your chin up and your shoulders pressed against the wall.

•**Push-ups.** They strengthen the chest, biceps, triceps and shoulders—all of which promote good posture. Traditional, on-the-floor push-ups are often too difficult for beginners…or

*Check first with your doctor before starting this—or any new—exercise program.

for those with limited upper-body strength. Wall push-ups involve the same basic movements but with less resistance—and they're good for people with back problems because they don't stress the spine.

What to do: Place your palms on a wall at about shoulder height, spaced slightly wider than the width of your shoulders. Back your feet a foot or two away from the wall—stepping farther back increases the difficulty... standing closer to the wall reduces it. Start with your elbows bent. Your face will be close to the wall.

Slowly extend your arms—while exhaling—to push away from the wall. Then inhale while returning to the starting position. Repeat as many times as you comfortably can—ideally, for 30 to 60 seconds.

•**Calf stretches.** Strong calves will improve your ability to walk and climb stairs.

What to do: Stand facing the wall, with both hands on the wall and your arms extended but slightly bent—keep this position throughout the exercise. Step back with your right foot. While holding this position, bend your left leg until you feel a stretch in your right calf. You can also slightly bend your right knee and drive it toward the same toe to increase the stretch. Relax into the stretch, and hold it for 10 seconds or more. Then switch legs and stretch the left calf.

•**Ankle strengthener.** Ankles are a commonly injured body part. People with weak ankles are more likely to have sprains. They are also more likely to have balance problems—the ankles are involved in *proprioception*, the body's ability to orient itself in space.

What to do: Stand facing a wall, with your feet about hip-width apart. Put both hands on the wall for support. Rise up on your toes, going as high as you can. Hold the position for a few seconds, then slowly lower your heels back down. Do this 25 times.

•**Bridge.** It strengthens the entire midsection, along with the ham-strings, glutes and lower back—all needed for good posture.

What to do: Lie on your back, with your buttocks 12 to 18 inches from the wall. Start by planting the soles of your feet flat against the wall so that your legs make a right angle.

Then, while squeezing your abdominal muscles, lift your hips while keeping your shoulder blades flat on the floor. Lift all the way up so that there is a straight line from your knees to your shoulders, then drop down one inch. This is the height to rise up to each time. Hold the pose for about 10 seconds, then lower back down—but *don't* let your bottom rest on the floor. Keeping it slightly elevated between movements will increase the intensity of the workout. Do this 25 times.

Make Exercise Safer and Much More Comfortable

Colin Milner, CEO of the International Council on Active Aging, a Vancouver, British Columbia–based organization dedicated to improving fitness and quality-of-life issues in older adults. Milner serves on the World Economic Forum's Global Agenda Council on Aging, is a contributor to the US Department of Health and Human Services' "Be Active Your Way" blog and is a recipient of the Canadian Fitness Professional Association's Lifetime Achievement Award.

L et's just face it. Exercise sometimes hurts. So when we fear that our bodies might rebel, we're tempted to put off exercise or even skip it.

That's a shame because it does not make sense to deprive ourselves of exercise—it's hands-down the most powerful health protector there is. So what's the solution?

By choosing the right workout aids, you can dramatically ease the discomfort of key exercise routines. *Here's what works best for...*

STRETCHING

Who among us isn't just a little—or a lot—stiff and achy at times? Stretching is perhaps the best exercise you can do to loosen up those tight, inflexible muscles. It will help limber you up and improve your range of motion—both of which make it easier to do day-to-day activities such as grabbing groceries off a high shelf.

But if you're not very flexible to begin with, stretching is likely to cause some discomfort.

What helps: Gaiam Multi-Grip Stretch Strap ($10.38,* Gaiam.com). With multiple handholds along the strap, this product allows you to ease into your stretches with greater control than you could on your own or if you relied on a regular strap without handholds.

WALKING

Walking is the easiest, most approachable workout there is. But if you've got pain due to arthritis, back problems or a hip or other joint replacement...or balance problems, even walking can be difficult.

Adding walking poles helps reduce impact on your joints, normalize your gait and improve your balance. The addition of poles also helps to boost your cardio endurance and increase your caloric burn—with poles, your heart rate will be 10% to 15% higher compared with traditional walking, and you'll burn about 400 calories per hour versus 280 calories.

What helps: ACTIVATOR Poles ($99.99 per pair, UrbanPoling.com). These aren't just any old walking poles. They feature bell-shaped, rubber tips for added grip and reduced vibration. With a doctor's prescription, this product may be covered by insurance.

Also: For people with peripheral neuropathy, a type of nerve damage that leads to numbness, tingling and/or weakness in the feet and other limbs, it can be tough to rely on walking as a form of exercise.

What helps: WalkJoy ($3,495 per pair, WalkJoy.com). This device is attached with straps worn below the knees. Sensors in the device signal healthy nerves around the knees (which are unaffected by peripheral neuropathy), letting your brain know that one foot has hit the ground and it's time to lift the toes of the opposite foot for another

*Prices subject to change.

step. WalkJoy is FDA-approved and available by prescription.

SWIMMING

Swimming is a great low-impact, whole-body exercise for people who are watching their weight, building cardio strength or looking for relief from arthritis pain.

For the average recreational swimmer, however, efficient breathing can be challenging. Many swimmers feel like they're struggling for air...or their necks tire or become painful from constantly twisting and lifting.

What helps: The Finis Swimmer's Snorkel ($35.99, FinisInc.com). Unlike many snorkels, which are designed for scuba divers, this product was created specifically for swimmers. Its adjustable head bracket lets you wear it with a swim cap and/or goggles while allowing you to keep your head in a fixed position so that you don't have to remove your mouth from the water to breathe.

CYCLING

Riding a bicycle is another great low-impact exercise. It has been shown to improve muscle strength and promote lung and heart health. The problem is, traditional bike saddles (on both stationary and road bikes) place a lot of pressure on the *perineum* (the area between the genitals and the anus). This contributes

---

EASY-TO-DO...

Quick Workout Motivation

Simply recalling an enjoyable workout, such as an invigorating hike or fun spin class, can motivate you to exercise more. In a recent study, participants who had a positive memory about a past workout session exercised moderately one more time over the next week than those who did not recall a pleasant memory.

Possible explanation: Thinking about an enjoyable workout session helped change participants' views about exercising.

Tip: Conjure up a pleasant memory before you begin your workout.

David Pillemer, EdD, professor of psychology, University of New Hampshire, Durham.

to pain and erectile dysfunction in men and numbness in women.

What helps: ISM Cruise Saddle ($99.95, ISMseat.com). This is a noseless saddle, which directly supports your "sits" bones (at the base of the buttocks) while easing pressure on the perineum. Research has found that no-nose saddles reduce most perineal pressure in male riders and improve penile blood flow when compared with traditional bike seats. No-nose saddles also reduce numbness in women.

The Heart Health Workout: Cuts Risk of Dying from Heart Disease Nearly in Half...

Barry A. Franklin, PhD, director of preventive cardiology/cardiac rehabilitation at William Beaumont Hospital in Royal Oak, Michigan. He is a past president of the American Association of Cardiovascular and Pulmonary Rehabilitation and the American College of Sports Medicine and coauthor of *One Heart, Two Feet*. For more information, go to CreativeWalking.com.

What if there were a piece of exercise equipment that could cut your risk of dying from heart disease by nearly half? This is actually possible by simply using a treadmill—in a strategic way. The approach is not complicated or even that difficult, but few people take advantage of it.

THE "MET" SECRET

We all know that walking is an excellent form of exercise. What makes a treadmill so efficient is that you can control your pace and/or incline so that you maintain your desired intensity and get the maximum benefit from your exercise routine.

The treadmill's winning secret is that it gives you the ability to monitor energy expenditure, also called a MET, which stands for metabolic equivalent. Every one MET increase in your fitness level cuts your risk for death from heart disease by 15%, so increasing METs by three, for example, will cut risk by 45%. Many treadmills display METs readings.

You can also estimate METs with an app for your smartphone or tablet. The Exercise Calculator for the iPhone or iPad displays METs when you enter your weight, type of activity and length of time exercising.

Simply put, METs allow you to track the intensity of your workout by estimating the amount of oxygen your muscles are burning to fuel you through various activities. For example, sitting requires one MET...and normal walking requires two to three METs—that is, two to three times as much oxygen and calories as you'd burn while relaxing in a chair. Light jogging requires eight METs...and running at a 6 mph pace, 10 METs.

With immediate feedback from your METs reading, you can effectively gauge how hard you're working out...and receive the motivation to push yourself at the safest and most effective intensity levels.

Important: If you've been sedentary, start your treadmill walking at 2 mph to 3 mph with no incline. Gradually increase your speed over the next eight to 10 weeks, then progress to graded treadmill walking or slow jogging. If symptoms such as shortness of breath, dizziness and/or chest pain develop, stop and tell your doctor.

Here's how to most effectively use a treadmill for specific exercise goals...

QUICK BUT EFFECTIVE WORKOUT

What to use: Incline *and* speed. When it comes to getting the most out of exercise, intensity and duration are inversely related. By combining higher treadmill inclines with increased speeds, you'll bolster your MET level and reach your target heart rate sooner. Working at your target heart rate helps improve fitness. With fast, graded treadmill walking, you can get a great workout in just 20 to 30 minutes.

Example: Increase speed slightly (0.1 mph to 0.2 mph) every minute for five minutes. Then increase the incline setting, which is measured as a percentage, by 0.5% (for example, going from 1% to 1.5% incline) and walk for five minutes. Alternate this sequence once or twice (increasing speed and incline each time) until you feel you're working hard, but can still carry on a conversation.

WEIGHT LOSS

What to use: Incline. With incline walking, more muscle mass—especially in the quadriceps and glutes—is activated with each stride. And the more treadmill incline you use, the more calories you'll burn.

A mere increase of just 1% on the incline setting (for example, going from 1% to 2%) at a comfortable walking speed (such as 1.5 mph to 2.5 mph) will boost your energy expenditure by about 10%, and I'll bet you won't even feel a difference. If you walk faster, you'll burn even more calories because you'll be working at a higher MET level.

Research shows that regular brisk walks of at least 30 minutes five or more days a week is the best approach to weight loss. Walking on level ground at 2 mph or 3 mph equates to about two or three METs. To help protect your knees, slow your pace as you gradually work up to higher levels of inclines.

Good news: At high inclines, walking may burn as many calories as jogging or running.

DON'T FORGET STRENGTH TRAINING

To get the most from your treadmill walking—or any cardio activity—be sure to add some resistance or strength training to further build your muscle strength. Strength training complements aerobic exercise, reducing your risk for heart disease. You'll also improve your insulin sensitivity (to help fight diabetes) and boost your bone mass (to guard against osteoporosis).

Best: Target various upper and lower body muscle groups, including the chest, back, shoulders, abdomen, quadriceps and hamstrings, using hand weights and/or weight machines. Some yoga poses can also increase muscle strength and endurance. Aim for eight to 10 exercises…and do at least one set of 10 to 15 reps per set, at least twice a week.

TAKE NOTE...

Best After-Workout Snacks

Best snacks after a workout to relieve sore muscles and begin muscle repair include collard greens for their phytochemicals…Brazil nuts for selenium, which helps prevent cell damage…chocolate milk to replenish glycogen and help build muscles…sweet potatoes, which are complex carbs that are packed with antioxidants.

Susan Kleiner, PhD, RD, sports nutritionist, Mercer Island, Washington, quoted in *Shape*.

BONUS TOOLS

You've probably seen people at the gym wearing ankle weights while walking on the treadmill. I'm not a fan. They can strain the lower extremities, increasing your risk for orthopedic or musculoskeletal problems.

Better approach: Try walking with a backpack carrying a comfortable amount of weight. You'll burn more calories than you would if you were walking without one. A snug fit will keep the weight close to your spine and hips—which may help you avoid balance problems and improve your bone density.

And don't forget your headphones. Music (whatever genre you like) can reduce perceived exertion and may make your workout seem easier. It can be more motivating than watching TV.

TREADMILL SAFETY

Treadmills are generally a safe way to exercise, but accidental falls can happen. *To stay safe…*

• **Always straddle the treadmill before turning it on,** and don't assume it will always start at a slow, comfortable speed.

• **Lightly hold the handrail for support while walking.**

• **Always warm up and cool down before and after the aerobic phase of your workout.** Never suddenly stop the treadmill.

5

The Natural Way

How to Live to 100: Best Ways to Add Healthy Years to Your Life

Will you live to 100... or even beyond? Certainly genetics is a major factor, but the number of years that you actually accrue—and how healthy you are during those years—frequently is within your control.

Consider: The number of centenarians—people who live to the ripe old age of 100 or beyond—increased by 51% between 1990 and 2000. The average life expectancy in the US is now 78.8 years, a record high.

Improvements in health care deserve some of the credit, but personal choice is a strong predictor of how long you'll live. About 70% of "normal," age-related declines—including those caused by heart disease, diabetes and other chronic diseases—are mainly due to lifestyle factors.

But which factors are the most important? Not smoking is one. But there are four other lifestyle changes that make the biggest difference when it comes to living a healthier, longer life. They will also improve your life right now by boosting your mood, energy and cognitive focus.

EXERCISE MORE AS YOU GET OLDER

Some exercise is better than none, but it's a myth that just a little exercise is enough. Walking to the mailbox or enjoying the occasional game of golf isn't enough.

Everyone should exercise hard at least five days a week. Make it six days if you're 50 or older. Tough workouts stress muscles,

Henry S. Lodge, MD, FACP, an internist and the Robert Burch Family Professor of Medicine at Columbia University Medical Center, New York City. He heads a private practice in New York City and is ranked one of the Best Doctors in America by Castle Connolly. He is author, with Chris Crowley, of *Younger Next Year* and *Younger Next Year Exercise Program*.

bones and blood vessels and cause adaptive microtrauma, small injuries that trigger the body's self-repair mechanisms.

Result: Healthier and stronger tissues.

A study that looked at 10,000 middle-aged men over a five-year period found that those who were fittest were three times less likely to die than those who were the least fit. Even more encouraging, men who were largely sedentary at the start of the study but who boosted their exercise levels reduced their mortality by half.

Suppose that you're 30 pounds overweight and a smoker, but you exercise every day. You'll still live longer than someone who is thin and doesn't smoke but does not exercise. (Obviously, you'll do even better if you give up the smokes and lose a few pounds.)

My advice: Lift weights a few days a week, and do serious aerobic exercise four days a week. You can vary your routine with other types of exercise such as yoga. Ideally, you'll exercise for about 60 minutes each time. During the aerobic workouts, keep your heart beating at approximately 60% to 65% of your maximum heart rate—and faster as you get in better shape.

I also advise patients to join a gym, even if they would rather not. Many people think that they'll get all of the exercise that they need by working out "informally"—by using a home treadmill, for example, or by going for runs or bike rides in the neighborhood. But most people don't stick with it.

In my experience, a gym membership is a good investment. Once you've written a check, you're already invested in making it work. Once you make it to the gym, you're going to exercise—and it's more fun to do it with others than alone.

Helpful: Sign up for classes or other group activities such as spin classes, aerobics sessions and Zumba that require you to be there at certain times. Or hire a personal trainer on a regular basis to give you a routine to follow.

GIVE UP WHITE FOODS

Sure, you've heard this before, but it bears repeating because it's crucial to living longer. Give up or strictly limit white potatoes, white rice, white bread and white pasta. Even though "simple" carbohydrates have only about half the calories of fat, they're more likely to cause weight gain because they act like pure sugar in the body. They cause surges in insulin that trigger inflammation and increase the risk for heart disease, diabetes and other chronic diseases.

Important: I don't recommend formal diets for weight loss. Calorie control obviously is important, but strict dieting rarely works. Most people will lose weight just by giving up junk food—and white, starchy foods are junk. Replace junk food with natural foods that haven't been processed or refined such as fruits, vegetables, whole grains, fish, etc.

Studies have shown that eating a Mediterranean-style diet (which actually is high in fat but includes the healthy foods above) is probably ideal for health as well as longevity. For more information on healthier eating, read Dr. Walter Willett's book *Eat, Drink and Be Healthy.*

LOG YOUR LIFE

Can you live longer just by writing down, every day, what you ate and how much you exercised? Surprisingly, the answer is yes.

Even though it's a bit of a hassle, keeping a daily diary of health-related details is a sign that you care. It's also a good form of accountability. You might be less likely to skip a day's exercise or chug down a supersized soft drink when you know that you'll have to confess it (if only to yourself).

The health software that now is standard issue on some smartphones makes it particularly easy to track your habits. The iPhone Health app, for example, automatically counts the number of steps you take and how far you have walked or run. You can use other features to track your weight and what you eat. I also like the apps *MapMyRide* (for cycling) and *MapMyRun* (for running).

STAY CONNECTED

People who have close friends and are engaged in their communities tend to live a lot longer than those who are loners. It makes sense because humans, like wolves, evolved as pack animals. We need people around us.

Single men, for example, have higher rates of heart disease and cancer than married men—and they tend to die years sooner. People who go home to an empty house after a heart attack are twice as likely to have a second heart attack within a few months. Those who are angry and isolated have four times the mortality rate of those who are happier.

My advice: Do whatever you can to connect with other people. Make plans with friends even when you would really rather be alone. Get involved in charities and other altruistic activities. Attend religious services. Take advantage of Meetup and other web-based social groups.

Obviously, someone who's naturally solitary will never want to become the life of the party. That's fine because what matters is the aggregate of your social connections. A few truly caring relationships can expand your life (and your life span) just as much as a wide social network.

Also, consider adopting a dog—or a cat, rabbit or bird. The emotional connections that we form with animals can rival, in terms of health benefits, those that we form with fellow humans.

One study, for example, looked at dog ownership in heart attack patients. People who didn't have a dog were six to eight times more likely to die of a second heart attack than those who did.

Not a dog lover? That's OK because any pet that you truly love and care for can offer the same benefits.

The Right Way to Take Your Vitamins: Avoid These Common Mistakes

Jacob Teitelbaum, MD, board-certified internist and nationally known expert in the fields of chronic fatigue syndrome, fibromyalgia, sleep and pain. Based in Kailua-Kona, Hawaii, he is author of numerous books, including *The Fatigue and Fibromyalgia Solution...Pain-Free 1-2-3...*and *Real Cause, Real Cure*, as well as the popular free smartphone app *Cures A–Z*. Vitality101.com

Many of us take vitamins and other nutritional supplements. In fact, researchers from Harvard analyzed data from nearly 125,000 middle-aged and older people and found that an astounding 88% of women and 81% of men took supplements.

Unfortunately, so many of us take nutritional supplements *wrong*. We do not take high-enough doses...or we take them at the wrong time of day...or we combine them with other supplements, foods or drugs that can block absorption.

Good news: I've counseled thousands of patients on the best ways to take vitamins, and I can assure you that taking them correctly can be simple and straightforward.

What you might be doing wrong—and how to quickly fix the problem...

Vitamin mistake #1: **You take a dose that's too low.** There are many nutrient-nutrient interactions that can reduce the absorption of individual nutrients by 5% to 10%.

Example: Iron cuts the absorption of zinc—the more iron in a supplement, the less zinc you're likely to absorb.

My advice: Don't take a multivitamin that supplies 100% of the "Daily Value" of nutrients, a level intended only to prevent deficiency diseases. Instead, take a multivitamin that supplies an *optimal* amount of nutrients—an amount that will easily overcome every absorption issue caused by nutrient-nutrient interactions.

For simplicity, use the B-vitamins as your reference point. Look for a product that supplies about 40 milligrams (mg) each of thiamin, riboflavin, niacin and vitamin B-6 (pyridoxine), and 200 micrograms (mcg) of vitamin B-12. These levels are safe *and* therapeutic, improving energy and mental clarity. When a product contains the above levels of these nutrients, it usually will have optimal levels of other nutrients as well.

***Vitamin mistake #2:* You take a dose that's too high.** It can be detrimental to your health to take high doses of vitamin A and vitamin E.

Reasons: Taking more than 3,000 international units (IU) of vitamin A (retinol) daily can increase your risk for osteoporosis, the bone-eroding disease. Vitamin E actually is a family of eight compounds called *tocopherols* and *tocotrienols*. Alpha-tocopherol—the compound commonly found in multivitamins—can be toxic in doses higher than 100 IU daily.

My advice: Take a multivitamin that contains no more than 3,000 IU of vitamin A total, with approximately one-half from retinol and one-half from beta-carotene (which turns into vitamin A in the body and does not cause osteoporosis).

Choose a multivitamin with no more than 100 IU of vitamin E. If you take the nutrient as a separate supplement for a specific condition, such as for breast tenderness, take it in the form of mixed tocopherols and tocotrienols.

***Vitamin mistake #3:* You try to take vitamins two or three times a day.** Taking vitamins in divided doses—two or even three times a day—is ideal because the body sustains higher blood levels of the nutrients. But very few people can stick with this type of regimen.

My advice: Take vitamins first thing in the morning, with breakfast. (The fat in the meal will help you absorb vitamins A, D and E, which are fat-soluble.) Yes, there's a tiny trade-off of effectiveness for convenience, but it's worth it.

Exception: If you take magnesium as a separate supplement, you might want to take it at bedtime for deeper sleep. Avoid magnesium oxide and magnesium hydroxide, both of which are poorly absorbed. Magnesium glycinate or magnesium malate is preferred.

***Vitamin mistake #4:* You take a second-rate formulation.** Vitamins come in a range of forms—tablets, caplets, capsules, chewables, softgels, liquids, powders—and some are better than others.

Vitamin tablets, for example, are a poor choice. They may not dissolve completely—and you can't absorb any nutrients from a pill that doesn't dissolve. Tablets (and some of the other forms listed above) also may contain binders, fillers and other additives. These supposedly "inert" compounds may have all kinds of unknown effects on the body.

My advice: I recommend powders, which are highly absorbable. Just add water and stir. My favorite is the Energy Revitalization System, from Enzymatic Therapy, which I formulated. (So that I can't be accused of profiting from my recommendation, I donate 100% of my royalties from sales to charity.) I recommend one scoop each morning combined with 5 grams (g) of ribose (a naturally occurring sugar) to optimize energy.

Don't like drinks? Try a combination of My Favorite Multiple Take One by Natrol plus two tablets of Jigsaw Sustained Release Magnesium plus two chewable ribose tablets (2 g to 3 g each).

***Vitamin mistake #5:* You take calcium.** One-third of people who take supplements take calcium—and I think just about every one of those people is making a mistake. The scientific evidence shows that taking a calcium supplement provides little or no protection against bone fractures, and research now links calcium supplements to increased risk for heart attacks and strokes.

My advice: I strongly recommend that you get your calcium from *food*, eating one or two servings of dairy a day. Almonds, broccoli and green leafy vegetables such as kale also are good calcium sources. Unlike supplemental calcium, calcium from food is safe. If you decide to take a calcium supplement for stronger bones, take no more than 100 mg to 200 mg daily, and always combine it with other bone-supporting nutrients, such as vitamin D, magnesium and vitamin K. Take these at night to help sleep.

***Vitamin mistake #6:* You don't realize that your medication can cause a nutrient deficiency.** Some medications block the absorption of specific nutrients. *In my clinical experience, the two worst offenders are...*

• **The diabetes drug *metformin*,** which can cause a B-12 deficiency.

What to do: Metformin is an excellent medication, but be sure to take a multivitamin containing at least 200 mcg of B-12 daily.

• **Proton pump inhibitors such as Nexium (*esomeprazole*),** which block the production of stomach acid and are prescribed for heartburn, ulcers and other gastrointestinal problems. Long-term use can cause deficiencies of magnesium and B-12.

What to do: Take a multivitamin with 200 mcg of B-12 and additional magnesium (200 mg daily)—and talk to your doctor about getting off the drug. (A gradual decrease in dosage is safest.) Proton pump inhibitors are toxic when used long term and addictive, causing rebound acid hyper-secretion when stopped. The solution? Improve digestion using plant-based digestive enzymes, deglycyrrhizinated licorice (DGL), marshmallow root and other stomach-healing supplements. Follow directions on the labels.

The New Nutrient Fix: Easy Ways to Correct 4 Often-Overlooked Deficiencies...

Dennis Goodman, MD, a board-certified cardiologist and clinical associate professor of medicine in the Leon H. Charney Division of Cardiology and director of Integrative Medicine, both at NYU Langone Medical Center in New York City. He is also author of *Magnificent Magnesium, The Thrill of Krill* and *Vitamin K2.* DennisGoodmanMD.com

If you eat a balanced diet, you may assume that you're getting all the nutrition you need. To play it safe, you might even take a multivitamin-mineral supplement. But is that enough? Probably not.

Four missing nutrients: Increasing evidence shows that there are four *little-known* nutritional deficiencies—each of which can threaten your health. The problem is, these deficiencies are not remedied by a typical multivitamin-mineral supplement and are extremely difficult to reverse through diet alone—even if you eat organic foods, which provide higher levels of some nutrients. *Here's what you're likely missing—and the nutrient fix you need...**

VITAMIN K-2

Vitamin K isn't even on most people's radar. But there are more than a dozen subtypes of this vitamin, including an important one known as *menaquinone* (vitamin K-2).

K-2 is crucial for both your bones and heart. Without sufficient K-2, osteocalcin, a protein that binds calcium to bone, cannot be activated. When calcium doesn't stay in bones, it can end up clogging your arteries, causing a heart attack or stroke.

Important finding: People with the lowest blood levels of vitamin K-2 had a 57% greater risk of dying from heart disease than those with the highest levels, according to research published in *The Journal of Nutrition.* People with low K-2 levels also are at increased risk for osteoporosis and bone fractures.

K-2 is found mainly in meat, eggs and dairy. But to get a bone- and heart-protecting level of K-2 from animal sources, you'd have to include in your daily diet at least eight pounds of beef, a gallon of milk, eight egg yolks and a gallon of yogurt. The only good nonanimal sources of K-2—fermented soybeans, found in foods such as tamari, miso and natto—aren't eaten regularly by most Americans.

My advice: Take a K-2 supplement—at least 45 micrograms (mcg) daily. Look for MenaQ7 (MK-7)—a long-acting and better-absorbed variety of K-2.

Good products: MenaQ7 from NattoPharma, MenaQ7.com...and MK-7 from NOW Foods, NowFoods.com.

Caution: If you take *warfarin* (Coumadin), ask your doctor before trying vitamin K-2—it can alter the drug's effectiveness.

*If you take medication, check with your doctor before trying any of these supplements to avoid potential interactions.

COENZYME Q10

Coenzyme Q10 (CoQ10) helps the body make *adenosine triphosphate* (ATP), the main energy source for cellular activity. But modern life steals CoQ10. You are probably deficient in this nutrient if you take a cholesterol-lowering statin…if you're exposed to high levels of air pollutants…or if you have a chronic disease. Research links low levels of CoQ10 to heart disease, Parkinson's disease, type 2 diabetes, male infertility and fibromyalgia.

CoQ10 is found in such foods as broccoli, nuts, beef and fatty fish—but only in small amounts.

My advice: Take a 100-milligram (mg) CoQ10 supplement daily. If you have side effects from taking a statin—such as muscle pain and weakness—consider taking 200 mg of CoQ10 daily. In my cardiology practice, I recommend SmartQ10, from Enzymatic Therapy, EnzymaticTherapy.com.

OMEGA-3s

Chronic, low-grade inflammation underlies many chronic health problems, including heart disease, type 2 diabetes, arthritis, cancer and Alzheimer's disease.

Omega-3 essential fatty acids—found in fatty fish, such as salmon, mackerel and tuna, and in oil-rich plant foods, such as walnuts and flaxseeds—are *anti-inflammatory*. In contrast, omega-6 essential fatty acids—found in baked goods (such as chips, crackers and cookies), cooking oils (such as corn oil, cottonseed oil and sunflower oil) and meat (especially processed meats and non-lean red meat)—are *pro-inflammatory*. Because the typical American diet has far too much omega-6 and not nearly enough omega-3, the majority of us have an omega-3 deficiency.

My advice: Take 500 mg of krill oil daily. I choose krill oil for myself and my patients rather than fish oil. Krill—small, shrimplike crustaceans—are at the bottom of the oceanic food chain and mostly harvested in the pristine waters around Antarctica, so their oil is less likely to be contaminated with mercury.

Krill oil also contains *phospholipids*, fatty substances that optimize the absorption of omega-3s. And because of that superior ab-

sorption, you need less—500 mg of krill oil is the therapeutic equivalent of 1 gram (g) to 2 g of fish oil.

If you are allergic to shellfish: Do not take krill oil.

MAGNESIUM

Eight out of 10 Americans unknowingly suffer from a chronic deficiency of this crucial nutrient. That deficiency causes or contributes to health problems, including heart attacks and other forms of cardiovascular disease (such as arrhythmias, heart failure and stroke), some forms of cancer, type 2 diabetes, obesity, osteoporosis, fatigue, depression and anxiety, migraines, muscle cramps and insomnia.

My advice: Magnesium is the *most* important supplement anyone can take. I recommend that women take 400 mg to 500 mg daily…and men take 500 mg to 600 mg daily. You can take it all at once or in divided doses—just take it! (If you have insomnia, consider taking your daily dose before bedtime to help you sleep.) I recommend Jigsaw Magnesium, from Jigsaw Health, JigsawHealth.com.

TAKE NOTE…

Fabulous Fiber

Fiber helps the brain, heart and more…

Brain: Adding 7 grams (g) of fiber daily may cut stroke risk by 7%.

Heart: For every 7 g of fiber daily, heart disease risk is lowered by 9%.

Waist: People who increased fiber intake to at least 30 g a day lost nearly as much weight as people on a complex, calorie-restricted diet.

Kidneys: Consuming more than 21 g of fiber daily may lower the risk for kidney stones by 22%.

Lungs: Fiber reduces inflammation and may lower the risk for chronic obstructive pulmonary disease (COPD) and other diseases.

Gut: Fiber helps balance bacteria levels, aiding digestion. *Added benefit:* Fiber slows the body's absorption of glucose, decreasing diabetes risk.

Studies from *British Medical Journal, Stroke, Journal of Nutrition, Annals of Internal Medicine, Journal of Urology, American Journal of Medicine, Journal of Molecular Biology, American Journal of Clinical Nutrition* and Mayo Clinic, reported in *Prevention*.

A well-absorbed form of magnesium malate, its sustained-release formula helps prevent diarrhea, a possible side effect of magnesium.

Whatever brand you use, look for magnesium malate, magnesium citrate or magnesium glycinate—the most absorbable forms. Avoid magnesium oxide—unless you want its stool-loosening effect to help ease constipation. You can also get magnesium in spray or cream forms online (check Ancient-Minerals. com or Amazon.com)—and by using Epsom salts (which is hydrated magnesium sulfate) in your bath!

---

14 Little Things You Can Do for a Healthier Heart

Joel K. Kahn, MD, a clinical professor of medicine at Wayne State University School of Medicine in Detroit and founder of the Kahn Center for Cardiac Longevity in Bloomfield Hills, Michigan. He is also an associate professor at Oakland University William Beaumont School of Medicine in Rochester, Michigan, and author of *The Whole Heart Solution.* DrJoelKahn.com

---

Heart disease is America's number-one killer. But just because it's a major health risk does not necessarily mean that you must make major lifestyle changes to avoid it. *Here are 14 simple and inexpensive ways to have a healthier heart...*

DOABLE DIET TIPS

1. Don't eat in the evening. Research suggests that the heart (and digestive system) benefits greatly from taking an 11-to-12-hour break from food every night. One study found that men who indulge in midnight snacks are 55% more likely to suffer from heart disease than men who don't. So if you plan to eat breakfast at 7 am, consider your kitchen closed after 7 or 8 pm.

Warning: You cannot produce the same health benefits by snacking at night and then skipping breakfast. This might create an 11-to-12-hour break from eating, but skipping breakfast actually *increases* the risk for heart attack and/or death—by 27%, according to one study. Our bodies and minds often are under considerable stress in the morning—that's when heart attack risk is greatest. Skipping the morning meal only adds to this stress.

2. Use apple pie spice as a topping on oatmeal and fruit. Some people enjoy it in coffee, too. This spice combo, which contains cinnamon, cloves, nutmeg and allspice, has been shown to reduce blood pressure, improve cholesterol levels and lower the risk for heart disease.

3. Take your time with your tea. Tea contains compounds called *flavonoids* that have been shown to significantly reduce the risk for heart disease—green tea is best of all. But you get the full benefits only if you have the patience to let the tea leaves steep—that is, soak in hot water—for at least three to five minutes before drinking.

4. Fill up on salad. It's no secret that being overweight is bad for the heart. But most people don't realize that they can lose weight without going hungry. Salad can make the stomach feel full without a lot of calories. But don't add nonvegetable ingredients such as cheese, meat and egg to salads...and opt for balsamic or red wine vinegar dressing—they are rich in nutrients, including artery-healing resveratrol.

As a bonus, vegetables and fruits contain nutrients that are great for the heart regardless of your weight—so great that eating a plant-rich diet could improve your blood pressure just as much as taking blood pressure medication. In fact, one study found that increasing consumption of fruits and vegetables from 1.5 to eight servings per day decreases the risk for heart attack or stroke by 30%.

One strategy: Become a vegetarian for breakfast and lunch. That way you still can enjoy meat at dinner, but your overall vegetable consumption will be increased.

5. Marinate meat before grilling it. Grilling meat triggers a dramatic increase in its "*advanced glycation end products*" (AGEs), which stiffen blood vessels and raise blood pressure, among other health drawbacks. If you're not willing to give up your grill, marinate meat for at least 30 minutes before cooking it. Marinating helps keep meat moist, which can slash

AGE levels in half. An effective marinade for this purpose is beer, though lemon juice or vinegar works well, too. You can add herbs and oil if you wish.

6. Sprinkle Italian seasoning mix onto salads, potatoes and soups. This zesty mix contains antioxidant-rich herbs such as oregano, sage, rosemary and thyme, which studies suggest reduce the risk for heart disease and cancer.

7. Avoid foods that contain dangerous additives. There are so many food additives that it's virtually impossible to keep track of them all. Focus on avoiding foods that list any of the following seven among their ingredients—each carries heart-related health risks. The seven are aspartame…BHA (butylated hydroxyanisole)…BHT (butylated hydroxytoluene)…saccharin…sodium nitrate…sodium sulfate…and monosodium glutamate (MSG).

8. Savor the first three bites of everything you eat. When people eat too fast, they also tend to eat too much. One way to slow down your eating is to force yourself to pay close attention to what you are eating. If you cannot do this for an entire meal or snack, at least do it for the first three mouthfuls of each food you consume. Chew these initial bites slowly and thoroughly. Give the food and its flavor your undivided attention, and you will end up eating less.

9. Prepare your lunch the night before if you won't be home for your midday meal. People who intend to make their lunch in the morning often are in too much of a rush to do so…then wind up resorting to fast food.

10. Buy organic when it counts. Higher pesticide levels in the blood predict higher cholesterol levels as well as cardiovascular disease. Organic food is free of pesticide—but it can be expensive. The smart compromise is to buy organic when it counts most—when traditionally grown produce is most likely to contain pesticide residue. According to the Environmental Working Group, the foods most likely to contain pesticide residue are apples, celery, cherry tomatoes, collard greens, cucumbers, grapes, hot peppers, kale, nectar-

HEART-HEALTHY SNACKS...

Peanut Power!

Peanuts may reduce risk for cardiovascular disease. People who reported the highest consumption of nuts—some tree nuts, but mainly peanuts—had 17% to 21% lower risk for death than those who reported the lowest nut consumption.

Study of 71,764 Americans and 134,265 Shanghai residents over 12 years by researchers at Vanderbilt University, Nashville, published in *JAMA Internal Medicine*.

Snack Combo for the Heart

Israeli researchers found that four ounces of pure pomegranate juice (not sweetened) and three dates (no added sugar), eaten together once a day, is hugely protective of heart health. It reduced oxidative stress in the arterial walls by as much as 33% while decreasing cholesterol by 28%.

Study by researchers at Technion-Israel Institute of Technology, led by Professor Michael Aviram of the Rappaport Faculty of Medicine and Rambam Medical Center, Haifa, Israel, published in *Food & Function*, a journal of The Royal Society of Chemistry.

Almonds Lower Blood Pressure

Men who ate a handful of almonds daily for four weeks had lower blood pressure and improved blood flow.

Study by researchers at Aston University in Birmingham, UK.

ines, peaches, potatoes, spinach, strawberries, summer squash and sweet bell peppers.

Important: If your options are eating conventionally farmed fruits and vegetables or not eating fruits and vegetables at all, definitely consume the conventionally grown produce. The health risks from small amounts of pesticide residue are much lower than the health risks from not eating produce.

EASY LIFESTYLE HABITS

11. Stand two to five minutes each hour. Recent research suggests that sitting for extended periods is horrible for your heart. Sitting slows your metabolism and reduces your ability to process glucose and cholesterol. But standing for as little as two to five minutes each hour seems to significantly reduce these health consequences (more standing is even better). Stand while making phone calls or during commercials. Buy a "standing desk," then stand when you use your computer.

12. Take walks after meals. Walking is good anytime, but walks after meals have special health benefits, particularly after rich desserts. A 20-minute postmeal stroll significantly improves the body's ability to manage blood sugar. Maintaining healthful blood sugar levels reduces risk for coronary artery blockage.

13. Exercise in brief but intense bursts. Research suggests that exercising as intensely as possible for 20 seconds...resting for 10 seconds...then repeating this seven more times provides nearly the same benefits for the heart as a far longer but less intense workout. Try this with an exercise bike, rowing machine, elliptical machine or any other form of exercise. Do an Internet search for "Tabata training" to learn more. There are free apps that can help you time these intervals. Download *Tabata Stopwatch* in the iTunes store if you use an Apple device...or *Tabata Timer for HIIT* from Google Play if you use an Android device.

Caution: Talk to your doctor. High-intensity training could be dangerous if you have a preexisting health condition.

14. Get sufficient sleep. One study found that the rates of heart disease for people who get seven to eight hours of sleep a night are nearly half those of people who get too little or too much sleep.

Better A-Fib Treatment

In a recent four-year study of overweight patients with atrial fibrillation (a-fib), 84% of those with a high level of *cardiorespiratory fitness* (a measure of how well the heart, lungs and muscles supply oxygen during workouts) had no arrhythmias, compared with 17% who had a low level of this type of fitness. How does one improve cardiorespiratory fitness? Work with your doctor to design an exercise program—and stick with it!

Some good options include: Cycling, brisk walking and swimming.

Prashanthan Sanders, MBBS, PhD, director, Centre for Heart Rhythm Disorders, The University of Adelaide, Australia.

Folic Acid Cuts Stroke Risk

According to a large study, supplements of the B vitamin decrease incidence of a first stroke in people with high blood pressure by 21%. People with normal blood pressure are likely to benefit, too. A standard daily multivitamin should provide adequate folic acid.

Better: Getting the vitamin from food, especially broccoli, beans (cooked from dried) and dark, leafy greens.

Also: Enriched grain products.

Meir Stampfer, MD, DrPH, professor of medicine at Harvard Medical School, Boston, and coauthor of an editorial published in *JAMA*.

How America's Top Diabetes Doctor Avoids Diabetes

George L. King, MD, chief scientific officer at the Boston-based Joslin Diabetes Center, one of the country's leading diabetes clinical care and research centers. He is also a professor of medicine at Harvard Medical School and author, with Royce Flippin, of *The Diabetes Reset.*

You might think that a diabetes researcher would never develop the disease that he's dedicated his life to studying. But I can't count on it.

My family's story: My father was diagnosed with diabetes at age 72 and was promptly placed on three medications to control his insulin levels.

What he did next made all the difference: Even though he began taking diabetes medication, he simultaneously went into action—walking an hour a day and going on the diet described below. A year and a half later, he no longer needed the prescriptions. He still had diabetes, but diet and exercise kept it under control.

As a diabetes researcher and physician whose own diabetes risk is increased by his family history, I've got a lot at stake in finding the absolute best ways to avoid and fight this disease.

Here are the steps I take to prevent diabetes—all of which can benefit you whether you want to avoid this disease or have already been diagnosed with it and are trying to control or even reverse it…

STEP 1: Follow a rural Asian diet (RAD). This diet includes the most healthful foods of a traditional Asian diet—it consists of 70% complex carbohydrates…15% fat…15% protein…and 15 grams (g) of fiber for every 1,000 calories. Don't worry too much about all these numbers—the diet is actually pretty simple to follow once you get the hang of it.

You might be surprised by "70% complex carbohydrates," since most doctors recommend lower daily intakes of carbohydrates. The difference is, I'm recommending high amounts of complex, unrefined (not processed) carbohydrates. This type of carb is highly desirable because it's found in foods—such as whole grains, legumes, vegetables and fruits—that are chock-full of fiber. If your goal is to reduce diabetes risk, fiber is the holy grail.

Why I do it: The RAD diet has been proven in research to promote weight loss…improve insulin sensitivity (a key factor in the development and treatment of diabetes) and glucose control…and decrease total cholesterol and LDL "bad" cholesterol levels.

To keep it simple, I advise patients to follow a 2-1-1 formula when creating meals—two portions of nonstarchy veggies (such as spinach, carrots or asparagus)…one portion of whole grains (such as brown rice or quinoa), legumes (such as lentils or chickpeas) or starchy veggies (such as sweet potatoes or winter squash)…and one portion of protein (such as salmon, lean beef, tofu or eggs). Have a piece of fruit (such as an apple or a pear) on the side. Portion size is also important. Portions fill a nine-inch-diameter plate, which is smaller than a typical 12-inch American dinner plate.

Helpful: I take my time when eating—I chew each bite at least 10 times before swallowing. Eating too quickly can cause glucose levels to peak higher than usual after a meal.

STEP 2: Fill up on dark green vegetables. I include dark, leafy greens in my diet *every day.* These leafy greens are one of the two portions of nonstarchy veggies in the 2-1-1 formula.

Why I do it: Dark green vegetables contain antioxidants and compounds that help your body fight insulin resistance (a main driver of diabetes).

My secret "power veggie": A Chinese vegetable called bitter melon. It is a good source of fiber and has been shown to lower blood sugar. True to its name, bitter melon tastes a little bitter but is delicious when used in soups and stir-fries. It is available at Asian groceries. Eat bitter melon as one of the two portions of nonstarchy veggies in the 2-1-1 formula.

STEP 3: Adopt an every-other-day workout routine. I try to not be sedentary and to walk as much as I can (by using a pedometer, I can tell whether I've reached my daily goal of 10,000 steps).

While this daily practice helps, it's not enough to significantly affect my diabetes risk. For that, I have an every-other-day workout routine that consists of 30 minutes of jogging on the treadmill (fast enough so that I'm breathing hard but can still carry on a conversation)…followed by 30 minutes of strength training (using handheld weights, resistance bands or weight machines).

Why I do it: Working out temporarily reduces your insulin resistance and activates enzymes and proteins that help your muscles use glucose instead of allowing the body to accumulate fat—a beneficial effect that lasts for 48 hours (the reason for my every-other-day routine). Strength training is crucial—your muscles are what really kick your body's glucose-burning into high gear. A weekly game of tennis helps shake up my routine.

STEP 4: Keep the temperature chilly. At the courts where I play tennis, the temperature is naturally cool, but I wear a very thin T-shirt that leaves my neck exposed. This helps activate the "brown fat" in my body. Most people have this special type of body fat—mainly around the neck, collarbone and shoulders.

Why I do it: Brown fat burns calories at high rates when triggered by the cold. To help burn brown fat, exercise in temperatures of 64°F or lower…set your home's thermostat in the mid-60s…and dress as lightly as possible in cool weather. Walking for 50 or 60 minutes a day in cool weather also helps.

STEP 5: Get the "sleep cure." I make a point to sleep at least six hours a night during the week and seven hours nightly on weekends.

Why I do it: Lack of sleep has been proven to dramatically harm the body's ability to properly metabolize glucose—a problem that sets the stage for diabetes. Research shows that seven to eight hours a night are ideal. However, because of my work schedule, I'm not always able to get that much sleep on weekdays. That's why I sleep a bit longer on weekends.

Research now shows that the body has some capacity to "catch up" on lost sleep and reverse some—but not all—of the damage that occurs to one's insulin sensitivity when you're sleep deprived.

---

4 Secret Cancer Fighters

The late Mitchell Gaynor, MD, founder and president of Gaynor Integrative Oncology in New York City and board-certified oncologist, internist and hematologist. He was also clinical assistant professor of medicine at Weill Cornell Medical College and is author of *The Gene Therapy Plan: Taking Control of Your Genetic Destiny with Diet and Lifestyle.*

My mother died of cancer at age 43, when I was nine years old. But I know I'm not a slave to my genetic destiny, doomed by DNA to die of the same disease. I know that I can do something about my cancer-prone genetic inheritance—and so can you.

The new science of *epigenetics* shows that it is possible to "upregulate" (trigger) the "expression" (activity) of powerful anticancer genes using a whole-foods diet, regular exercise, restful sleep, stress reduction—and concentrated nutritional and herbal compounds.

These natural compounds can activate genes that tell the body to turbocharge the immune system so that it can locate cancer cells…kill those cells…douse chronic, low-grade inflammation, which generates "growth factors" that fuel cancer…decrease the liver's production of *insulin-like growth factor one* (IGF), the most deadly "tumor promoter"…reduce a tumor's cancer-spreading blood supply…and even improve the effectiveness of chemotherapy.

In addition to taking vitamin D daily, I recommend these four powerful anticancer supplements for preventing or controlling cancer or stopping its recurrence. Take one, two or all four. At the dosages recommended, they are very safe. Of course, always check with your doctor before taking any new supplement.

MAGNOLIA EXTRACT

This herbal supplement from the bark of a magnolia tree contains *honokiol*, which has anticancer functions—it is anti-inflammatory and anti-angiogenic (limiting blood supply to tumors), and it targets many biochemical compounds that "signal" cancer to start and to grow, such as *nuclear factor-kappaB* and *epidermal growth factor receptor.*

Scientific research: More than 200 studies show that honokiol (and *magnolol*, another compound in magnolia bark) can fight cancer. In a recent cellular study, published in *International Journal of Oncology*, honokiol activated a gene that "suppressed" the spread of kidney cancer and deactivated two genes that allow kidney cancer cells to invade and colonize the surrounding tissue (metastasize).

Typical dosage: 200 milligrams (mg), daily.

Suggested product: Magnolia Extract from NutriCology. (I have no financial interest in this or any other product or brand that I recommend using.)

ARTICHOKE EXTRACT

This extract from artichoke leaves contains *rutin, quercetin, gallic acid* and *chlorogenic acid*—all of which have been shown in laboratory studies to kill a variety of cancer cells, including colon, breast and liver cancers, and leukemia. Artichoke extract also contains *cynarin*, which decreases inflammation. Plus, the extract has been shown in people to improve *insulin sensitivity*, the body's ability to utilize the glucose-regulating hormone insulin. When insulin is used efficiently, the body makes less insulin—and less cancer-sparking IGF.

Recent study: A cellular study published in *Asian Pacific Journal of Cancer Prevention* showed that artichoke extract triggered tumor suppressor genes.

Typical dosage: 320 mg, once daily.

Suggested product: Artichoke Extract from Enzymatic Therapy.

BLACK CUMIN SEED OIL

Many years ago, a patient of mine with prostate cancer started taking black cumin seed oil (*Nigella sativa*) with honey, three times a day, on the recommendation of a naturopathic physician. His Gleason score (a measure of the severity of prostate cancer) went from nine on a scale of one to 10 (an aggressive, invasive cancer with poor prognosis) to six—essentially, a precancerous lesion. Amazed, I started investigating this compound, which has been used in Turkish cooking for millennia—and started taking it myself, adding the seed to blended shakes and the oil to foods as seasoning. I recommend that patients use the oil—rich in *thymoquinone*, which is found in few other foods—either in their diets or as a supplement.

Compelling research: Researchers at Barbara Ann Karmanos Cancer Institute at Wayne State University School of Medicine in Detroit reviewed hundreds of cellular and animal studies on thymoquinone and cancer and concluded that the compound is anti-inflammatory...stops cancer cells from dividing and spreading by triggering their death...limits the formation of blood vessels that nourish the tumor (angiogenesis)...and "sensitizes" cells to chemotherapy.

Example: In a recent animal study, published in *Archives of Medical Science*, researchers discovered that thymoquinone "decreased

---

HEALTHY RECIPE...
Anticancer Smoothie

This drink is rich in anticancer compounds.

Examples: The *sulforaphane* from broccoli promotes the activation of "tumor suppressor" genes. The *quercetin* from apples inhibits tyrosine kinase, an enzyme associated with cancer. The *lauric acid* from coconut milk is linked to a low risk for breast cancer. And the *curcumin* from turmeric keeps cancer cells from replicating. Drink it daily. *Ingredients...*

½ cup coconut water
¼ cup broccoli
1 peeled cucumber
¼ cup watercress
1 apple, cored with peel
1 Tablespoon coconut milk powder
⅛ teaspoon ground turmeric

Blend one minute on medium. Pour through a strainer.

---

the expression" of both BRCA1 and BRCA2 genes—genes that increase the risk for breast cancer three- to five-fold and the risk for ovarian cancer as much as 30-fold.

Typical dosage: 500 mg, twice daily.

Suggested product: Black Seed Oil from Amazing Herbs.

BEE PROPOLIS, BEE POLLEN AND ROYAL JELLY

Bee propolis (a waxlike material used by bees to repair holes in hives) is rich in *caffeic acid phenethyl ester* (CAPE), *chrysin* and *cinnamic acid*, compounds that affect cancer genes. Studies show they are immune-strengthening, anti-inflammatory and anti-angiogenic and can reduce the growth of many cancers, including colon, prostate and kidney. Bee propolis also has been used clinically to reduce mouth sores caused by chemotherapy and radiation.

Recent study: In a cellular study on prostate cancer from the University of Texas Medical Branch, researchers found that CAPE boosted the cancer-killing power of chemotherapeutic drugs.

Another cellular study shows that bee pollen can inhibit *vascular endothelial growth factor* (VEGF), which helps create blood supply to tumors.

Royal jelly (a milky secretion produced by worker bees) contains several epigenetic factors. It has been shown to suppress the blood supply to tumors.

Typical dosage: 500 mg, once daily.

Suggested product: Triple Bee Complex from Y.S. Organic Bee Farms, which contains bee propolis, bee pollen and royal jelly.

Caution: People who are allergic to bee stings should not take bee products.

The Best of Integrative Cancer Care

Dwight McKee, MD, a medical oncologist based in Aptos, California, who is also board-certified in nutrition and integrative and holistic medicine. He edited several issues of *Cancer Strategies Journal* and coauthored the book *Herb, Nutrient, and Drug Interactions: Clinical Implications and Therapeutic Strategies.* Dr. McKee is also coauthor of *After Cancer Care: The Definitive Self-Care Guide to Getting and Staying Well for Patients After Cancer.*

Cancer is a complex disease—elusive and difficult to control, let alone cure. To get the best possible outcome, you want to have all hands on deck.

More than the conventional approach: While modern oncology has given us powerful weapons to fight cancer—drugs, surgery and radiation that attack tumors head on—the most effective integrative cancer therapies focus on the *cancer patient*, bolstering his/her natural defenses to help suppress tumor growth. Combining these approaches not only fills in gaps but also creates a powerful synergy.

BUILD YOUR DEFENSES

While there are a multitude of integrative approaches now available for cancer patients, ranging from acupuncture and massage to aromatherapy and music therapy, it's crucial to fortify your body's defenses to fight the inflammation associated with cancer. *Here's how…*

• **Diet.** Strive for a plant-based diet (especially cruciferous vegetables and berries—both are extremely rich in cancer-fighting nutrients) with plenty of whole grains, nuts and omega-3–rich fatty fish (omega-3s have been linked to reduced cancer risk). Cut back on animal proteins and sugar—these foods are associated with cancer-promoting inflammation.

• **Exercise.** Try to get 150 minutes weekly of moderately vigorous exercise (such as brisk walking) to help optimize your body's own cancer-fighting abilities. An ideal regimen could include some aerobic activity (such as cycling)…some stretching (such as yoga or tai chi)…and some strength training (with hand weights or resistance bands).

• **Stress reduction.** The first weeks after diagnosis are likely to be the most stressful of your life.

There are a myriad of ways to control stress, including meditation, hypnosis, yoga and tai chi, but one method that seems particularly effective is progressive muscle relaxation, which involves systematically relaxing all the muscle groups in the body, one after another. Twenty minutes daily has been shown to provide major benefits to people with cancer.

For a free video demonstrating progressive muscle relaxation, go to: CMHC.utexas.edu and then search for "Progressive Muscle Relaxation."

• **Herbs and supplements.** While adopting the inflammation-fighting lifestyle practices described earlier, anti-inflammatory herbs, such as curcumin and boswellia, can be powerful aids.

In addition, a typical herb-and-supplement regimen for a colon cancer patient, for example, may include some combination of the following—Vitamin D, green tea extract, resveratrol, grape seed extract, probiotics and omega-3 fatty acids.

Important: For specific advice on herbs and supplements, work with a skilled, experienced complementary/alternative doctor or herbalist (see below).

GETTING RID OF THE TUMOR

While conventional methods, such as surgery, radiation and chemotherapy, can be quite effective, they have important downsides, too. For example, chemotherapy and radiation not only have harsh side effects, including nausea and hair loss, but they also suppress the immune system at a time when it should be working overtime to fight the cancer.

Newer alternatives: The immune-suppressing effects of chemo and radiation can be avoided with *thermal ablation*. With this approach, doctors insert a needle into the tumor, often guided by computed tomography (CT) imaging, to kill the cancer cells with heat (*radiofrequency* or *microwave ablation*) or freezing (*cryoablation*). *Irreversible electroporation* (the NanoKnife) uses electrical pulses to kill cancer cells by disrupting their cell membranes. These methods are also much less invasive and traumatic than surgery.

Right now, ablation is mainly used for tumors that can't be treated with conventional surgery, due to their location or number, and for isolated metastases in the lung and liver. But ablation and electroporation have the potential to replace a considerable amount of surgery.

IMMUNOTHERAPY

Scientists are actively developing new medications that help undo the tumor's ability to produce chemicals that inactivate the body's cancer-fighting immune cells.

For instance: Both *ipilimumab* (Yervoy) and *pembrolizumab* (Keytruda) have been approved for the treatment of melanoma. Clinical trials to investigate their use against a wider range of malignancies, including certain kinds of lung cancer, and bladder, colon and metastatic prostate cancer, are also under way. For details on clinical trials involving these drugs, check ClinicalTrials.gov.

Because these drugs target molecular mechanisms driving cancer, they are far less toxic than conventional chemotherapy. The drugs are, however, extremely expensive (costing up to $150,000 a year). If insurance won't cover the drug and a clinical trial is not available, sometimes the pharmaceutical manufacturer will donate it to a patient without the financial resources to purchase it so that it can be administered by his/her oncologist.

GETTING THE HELP YOU NEED

It's risky for cancer patients to try to treat themselves with integrative approaches. Some therapies, including certain herbs, such as St. John's wort, may even interfere with conventional treatment. But finding oncologists, herbalists and other health-care professionals who are knowledgeable about the latest approaches in integrative cancer care is also challenging.

To locate a health-care professional who specializes in integrative oncology: Ask for a referral from your doctor or consult the Society for Integrative Oncology, IntegrativeOnc. org. When you find an experienced integrative professional, ask him/her to work with your primary oncologist in coordinating your care.

B-3 May Reduce Skin Cancer Risk

Risk for some types of skin cancer can be reduced by taking a vitamin B-3 derivative called *nicotinamide*, in addition to using sunscreen.

Details: Nearly 400 adults who previously had basal cell or squamous cell carcinomas took 500 milligrams (mg) of nicotinamide twice daily. After a year, their rate of new skin cancers was 23% lower than that of those who didn't take nicotinamide, which enhances the DNA in sun-damaged cells.

Note: Talk to your doctor before taking nicotinamide—it can interact with medications.

Diona Damian, PhD, professor of dermatology, The University of Sydney Medical School.

Vitamin D Fights Cancer

The late Mitchell Gaynor, MD, founder and president of Gaynor Integrative Oncology in New York City. He is author of *The Gene Therapy Plan.*

Vitamin D is important for cancer control. *Recent research:* Women with breast cancer who had the highest levels of vitamin D were 44% more likely to survive the disease. When researchers at University of California, San Diego, looked at patients with colon cancer, those with the highest levels were 37% more likely to survive than those with the lowest.

Other recent cancer studies show that people with high levels of vitamin D have a 25% reduced risk for bladder cancer…54% reduced risk for melanoma…and 52% greater chance of surviving lymphoma.

The only way to accurately determine if you have a low level of vitamin D is to test your blood for *25-hydroxyvitamin D*, a metabolite of vitamin D-3. I recommend a test three times a year, in September, January and May.

What to do: Ask your doctor for a test…or order a test yourself from DirectLabs.com…or order a home test from the Vitamin D Council (VitaminDCouncil.com).

I recommend aiming for a blood level between 50 ng/mL and 90 ng/mL. It is impossible to achieve the recommended level from foods alone—even a D-rich diet provides a maximum of 350 international units (IU) daily.

Better: Take a vitamin D supplement, 1,000 IU to 5,000 IU daily.

Surprising Cure for Back Pain: It's Not Drugs, Exercise or Surgery!

Todd Sinett, DC, chiropractor and founder/owner of Midtown Integrative Health & Wellness in New York City. He has served as a clinical expert for many television programs, including *FoxMD* and *Good Day New York*. He is author of *3 Weeks to a Better Back: Solutions for Healing the Structural, Nutritional and Emotional Causes of Back Pain*.

If you have persistent back pain, most doctors look for *structural* problems—a herniated disc, for example, or a misaligned spine. These can be real issues, but they point to a solution for only a small percentage of patients.

Surprisingly, back pain can be the result of poor nutrition and poor digestion, which causes chronic inflammation that irritates muscles, ligaments, tendons and/or nerves. A recent study in *Asian Spine Journal* found that nearly one-third of women and one-quarter of men with back pain also had food intolerances or other gastrointestinal complaints.

Dietary changes won't always eliminate back pain (although they might), but they often reduce pain significantly. If you rate your pain as an eight, for example, changing your diet could reduce it to a manageable two or three. *What to do…*

•**Get enough fiber.** If you're often constipated or have infrequent bowel movements, you'll have buildups of toxins that increase inflammation and back pain. A high-fiber diet can fix this and reduce your back pain.

My advice: Look at your stool. It should be more or less smooth (and should pass easily). If it is lumpy and hard, you probably need more fiber. Increase your water, fruit and vegetable intake.

•**Cut back on caffeine.** Caffeine is a stimulant that increases levels of cortisol, a hormone that triggers inflammation. People who drink a lot of coffee or other caffeinated beverages are more likely to have painful muscle cramps and spasms.

My advice: Eliminate caffeine for two to three weeks. If this makes a big improvement, give it up altogether. If it doesn't help, you can go back to it because caffeine isn't the culprit.

•**Stay well-hydrated.** Many of my patients don't drink water very often. This is a problem because you need water to improve digestion and reduce inflammation—and because people who don't drink much water often consume less healthful beverages, such as sodas. Water also helps lubricate the spinal discs and can help prevent fissures, cracks in the discs that can allow the soft middle portion to bulge out and press against a nerve.

Everyone with back pain should drink between four and 10 glasses of water a day. The first thing I do every morning is drink a big glass of water. If you're not a fan of plain water, you can spruce it up with a squeeze of lemon or lime or substitute watered-down juice (half juice, half water).

• **Eliminate *all* added sugar.** The average American consumes about 175 pounds of sugar a year—from soft drinks, desserts and even packaged foods that you wouldn't imagine are loaded with sugar, such as white bread, salad dressing, ketchup and pasta sauce.

The rapid rise in glucose (blood sugar) that occurs when you eat sweetened foods triggers the production of *cytokines,* proteins secreted by immune cells that increase inflammation. A high-sugar diet also irritates the digestive tract, which can lead to back pain.

My advice: Give up all added sugar for at least three weeks. It takes about two weeks for existing inflammation to "calm." Staying off added sugar for an additional week will help reinforce the change in your usual habits. After that, you can reintroduce a small amount of sugar—by having an occasional dessert, for example, or adding a small amount of sugar to your morning coffee.

If you add back a bit of sugar and your pain doesn't increase, you'll know that you can enjoy *some* sugar. On the other hand, you might notice that you're having more back pain again, in which case you'll want to cut out sugar.

• **Eat more organic produce.** Most people know that antioxidants in fruits and vegetables—substances such as vitamin C, lycopene and indole-3-carbinol—can reduce levels of cell-damaging molecules (free radicals) that cause inflammation. In my experience, getting more antioxidants isn't as effective for pain as improving digestion (with fiber, cutting back on sugar, etc.), but it can help. I tell patients to buy organic produce because it won't be tainted with pesticides or other inflammatory chemicals. Also, a recent study found that organic corn contained 58% more antioxidants and that organic marionberries (a type of blackberry) had up to 50% more antioxidants than their nonorganic counterparts.

• **Look for sensitivities.** The healthiest diet in the world won't improve back pain if you're eating foods that trigger a reaction in you. Many foods (including foods considered healthy, such as broccoli) can trigger symptoms in some people. In addition to pain, these symptoms could include digestive irrita-

tion, sleepiness after a meal, fogginess, achiness and/or congestion.

To find out whether you're sensitive to one or more foods, track what you eat with a journal. When you notice an increase in pain, you can review the journal and find the food(s) that might be responsible. In addition to the foods mentioned in this article, dairy and gluten are common offenders.

My advice: When you identify a likely food suspect—maybe you drank a beer on the day your back got worse—give it up for a few weeks. If your symptoms improve, test your conclusion by having a small amount of that food or beverage. If the pain increases again, you'll know that you have to avoid that food in the future. Or you can go to a gastroenterologist, allergist, nutritionist or integrative medical doctor for food-sensitivity testing.

---

5 Hidden Causes of Pain: It's Crucial to Find the *Real* Culprit...

Vijay Vad, MD, a sports medicine specialist at the Hospital for Special Surgery and assistant professor of rehabilitation medicine at Weill Cornell Medical College, both in New York City. He is also the founder of the Vad Foundation, VijayVad.com, an organization that supports medical research related to back pain and arthritis, and author of *Stop Pain: Inflammation Relief for an Active Life.*

D o you have arthritis, backaches or some other type of nagging pain that just won't go away?

Why pain often persists: For a significant number of people who chalk up their pain to a creaky joint, muscle aches or some other common problem, the true culprit actually has never been properly diagnosed.

But don't give up. One of the following conditions may be at the root of your pain—or at least making it much worse. *The good news is that there's plenty you can do to treat these hidden causes of pain...*

VITAMIN D DEFICIENCY

What does your backache have to do with the amount of vitamin D in your body? More than you might think, according to recent research.

Here's why: Vitamin D is needed for normal bone metabolism. People who don't produce enough are especially susceptible to low-back pain, possibly because the vertebrae become weakened. Low vitamin D levels also have been linked to hip pain and knee pain.

My advice: Get your vitamin D level tested once a year, particularly if you live in the Northeastern US or the Pacific Northwest. Limited sun exposure in these areas can make it difficult for the body to synthesize enough vitamin D, and it is difficult to get adequate amounts of this vitamin from food.

If your vitamin D level is low (most experts put the optimal blood level between 20 ng/mL and 36 ng/mL), take a daily supplement that provides 1,000 international units (IU) to 2,000 IU…and continue to get tested annually.

LOW THYROID

Underactive thyroid gland (hypothyroidism) is more common than most people realize. Even though the condition is most often found in women, it can affect men, too. The blood tests used to detect the condition are simple and inexpensive, yet few doctors order the testing routinely, as they should.

Thyroid hormones are real workhorses in the body—for example, they help regulate how many calories you burn, your heart rate and body temperature. If you have low thyroid levels, you're likely to suffer from fatigue, sensitivity to cold and unexplained weight gain.

What's not so well-known is that people with hypothyroidism tend to have nagging muscle and joint pain. This is because low thyroid can accelerate the loss of cartilage in those who already have a touch of arthritis.

My advice: If you have arthritis or any type of joint or muscle pain that has unexpectedly worsened, ask your doctor for a thyroid test. This advice applies to men, too. A *thyroid function panel* measures blood levels of thyroid stimulating hormone (TSH), along with levels of different thyroid hormones. A normal TSH level is typically between 0.4 mlU/L and 4.0 mlU/L.

Even if your TSH level is "borderline," your thyroid may be contributing to your pain, so ask your doctor about medication. Thyroid-replacement hormones, such as Synthroid or Levothroid, mimic the effects of natural thyroid hormone and can start to relieve symptoms, including thyroid-related arthritis pain, within a month.

NOT ENOUGH ESTROGEN

Women tend to experience more pain overall once they go through menopause—not necessarily because of pain-causing conditions, but because the body's drop in estrogen lowers their pain tolerance.

Example: Knee pain that you might have rated as a 5 (on a 1-to-10 scale) before menopause might now feel like an 8. Pain sensitivity is higher in postmenopausal women who also have low thyroid.

My advice: Try supplemental curcumin. This potent anti-inflammatory reduces pain and improves joint flexibility. Most postmenopausal women (and men, too!) notice an improvement when they take it.

Dose: 2,000 mg daily. This supplement is generally safe for everyone to use, but consult your doctor first, especially if you take any medication (it can interact with some drugs, such as anticoagulants)…or if you have gallstones, since it could increase painful symptoms.

Good product: Northeast Natural's Triple Curc, ActiveBodyActiveMind.com.

If this doesn't give you adequate pain relief, you may also want to consider estrogen replacement. It decreases pain sensitivity and reduces the loss of joint cartilage.

Important: Estrogen replacement can increase risk for heart disease, stroke and breast cancer in some women, so ask your doctor to help you sort out the pros and cons.

LYME DISEASE

This tick-borne illness can be easily treated (usually with a three-week course of antibiotics)—*if* it's detected early. But many people don't know they have it, in part because the test isn't always accurate.

What happens: The bacterium that causes Lyme can destroy joint cartilage. Many people with Lyme know that something's wrong, but it often takes months—and multiple visits with different specialists—to get an accurate diagnosis.

My advice: If you reside in an area where ticks and Lyme disease are common, do not wait to get help. The symptoms might include muscle or joint pain, unexplained fatigue and/or a burning sensation that affects your whole body. Treating Lyme disease quickly reduces the risk of lingering joint pain and other symptoms.

If you test negative but still suspect that your pain may be caused by the disease, consider seeing a doctor who specializes in diagnosing Lyme for a second opinion. To find such a specialist near you, consult the International Lyme and Associated Diseases Society at ILADS.org.

POOR SLEEP

People who suffer from chronic pain often don't sleep well. But it also works the other way—less deep sleep lowers your tolerance to pain.

Even if you think that you sleep well, you may not be getting enough rapid eye movement (REM) sleep—the more time you spend in this stage of sleep, the better equipped your body will be at tolerating pain.

My advice: Get at least 30 minutes of aerobic exercise every day. This type of exercise increases levels of deep sleep, which is needed for you to get adequate REM sleep.

Best Natural Remedies for Migraines: Kill the Pain Without the Drugs

Jay S. Cohen, MD, a widely recognized expert on prescription drugs and natural alternatives. He is author of *15 Natural Remedies for Migraine Headaches* and a member of both the psychiatry and psychopharmacology departments at University of California, San Diego.

Migraine headaches can be awful—and many people find that the side effects of the prescription medications given to prevent or treat them can be just as bad. For instance, listed among the numerous possible adverse effects for *propranolol,* a commonly prescribed migraine medication, are vertigo, facial swelling, receding gums, cardiac arrhythmia—and, believe it or not, headache.

However, compelling research has shown that certain natural remedies help prevent, soothe and reduce the frequency of migraine headaches—without the side effects of drugs.

Important: Check with your doctor to make sure that none of these natural treatments will interact with any other medications that you take or conditions that you have. Then I suggest working through the list to see what helps you. You also can combine remedies, such as riboflavin, magnesium and CoQ10, but always check with your doctor.

RIBOFLAVIN

Also called vitamin B-2, riboflavin occurs naturally in certain foods. It helps convert food into energy…it's an antioxidant that fights free-radical damage…and it helps activate other forms of vitamin B.

How riboflavin helps migraines: It is believed that some migraines occur because oxygen is not being properly metabolized in the *mitochondria* (the so-called "power plants" of cells), so riboflavin's energy-boosting function may help prevent this type of migraine.

The research: The first published study evaluating riboflavin for migraine therapy reported that taking 5 milligrams (mg) three times daily over several months diminished migraine frequency—some subjects said that taking hourly doses halted acute migraines.

Studies done in 1994 and 1998 found that taking 400 mg/day of riboflavin helped reduce frequency and severity of migraines, with the best results seen in the third month of therapy. A 2004 study of migraine patients who had not responded to other therapies yielded a 50% reduction in migraine frequency for patients who took riboflavin daily.

How to take riboflavin: I suggest 400 mg daily. It's safe to take riboflavin indefinitely. Some people notice improvement quickly, but others see benefits only after three or four months of taking riboflavin daily. A small percentage of people find that riboflavin makes their faces flush and/or report digestive upset—if that happens to you, you might try dividing your dose in half (200 mg, morning and night) or just take 200 mg/day.

COENZYME Q10

Also called *ubiquinone*, CoQ10 is a substance that occurs naturally in the body that helps with mitochondrial function and energy production. It's also an antioxidant that may help stem inflammation.

How CoQ10 helps migraines: CoQ10 works similarly to riboflavin, supporting cellular energy production. Its antioxidant power is so strong that it's often recommended for people with certain types of heart disease and muscular and nervous system problems.

The research: Several small studies found that taking CoQ10 reduced migraine frequency. In a 2002 study of 32 adults taking 150 mg/day, 61% said that the days they experienced migraines were down by 50% or more. A 2005 study found that 48% of participants experienced a 50% or greater decrease in frequency, and a 2007 study of children and adolescents had similar results.

How to take CoQ10: I typically advise patients to start with a dose of 150 mg/day and, if needed, work their way up to taking three daily doses of 100 mg (morning, noon and night). One percent of people report some stomach upset with CoQ10—if you're in that group, stop taking CoQ10.

MAGNESIUM

The vast majority of Americans are deficient in magnesium, which is a problem because it is essential to the healthy function of muscles and the nervous system. I believe magnesium is very helpful for people with a deficiency—not so much for those whose magnesium levels already are healthy.

How magnesium helps migraines: Magnesium plays a role in many cellular processes and also is responsible for smooth-muscle activity in the nerves and arteries—both factors in migraines. Also, magnesium deficiency has been shown to cause spasms of the cerebral arteries, associated with migraine.

The research: A 1995 study reported that intravenous delivery of 1,000 mg of magnesium was effective at halting migraines. Studies examining the use of oral magnesium (600 mg/day) to prevent migraines were done in 1996 and 2008 and found that it reduced both the frequency and severity of the headaches.

How to take magnesium: A good dose to begin with is 100 mg twice daily. Gradually work your way up to 400 mg/day.

5-HTP

5-Hydroxytryptophan (5-HTP) is a building block used by the body to produce serotonin, a neurotransmitter that aids cellular communication and also is associated with mood. Available in many foods, 5-HTP is produced from the amino acid tryptophan.

How 5-HTP helps migraines: 5-HTP gets converted by the body to serotonin (found in the nervous system and the gut), which is involved in the conduction of pain signals and the dilation/constriction of blood vessels—both relevant to migraine pain.

The research: A 1973 study compared the efficacy of 5-HTP therapy (200 mg/day) and a prescription medication in 20 patients and found identical results—both treatments achieved a 55% reduction in frequency, and the 5-HTP patients who continued taking the supplement reported continual improvement. Subsequent studies found 5-HTP effective at soothing the pain of migraines already in progress.

How to take 5-HTP: Begin with a small dose (50 mg to 100 mg), and if need be, work your way up to the maximum daily dosage (300 mg to 400 mg), taken at bedtime. Side effects are mild and may include gastrointestinal problems and weird dreams.

MELATONIN

This sleep-promoting hormone has numerous positive effects, including suppression of the substances that promote pain. It also fosters anti-inflammatory activity, regulation of serotonin and nerve and blood vessel interaction.

How melatonin helps migraines: A theory about one possible cause of migraine relates to an imbalance in the relationship between the hypothalamus and the pineal gland that affects adequate melatonin production.

The research: A 2004 study followed 34 adult patients who were given a nightly melatonin dose of 3 mg over three months—25% stopped getting migraines altogether and 80% reported a 50% or greater reduction in frequency. A 2008 study examining children and adolescents taking 3 mg of melatonin at bedtime found a 50% or greater reduction in frequency for 71% of participants.

How to take melatonin: Start with a dose of 0.5 mg or 1 mg and go up to 2, 3 or 5 mg, depending on your reaction. Take melatonin in the evening, preventively, or as treatment for an acute migraine. Melatonin yields superior results and has far fewer side effects when compared with common migraine drugs.

Save Your Sight: Natural Ways to Fight Common Eye Problems

Jeffrey R. Anshel, OD, founder of the Ocular Nutrition Society and president of Corporate Vision Consulting, based in Encinitas, California, where he also has the private optometry practice E Street Eyes. He is author of *What You Must Know About Food and Supplements for Optimal Vision Care: Ocular Nutrition Handbook.* SmartMedicineforYourEyes.com

---

Vision problems in the US have increased at alarming rates, including a 19% increase in cataracts and a 25% increase in macular degeneration since 2000.

Why the increase? Americans are living longer, and eyes with a lot of mileage are more likely to break down. But not getting the right nutrients plays a big role, too—and the right foods and supplements can make a big difference.

Of course, people with eye symptoms or a diagnosed eye disease should work closely with their doctors. I also recommend medical supervision for people who are taking multiple supplements.

But here are common eye problems and the foods and supplements that can fight them…

DRY EYES

The eyes naturally get drier with age, but *dry-eye syndrome*—a chronic problem with the quantity and quality of tears—often is due to nutritional deficiencies. Poor nutrition can permit damaging free radicals to accumulate in the glands that produce tears.

What to do: Take one-half teaspoon of cod liver oil twice a week. It's an excellent source of DHA (*docosahexaenoic acid,* an omega-3 fatty acid) and vitamins A and D, nutrients that improve the quality of tears and help them lubricate more effectively.

Also helpful: BioTears, an oral supplement that includes curcumin and other eye-protecting ingredients. (I am on the scientific advisory board of BioSyntrx, which makes BioTears and Eye & Body Complete, see below, but I have no financial interest in the company.) I have found improvement in about 80% of patients who take BioTears. Follow the directions on the label.

CATARACTS

Cataracts typically are caused by the age-related clumping of proteins in the crystalline lens of the eyes. More than half of Americans will have cataracts by the time they're 80.

What to do: Eat spinach, kale and other dark leafy greens every day. They contain *lutein,* an antioxidant that reduces the free-radical damage that increases cataract risk. (Lutein and *zeaxanthin,* another antioxidant, are the only carotenoids that concentrate in the lenses of the eyes.)

Important: Cook kale or other leafy greens with a little bit of oil…or eat them with a meal that contains olive oil or other fats. The carotenoids are fat-soluble, so they require a little fat for maximal absorption.

I also advise patients to take 500 milligrams (mg) of vitamin C three or four times a day (cut back if you get diarrhea). One study found that those who took vitamin C supplements for 10 years were 64% less likely to have cataracts.

The supplement Eye & Body Complete contains a mix of eye-protecting compounds, including bioflavonoids, bilberry and vitamins A and D. Follow instructions on the label.

COMPUTER VISION SYNDROME

The National Institute of Occupational Safety and Health reports that 88% of people who work at a computer for more than three hours a day complain of computer-related problems, including blurred vision, headaches, neck pain and eye dryness.

What to do: Take a supplement that contains about 6 mg of *astaxanthin*, a carotenoid. It reduces eyestrain by improving the stamina of eye muscles.

Also helpful: The 20/20/20 rule. After every 20 minutes on a computer, take 20 seconds and look 20 feet away.

REDUCED NIGHT VISION

True night blindness (*nyctalopia*) is rare in the US, but many older adults find that they struggle to see at night, which can make night driving difficult.

What to do: Take a daily supplement that includes one-half mg of copper and 25 mg of zinc. Zinc deficiencies have been associated with poor night vision—and you'll need the extra copper to "balance" the zinc. Zinc helps the body produce vitamin A, which is required by the retina to detect light.

Also helpful: The foods for AMD (below).

AGE-RELATED MACULAR DEGENERATION (AMD)

This serious disease is the leading cause of blindness in older adults. Most people with AMD first will notice that their vision has become slightly hazy. As the disease progresses, it can cause a large blurred area in the center of the field of vision.

What to do: Eat several weekly servings of spinach or other brightly colored vegetables, such as kale and yellow peppers, or egg yolks. The nutrients and antioxidants in these foods can help slow the progression of AMD. The National Eye Institute's Age-Related Eye Disease Study (AREDS) reported that patients who already had macular degeneration and had adequate intakes of beta-carotene, zinc, copper and vitamins C and E were 25% less likely to develop an advanced form of the disease.

Also helpful: The Eye & Body Complete supplement, mentioned earlier. It contains all of the ingredients used in the original AREDS study—plus many others, including generous amounts of lutein and zeaxanthin that were included in a follow-up study, known as AREDS2—and was found to have positive effects.

Better Vision in 6 Weeks or Less: Without New Glasses or Surgery

Larry Jebrock, OD, a board-certified, licensed optometrist who emphasizes nonsurgical vision improvement and behavioral optometry. He is founder and director of Natural Vision Correction, Orthokeratology & Vision Therapy, in Novato, California. He is a former instructor for the California Optometric Association and a consultant for companies on the effects of prolonged computer use and video display terminals on the vision system. EyeExercises.com

---

If you're over 40, it's likely that you're not seeing as well as when you were younger—and if you're over 60, it's nearly certain that your eyesight has declined.

Breakthrough approach: Behavioral optometry—using *eye exercises* to improve vision—is an effective but usually overlooked method for stopping, slowing and even reversing the age-related decline of eyesight.

VISION PROBLEMS

If your eyesight has declined, you probably have *presbyopia*, a decrease in your ability to focus and see clearly at close distances, such as when you're reading or looking at the computer.

You also might have diminished *contrast sensitivity*—less light is reaching the retina, the lining at the back of the inner eye that transforms light into electrical impulses that are sent to the visual cortex in the brain. As a result, vision is "washed out" and the contrast between objects becomes less distinct. It may be difficult to see the difference between the sidewalk curb and the street, for example. Lessened contrast sensitivity also worsens glare from headlights at night or sun reflecting off windshields during the day.

The danger: Poor contrast sensitivity increases the risk for falls and car accidents.

Aging also decreases overall visual acuity, or sharpness of vision. And visual reaction time is diminished. It takes longer for the brain to register what has been seen.

The typical solutions to declining vision are corrective lenses (eyeglasses or contacts) and Lasik laser surgery, in which the cornea is reshaped. But for many people, stronger corrective lenses are needed every six to 18 months, as vision continues to worsen…and Lasik surgery often is not covered by insurance, doesn't always restore perfect vision and can cause dry eyes, glare and hazy vision.

EXERCISES WORK

New scientific evidence: Researchers from University of California, Riverside and Brown University used eye exercises to improve the eyesight of 16 younger people (average age 22) and 16 older people (average age 71), and published their results in *Psychological Science*.

After just seven days, diminished contrast sensitivity was *eliminated* in the older group—in other words, their contrast sensitivity reversed, becoming the same as that of the younger group. And both younger and older adults had improved visual acuity in the problem areas common to their age—older people saw *near* objects more clearly, and younger people saw *far* objects more clearly.

Here are three vision-restoring exercises you can do at home. Results can be immediate or take up to six weeks. Once your eyes have improved, keep up the exercises, but you can do them less often. Your eyeglass/contact

prescription may change, so see your eye-care professional.

• **Improve near vision and far vision.** Practice this simple eye exercise for three or four minutes a few days a week.

Instructions: Look at a calendar on a wall about 10 feet away. In your hand, have another object with numbers or letters, such as a small calendar or an open book. Cover the left eye with your hand. Look back and forth from the far object to the near object, focusing on and calling out a letter or number from each.

Example: The "J" in June from the far calendar and the "12" in June 12 from the near calendar. Do this five to 10 times, calling out a different letter or number each time. Cover the right eye, and repeat the exercise. (You also can use an eye patch to cover one eye and then the other.)

Bonus benefit: It's common after a car accident for the person who is at fault to say that he "never saw" the other vehicle. I call this *inattentional blindness*—your eyes are on the road, but your vision system is not fully activated, because you're thinking or moving or otherwise preoccupied. The near-far exercise also improves visual attention.

• **Improve peripheral vision—the "other" visual system.** Corrective lenses correct only *central vision*, when the eyes focus straight ahead, so that you can read, drive and see details sharply. But there are *two* key parts to the visual system—central and peripheral vision. And improving peripheral vision improves every aspect of seeing, from visual acuity to contrast sensitivity.

Everyday enemy of peripheral vision: Stress. Under stress, people see less, remember less and typically the visual field constricts. But there's a simple exercise called "palming" that relieves stress and eases eyestrain.

Instructions: Sit at a table with your elbows on the table. (Put a pillow under your elbows if that's more comfortable.) Breathe easily and deeply, relaxing your body. Close your eyes, and notice what you're seeing—it's likely there will be visual "chatter," such as spots and flashes of light. Now cup your palms over your closed eyes, and visualize (create mental imagery of) blackness.

Example: Visualize yourself out on the ocean on a moonless night on a black ship on a black sea. The goal of the exercise is to see complete blackness.

Relaxing, breathing deeply, blocking out light and "visual chatter"—and even the warmth of your palms—relaxes the visual system and helps to open up peripheral vision.

Do the exercise for as long as you like, from 30 seconds to 30 minutes.

•**Improve "binocularity"**—seeing out of both eyes. A common but little-recognized vision problem in older adults is a lack of *binocularity*—one eye is not processing visual detail, which decreases visual acuity and depth perception (crucial for stepping off a curb or walking up stairs without stumbling or falling). This exercise can help you see with both eyes.

For this exercise you'll need a Brock String, named after its inventor, the optometrist Frederick Brock. It's a simple device—a 10- or 12-foot string with several colored beads on it. (The Brock String is widely available online for around $10 or less.)

Instructions: Attach one end of the string securely to a wall with a nail, tack or tape. Sit 10 feet away from the wall, holding the string so that there is no slack. The closest bead should be about four feet from your eyes.

Hold the string to the side of your nose and look *directly* at the closest bead, using both eyes—you should see two strings going toward the bead and crossing either in front of or behind the bead. You're "seeing double" because the device is engineered to generate a double-image, similar to what you might see when your eyes are relaxed and unfocused. This experience helps you become aware that you're seeing out of both eyes. If you see only *one* string, you're not seeing fully out of both eyes. And if the strings *cross in front of* or *behind* the bead, your eyes aren't aimed right at the bead. *The goals of the exercise…*

•Keep both strings "turned on" (your eyes will get a "feel" for how to do this).

•The strings should cross at the bead—if the string crosses ahead of the bead, look a few

inches beyond the bead…if the string crosses behind the bead, look in front of the bead.

Do the exercise for three or four minutes, two or three times a week.

For a Sharper Brain, Eat These 4 Foods

Drew Ramsey, MD, an assistant clinical professor of psychiatry at Columbia University College of Physicians and Surgeons in New York City. Dr. Ramsey is also co-author of *The Happiness Diet: A Nutritional Prescription for a Sharp Brain, Balanced Mood, and Lean, Energized Body* and *Fifty Shades of Kale: 50 Fresh and Satisfying Recipes That Are Bound to Please.*

We all know that a strong cup of coffee can give us that extra mental boost we may need to complete a brain-draining project or meet a tight deadline.

What works even better: Strategic eating is a healthful and reliable way to improve your ability to concentrate for the long haul—not just for a few hours at a time when you're hyped-up on caffeine.

There's no single food that will suddenly have you speed-reading a book in one sitting, but you can improve your overall powers of concentration by including the following foods in your diet…

•**Eggs.** When it comes to mental focus, it doesn't get much better than eggs! They're a leading source of a nutrient called *choline*, a precursor to the neurotransmitter *acetylcholine*—a key molecule of learning.

Eggs (including the yolks) also contain a variety of B vitamins, most of which have been stripped from the refined carbs that are so ubiquitous in the typical American diet. In particular, eggs are rich in vitamins B-6 and B-12, which are crucial for carrying out most cognitive functions (three large eggs will give you about half of your daily B-12 requirement)… and vitamin B-9 (also known as folate).

For optimal brain health, include up to 12 eggs in your diet each week. While cholesterol in one's diet has only a minimal effect on blood levels of cholesterol, consult your doctor for advice on appropriate intake of eggs if cholesterol is a concern.

•**Mussels.** Three ounces of mussels—which is a modest serving—contain 20 micrograms (mcg) of vitamin B-12 (that's nearly 10 times your daily requirement). Even a mild deficiency of this crucial brain-boosting vitamin can impair concentration and lead to fuzzy thinking.

But that's not all. Three ounces of mussels will also give you 430 milligrams (mg) of *docosahexaenoic acid* (DHA)—the equivalent of two to three typical fish oil supplement capsules. DHA is a type of omega-3 fatty acid needed for healthy brain function. Mussels are also loaded with zinc, a nutritional workhorse involved in more than 100 chemical reactions in the brain. Enjoy mussels twice a month.

Don't like mussels? Other smart brain-boosting seafood selections include oysters (six oysters deliver three to four times your daily zinc needs)…anchovies, which have more omega-3s than tuna…and clams, which are an excellent source of vitamin B-12.

Tasty choices: Caesar salad with anchovies…clam chowder…or pasta alle vongole (with clams).

GOOD TO KNOW...

How to Add 5 Years of Brainpower

Eating the right five foods can postpone brain aging by five years.

Recent study: Adults age 65 and older who frequently ate at least five foods from the Mediterranean diet (such as fish, vegetables, fruit, whole grains, legumes and olive oil) and consumed moderate amounts of wine and low amounts of dairy, meat and poultry were found to have larger brain volumes than those who didn't eat this way. The difference in brain volume was comparable to about five fewer years of brain aging.

Theory: The Mediterranean diet may help slow the loss of brain cells during aging.

Yian Gu, PhD, assistant professor, neuropsychology, Columbia University College of Physicians & Surgeons, New York City.

•**Beef.** You've probably heard that eating too much red meat is linked to heart disease and even some types of cancer. However, you can minimize these risks and maximize your brainpower with a few small servings per week.

Here's why: Beef is a potent source of *heme iron* (the most absorbable form), which is needed to transport oxygen through the blood and to the brain.

What I recommend: Opt for grass-fed beef. It has fewer calories, less fat and more nutrients (such as vitamin E) than conventional beef. Meat from grass-fed animals has two to three times more *conjugated linoleic acid* (CLA) than meat from grain-fed animals. CLA helps protect the brain by counteracting the effects of harmful stress hormones.

Try to have grass-fed beef once or twice a week—but give it a supporting role instead of making it the star of your meal. Think grass-fed vegetable beef stew instead of a large steak.

Note: Even though grass-fed beef is more expensive than conventional beef, you can save by opting for nontraditional cuts, such as beef shank, stew meats and roasts. If you are a vegetarian or vegan, black beans are an excellent substitute.

•**Cruciferous vegetables.** Take your pick—the list includes brussels sprouts, kale, arugula, bok choy, cauliflower and collard greens. As members of the *Brassica* plant family, these veggies contain sulfur-based anti-inflammatory compounds that help protect the brain. One of these compounds, *sulforaphane*, has even been shown to improve memory and learning after brain injury.

Aim for at least two cups of cruciferous vegetables daily—I put that much in my kale-blueberry smoothie every morning!

Note: Consult your doctor before changing the amount of leafy greens you eat if you take *warfarin*, a blood thinner, since vitamin K–rich foods may interact.

Other good choices: Add purple cabbage to a stir-fry…or mash cauliflower instead of potatoes and season with brain-boosting turmeric and black pepper (to increase the absorption of turmeric).

Dr. Kosik's Alzheimer's Prevention Plan: 6 Powerful Secrets

Kenneth S. Kosik, MD, the Harriman Professor of Neuroscience Research and codirector of the Neuroscience Research Institute at the University of California, Santa Barbara, where he specializes in the causes and treatments of neurodegeneration, particularly Alzheimer's disease. Dr. Kosik is coauthor of *Outsmarting Alzheimer's*. KennethSKosikMD.com

I f someone told you that there was a pill with no side effects and strong evidence showing that it helps prevent Alzheimer's disease, would you take it? Of course, you would!

The truth is, there's no such "magic bullet," but most adults *do* have the ability to dramatically decrease their odds of getting this dreaded disease.

A window of opportunity: According to the latest scientific evidence, slowing or blocking Alzheimer's plaques (buildups of dangerous protein fragments), which are now known to develop years before memory loss and other symptoms are noticeable, could be the key to stopping this disease.

To learn more, we spoke with Dr. Kenneth S. Kosik, a renowned neuroscientist who has researched Alzheimer's for 25 years. He shared with us the habits that he incorporates into his daily routine to help prevent Alzheimer's…

STEP 1: Make exercise exciting. You may know that frequent exercise—particularly aerobic exercise, which promotes blood flow to the brain—is the most effective Alzheimer's prevention strategy. Unfortunately, many people become bored and stop exercising.

Scientific evidence: Because exercise raises levels of *brain-derived neurotrophic factor*, it promotes the growth of new brain cells and may help prevent shrinkage of the *hippocampus* (a part of the brain involved in memory).

What I do: Most days, I spend 35 minutes on an elliptical trainer, followed by some weight training (increasing muscle mass helps prevent diabetes—an Alzheimer's risk factor). To break up the monotony, I go mountain biking on sunny days. I advise patients who have

---

TAKE NOTE...

Good News for Coffee Lovers!

Drinking three to five cups of coffee per day could cut your risk of developing Alzheimer's disease by 20%, according to a recent analysis.

Why: Coffee is naturally high in polyphenols, which reduce inflammation and slow the deterioration of brain cells. If you're not a coffee drinker, you can get polyphenols with a diet that includes plenty of fish, fresh fruits and vegetables, and olive oil.

Arfan Ikram, MD, PhD, associate professor of neuroepidemiology, Erasmus Medical Center, Rotterdam, the Netherlands.

---

trouble sticking to an exercise regimen to try out the new virtual-reality equipment available in many gyms. While riding a stationary bike, for example, you can watch a monitor that puts you in the Tour de France!

Also helpful: To keep your exercise regimen exciting, go dancing. A recent 20-year study found that dancing reduced dementia risk more than *any* other type of exercise—perhaps because many types of dancing (such as tango, salsa and Zumba) involve learning new steps and aerobic activity. Do the type of dancing that appeals to you most.

STEP 2: Keep your eating plan simple. A nutritious diet is important for Alzheimer's prevention, but many people assume that they'll have to make massive changes, so they get overwhelmed and don't even try. To avoid this trap, keep it simple—all healthful diets have a few common elements, including an emphasis on antioxidant-rich foods (such as fruit and vegetables)…not too much red meat…and a limited amount of processed foods that are high in sugar, fat or additives.

Scientific evidence: Research has shown that people who consume more than four daily servings of vegetables have a 40% lower rate of cognitive decline than those who get less than one daily serving.

What I do: I try to consume more vegetables, in particular broccoli, cauliflower and other crucifers—there is strong evidence of their brain-protective effects.

Helpful: I'm not a veggie lover, so I roast vegetables with olive oil in the oven to make them more appetizing. Whenever possible, I use brain-healthy spices such as rosemary and turmeric.

STEP 3: Guard your sleep. During the day, harmful waste products accumulate in the brain. These wastes, including the *amyloid* protein that's linked to Alzheimer's, are mainly eliminated at night during deep (stages 3 and 4) sleep.

Scientific evidence: In a long-term Swedish study, men who reported poor sleep were 1.5 times more likely to develop Alzheimer's than those with better sleep.

Regardless of your age, you need a good night's sleep. While ideal sleep times vary depending on the person, sleeping less than six hours or more than nine hours nightly is linked to increased risk for cardiovascular disease—another Alzheimer's risk factor. If you don't feel rested when you wake up, talk to your doctor about your sleep quality.

What I do: I often take a 10-minute nap during the day. Brief naps (especially between 2 pm and 4 pm, which syncs with most people's circadian rhythms) can be restorative.

STEP 4: Don't be a loner. Having regular social interaction is strongly associated with healthy aging.

Scientific evidence: Older adults who frequently spend time with others—for example, sharing meals and volunteering—have about a 70% lower rate of cognitive decline than those who don't socialize much.

What I do: To stay socially active, I regularly Skype, attend conferences and stay in touch with other scientists and postdoc students.

If you're lonely, any form of social interaction is better than none. One study found that people who used computers regularly—to write e-mails, for example—were less lonely than those who didn't. If you can't connect in person, do a video chat or Facebook update at least once a day.

Also helpful: Having a pet. Pets are sometimes better listeners than spouses!

STEP 5: Stay calm. People who are often stressed are more likely to experience brain shrinkage.

Scientific evidence: In a three-year study of people with mild cognitive impairment (a condition that often precedes Alzheimer's), those with severe anxiety had a 135% increased risk for Alzheimer's, compared with those who were calmer.

What I do: I go for long walks.

Other great stress reducers: Having a positive mental attitude, deep breathing, yoga, tai chi, meditation—and even watching funny movies. Practice what works for you.

STEP 6: Push yourself intellectually. So-called "brain workouts" help prevent Alzheimer's—perhaps by increasing *cognitive reserve* (the stored memories/cognitive skills that you can draw on later in life)…and possibly by accelerating the growth of new brain cells.

Scientific evidence: In an important study, older adults (including those with a genetic risk factor for Alzheimer's) who frequently read, played board games or engaged in other mental activities were able to postpone the development of the disease by almost a decade.

But don't fool yourself—if you're an accomplished pianist, then banging out a tune won't help much even though a nonmusician is likely to benefit from learning to play. *Push* your mental abilities—do math problems in your head, memorize a poem, become a tutor, etc.

What I do: To challenge myself intellectually, I read novels and practice my foreign language skills—I do research in Latin America, so I work on my Spanish.

A Gentle Way to Break the Sugar Habit

Jacob Teitelbaum, MD, board-certified internist and nationally known expert in the fields of chronic fatigue syndrome, fibromyalgia, sleep and pain, Kailua-Kona, Hawaii. Dr. Teitelbaum is also author of numerous books as well as the popular free smartphone app *Cures A–Z.* Vitality101.com

P eople may like to joke about having a "sweet tooth," but it's really no laughing matter.

The craving for sweets can be just as intense as cravings for drugs or alcohol. The comparison is apt because sweets trigger some of the same brain changes that occur in people who use cocaine or other highly addictive substances—and can be even *harder* to give up. So what's the harm in having a daily sugar fix?

What the research now says: While we've long known that overindulging in sugar can lead to cavities and weight gain (and related risks such as diabetes), a growing body of research now shows a far broader range of potential harms. These include increased risks for high blood pressure and heart disease…certain types of cancer (such as malignancies of the breast and pancreas)…kidney disease…liver failure…migraines…osteoporosis…and cognitive decline. Too much sugar has also been linked to fatigue, anxiety and depression.

Wondering if you are a sugar addict? As with most addictions, if you feel the need to ask the question, you likely are! (See next page for a self-test.)

SUGAR OVERLOAD

A little sugar won't hurt, but most people get *much* more than the daily maximum amount of added sugar recommended by the American Heart Association (AHA)—100 calories for women and 150 calories for men, which is roughly equal to six to nine teaspoons of sugar or 25 grams (g) to 37 g.

And it adds up fast. Most sodas and many fruit drinks have up to three-quarters of a teaspoon of sugar per ounce. It's also hidden in places you might not expect. Many flavored six-ounce yogurts have seven teaspoons of sugar…a half-cup serving of coleslaw has 2.5 teaspoons…and one-half cup of spaghetti sauce has almost two teaspoons.

CUT THE CRAVINGS

With sugar's addictive qualities, cutting back is no easy feat. Some people try to go cold turkey for a few days (forgoing even foods that contain natural sugar) to prime themselves for a longer-term low-sugar diet. For many people, however, this approach is too drastic.

A gentle way to rein in your sugar intake: Start by cutting back on the *highest-sugar foods* in your diet—sweet beverages, candy and other sugary desserts. You'll still be getting some added sugar in foods you may not expect (such as condiments, including salad dressing, sauces and ketchup…granola…and even many types of bread). But if sugar is listed as one of the top three ingredients on a food or drink label (meaning the sugar content is high), don't have it.

Important: When you're checking labels, be aware that added sugar may appear under such terms as *sucrose, maltose, glucose* or *dextrose*…and, of course, high-fructose corn syrup, molasses, honey, etc. A lot of restaurant food is also notoriously high in sugar—including ethnic foods, such as Chinese and Thai.

Keep it simple: Your goal is to significantly cut back on added sugar—that is, sugars and syrups added to food or beverages during preparation and processing. Aim for the AHA's guideline (six teaspoons a day for women…and nine for men). To calculate teaspoons, divide the number of grams by four. Also avoid foods with white flour, found in many breads and pastas—the body rapidly converts it to sugar. But if it's a whole food without a label—such as a fruit or veggie—then you can safely assume that it's OK to eat.

If you've been getting too much sugar, you'll probably experience irritability, loss of energy and other withdrawal symptoms when you first cut back, but they usually fade within 10 days. You'll then have more energy, suffer less aches and pains and feel dramatically better!

Helpful while you're cutting back…*

• **Replace added sugar with stevia.** This plant-based sweetener has no calories, and it doesn't cause the insulin spikes that occur with sugar…or increase risk for diabetes.

Stevia is 200 to 300 times sweeter than sugar, so you can use just a small amount in your coffee or tea…and use it for baking (follow label instructions for the correct amount). Some brands of stevia have a bitter aftertaste due to poor filtering.

Good products: Body Ecology's Liquid Stevia Concentrate…Stevita…Truvia…Pure Via.

*If you have diabetes or take any type of medication, consult your doctor before changing your diet and/or taking supplements.

•**Take ribose.** It's a special type of sugar that is made by the body to create energy. You can use ribose in supplement form to replace the sugar energy "high" you may miss when you phase out sweets. Research has shown that it increases healthy energy by an average of 60% within three weeks.

My advice: Add a 5,000-milligram (mg) scoop of ribose powder twice daily to any food or drink. Ribose powder looks and tastes like sugar but doesn't raise blood sugar (it can lower blood sugar in people with diabetes). Use less if you feel too energized.

•**Eat low-glycemic foods.** The glycemic index (GI) rates foods by how quickly they raise blood sugar. High-glycemic foods, including white bread and white rice, raise blood sugar nearly as quickly as pure sugar—and increase sugar cravings. Foods rated 70 or above cause rapid rises in blood sugar…those with a GI below 55 have little effect (those in between have an intermediate effect). Choose foods at the lower end of the scale.

Examples: Whole grains, legumes, non-starchy vegetables, nuts and eggs.

For the GI of specific foods, go to Glycemic Index.com and use the search function.

WHAT TYPE OF SUGAR ADDICT ARE YOU?
The four main types of sugar addiction…

TYPE 1: Low energy. Do you repeatedly crave sweets or caffeine to give you the energy you need to get through the day?

What helps: Take a multinutrient powder. Nutrient deficiencies can cause fatigue while increasing both appetite and sugar cravings.

Good product: Energy Revitalization System multinutrient powder. (I developed this product but donate 100% of my royalties to charity.) Take one-half to one scoop daily. You can blend it with milk, water or yogurt. For extra energy, add a scoop of ribose (see above).

TYPE 2: Overtaxed adrenal glands. Do you constantly feel stressed-out? Are you irritable when you're hungry? These are both red flags for another common cause of sugar addiction—*adrenal insufficiency*, a stress-related reduction in adrenal hormones.

What helps: Drink one cup of licorice root tea each morning. This helps the adrenal hormones that are made by your body last longer.

Caution: If you have high blood pressure or take any type of medication, ask your doctor before trying licorice root tea.

Adrenal function is also supported by vitamins C and B-5 (the Energy Revitalization System multinutrient powder mentioned above provides healthful levels).

TYPE 3: Candida overgrowth. Do you have chronic nasal congestion, sinusitis or irritable bowel syndrome? These conditions may indicate hidden *Candida* (yeast) overgrowth. Yeasts thrive on sugar and release a chemical that causes sugar cravings.

What helps: A good enteric-coated probiotic (such as Optima) will fight Candida overgrowth. It is also worth seeing a holistic physician (check the American Board of Integrative Holistic Medicine, ABIHM.org, for a referral) to help you get rid of Candida.

TYPE 4: Imbalanced hormones. In premenopausal and menopausal women, changes in estrogen and progesterone can lead to mood changes that improve when sugar is eaten. Men can be affected by midlife drops in testosterone, which also can trigger sugar cravings.

What helps: Eating a handful of edamame daily may help balance hormone levels in women with premenstrual syndrome (PMS) and ease menopausal symptoms, such as hot flashes. Women and men who suffer from hormonally driven sugar cravings may also want to ask their doctors about natural hormone replacement.

6

On a Personal Note

Sexy Smoothies and More to Improve Your Sex Life...and Help Your Heart

Everybody knows about the "little blue pill" (also known as Viagra). Viagra and similar drugs can help men perform sexually by opening up and relaxing blood vessels in the penis. But some men suffer from headaches, stomach upset and other side effects. And women? There doesn't seem to be an effective oral medication to help them with sexual enjoyment.

A safe option: Many fruits and vegetables can improve sexual functioning in much the same way that prescription medications do—and they help women, too.

Hard to believe? It's true. These foods, including bananas, kale and watermelon, are rich in inorganic compounds, such as *nitrate* and *nitrite*, and other compounds that play a key role in men's—and women's—sexual arousal, performance and response. These compounds are such powerhouses because they have the ability to increase levels of *nitric oxide* (NO)—a molecule that dilates blood vessels and increases blood flow to many organs, including the sexual organs.

Bonus: NO's beneficial effect on blood vessels also helps reduce heart disease risk by lowering blood pressure. *Tasty recipes to improve your sex life—and heart health...**

*Some ingredients used in these recipes may interact with certain medications—such as *warfarin* (Coumadin) and blood pressure or erectile dysfunction drugs. Consult your doctor.

Mark A. Moyad, MD, MPH, the Jenkins/Pokempner Director of Preventive & Alternative Medicine in the department of urology at the University of Michigan Medical Center in Ann Arbor. Dr. Moyad, who specializes in nondrug medicinal therapies, is the lead author of more than 150 medical articles and 11 books, including *The Supplement Handbook*. He created the recipes in this article with his wife, Mia Moyad.

111

SEXY SMOOTHIE

Blend (start on "low" and increase to "high"): One-half cup of ice...one cup of unsweetened coconut water...one-half cup of shredded kale...one-half frozen banana...one-half cup of your favorite frozen berries (for some extra sweetness, if desired)...one to two pitted prunes...plus one tablespoon of L-citrulline (an amino acid that creates NO) or dried Panax ginseng powder (an herb that promotes sexual desire).

Why it works: Bananas are a great source of nitrate and nitrite. Coconut water, bananas and kale are rich sources of blood pressure–lowering potassium...and prunes deliver fiber, which helps control blood sugar—important for heart health and blood pressure control.

L-citrulline is the closest thing there is to an over-the-counter Viagra. It's available as a powder or in capsule form (empty out two or three capsules to get 1,000 milligrams (mg) to 1,500 mg of powder...or simply swallow them with your smoothie).

Good product: Source Naturals' L-Citrulline powder, VitaminShoppe.com.

Red Panax ginseng has been found in research to significantly improve sexual arousal in menopausal women. Select a brand with at least 8% *ginsenosides* (the main active components of Panax ginseng).

Good product: NuSci Panax Ginseng Extract Powder, Standardized 10% Ginsenosides, *Amazon.com.*

Note: Breast cancer patients should not use ginseng products.

HIGH-OCTANE SMOOTHIE

Blend (start on "low" and increase to "high"): One cup of ice...one cup of almond milk...two tablespoons of natural, no-sugar-added peanut butter...one-half frozen banana...one-half-inch jalapeño or a dash of cayenne pepper...one teaspoon of coconut or palm oil...and one tablespoon of cacao powder.

Why it works: This smoothie lifts your energy levels—crucial for a good sex life. Peanut butter is a stellar source of protein, which helps maintain metabolism and muscle function. If you don't like peanut butter, try another nut butter—or a scoop of flavored protein powder.

Good product: Jay Robb Whey Protein Powder, GNC.com.

Capsaicin, the compound responsible for the fiery heat of jalapeño and cayenne pepper, increases NO and blood flow throughout the body. Coconut and palm oils provide a type of healthful fat that is easily used by the body for energy. Cacao contains *anandamide,* a feel-good neurotransmitter, and just enough caffeine for a little natural lift.

WATERMELON SANGRIA

Combine: One bottle of red wine with a sliced orange, lemon and lime, plus two cups of club soda. Then add one cup of watermelon juice (buy it online or make your own) and one cup of shaved watermelon rind (shave the white part of the rind on the inside of the watermelon).

Why it works: This summer cocktail features heart-healthy red wine. What makes this recipe different is the L-citrulline (found in watermelon juice and rind), which improves NO production. The alcohol will lower inhibitions to help put you in the mood for sex. But don't have more than two four- to six-ounce glasses. Too much will steal your mojo!

GOOD TO KNOW...

How Often Should You Have Sex?

Studies of more than 30,000 people show that couples who make love once a week report the highest level of happiness—more than those who have sex less frequently but no less than those who exceed a weekly tryst.

Explanation: Weekly sex is optimal to maintain an intimate connection between partners with busy lives.

Amy Muise, PhD, postdoctoral fellow, University of Toronto, Ontario, Canada.

ED Drugs Don't Ensure Satisfying Sex

Many older men with erectile dysfunction (ED) who used Viagra, Cialis, Levitra and similar medicines still expressed concern about their level of desire, frequency of sexual activity, erectile function and other aspects of their sex lives. Doctors need to give patients realistic expectations…and treat any psychological or relationship issues.

Study of more than 2,600 men, ages 51 to 87, by researchers at The University of Manchester and NatCen Social Research, London, both in the UK, published in International Journal of Impotence Research.

Move Over Viagra!

Men who consumed the most flavonoid-rich foods (such as blueberries, apples, citrus fruits and red wine) had a 10% reduced risk for erectile dysfunction (ED) compared with those who ate the least, a recent 30-year study has found.

Possible reason: Flavonoids enhance blood vessel function and reduce inflammation, both of which improve blood flow to the penis.

Bonus: Men who were also physically active (brisk walking for two to five hours per week) cut their risk for ED by up to 21%.

Eric Rimm, ScD, professor of epidemiology and nutrition, Harvard T.H. Chan School of Public Health, Boston.

ED Linked to Low Vitamin D

Men with vitamin D deficiency are 32% more likely to have erectile dysfunction (ED) than men who are not deficient. Men with erectile dysfunction symptoms should have cardiovascular risk factors measured—such as blood pressure and lipid and glucose levels—because up to 80% of ED is thought to have vascular causes. But vitamin D measurement also is useful—the vitamin has a role in regulating blood pressure, glucose and inflammation.

Erin D. Michos, MD, MHS, FACC, associate director of preventive cardiology at the Ciccarone Center for the Prevention of Heart Disease, Baltimore, and leader of a study presented at a recent American Heart Association meeting.

Sex and Your Heart

Contrary to commonly held beliefs, sex is not associated with heart attack. A 10-year study of more than 500 patients recovering from heart attacks found that less than 1% had their heart attack within an hour of having sex. Additionally, second heart attacks were not linked to sexual activity.

Explanation: Sexual intercourse generally involves physical activity no more strenuous than a brisk walk or climbing two flights of stairs.

Dietrich Rothenbacher, MD, MPH, professor of epidemiology, Ulm University, Germany.

"Viagra" for Women?

The new "female Viagra" boosts libido only moderately. *Flibanserin* was approved by the FDA in 2015. Unlike Viagra for men, which increases penile blood flow, flibanserin affects the brain and changes levels of *serotonin, norepinephrine* and *dopamine* to enhance sexual mood. Side effects include dizziness, fatigue, anxiety, dry mouth, insomnia and nausea.

Natural alternative: ArginMax, which has been shown in clinical studies to boost women's sexual response. It contains L-arginine (an amino acid), herbs, vitamins and minerals. Side effects include headache and nausea.

Laurie Steelsmith, ND, LAc, medical director of Steelsmith Natural Health Center, Honolulu, and coauthor of *Great Sex, Naturally.*

Pesticides May Affect Sperm Health

Men enrolled in a fertility study who ate produce that typically contains more pesticide residue—strawberries, spinach, apples, peaches and peppers—had lower sperm counts and a lower percentage of normal sperm than men who ate produce that usually has less pesticide residue, including avocados, asparagus, onions and cabbage.

Study of data from 155 men by researchers at Harvard T.H. Chan School of Public Health, Boston, published in *Human Reproduction*.

Latest Thinking on the PSA Debate

H. Ballentine Carter, MD, a professor of urology and oncology and the director of adult urology at Johns Hopkins University School of Medicine in Baltimore. He has published more than 200 papers and 32 textbook chapters on male urologic health. Dr. Carter is also coauthor of *The Whole Life Prostate Book*.

The prostate-specific antigen (PSA) test is the most controversial health issue facing men today. Many consider it crucial for early detection and treatment of prostate cancer, noting that in the years after it was approved, the number of prostate cancer deaths dropped by 40%.

The catch-22: Even though some experts believe that PSA testing has played a key role in reducing the number of deaths from prostate cancer, it can't differentiate harmless cancers (the majority) from aggressive ones. Studies have shown that men whose levels test high are only marginally less likely to die from prostate cancer, on average, than those who were never tested…and they're more likely to have biopsies, surgeries and other risky treatments that will make no difference in their long-term health.

That's why a 2012 task force advised against widespread screening. Within a year, PSA testing had dropped by 28%—but there was a corresponding decline in the diagnoses of potentially risky cancers.

To sort through the issues, we spoke with H. Ballentine Carter, MD, an internationally recognized expert in the diagnosis and treatment of prostate cancer.

•**Isn't early cancer detection always a good thing?** Not for prostate cancer. Most tumors discovered by routine PSA tests are *indolent*—slow-growing cancers that pose no risk to a man's long-term health. The tests do find some dangerous cancers, but not many. Over a 10-year period, only one life will be saved for every 1,000 men who are screened.

It's tempting to argue that saving the lives of a few men (particularly if you're one of them) outweighs the inconvenience for the thousands who aren't helped. But the test isn't merely a bother for those who test positive. Many of these men will be subjected to biopsies and other treatments, including surgery—and possible complications such as incontinence and impotence—for cancers that never would have been a threat.

•**Do you agree with the guidelines for curtailed testing?** It's worth pointing out that no government agency has ever recommended mass PSA screening. It's an important test for select men, but it's not for everyone—and it needs to be used more judiciously.

Consider an 80-year-old man who is expected to live for another five or 10 years. Does he need to have a PSA test? Probably not, because most prostate cancers are slow-growing. He's unlikely to die from prostate cancer, even if cancer cells are already present.

But a man in his 50s should consider having the test every two years. If his PSA is low—for example, between 0 ng/ml and 2.5 ng/ml—he can rest easy. If his level is high—10 ng/ml or above—he can work with his doctor to decide if he needs a biopsy or other tests/treatments.

•**Won't reduced screening cause more cancer deaths?** In the year after the 2012 task force recommended against routine PSA testing, the number of prostate cancer diagnoses dropped. Much of the reduction involved low-risk cancers, but there was also a reduction in the diagnoses of higher-risk cancers, according to a study published in *The Journal of Urology*. This is potentially worrisome, although it's unclear whether the "missed" diagnoses will eventually lead to more cancer deaths. The goal for now is *smarter* testing, not more testing.

•**What do you mean by "smarter"?** The PSA test can't distinguish meaningless tumors from lethal cancers. Yet some doctors urge men to undergo biopsies based on a single high reading. That's a mistake.

If a man's PSA is, say, 10 ng/ml, that's concerning. But what if the high reading is transitory and caused by something other than cancer? What if the lab made an error?

Even when a high PSA is caused by cancer, a single high reading might not mean it's a lethal cancer. I worry more about PSA *velocity*—the amount that PSA increases over time and how quickly it rises. A continuously rising PSA—especially more than one point per year—can point to an aggressive cancer.

• **What if my PSA tests high?** Don't panic. All sorts of things besides cancer can cause a high PSA reading—infection, inflammation and even ejaculation within the past 48 hours can cause a temporary increase. Your doctor should recommend a repeat test within a few weeks or months, possibly followed by annual or semiannual testing. Do not agree to a biopsy unless your doctor is convinced that cancer is a strong possibility.

Also helpful: A new test approved by the FDA in 2012, the *prostate health index* (PHI), looks at different types of prostate cancer-specific biomarkers—total PSA, free PSA and pro-PSA. The score from the *combined* factors is more reliable than PSA alone. Research has shown that this type of testing—along with even newer tests, such as the 4Kscore, that look for other cancer "markers"—can reduce unnecessary biopsies by about 30%.

• **What's the "sweet spot" between too much testing and not enough?** When the task force guidelines were issued, PSA tests were overused. Also, only about 10% of men who were tested and diagnosed with prostate cancer were managed with *active surveillance*. This approach doesn't rush men into treatment—they undergo monitoring that may include digital rectal exams and biopsies. The goal is to determine more precisely which men will truly benefit from treatment.

Active surveillance is now used in up to 40% of patients. This is good and might encourage *more* testing because men will be reassured that they'll be treated only for cancers that pose a real threat.

• **What advice do you have for men who want to be tested?** A healthy man, without a family history of prostate cancer (in his father, brother or son), should consider having a PSA test between the ages of 50 and 55 and then every two years but *only* after a conversation with his doctor about potential risks and benefits. Men with a family history of prostate cancer and African-American men—both of whom are at increased risk—should ask their doctors about earlier testing.

A man needs to ask himself if he can deal with the stress if his PSA is high, suggesting that he might have cancer. Can he live with the idea that he *might* have a "harmless" cancer? Or will he insist on a biopsy that might lead to unnecessary surgery or other treatments? That's exactly what we're trying to avoid.

Wait-and-Watch Warning

An analysis of more than 3,600 prostate cancer patients undergoing "watchful waiting" discovered that less than 5% were monitored appropriately, which means receiving routine prostate-specific antigen (PSA) tests, physical exams and at least one additional prostate biopsy within a two-year period of time. Inadequate monitoring puts these men at risk of having their cancer progress without them knowing it.

Karim Chamie, MD, MSHS, assistant professor of urology, David Geffen School of Medicine, University of California, Los Angeles.

Powerful Prostate Protection

In a recent study, 37 men with low-grade prostate cancers took 4,000 international units (IU) of vitamin D-3 daily for one year after being diagnosed. In most of the men, their cancers decreased or did not grow.

Possible reason: Vitamin D-3 has anti-inflammatory effects. Inflammation is believed to promote the growth of cancer cells.

Consult your doctor.

Bruce Hollis, PhD, professor of medicine, Medical University of South Carolina, Charleston.

Prostate Cancer and Statins

Men with advanced prostate cancer may benefit from statin drugs. Standard treatment for advanced prostate cancer is *androgen deprivation therapy* (ADT). Men taking statins and ADT were 17% less likely to have disease progression compared with men who did not take a statin.

Possible reason: Statins stop a precursor of testosterone called DHEA-S from entering cancer cells.

Philip Kantoff, MD, chief of solid tumor oncology at Dana-Farber Cancer Institute, Boston, and leader of a study of 926 men published in *JAMA Oncology*.

Better Prostate Cancer Treatment

A study of more than 3,500 men with prostate cancer that spread to nearby lymph nodes found that the five-year survival rate of those who received androgen-deprivation therapy (ADT) *plus* radiation was 50% higher than for those who received only ADT.

Explanation: Radiation appeared to prevent further spread of cancer cells.

Jason A. Efstathiou, MD, DPhil, associate professor of radiation oncology, Massachusetts General Hospital, Boston.

Prostate Cancer Recovery Tip

Just a little exercise goes a long way in healing after prostate cancer. A review of more than 51,500 prostate cancer survivors found that those who walked at an easy pace for three hours per week had less fatigue, depression and weight problems (common post-treatment issues) than those who didn't walk as much. Picking up the pace was also beneficial—men who walked briskly for only 90 minutes a week showed similar improvements. About half the men had surgery, and 40% received radiation as their primary treatment.

Siobhan M. Phillips, PhD, assistant professor of preventive medicine at Northwestern University Feinberg School of Medicine, Chicago.

Alternative to Tamoxifen?

Laurie Steelsmith, ND, LAc, medical director of Steelsmith Natural Health Center, Honolulu. She is a licensed naturopathic physician and acupuncturist and coauthor of *Great Sex, Naturally*.

Tamoxifen is a synthetic hormone that blocks the action of estrogen and reduces the risk for certain types of breast cancer. Side effects may include hot flashes, menstrual changes, weight gain or loss and, rarely, such serious problems as clots in the lungs and stroke.

We don't have long-term research on dietary supplements that can prevent breast cancer as we do with tamoxifen. But some supplements appear to have estrogen-blocking effects or other protective properties. *These include...*

•**Calcium d-glucarate**—a combination of calcium and glucaric acid—is found in apples, cabbage and certain other fruits and vegetables. It also is produced naturally in the human body in small amounts.

Typical supplement dose: 1,500 milligrams (mg) daily.

•**DIM (*diindolylmethane*)** is produced in the body when broccoli, cauliflower and other cruciferous vegetables are digested.

Typical supplement dose: 300 mg daily.

I recommend to patients that they take these supplements if they are at unusually high risk for breast cancer, and I have patients take these supplements when on tamoxifen (in addition to the drug). But always talk with your doctor about what is right for you.

Diet also is very important in keeping the breasts healthy. Avoid alcohol, saturated fats and sugar. Opt for organic foods. Eat plenty of vegetables (especially cruciferous ones such as broccoli and cauliflower), leafy greens, lean protein (beans, chicken breast, salmon), low-glycemic fruits (apples, cherries, grapefruit) and complex, nonglutinous grains (brown rice, oatmeal, quinoa).

TAKE NOTE...

Lower Breast Cancer Risk by Doing This...

Longer gaps between the last food eaten in the evening and the first food eaten the next morning may reduce breast cancer risk. The longer the gap, the better the control over blood glucose concentrations—and this may lower risk for breast cancer. Each three-hour increase is associated with a 4% lower glucose level after eating, no matter how much food a woman consumes.

Study of dietary data for 2,212 women and glucose readings for 1,066 women by researchers in the cancer-prevention program, University of California, San Diego, published in Cancer Epidemiology, Biomarkers & Prevention.

Dense Breasts? You May Not Need Extra Screening

Not all women with dense breasts need additional screening for breast cancer. Women with dense breasts have a higher risk

for breast cancers, but only 24% benefit from extra screening. A calculator (Tools.bcsc-scc.org/BC5yearrisk/intro.htm) from the National Cancer Institute's Breast Cancer Surveillance Consortium can help women ages 35 to 79 decide whether extra screening is warranted. Discuss the results with your doctor.

Karla Kerlikowske, MD, professor in the departments of medicine and epidemiology/biostatistics at University of California, San Francisco, and an internationally recognized expert on breast cancer screening.

Mammograms May Predict Heart Disease

A recent study of 371 women who had a digital mammogram and a chest computed tomography (CT) scan found that women whose mammograms revealed deposits of calcium in breast arteries were also more likely to have calcium deposits in coronary arteries, putting them at higher risk for cardiovascular disease.

If your mammogram indicates vascular calcification: Talk to your doctor about heart tests, such as a coronary calcium CT scan.

Laurie Margolies, MD, associate professor of radiology, Icahn School of Medicine at Mount Sinai, New York City.

MRI vs. Mammogram

Recent research indicates that for women at high risk for breast cancer, an MRI can significantly improve cancer detection rates by as much as 90%. But there is currently no evidence that MRIs find additional cancers in women at average risk for the disease.

Start by talking to your doctor about such factors as your family history of the disease and any known genetic mutation you might have that predisposes you to breast cancer. Also, there are some excellent online resources, such as the American Cancer Society, that can point you toward your appropriate risk group. If you do fall into a high-risk category, talk to your doctor about whether an MRI is right for you. For patients with an average risk for breast cancer, routine mammography still is the recommended method of screening.

Constance D. Lehman, MD, PhD, FACR, professor and vice-chair of radiology, section head of breast imaging, University of Washington School of Medicine, Seattle, and director of imaging at Seattle Cancer Care Alliance.

How to Beat Breast Cancer: Good News... but Misunderstandings Abound

Elisa Port, MD, chief of breast surgery at Mount Sinai Medical Center, director of the Dubin Breast Center and an associate professor of surgery at the Icahn School of Medicine at Mount Sinai in New York City. Her research interests include sentinel lymph node biopsies, the use of MRIs in high-risk patients and the use of PET scanning for breast cancer. She is author of *The New Generation Breast Cancer Book: How to Navigate Your Diagnosis and Treatment Options—and Remain Optimistic—in an Age of Information Overload.*

One-third of all new cancers diagnosed in women are breast cancers. The American Cancer Society estimates that more than 230,000 cases of invasive breast cancer will be diagnosed in the US in 2015.

But no one should let the fear of breast cancer obscure some very encouraging facts. The overall five-year survival rate from breast cancer now is close to 90%. Less than 7% of breast cancers are diagnosed before the age of 40—those diagnosed later in life tend to be easier to treat. Many women with breast cancer will never need highly aggressive (or disfiguring) treatments.

Despite such good news, misunderstandings about breast cancer are common. *Here's what you need to know now...*

•**Lumpectomy often is the best choice.** Many women assume that a mastectomy is the "safest" way to beat breast cancer. It makes

intuitive sense that removing an entire breast would improve long-term survival.

Not true: Survival has nothing to do with the amount of additional healthy tissue that's removed during surgery. About 60% to 75% of breast cancer surgeries are lumpectomies, in which only a small amount of tissue is removed. If your doctor gives you a choice, you can assume that the probability of survival for both procedures will be essentially the same.

The advantages of lumpectomy are obvious. The surgery is less extensive and women need less anesthesia, both of which are associated with shorter recovery time—and the breast probably will look much the same as it did before the surgery.

Downside of lumpectomy: About 25% of women will need a second procedure to remove cancer cells that were left behind during the first surgery if clear "margins" aren't achieved. Most patients will require a five-to-seven-week-long course of radiation. And the risk of the cancer coming back is slightly higher (usually less than 5%) in women who choose a lumpectomy rather than mastectomy (1% to 2%). Despite the slightly higher risk for local recurrence in the breast, the survival rates between lumpectomy and mastectomy are the same for women who are eligible for both.

A lumpectomy often is the best choice for tumors that are smaller than 4 centimeters (cm) to 5 cm. Some women feel that they'll have peace of mind only when the entire breast is removed. This can be a valid decision as long as you understand that the medical outcomes are roughly the same.

Of course, there is no "one size fits all," and absolutely, there are cases where a mastectomy is the better choice for an individual patient. For example, most women who are genetically predisposed to breast cancer and test positive for the BRCA genes are at much higher risk for recurrence with lumpectomy alone. In these cases, mastectomy—and often removal of both breasts, bilateral mastectomy—is recommended.

•**You may respond well to neoadjuvant chemotherapy.** Chemotherapy usually is considered for women whose cancer has spread to the lymph nodes and for those with large tumors. It's typically given after surgery. For certain types of cancer, however, a different approach is highly effective. In this approach, the chemotherapy is given first.

This therapy, called *neoadjuvant chemotherapy*, is used to shrink a tumor prior to surgery. In some cases, it will allow women who would otherwise need a more extensive surgery, such as a mastectomy, to have a lumpectomy instead. It's also the only recommended approach for women with inflammatory breast cancer, which involves the whole breast along with the overlying skin. It also can be a good choice for women with "triple negative" cancers, which don't respond to hormonal treatments (see below), and those with HER2/neu-positive cancers. In some cases, this treatment shrinks a tumor so much that surgeons can find no residual cancer (but surgery still is necessary to ensure that this is the case).

•**Consider using medications that block hormones.** Between 60% and 70% of all newly diagnosed breast cancers are estrogen/progesterone-receptor positive. This means that exposure to these hormones can increase the risk for a recurrence.

Women with these types of cancers are almost always advised to take medication that reduces their risks. *Tamoxifen* (Nolvadex) is recommended for women prior to menopause. *Aromatase inhibitors* (such as *letrozole*, or Femara) are used after menopause.

The medications kill tumor cells that might have spread beyond the breast…reduce the risk that cancer will come back in a treated breast…and reduce the risk for cancer in the opposite breast. Women who take them can reduce their risk for a cancer recurrence by 40% to 50%. Patients usually take one pill a day and continue the treatment for five to 10 years.

Important: Recent research has shown that premenopausal women who take tamoxifen for 10 years usually have a greater reduction in cancer recurrences than those who take it for only five years.

The medications can bring on unpleasant, menopause-like side effects, such as hot flashes and/or vaginal dryness. Tamoxifen also is associated with some rare but serious side effects such as a slightly higher risk for uterine cancer and blood clots, and aromatase inhibitors can affect bone density, which can be a problem for women with osteoporosis. But the side effects usually are minor, and many women feel the side effects are an acceptable trade-off for the superior protection.

WHAT ELSE CAN YOU DO?

Studies have shown that surgeons who treat a lot of patients (more than 50 cases a year) have better results. Ask your doctor to recommend a surgeon who specializes in breast cancer. *Also helpful…*

•**Ask your doctor if being in a clinical trial makes sense for you.** Most clinical trials are conducted by top hospitals and doctors. You will get very sophisticated (and attentive) care. In many cases, even if you're assigned to a control group, you still will get the same treatment that you would have gotten if you hadn't joined the study. Those in the "active" group will get something that's expected to be at least as good—and possibly better.

Even if your doctor isn't personally involved in a clinical trial, he/she can talk you through the issues, including the pros and cons of participating…where to look for studies that involve your type of cancer…and what the studies are likely to involve.

•**Keep your weight down.** There is no evidence that specific dietary changes affect recovery from breast cancer. However, there is good evidence that maintaining a healthy weight is important, particularly for women with estrogen-sensitive cancers. (Much of a postmenopausal woman's estrogen is produced by fatty tissue.) Women who maintain a healthy weight may have up to a 5% survival advantage compared with those who are obese. Normal-weight women are less likely to get postsurgical infections and blood clots—particularly important for those who take tamoxifen, which slightly increases the risk for clots.

There isn't clear evidence that regular exercise helps prevent breast cancer, but I have found that cancer patients who exercise tend to recover more quickly—and of course, they find it easier to maintain a healthy weight.

Cut Heart Disease Risk During Radiation for Breast Cancer

Women who have had radiation for breast cancer on their left sides are at higher risk for heart disease.

But: Women who hold their breath during radiation pulses reduce radiation exposure to their hearts by as much as 62%, thus reducing damage to their hearts.

Study of 81 women for eight years after radiation treatments by researchers at Thomas Jefferson University, Philadelphia, published in *Practical Radiation Oncology.*

Help for Clitoral Pain

Women with clitoral pain, itching or burning may have a fungal problem. Flare-ups of the yeast *Candida*, a common fungus, can be triggered by antibiotics or certain other drugs, alcoholic drinks or a diet with too much sugar or gluten.

Self-defense: Reduce consumption of sugar, starch and alcohol. Eat plenty of garlic. Treat the affected area with coconut oil (three or four times daily) or drink three drops of oil of oregano daily in a glass of water.

Also helpful: Swallow one olive leaf capsule twice daily after meals. Insert a gauze-wrapped garlic clove in the vagina for 30 minutes a day.

If the problem persists for more than a week, consult a physician, who may suggest using *nystatin, tioconazole* or another type of pharmaceutical.

Barbara Bartlik, MD, sex therapist in private practice and clinical assistant professor of psychiatry and obstetrics, Weill Cornell Medical College, New York City. She is past-president of the Women's Medical Association.

GOOD NEWS...

There Is Hope for Ovarian Cancer Patients

Ovarian cancer is not an automatic death sentence. More than 30% of women diagnosed with ovarian cancer survived more than 10 years after diagnosis.

Analysis of more than 11,500 women by researchers in the Department of Public Health Sciences at University of California-Davis, published in *Journal of Obstetrics and Gynecology.*

Aspirin Protects Against Ovarian Cancer

Low-dose aspirin may reduce risk for ovarian cancer. Women who took low-dose aspirin (less than 100 milligrams) daily to protect against cardiovascular disease were 34% less likely to develop ovarian cancer. This may be especially important to women with BRCA genetic mutations, which raise the risk for both breast and ovarian cancers.

Caution: Aspirin has potential side effects, so discuss all the risks and benefits with your doctor.

Analysis of 12 studies of aspirin use by researchers at the National Cancer Institute, Bethesda, Maryland, published in *Journal of the National Cancer Institute.*

Popular Heart Med May Help Ovarian Cancer

In a recent retrospective study, researchers found that ovarian cancer patients who took "nonselective" beta-blockers, such as *carvedilol* (Coreg) and *propranolol* (Inderal), while undergoing treatment for ovarian cancer lived more than twice as long as patients who did not use the drugs.

Possible reason: The medications inhibit mechanisms that are involved in the growth and spreading of tumors.

Anil Sood, MD, director of Blanton-Davis Ovarian Cancer Research Program, University of Texas MD Anderson Cancer Center, Houston, and senior author of a study published in *Cancer*.

This Lifesaving Cancer Treatment Is Often Not Used

Maurie Markman, MD, an oncologist and president of Medicine and Science at Cancer Treatment Centers of America, which has hospitals in Atlanta, Chicago, Philadelphia, Phoenix and Tulsa. CancerCenter.com

Three major US studies have concluded that a treatment known as *intraperitoneal* (IP) *therapy* often extends the lives of women diagnosed with ovarian cancer. One study found that IP therapy reduces the risk for death within the 10 years following treatment by 23%.

Yet according to some estimates, fewer than half of ovarian cancer patients receive IP therapy, which involves pumping chemotherapy drugs directly into the abdominal cavity. Many patients are not even told about it.

Why is IP therapy not more widely used? *Several reasons...*

• **Pharmaceutical companies are not pushing it.** IP therapy uses generic drugs, so there's no big company promoting it to doctors.

• **The procedure is time-consuming, unprofitable and unfamiliar to many doctors.** Some oncologists do not provide IP therapy simply because they have no experience with it. They have very little economic incentive to learn—pumping chemotherapy drugs into the abdomen takes significantly more time and effort than simply setting up a traditional IV. (IP therapy is used in conjunction with intravenous delivery of chemotherapy drugs, not instead of it.)

• **There are side effects.** IP therapy can cause increased discomfort for patients, including painful abdominal bloating during

---

GOOD TO KNOW...

Many Hysterectomies Aren't Necessary

One in five women who had a hysterectomy may not have needed it. More than 400,000 hysterectomies are performed in the US each year. Nearly 18% were done for benign indications, such as uterine bleeding, fibroids and endometriosis, that could have been treated without surgery.

Study of 3,400 women by researchers at University of Michigan, Ann Arbor, published in American Journal of Obstetrics & Gynecology.

---

treatment. The process also is more invasive than traditional IV delivery—typically a catheter is inserted into the abdomen, which occasionally leads to infection. But any side effects are temporary, and any infection is likely to be treatable.

If you are diagnosed with ovarian cancer: Ask your oncologist if IP therapy is an option. If your oncologist doesn't seem to be well-informed about IP therapy or simply says he/she doesn't do it, ask for a referral to an oncologist who does use the therapy. If your oncologist cannot provide such a referral, contact the American Cancer Society (Cancer.org) and/or the American Society of Clinical Oncology (ASCO.org) and ask for a referral to a gynecological oncologist in your area who has experience with IP therapy.

Embarrassing Symptoms

Jamison Starbuck, ND, a naturopathic physician in family practice and a guest lecturer at the University of Montana, both in Missoula. She is also a past president of the American Association of Naturopathic Physicians and a contributing editor to *The Alternative Advisor: The Complete Guide to Natural Therapies and Alternative Treatments.* DrJamisonStarbuck.com

"I'm just so embarrassed about this!" is a phrase that most doctors hear often. I always offer some reassurance, but it's disheartening to know that for every patient who

121

does speak up, there are likely numerous others who are risking their health by failing to mention these issues to their doctors. The topics that tend to give patients the hardest time are those related to the rectal area or genital area. I wish patients realized that, for doctors, these areas might as well be an elbow or a knee! *If you have a health complaint affecting one of the following parts of the body, do yourself a big favor and tell your doctor…*

• **Rectal area.** This includes bowel habits. I recall a 37-year-old man who didn't come to see me with his frequent diarrhea until he suffered 30 episodes in one day. He had been feeling lousy and having frequent bowel movements for several months but was "mortified" to talk about it. By the time he came to my office, he was severely dehydrated and malnourished and had to be hospitalized for several days. It turns out he was suffering from Crohn's disease, a serious inflammatory bowel disease. Ordinarily, it can be controlled without hospitalization—as long as you consult a doctor in the early days of the illness.

So please see your doctor if you have any significant change in bowel function (including diarrhea or constipation…or frequency), which lasts more than a few days—especially if it's accompanied by pain, vomiting and/or fever. Such changes may also indicate infec-

tion or cancer—both of which can be fatal if not treated promptly.

Another common condition is frequent rectal itching. Dietary habits, particularly consuming too much sugar (which promotes inflammation and yeast) or coffee (which is drying to tissues), often cause this uncomfortable condition, but it's best to be evaluated by your doctor to rule out infection, allergies or other causes.

There's also rectal bleeding. The cause may be something simple such as hemorrhoids or intestinal tract irritation from drugs (including laxatives or antibiotics) or organisms (such as *Salmonella* and other bacteria sometimes found in food).

But rectal bleeding can also be a red flag for cancer, so talk to your doctor immediately if you experience it. (If you have hemorrhoids, let your doctor know if bleeding lasts for more than a couple of days.)

• **Genital area.** While a number of conditions can affect the genital area, among the most common are jock itch and vaginitis. It's unfortunate that so many patients are reluctant to bring up the telltale symptoms—itching and a rash in the groin area can signal jock itch…itching near the outside of the vagina and an abnormal, sometimes smelly, generally white discharge often mean vaginitis. Both conditions often have a common cause—yeast, which is usually treatable with a simple natural remedy.

My protocol for yeast: Until symptoms subside, completely avoid foods on which yeast flourishes, such as bread, pasta and desserts… and take a probiotic supplement—at least 6 billion live organisms per dose—twice daily for at least a month.

Also: Apply a white vinegar/water solution (two tablespoons of vinegar in a pint of water) topically to the yeast. Men can spray it directly on the area of jock itch three times daily until it's gone…women can use a vaginal douche nightly until the yeast infection is eliminated, usually within three to five nights.

TAKE NOTE…

A Juice That Relieves Menopause Symptoms

Women who drank about seven ounces of unsalted tomato juice twice a day for eight weeks reported a 16% improvement in hot flashes, fatigue and irritability.

Reason for the improvement: Tomatoes contain lycopene and *gamma-aminobutyric acid* (GABA). Lycopene reduces stress, and GABA helps ease hot flashes.

Study of 93 women by researchers at Tokyo Medical and Dental University, Japan, published in *Nutrition Journal*.

Secrets to Staying "Regular": 7 Mistakes That Can Lead to Constipation

Anish Sheth, MD, a gastroenterologist at Princeton Medical Group and an attending physician at the University Medical Center of Princeton at Plainsboro, New Jersey. He is a member of the American Gastroenterology Association, American College of Gastroenterology and the American Association for the Study of Liver Disease, and coauthor of *What's Your Poo Telling You?*

With so much attention being focused these days on irritable bowel syndrome (IBS), colitis, diverticular disease and other gastrointestinal (GI) problems, many people forget about the granddaddy of them all—constipation.

It's hands down one of the most common GI challenges, and 15% of American adults regularly suffer from the condition. And if you believe TV and magazine advertisements, more fiber (often from a supplement) is the solution.

What you're not being told: While fiber is helpful, it's not always the answer. In fact, constipation isn't as straightforward as most people think. There are many common mistakes that prevent some people from getting relief from constipation—and cause others to worry unnecessarily.

Among the most common…

MISTAKE #1: Assuming that "normal" means daily. Constipation is usually defined as having fewer than three bowel movements a week. But there's a wide range of "normal"—some people routinely have three bowel movements a week…others go three times every day.

Doctors usually do not worry about a few missed bowel movements. There is almost always a simple explanation—travel, a new medication (see below), changes in diet or simply a busy schedule that causes people to delay using the toilet.

When to be concerned: When constipation is persistent—especially when it occurs along with other symptoms, such as lumpy, hard stools, straining to have a bowel movement and/or feeling as though you can't completely empty the stool from your rectum. It's also cause for concern when someone's normal bowel habits suddenly change for no obvious reason. This could indicate irritable bowel syndrome, a thyroid condition or even colon cancer.

MISTAKE #2: Not taking medication into account. Many prescription and over-the-counter drugs as well as supplements can cause constipation as a side effect. People who aren't aware of this may resort to treatments, such as enemas, that they don't really need—or book unnecessary visits with their doctors.

Psychiatric medications, including tricyclic antidepressants, such as *imipramine* (Tofranil) and *amitriptyline* (Elavil), are notorious for causing constipation.

Other offenders: Blood pressure drugs, including calcium channel blockers and beta-blockers…narcotic painkillers…antihistamines such as Benadryl…and iron supplements.

My advice: If a new medication is causing constipation, ask your doctor if you can get by with a lower dose—or switch to a different drug. If that's not possible, you might need to be more aggressive with lifestyle changes—such as drinking more water and getting more exercise—both help keep stools soft and intestinal muscles active.

MISTAKE #3: Depending only on fiber. Getting more fiber from plant foods (especially pears, apples and sweet potatoes—all with skins on—and cooked greens) will usually increase the frequency and comfort of bowel movements…but not for everyone.

A form of constipation known as *slow-transit constipation* (STC) occurs when the intestinal muscles contract less often and with less force than normal. Some patients with STC improve when they get more fiber, but others will still need laxatives or other treatments.

My advice: If you have constipation that hasn't responded to dietary changes, ask your doctor whether you might have STC. You may need a *colonic transit study*, which involves swallowing a capsule containing a small amount of material that can be traced with

X-rays to show its movement over a period of several days. This test will help your radiologist and gastroenterologist determine how quickly stool moves through your colon.

MISTAKE #4: Rejecting laxatives. Many people have the mistaken notion that laxatives should *always* be avoided. Admittedly, some of the laxatives used in the past were harsh—people who took them were nervous about being more than a few steps away from a bathroom. But newer laxatives are much gentler.

I usually recommend one of the *osmotic* laxatives, such as *polyethylene glycol 3350* (MiraLAX) or good old Milk of Magnesia. They help stool retain fluid, which softens stools and stimulates bowel movements. It's obviously preferable to have "natural" bowel movements, but these laxatives are gentle enough for long-term use (under a doctor's supervision) and can be a good choice for those with health problems (such as Parkinson's) that often cause constipation.

Note: People with heart or kidney failure should avoid these laxatives—they can cause dehydration and/or a mineral imbalance.

MISTAKE #5: Not checking the bowel. Some people would rather not see what comes out (others closely examine their stools). I advise patients to take at least a quick look before they flush. The appearance of stools can provide important information about your GI health.

Color is a big one. Stools that are extremely dark could be a sign of intestinal bleeding. Bright red can indicate a recent meal of beets, a bleeding hemorrhoid or even colon cancer. Gray can mean that something's obstructing the flow of bile to the intestine.

Texture/shape is also important. Stools that are hard and pelletlike can indicate more severe constipation, which could have many underlying causes, including chronic conditions such as thyroid problems, diabetes or Parkinson's disease. "Floaters" are usually normal (they're caused by gas in the stools) but can also be a sign of conditions that impair fat absorption, such as pancreatitis. (For more on different types of stool, see "How to Talk About Bowel Movements" at right.)

MISTAKE #6: Avoiding enemas. Simple fixes might not help when you haven't had a bowel movement for a week or two. Stools that stay that long in the intestine can become almost rocklike and painful to pass. Enemas are also the best treatment for fecal impaction, a hard-stool blockage that's usually caused by lengthy constipation.

An enema, available as an over-the-counter saline laxative, increases the flow of water into the intestine. It softens hard stools and usually promotes a bowel movement within a few minutes. Follow package instructions. Fecal impaction that is not relieved by an enema may require a health-care provider to manually remove stool.

MISTAKE #7: Not eating enough prunes. Your grandparents were right—prunes (and prune juice) are an effective treatment for constipation. Prunes are high in fiber, but the main benefit comes from sorbitol, a sugar that draws water into the intestine. Two servings of prunes (about 10 fruits) contain 12 grams (g) of sorbitol…and eight ounces of juice has about 15 g.

Note: Drinking warm prune juice seems to be more effective at relieving constipation in some people. If you don't like prunes, consider trying rhubarb, artichokes and/or peaches—all of which promote regular bowel movements.

Important: If you're prone to constipation, limit your intake of processed foods, cheese and meat—these foods can slow down your digestive system.

HOW TO TALK ABOUT BOWEL MOVEMENTS

If you've been constipated or your doctor asks about your bowel movements, how do you describe them? You might feel awkward or at a loss for words, but help is available.

The Bristol Stool Form Scale is a detailed guide to the usual textures and shapes.

Check this link for descriptions of the different types of bowel movements: Bowel Control.nih.gov/bristol.aspx.

More Young People Are Getting Colon Cancer

One in seven colon cancer patients is now under age 50—the age at which screening is recommended to start. Younger patients are more likely to have advanced cancer—although they live slightly longer without recurrence after being treated, because doctors tend to treat them aggressively. People with a family history of colon cancer…and those with risk factors such as smoking, obesity and physical inactivity…should consider starting screening before age 50. Ask your doctor for details.

Analysis of data on nearly 260,000 patients diagnosed with colon cancer between 1998 and 2011 by researchers at University of Michigan, Ann Arbor, published in *Cancer*.

Secrets to Getting the Best Colonoscopy

Douglas K. Rex, MD, a Distinguished Professor of Medicine at Indiana University School of Medicine and director of endoscopy at Indiana University Hospital, both in Indianapolis. He is coauthor of the colorectal cancer screening recommendations of the American College of Gastroenterology as well as current chair of the US Multi-Society Task Force on Colorectal Cancer and coauthor of the recommendations on quality in colonoscopy for this group.

If you are age 50 or older, chances are you have had a colonoscopy—and maybe more than one. If so, you've taken a crucial step in protecting your health.

Why this test is so important: It is estimated that if every person age 50 and older had a colonoscopy, 64% of people who have colorectal cancer would have never developed the disease.

But since you are going to the trouble to get this test (and we all know the bowel-cleansing prep is no picnic), then it also makes sense to make sure you're getting the best possible screening. *How to ensure that you get the maximum cancer protection from your colonoscopy exam…*

INTERESTING FINDING…

A Vitamin for IBS?

There's no known cure for the diarrhea, constipation and/or urgency of irritable bowel syndrome (IBS), but a recent study found that 82% of IBS sufferers were also low in vitamin D (less than 20 ng/mL). Most of those whose vitamin D levels returned to normal after taking a supplement for 12 weeks had improved IBS symptoms, but more research is needed to statistically link the two.

Simon Tazzyman, PhD, postdoctoral researcher, The University of Sheffield, UK.

HOW GOOD IS YOUR DOCTOR?

One of the most important aspects of a colonoscopy is the doctor's ability to detect a type of polyp called an *adenoma*—the doctor's so-called "adenoma detection rate" (ADR). This varies widely depending on the doctor's skill.

If your doctor has a low ADR, you're more likely to get colon cancer before your next colonoscopy. Gastroenterologists are more likely to have good ADRs than primary care physicians and general surgeons who might perform colonoscopies, but there's a wide range of performance within each group.

Precisely defined, a doctor's ADR is the percentage of screening colonoscopies in patients age 50 or older during which he/she detects one or more adenomas.

My advice: Look for a doctor with an ADR of 20% or higher in women and 30% or higher in men (who have more adenomas)…or a "mixed-gender" rate of 25% or higher—in other words, the doctor detects at least one adenoma in 25% of the screening colonoscopies he conducts.

Startling recent finding: A 10-year study published in *The New England Journal of Medicine* evaluated more than 300,000 colonoscopies conducted by 136 gastroenterologists—and found that for every 1% increase in ADR, there was a 3% reduction in the risk of developing colorectal cancer before the next colonoscopy. This means that having your colonoscopy performed by a doctor with a high ADR (as described earlier) is a must for optimal screening. But how does a patient ask

125

about his doctor's ADR without seeming to question the physician's competence?

My advice: Ask about your doctor's ADR *on the phone*, during the colonoscopy scheduling process, when you are talking to an administrator or a nurse. If that person doesn't know, request that someone get back to you with the number. That will make your query less confrontational.

However: Even your doctor may not know his own ADR. Monitoring of ADRs is endorsed by several professional medical societies, such as the American Society for Gastrointestinal Endoscopy and the American College of Gastroenterology, but there is no law mandating that doctors must track it. Or your doctor may refuse to disclose his ADR—a response you should find concerning. If you don't get the information you need from your doctor, it's probably a good idea to find a new one.

Also important: Make sure your colonoscopy is being performed with a high-definition colonoscope, the current state-of-the-art in colonoscopy. Inquire about this when you ask about a doctor's ADR.

A BETTER BOWEL PREP

Another key to a truly preventive colonoscopy is the *preparation*. Before the procedure, a patient drinks a defecation-inducing liquid (prep) that cleanses the rectum and colon of stool so that the doctor can clearly see the lining. In some patients, a four-liter prep (about one gallon), or even more, is best for optimal cleansing. If you don't have a condition associated with slow bowel motility, such as chronic constipation, or use constipating medications such as opioids, you may be eligible for one of the regimens that requires only two or three liters of fluid. (A pill preparation is also available, but it is seldom used because it can cause kidney damage.) Ask your doctor what regimen will give you the best combination of excellent cleansing and tolerability.

A common mistake: Many people think that they can drink the prep one to two days before the procedure and then drink nothing but clear fluids (such as Gatorade, apple juice or water) until the day of the colonoscopy.

But even during the prep, the small intestine (the section of bowel after the stomach and before the colon) continues to produce *chyme*, a thick, mucousy secretion that sticks to the walls of the ascending colon—so that seven to eight hours after drinking the prep the colon is no longer completely clean.

Best: A *split prep*, with half the prep ingested the day before the procedure and half ingested four to five hours before (the middle of the night when the colonoscopy is scheduled for the morning...or the morning when the colonoscopy is scheduled for the afternoon).

Scientific evidence: Split preparation improves ADR by 26%, according to a study in *Gastrointestinal Endoscopy*.

Also helpful: Drinking the prep can be difficult, even nauseating. *How to make it more palatable*...

Chill the liquid thoroughly, and drink it with a straw. Follow each swallow with ginger ale or another good-tasting clear liquid. Suck on a clear menthol lozenge after you drink the prep. And if you throw up the prep, wait 30 minutes (until you feel less nauseated) and then continue drinking the prep as instructed—it can still work.

Several recent studies have found that eating a fiber-free diet all or part of the day prior to colonoscopy allows for better cleansing of the colon. Some doctors advise avoiding high-fiber foods such as corn, seeds and nuts for about a *week* before a colonoscopy. Ask your doctor what he advises for you.

Quitting or Just Cutting Back? Surprises on the Road to Sobriety

Jack Canfield, cocreator of the Chicken Soup for the Soul book series and CEO of Canfield Training Group, a Santa Barbara–based corporate training company...and Dave Andrews, a leading sobriety coach and founder of The 30-Day Solution, LLC. The pair are coauthors of *The 30-Day Sobriety Solution: How to Quit or Cut Back Drinking in the Privacy of Your Own Home.* For more information, go to The30DaySolution.com

Nearly one-third of all American adults drink excessively. Many of these drinkers eventually will decide that alcohol is harming their health and happiness and try to quit or at least cut way back. *Knowing these surprising facts could improve your odds of succeeding...*

• **If you have an alcohol problem, you have a sugar problem, too.** Alcohol is basically fermented sugar. So when heavy drinkers quit drinking, their bodies don't just crave alcohol...they also crave the large quantities of sugar that they're used to consuming.

What to do: Giving up drinking is challenge enough—do not force yourself to give up sugar at the same time. For at least your first month of your sobriety, keep your blood sugar levels up by eating whenever you feel hungry—at least once every five hours...never skipping a meal, especially breakfast...and consuming plenty of fruit, which satiates cravings for sugar, without resorting to unhealthy treats such as candy.

• **Willpower alone is never enough to overcome excessive drinking.** People who have tried to quit drinking without success in the past often conclude that they lack sufficient willpower to remain sober. In truth, no one has enough willpower to permanently stop doing something they very much want to do. The secret to giving up alcohol is to find a way to decrease your desire to drink so that you are not as dependent on willpower to quit.

What to do: Whenever you feel the urge to drink, imagine what your life will be like in five or 10 years if you continue drinking heavily, versus what it could be like if you stop. *For example, consider...*

• How healthy you could be if you quit, versus how unhealthy you could be if you continue.

• How much you would accomplish if you were always sober, versus all the hours you would have wasted drinking or being drunk.

• How much money you could have saved, versus how much you would have spent on alcohol.

• How respected you could be, versus the embarrassments you might have endured with continued heavy drinking—such as behaving like a buffoon at parties.

Drinkers tend to associate drinking with pleasure and quitting with pain—that's why it takes willpower to quit. Reflecting on the *long-term* pain of drinking and *long-term* pleasure

of stopping helps reverse this association, so sobriety no longer feels like an endless struggle against desire.

• **Giving up drinking can lead to chemically induced feelings of depression.** The brains of heavy drinkers often produce the "positive thinking" neurotransmitters *dopamine* and *serotonin* only when alcohol is in the bloodstream. When these people suddenly stop drinking (or cut way back on their alcohol intake), the loss of these upbeat mood-triggering neurochemicals leaves them feeling depressed. Some inevitably conclude that they need alcohol to be happy and start drinking again.

What to do: Your brain eventually will start producing dopamine and serotonin without alcohol again, but it could take as long as 90 days (or in rare cases, even longer). For at least the first three months of sobriety, regularly consume foods that contain omega-3 fats, such as wild-caught salmon, sardines, herring, anchovies and mackerel—these have been shown to significantly raise dopamine levels.

Also consume foods that contain *gamma-aminobutyric acid* (GABA), such as cherry tomatoes, shrimp and bananas—these can beneficially alter the brain's serotonin balance. Taking dietary supplements containing GABA or omega-3 could help, too. But speak to your doctor before taking supplements.

You could end up feeling mentally foggy. People assume that they will feel sharper when they stop drinking, and for light drinkers and weekend bingers, this usually is true. But when heavy daily drinkers first quit, they often find their thinking becoming foggier. This stems from the chemical changes occurring in the brain as it readjusts to life without alcohol, and it generally lasts several weeks.

What to do: Exercising regularly and drinking plenty of water during this foggy brain period seems to help. Some people find that listening to or playing music helps focus the mind during this period, too.

• **You don't have to hit rock bottom to quit.** There is a common misconception that drinkers cannot successfully give up drinking until they "hit bottom," which might involve going on a prolonged bender...losing a job or

127

spouse because of drinking...or getting arrested for drunk driving. In truth, the only reason heavy drinkers tend not to quit until they "hit bottom" is that until then they generally are not willing to admit that they have a serious drinking problem.

What to do: Stop searching for reasons why your drinking is not a problem, and instead honestly consider the question, *Would my life be better without alcohol?* If you answer yes, then you have a problem and should quit.

• **Quitting drinking earns you free time—** but that time could be dangerous to your sobriety. Heavy drinkers who quit often are amazed by how much more time they suddenly have. Not only does quitting free up the hours they previously spent drinking, it frees up the hours they previously spent too drunk to do anything productive—and the hours they spent sleeping off hangovers.

What to do: Find constructive and/or enjoyable things to fill this newfound time. Boredom is a sobriety killer—former drinkers sometimes return to the bottle simply because they can't think of anything else to do.

If you don't have projects and hobbies in mind, try getting exercise outdoors...learning to play a musical instrument...or starting a home-improvement project.

Or you can volunteer with nonprofits...take adult-education classes...or use websites such as MeetUp.com to find nonalcohol-related gatherings.

Activities that involve spending time with people who are not drinking are best. Excessive drinking often is at some level a substitute for love and human connection. If people you love insist on getting intoxicated when you're together, it's important to not spend time with them when they're drunk. Ultimately, if they don't change, they are going to want you to drink, so spending time with them while they are intoxicated can be risky. Without coming across as judgmental or resentful, explain that you love them but that you need to make this change for your own well-being.

TRICK TO OVERCOME CRAVINGS

Overcoming cravings to drink could be as simple as tapping your fingers. Gently tapping your fingers on certain spots on your body can help control alcohol cravings (other cravings, too). That might sound unlikely, but decades of research confirms that this really does work for most people. One study found that it can reduce cravings by an astonishing 83%.

How is that possible? Experiencing cravings makes people feel stressed, which causes the body to release stress hormones. But gentle tapping in certain spots encourages the body to instead release both dopamine and serotonin, the positive-feeling neurotransmitters discussed earlier.

What to do: When you feel like you need a drink, use your index and middle fingers to gently tap five to seven times on each of the following eight spots...

• **The top of your head**
• **One of your eyebrows**
• **Just beyond the outer corner of one of your eyes**
• **Just under one of your eyes**
• **Just under your nose**
• **On your chin**
• **On your collarbone**
• **In one of your armpits**

Not coincidentally, these are among the spots that acupuncturists have been targeting with their needles for thousands of years. (For more details, search "EFT Tapping Therapy" on YouTube.)

7

Moneywise

My Worst Money Mistake: 6 Financial Experts Fess Up

Even the shrewdest of financial experts make terrible money mistakes from time to time—these big mistakes can be very expensive, but they frequently offer important lessons for the future.

We asked six money mavens to recall some of the most painful mistakes they have made with their own finances and what lessons can be learned from those mistakes that benefit consumers, savers, borrowers and investors. The experts came up with painful memories that range from a credit card addiction and an emotionally wrenching estate-planning blunder to a scary health insurance stumble and an unfortunate venture that involved 17 dairy cows.

CREDIT CARD REWARDS TRIGGERED AN ADDICTION
Curtis Arnold, CEO

At the beginning of 2000, I started using an American Express card that had a generous cash rewards program. I funneled so much spending through the card that it soon became a game to see how many points I could rack up. Through the end of 2014, I had earned a total of $8,425 in rebates. But over that period, I spent $708,442.45 to get those rewards. And I probably spent 10% more than I should

Curtis Arnold, founder of CardRatings.com and Best PrepaidDebitCards.com.

Allan S. Roth, CFP, CPA, principal of Wealth Logic, LLC, a financial advisory firm in Colorado Springs.

Herbert E. Nass, Esq., founding partner of Herbert E. Nass & Associates, a New York City law firm specializing in wills, estates, probate and trusts.

Charles B. Inlander, a consumer advocate and health-care consultant based in Fogelsville, Pennsylvania.

Edgar Dworsky, founder of the consumer-protection websites ConsumerWorld.org and Mouseprint.org, based in Somerville, Massachusetts.

Edward Mendlowitz, CPA, a partner at the accounting firm WithumSmith+Brown, New Brunswick, New Jersey.

have—a wasted $70,000 that I could have put in my retirement account instead of spending on unnecessary things. Since I never carried a balance and always paid my card in full each month, I reasoned that I was being shrewd and beating the system. Early this year, I sat down and reviewed my purchase history and realized the error of my ways.

Lesson learned: Don't use rewards points as a justification for spending on items that you don't need and/or that would stretch you financially.

A TINY FEE WASTED $20,000
Allan S. Roth, CFP, CPA

Back in 1990, I invested about $25,000 in the Dreyfus Standard & Poor's 500 stock index fund. I felt smart in choosing a well-respected, broadly diversified mutual fund that charged a much lower expense ratio than actively managed funds. I didn't do enough research to find out that, over the following years, this fund charged between two and 10 times as much as the least expensive S&P 500 fund. And I didn't realize how much money the higher fees were costing me until a decade later. I eventually switched half of the holdings to another, less expensive fund, but I didn't shift all of the investment because I was reluctant to pay capital gains taxes on my profits in the Dreyfus fund. This short-sightedness has cost me about $20,000 overall that has gone into Dreyfus's pocket instead of mine.

Lesson learned: Don't assume that a fund has the lowest fees until you check similar funds—and realize how costly the difference can be.

WHY THREE EXECUTORS ARE BETTER THAN TWO
Herbert E. Nass, Esq.

In 1992, my mother decided to name my sister and me as co-executors of her will. After Mom died, administering her estate strained my relationship with my sister. We disagreed on various issues and got locked into stalemates that caused some hurt feelings.

Lesson learned: Having three executors with one vote each provides a practical way to break deadlocks. In my own will, my wife and I have named our two children to be the "successor" executors after both my wife and I have died, and we have added a third executor—a trusted family friend—who will be able to break any tie votes and attempt to minimize hurt feelings.

AN EXPENSIVE HEALTH INSURANCE BARGAIN
Charles B. Inlander

When I began my business a decade ago, I selected a health insurance plan with a monthly premium of $300 and a deductible of $10,000 instead of the $600/$2,000 option. Higher premiums seemed like a waste of money because I rarely went to doctors and figured I could set aside the savings from lower premiums if there ever were an emergency. Within a few months, I needed unexpected prostate surgery. Not only did I have to come up with an enormous sum out-of-pocket, but I also had to endure the stress of this financial hardship while trying to deal with and recover from a frightening and difficult illness.

Lesson learned: Select the most comprehensive health plan available even if you have to make sacrifices to afford it each month. Hospital health-care costs are so high that if you or a family member suffers just one major health crisis, it can make years of paying higher premiums the more economical choice.

THE WRONG STOVE
Edgar Dworsky

I had to replace my kitchen stove three years ago. My local Sears did not have a floor model of the exact $1,000 gas range with stainless steel knobs that I wanted, but a salesperson showed me a picture of the one I wanted on the Sears website and I ordered it. When it was delivered, it was not the same as the one pictured. I had neglected to look at the details on the web page. Sears did agree to replace the stove with the one pictured but only after a lot of aggravation and expense—I had arranged for a plumber and electrician to be there for installation.

Lesson learned: Retailers often post stock photos that may not exactly match what you think you are buying. Make sure the features and specifications listed are the ones you want and see it in person if at all possible.

BETTER WAYS...

11 Ways to Save Money with Your Spouse

1) Have a savings competition—see who can save the most in 30 days...2) Decide together where you want to allocate funds and where you want to save...3) Create a budget—track all spending for a month or two...4) Use a budget-tracking app, such as *Home Budget with Sync*...5) Do not hide spending except for occasional gifts...6) Live off one income, and save the other...7) Have a joint bank account to reduce fees and stay in financial touch with each other...8) Have date nights during the week, when many prices are lower than on Friday and Saturday...9) Plan meals to save on groceries by buying in bulk, on sale and with coupons...10) Use daily deals from sites such as Groupon and Living Social...11) Share restaurant meals—for example, one appetizer plus one main course for the two of you.

Roundup of couples' money-saving ideas, reported at Philly.com.

A MISBEGOTTEN HERD OF COWS
Edward Mendlowitz, CPA

In 1985, I bought a herd of 17 Holstein dairy cows at public auction for $175,000. I knew nothing about commodity investing and had no interest in becoming a gentleman farmer. But the tax breaks were too good to resist. I put up $20,000 and financed the remainder over five years. In the meantime, I qualified for investment tax credits that gave me $40,000 in initial tax savings. Two years later, Congress eliminated that tax shelter. One of my Holsteins was struck by lightning and killed. Then the US government reduced its support of milk prices and the herd's value plummeted. I sold the cattle at nearly a total loss.

Lesson learned: Many investments, ranging from buying a home to investing in real estate or municipal bonds, offer attractive tax breaks. But reducing your tax bill is just one factor in deciding to invest—and typically not the most crucial one. You need to consider the current value of the investment, your time frame for holding it, the potential for appreciation or loss and what purpose the investment will serve in your portfolio and/or your life.

No More Fights About Money!

To help resolve money conflicts with your spouse, ask questions about what early memories may be affecting your spouse's behavior—what are your most painful and most joyful money memories? How did those experiences shape the way you feel about money? What three things did your parents teach you about money? Did you feel that your family was rich, poor or middle class when you were growing up? What is your greatest financial fear?

Roundup of financial planners and counselors who focus on financial communication, reported in The Wall Street Journal.

Are You Too Cheap? The Dangers of Being an Underspender

Brad Klontz, PsyD, CFP, executive director of financial psychology and behavioral finance at Occidental Asset Management, LLC, an investment advisory firm based in San Francisco. He also is an associate professor of personal financial planning at Kansas State University and coauthor of Mind Over Money: Overcoming the Money Disorders That Threaten Our Financial Health. OccamLLC.net

Some individuals struggle to control their spending...others struggle to spend at all. The latter are *extreme underspenders*—and that isn't a good thing. We asked psychologist and financial planner Brad Klontz to explain why this could be a big problem and what an underspender can do to overcome it...

UNHAPPY AND UNHEALTHY

People who can't bring themselves to part with money might seem like role models to many, but they often live unhappy lives of unnecessary deprivation. They even might be unhealthy because they won't pay for preventive medical or dental care. Even in cases where underspending isn't quite that extreme, it still can lead people to live drab, monotonous lives—lives in which they are not terribly unhappy, but because they don't do things and try things that require shelling out some cash, they are not really as happy as they could be.

It's not clear how common extreme underspending is. Underspenders rarely seek help because they generally don't believe they have a problem—in even the most extreme cases, they tend to consider themselves fiscally prudent, not miserly. But extreme underspenders often cost themselves money in the long run by refusing to spend what's required to properly maintain their bodies, homes, cars and other possessions.

THE ROOTS OF UNDERSPENDING

Financial fears are at the heart of extreme underspending. To an impartial observer, it might seem that these underspenders have no money worries—they tend to have plenty of savings and very low expenses. But in the mind of an underspender, there is always a danger of going broke that must be addressed—by not spending.

This fear typically is rooted in family history. Many extreme underspenders grew up in households that were chronically short of money...or that experienced a severe financial shock, such as a bankruptcy, or a financial threat at some point. Others grew up in households where there was sufficient money but where one or both parents harbored money-related anxieties that dated back to their own childhoods.

FACING THE REALITY

Before you can solve your problem, you have to acknowledge you have one...

• **Ask yourself whether your financial caution is reasonable or excessive.** Extreme underspenders typically cannot answer this question on their own—they truly believe that they are acting reasonably. If one or more telltale signs apply to you, ask your spouse, siblings, adult children and anyone you trust whether they think your frugality is excessive. These signs include the following—you are regularly accused of being cheap, perhaps in a joking way...you chronically decline to seek medical or dental treatment for fear it is too

expensive...you avoid doing things that sound enjoyable, even though you have enough income and savings to cover the cost...you frequently worry about running out of money, even though your income is well in excess of your expenses.

Alternative: Pay a fee-only financial planner a few hundred dollars to examine your financial situation and weigh in on whether you are spending much less than you safely could. (If you cannot bring yourself to pay a planner to do this, consider that to be one of the signs that you really do have a problem.)

• **Trace your financial anxieties back to their source.** Do you recall serious financial problems or anxieties in your household when you were a child or a young adult? If not, ask your siblings, parents or other surviving family members whether they are aware of any money problems or anxieties during your formative years. Learning the root cause of your underspending will make it easier to admit that this underspending stems from an irrational fear, not fiscal prudence. Some people find that seeing a therapist can help them cope with fears rooted in the past.

• **Reflect on whether your underspending is helping you or hurting you.** Has your extreme frugality made you happier...or has it cost you opportunities to enjoy your life? Has it caused strife with your loved ones? Can you think of times when trying to save a small amount of money cost you a larger amount? As you look back, are there things you have not done that give you pangs of wistfulness, such as trips you could have taken...events you could have attended...hobbies that interest you that you could have pursued...and possessions you could have owned that would have brought you pleasure?

SOLVING THE PROBLEM

Steps you can take…

•**Pay a financial planner to determine how much you can safely spend without any realistic risk of running out of money.** If you see a financial pro to determine whether you have a problem, as mentioned above, also ask him/her to provide this advice. This won't just make it mentally easier for you to spend money…it also will help you sleep easier at night knowing that your fears about running out of money are not justified.

•**Make a few purchases that you can reframe as savings.** What could you spend a small amount on today that could save you a larger amount tomorrow? This might include obtaining preventive health or dental care…having maintenance work done on your home or car…purchasing sufficient homeowner's, auto and/or umbrella insurance to protect you against a financial disaster…or buying nutritious food rather than cheaper but unhealthful food. "Money saving" purchases such as these can serve as initial, small steps toward more reasonable (and more fulfilling) spending habits.

Alternative: Buy gifts for people you care about. You may find it easier to spend on loved ones than to spend on yourself.

•**Force yourself to spend money on something purely for yourself—and completely frivolous.** This will be extremely difficult, but it must be done—underspending is rooted in anxiety, and the most effective treatment for anxiety is facing the thing you fear.

Example: Get a massage. Almost every extreme underspender I have ever met considered massages a total waste of money…but after trying one, most admitted that they enjoyed it—and this helped them realize that enjoyment is a legitimate reason for spending money.

•**Make it a monthly habit.** Onetime financial frivolity is not enough to alter a lifetime of underspending. At least once a month, make a purchase that you consider frivolous but that brings you enjoyment. The amount you spend should be large enough to make you uncom-

fortable but not so large that it greatly affects your bottom line.

Meanwhile, start making a list of pricey things that might be enjoyable to you—this might include renting a vacation home or upgrading to a bigger TV. Once you become comfortable with your small monthly frivolous purchase, choose something from this list of larger purchases that you can fit into the safe financial parameters provided by the planner you spoke with and give it a try.

Beware of Linking Bank Accounts to an App

Some apps help with budgeting, tax preparation and other financial matters. But giving an app your user ID and password for a bank account could make you responsible if the app gets hacked and your money is stolen. Many banks state in their online user agreements that they are not liable if you lose money because you gave your access credentials to third parties. Your actual loss may be capped at $50 or $500, depending on circumstances, under federal banking regulations. But it may take much time and effort to get even a partial refund from your bank.

Self-defense: Don't give out your banking credentials anywhere beyond the bank itself.

Credit.com

Great Credit Cards Now

Odysseas Papadimitriou, CEO of Evolution Finance, Inc., based in Washington, DC, parent of CardHub.com, an online credit card comparison website.

The come-ons are tempting. There are credit cards that offer 2% cash back on all purchases…cards that offer 5% or even 6% cash back in certain spending categories…cards that offer hundreds of dollars just for signing up and using them for a while…

and cards that charge 0% interest for as long as 21 months.

But in the fine-print–laden world of credit cards, even those with desirable features can have pitfalls that cardholders must avoid to get the full benefit. We asked credit card expert Odysseas Papadimitriou to look at the pluses and minuses and choose the best cards in a range of categories (with no annual fee unless otherwise noted)...*

REWARDS CARDS

Best for straightforward cash back: Citi Double Cash MasterCard offers 2% cash back on all purchases, with no caps on how much you can earn. Rewards can be claimed as a check, statement credit or gift card whenever a $25 reward threshold is reached. Rather than getting 2% back immediately on purchases, cardholders earn 1% on each dollar spent and then another 1% on each dollar when paying the bill. Unredeemed rewards balances expire if additional rewards are not earned for 12 months.

Annual percentage rate (APR) interest on unpaid balances: 13.24% to 23.24% following an 18-month 0% introductory rate on balance transfers. Citi.com

Best travel rewards: Citi ThankYou Premier MasterCard offers three points per dollar spent on travel-related expenses, including airfares, trains, hotels, car rentals, gas, road tolls and campgrounds...two points on meals and entertainment...and one point on other purchases. Points are not capped, do not expire and can be redeemed in a range of ways, including gift cards.

Example of maximum rewards: You spend $1,667 on a round-trip flight and hotel, which gets you 5,000 points that you redeem for a $50 Home Depot gift card—equivalent to a 3% return. ThankYou Premier has a $95 annual fee, but it is waived in the first year.

APR: 14.24% to 23.24%. Citi.com

Best gas card that can be used at any gas station: PenFed Platinum Cash Rewards Plus Visa pays 5% cash back on gas purchases

*Fees, interest rates and other details of programs were accurate as of late-August 2016.

if you join the Pentagon Federal Credit Union (join by making a donation of as little as $14 to a specified nonprofit)...and establish another account with PenFed, such as a money-market savings account...or a checking account with direct deposit and a $250 minimum balance...or a home-equity loan/line of credit. (If you do not have one of the accounts listed above, the card gets you 3% back on gas and you must pay a $25 annual fee.) Rewards are not capped and are automatically credited to your account.

APR: 10.24% to 17.99%. PenFed.org

Best single-brand gas card: Marathon Visa pays a 25-cent rebate on each gallon of Marathon gas you charge during months when your total charges are at least $1,000. You will earn 15 cents back per gallon in months that you charge between $500 and $999.99...and 5 cents in months that you charge less than $500. A Marathon Cash Card, redeemable at Marathon stations, will be sent whenever your rewards balance reaches $25. Marathon stations are in many southeastern and central states.

APR: From 17.24% to 25.24%. Comenity.net/Marathon

Alternative: Chevron/Texaco Visa deducts three cents per gallon (which is 1% at $2.15/gallon) off your statement when you purchase gas at Chevron and Texaco stations plus an additional 20 cents per gallon in months when you spend at least $1,000 (9%) or an additional 10 cents per gallon in months when you spend between $300 and $999.99 (5%). Gas credits are capped at $300 per year.

APR: 27.24%. ChevronTexacoCards.com

Best for grocery purchases: Blue Cash Preferred from American Express pays 6% cash back on up to $6,000 a year in grocery-store spending—that's a potential $360 back a year, more than enough to justify the $75 annual fee. Cardholders also earn 3% cash back on gas and purchases at select department stores...and 1% on most other purchases. Cash back is received as a statement credit.

APR: 13.24% to 23.24% following a 12-month 0% introductory rate. AmericanExpress.com

CARDS WITH LOW INTEREST RATES

Best for low ongoing interest rates: Simmons Bank Visa Platinum recently had the lowest APR among cards that do not charge an annual fee—7.50%. Simmons typically offers among the lowest rates, although some other cards have lower introductory rates for limited periods. SimmonsFirst.com

Best card for a low introductory rate: Citi Diamond Preferred MasterCard has a 0% introductory rate that lasts 21 months for new purchases and balance transfers. Its balance transfer fee is 3%.

APR: 12.24% to 22.24% after the introductory period. Citi.com

Best card for balance transfers: Chase Slate features no transfer fee for the first 60 days your account is open (after that, the fee is 5%), no annual fee and a 0% introductory rate for transfers (as well as for new purchases) that lasts 15 months.

APR: 13.24% to 23.24% after the introductory period. CreditCards.Chase.com

CARDS WITH SPECIAL FEATURES

Best card for a variety of perks: Chase Sapphire Preferred Visa provides a vast array of perks that are especially attractive now as many other cards cut back their perks. It extends many manufacturer warranties for an additional year...provides coverage of up to $500 for items stolen or damaged during the first 120 days of ownership...and supplies trip-cancellation insurance of up to $10,000 per trip and no foreign transaction fees, to name just a few perks. Cardholders earn two points per dollar spent on travel and dining...one point per dollar on other purchases...and 50,000 in bonus points for spending at least $4,000 in the first three months. Points can be redeemed for travel expenses or transferred to certain frequent-flier and hotel points programs, among other options. The $95 annual fee is waived in the first year.

APR: 16.24% to 23.24%. CreditCards.Chase. com

Best card for college students: Journey Student Rewards from Capital One offers 1% cash back on all purchases, plus 0.25% bonus

---

for paying the card's bill on time, for a total 1.25% cash back. (Cardholders do not need to pay the bill in full to qualify for the bonus.) That's a very generous rewards program for a card issued to students who have very limited credit histories. Rewards are uncapped, do not expire and can be received as a statement credit or check.

APR: 20.24%. CapitalOne.com

Best for people who have low credit scores or limited credit history: Harley-Davidson Visa Secured Card is a "secured card"—cardholders deposit between $300 and $5,000 in a savings account with the credit card's issuer. The amount deposited serves as the credit limit. Unlike many other secured cards, this one has no annual, monthly or account-processing fee. It even has a rewards program, though one that's useful only for Harley fans. Cardholders earn one point per dollar spent. They can request a $25 gift card when they reach 2,500 points. The gift cards can be redeemed only in Harley dealerships or at the company's online store (H-D.com/store).

APR: 23.24%. H-DVisa.com

BEST CREDIT CARD FOR SMALL BUSINESS

Chase Ink Cash Visa offers 5% cash back at office-supply stores and on cell-phone and Internet bills, on up to $25,000 spent per year...2% cash back at gas stations and restaurants, on up to $25,000 spent per year...and 1% on everything else, with no limit. Cardholders can earn a $200 bonus by spending $3,000 in their first three months with the card. Other small-business cards, including Chase Ink Plus, have slightly more generous rewards programs—but unlike Ink Cash, they charge annual fees. Rewards don't expire and can be account credits or electronically deposited into bank accounts.

APR: 13.49% to 19.49%. CreditCards.Chase. com

You Can Avoid Credit Card Balance-Transfer Fees

Scott Bilker, founder of DebtSmart, a credit-management website. He is author of several books about credit cards, including *Talk Your Way Out of Credit Card Debt*. DebtSmart.com

I f you want to lower the interest rate on your credit card balance, you might choose to transfer the balance to a new credit card, possibly one with an interest rate as low as 0%.

But be careful—there might be a "balance-transfer fee" equal to 3% or 4% of the amount transferred. That's a hefty $300 or $400 fee if you transfer $10,000.

How to avoid a fee…

Look for a card that offers low balance-transfer fees in addition to low interest rates. For example, Chase Slate is a no-annual-fee card that waives its 5% balance transfer fee for transfers made within 60 days of opening an account and offers a 0% interest rate on the money transferred as well as on new purchases for 15 months (ChaseSlate.com).

Credit card terms and offers change frequently, so search online for the phrase "best balance-transfer credit cards" to find other appealing deals.

If you apply for a card and are declined…

Call the issuers of credit cards that you already have. Start with cards that you have used responsibly for years with few, if any, late payments or other problems and on which you are currently not carrying a balance. Say that you are thinking about transferring your debt to a new card—mention a specific one and its attractive balance-transfer offer—but that first

you want to find out what transfer deals your existing card could provide. Your card issuer might offer you better transfer terms than it is advertising because you are a responsible borrower.

Example: An issuer might offer to cap its transfer fee at $100 or $200 rather than require you to pay its 3% or 4% fee on the entire amount. If a phone rep does not offer an attractive deal, ask to speak to a supervisor.

Credit Cards with the Most/Least Fees

The credit card with the most fees has 12 of them. The card is from First Premier Bank, whose fees include a $25 charge to get a $100 higher credit limit. The card with the fewest fees is PenFed Promise Visa, which has none. And the average among 100 cards surveyed is six fees. The most common fees are for late payments (ranging from $10 to $49) and cash advances (typically $10 or 5% of the amount advanced).

For a list of fees, go to CreditCards.com/credit-card-news/fee-survey.php.

Matt Schulz, senior analyst for CreditCards.com, which conducted the survey.

Price Protection Varies

CreditCards.com

P rice protection varies among different credit cards. This feature refunds you the difference in price if an item you bought on the card shows up at a lower price within a specified time. Price protection is a free benefit on certain cards from Citibank, Capital One, Chase, MasterCard and Discover—but not American Express. American Express had a program called Best Value Guarantee, but it has been phased out. The easiest program to use is Citi's Price Rewind—you register your purchase and submit the receipt online, and the service automatically scans for a lower price and sends you a refund if it finds one. One Citi customer was recently sent a check for $120 after buying a laptop because Citi's program found a cheaper price.

Other plans are more complex: You call a customer-service line to make a claim, receive a form by mail, then send it with the receipt and proof of the lower price to the card issuer. These programs are best used when buying big-ticket items.

Helpful: Watch prices yourself using price-monitoring sites such as TrackIf.com, CamelCamelCamel.com and GetInvisibleHand.com.

Vanishing Credit Card Perks

Bill Hardekopf, CEO, LowCards.com, Birmingham, Alabama, and coauthor of *The Credit Card Guidebook.*

Credit card issuers have been cutting back on card benefits—a move that could cost you money and cause you hassle. The benefits being cut back include reimbursement for newly purchased items that are damaged or stolen...reimbursement if a store won't let you return a newly purchased item that you're not satisfied with...roadside assistance...insurance coverage for rental-car damage or theft, as well as coverage for baggage delay or loss and for travel delays...and concierge assistance hotlines for help with travel planning and emergencies.

If you don't pay attention to mailings from your cards' issuers, you might think that you still are getting benefits that are no longer available, so be sure to read those mailings and check card-issuer websites to decide which perks are most important to you when using or applying for cards. By cutting back, the credit card companies are seeking to save money partly in anticipation of a greater number of defaults by consumers on variable-rate credit card balances if interest rates start to rise.

Popular credit cards that are cutting back benefits include...

• **Bank of America Better Balance Rewards MasterCard**—no more reimbursement for newly purchased items that you don't want...roadside assistance...travel assistance.

• **Discover Card**—no more roadside assistance...insurance for baggage delay, travel delay and lost luggage...travel assistance.

More cards may cut back similar benefits over the coming year. Check those mailings!

Little-Known Credit Card Perks

ConsumerReports.org

There are many valuable credit card perks that consumers might not know about. *See below...*

• **Missed-connection insurance**—a credit card may cover a hotel stay, taxi to the hotel, meals, toiletries and other costs if you are delayed more than a certain period. Some cards will cover up to $500 in expenses.

• **Baggage-delay insurance**—some credit cards cover purchases of $100 per day for up to five days if your baggage is delayed after a flight charged on the card.

• **Cell phone replacement**—if your phone is stolen and you pay your monthly bill with certain credit cards, you may be entitled to a new phone.

• **Price-drop protection**—some cards give partial or complete refunds on purchases if the item's price falls after you buy it.

• **Extended warranties**—some cards extend manufacturers' warranties for various periods. Check each card's conditions.

Beware Rewards Gaps

Be on the lookout for rewards gaps with credit cards. Groceries do not usually get rewards points if bought at warehouse clubs, such as Sam's Club, or big-box retailers. Dining generally excludes restaurants within places such as hotels and stadiums. Travel may exclude tourist attractions, taxis and tolls.

Clever approach: If you earn rewards at supermarkets but not at warehouse clubs, for example, buy gift cards at supermarkets and use them at warehouse clubs.

Bill Hardekopf, CEO, LowCards.com, Birmingham, Alabama, and coauthor of *The Credit Card Guidebook*.

---

4 Ways to Bump Up Your Credit Score

Greg McBride, CFA, senior vice president and chief financial analyst, Bankrate.com.

Below are four measures you can take that will help you to increase your credit score…

• **Keep the percentage of revolving credit you use**—such as credit cards—to 30% or less, and ideally no more than 10%, of the total revolving credit you have.

• **Leave favorable old accounts on your credit report**—that means debt you have paid off as agreed, such as a car loan or even a credit card you've had for a long time.

• **When shopping for home, auto or student loans, make all of your applications within a short time period**—ideally within

14 days. Each credit application causes your score to decline slightly, but multiple applications in a short period of time are treated as a single inquiry, so it is OK to shop around.

• **Always pay bills on time, and aim to pay down your debts over time.**

Helpful: You are allowed one free report a year from each of the credit bureaus—Equifax, Experian and TransUnion—and you can request those free credit reports at the website AnnualCreditReport.com. The site myBankrate.com provides free access to your TransUnion credit report and credit score each month.

MONEYSMARTS…

Do You Check Your Credit Report?

Thirty-five percent of Americans say they have never looked at their credit report—including 44% of senior citizens and 41% of millennials. That is even though all adults are entitled to one free report per year from each of the three major credit bureaus—Equifax, Experian and TransUnion.

Bankrate.com

New Rules Could Boost Your Credit Score

John Ulzheimer, president of The Ulzheimer Group, a consulting firm focusing on credit reporting and scoring, Atlanta. He previously worked for Equifax Credit Information Services and Fair Isaac Corp., which designed the FICO credit-scoring system. JohnUlzheimer.com

---

The major credit-reporting agencies have agreed to make various policy changes that could boost your credit scores. *What you can expect now…*

• **More help with errors.** Up to now, if you complained to a credit-reporting agency about an inaccurate entry on your credit report, the agency simply passed your complaint along to the creditor…then refused to adjust or remove the problematic entry if the creditor would not admit that there was a mistake. Under the new rules, if you provide documentation but a creditor does not back off its contention, the credit bureaus must assign an agent to review the documentation and could then change the entry despite the creditor's resistance.

• **More time to resolve medical bills.** Under the old rules, your credit report could show a collection—a debt that has been referred to a debt-collection agency—simply because a health insurance company was slow to pay a claim. Collections could lower your credit score by 100 points under certain circumstances. Under the new rules, medical collections cannot be reported to the credit bureaus any sooner than 180 days after the date that the debt becomes delinquent, giving the insurance claim and payment process time to run its course.

• **No more credit score penalties for unpaid tickets and fines.** Currently an unpaid parking ticket or overdue library book fine can end up as a "collection account." Under the new rules, credit reports will not be allowed to include charges if you did not enter into a contract or sign an agreement to pay them.

Fix Errors on Your Credit Report Using New Rules

Credit-reporting agencies Experian, Equifax and TransUnion now must consider documentation that you submit—such as a letter from your bank confirming that your loan payments are up-to-date—to be possible proof of a mistake on your credit report. Under the old rules, the process often stopped short as soon as a credit agency contacted a bank and a bank employee said there was no mistake, even if the employee was incorrect.

John Ulzheimer, president of The Ulzheimer Group, a consulting firm focusing on credit reporting and scoring, Atlanta. JohnUlzheimer.com

How to Earn Much More Interest on Your Cash: A Smart New CD Strategy

Allan S. Roth, CFP, CPA, principal of Wealth Logic, LLC, a financial advisory firm in Colorado Springs that serves clients with investments ranging from $10,000 to $50 million. He is author of *How a Second Grader Beats Wall Street: Golden Rules Any Investor Can Learn.* DaretoBeDull.com

As interest rates have plunged, investments in certificates of deposit (CDs) have decreased by $800 million since 2006, or 32%. And no wonder, with one-year CDs yielding a mere 0.21%,* on average…and three-year CDs averaging just 0.48%. But for investors who need their portfolios to generate income, now actually is a good time for them to consider CDs again as a safe, attractive place to stash some cash.

Reason: Now that the Federal Reserve has started to push up interest rates, bond fund performance could sink and possibly even turn negative, marking the end of the long bull market in bonds. Even individual bonds could become unattractive in cases where you have to sell them before maturity.

To squeeze the most income out of CDs (and bank accounts), you need to consider using some or all of the following strategies…

BUILD A BARBELL INSTEAD OF A LADDER

The classic CD-investing strategy in a time of rising interest rates has been to create a *ladder* of CDs with staggered maturity dates, typically stretching from three months to five years. That way, you keep earning interest… and as the CDs successively mature, you can redeploy the principal to pay living expenses and/or invest in new CDs, presumably at higher and higher yields. But most short-term CD yields were so low recently that a traditional ladder would produce mediocre results. The highest yields on CDs maturing in one year or less were lower than what's available from some savings accounts, which, in contrast to

*Rates as of late-August 2016.

CDs, allow you to withdraw money at any time without penalty.

Better: Use a *barbell* strategy. It gives you exposure to some of the highest yields on CDs today plus great flexibility if you suddenly need cash or when interest rates rise. With this strategy, you don't have to guess when rates will rise or by how much.

At one end of the barbell, you keep your short-term savings (cash that you need quick access to) in a savings or money-market account at an online bank or credit union. These accounts were recently paying an annual percentage yield (APY) as high as 1.11%, better than the best three-, six- or nine-month bank CDs.

At the other end of the barbell, stash your longer-term savings (cash that you won't need to access for a year or more) in five-year bank CDs that offer *low early-withdrawal penalties*. With most long-term CDs, you must sacrifice a full year's worth of interest if you want to cash out before a CD matures to take advantage of rising interest rates. But with low-penalty CDs, you typically sacrifice just six months of interest. The highest-paying low-penalty five-year CD recently offered a 2.25% APY, only slightly lower than the 2.27% APY for the highest-paying five-year CD with a 12-month penalty—and that higher-paying CD requires a $100,000 minimum deposit.

What this means: If interest rates don't rise or rise minimally for the next five years, you earn nearly the highest yield available. If, however, rates do rise, cashing out early doesn't cost you too much.

Example: You invest $100,000 in a five-year CD with a 2.25% APY and a six-month penalty. One year later, you decide to cash out and reinvest in a new, higher-yielding CD. After paying the penalty, you have earned $1,130 in interest (an APY equivalent to 1.13%). That's just slightly less than if you had invested the money in today's best-available one-year CD (1.23%). If you cash out that five-year CD in Year 2, you would earn $3,380 in interest (equivalent to a 1.69% APY, which actually is more than the best-available two-year CD now, 1.4%). Cash out in Year 3, and you would earn $5,640 in interest (equivalent to a 1.88% APY versus 1.5% for today's best-available

three-year CD). Cash out in Year 4, and you would earn $7,880 in interest (equivalent to a 1.97% APY versus 1.92% for today's best-available four-year CD).

Helpful: Use the free online calculator at *DepositAccounts.com/tools/ewp-calculator. aspx* to compare early-withdrawal penalties on CDs and test what the yields would be, based on the rates being paid, the penalty and when the money is withdrawn.

CONSIDER A BROKERED CD

If you want even higher yields and are willing to take on a little more complexity, consider a CD that is sold by a brokerage but is issued by a bank and insured by the Federal Deposit Insurance Corporation (FDIC) up to $250,000 per depositor. Many brokerages offer newly issued 10-year CDs as well as older 10-year CDs that were bought by customers in the past and have less than 10 years left until maturity. Buyers of the older CDs often can get higher annual yields than with newly issued CDs.

Helpful: Right now, the highest-yielding 10-year CDs on the secondary market tend to have about nine years left before maturity.

Example: I recently bought a Synchrony Bank CD on the secondary market through Fidelity Investments. It yields 3.11% and matures on July 11, 2024. That's a far better annual yield than you can get from any bank CD, Treasury bond or even a high-quality corporate bond with a similar maturity date.

SOME CAVEATS WHEN BUYING BROKERED CDs...

●**Invest only money that you won't need back before maturity.**

Reason: If interest rates rise, you won't be able to easily cash out the CD and pay a small early-withdrawal penalty, as you could with a CD bought directly from a bank. Your brokerage would have to try to sell it for you on the open market, and in that case, it would probably sell for less than you paid for it because investors presumably would have a choice of buying newly issued CDs with similar maturity dates and higher yields than yours.

●**Choose a large, reputable brokerage,** such as Fidelity, Vanguard or Schwab—they are most likely to give you a good deal.

• **Make sure that your CD is "noncallable."** Banks sometimes retain the right to "call" (buy back) a CD from you before maturity if interest rates drop substantially below the rate you're receiving. Don't buy a CD with this feature.

AVOID GIMMICKS

To boost yields for savers, many banks offer "bump-up" CDs. But they often are crafted to favor the banks rather than investors. *Example*: Bump-up CDs typically offer a lower interest rate than a comparable regular CD but allow you to raise the rate at least once if interest rates rise during the term of your CD. However, when rates rise, you don't receive the most attractive new CD rate available. You get whatever rate your specific bank decides to offer.

Home Loan Smarts

Roundup of experts in the area of home loans, reported at MoneyTalksNews.com.

Thinking of getting a home-equity loan? *Ask yourself the following six important questions…*

Why am I borrowing? Focus on how taking the loan will move you closer to your financial goals—do not borrow for things such as vacations or cars that are either onetime events or depreciate quickly. *Is my home-improvement project worth it?* New roofs, major remodels or deferred maintenance may be necessary, but not every project increases the value of your home. *Should I consolidate debt?* This might make sense—but only if you change the habits that led to debt trouble in the first place. *Should I pay off student debt with a home-equity loan?* Student loans have protections that may be valuable, and refinancing them may be better than taking out a home loan. *Should I take a loan and use it to further my education?* First look into federal student aid and federal tax credits for education costs. *How big a loan should I take?* Decide how much you really need and how you will pay the loan back.

Ask a financial or tax adviser for details.

New Disclosure Requirement May Delay Home Buying

The federal disclosure requirement, which became effective in October 2015, is intended to make it easier for buyers to understand lenders' rate and fee quotes. Lenders must provide disclosures to buyers twice, at specific times in the loan process.

The first disclosure, *Loan Estimate*, shows rate quote, loan term, line-item fees and cash needed to close—and the lender cannot perform critical tasks, such as ordering an appraisal, until the buyer approves this form. The Loan Estimate must be given within three days of a mortgage application. The second form, *Closing Disclosure*, gives more detail on closing costs and must be given at least three days before closing. The new rules could add about a week to the closing process—more if the purchase happens near a weekend or holiday.

FoxBusiness.com

BETTER WAYS…

Savings Bond Mistakes… and How to Avoid Them

• **Cashing in your oldest bonds first**—they may earn the highest interest, possibly as much as 5%.

• **Looking only at bonds' face amounts when deciding how many to redeem**—this could lead to high taxable income after interest is added.

• **Cashing in many bonds at once**—taxable interest could put you in a higher tax bracket.

• **Redeeming a bond on the day or in the week before its six-month interest payment will be paid**—find out the schedule and bond values with free calculators at TreasuryDirect. gov and SavingsBonds.com.

Jane Bryant Quinn, personal-finance columnist, writing in *AARP Bulletin*.

Better Time to Buy a Home?

Buy a new home at the end of the month to improve your short-term cash flow. Mortgage interest is paid in arrears—after the month has ended. At closing, buyers pay accrued interest from the time they close through the last day of the month. So the later in the month you close, the less accrued interest you pay at closing.

Example: If you have a $240,000 loan at an annual rate of 4.5%, daily interest is $29.60. Closing on the first day of a 30-day month would mean paying $888 in prepaid interest at closing. Closing on the last day would mean paying $29.60—a savings of $858.40 at closing.

In the long run, the total you pay comes out the same, and prepaid interest may be unimportant if, for example, you need to move early in the month. But if you have a flexible moving date and tight cash flow approaching closing, a late-in-month closing date may be better.

A roundup of experts on mortgages, reported at GoBankingRates.com.

GOOD TO KNOW...

The Most Affordable Cities

The 15 most affordable cities in the US have reasonable housing costs, commuting costs, utility bills and everyday living expenses.

Top choice: Akron, Ohio. The median listing price of homes was recently $120,450...median household income was $45,628...percentage of monthly income spent on housing, utilities and commuting was 28.9%.

Other most affordable cities are: Dayton, Ohio...Louisville, Kentucky...Kansas City, Missouri...Wichita, Kansas...Little Rock, Arkansas ...Cleveland...Toledo, Ohio...Syracuse, New York ...St. Louis...Rochester, New York...Indianapolis...Grand Rapids, Michigan...Gary, Indiana... Columbia, South Carolina.

Calculations by real estate website Trulia, reported at CBSNews.com.

Condo Mortgages Easier to Get Now

After the housing-market crash, some lenders required condominium down payments as high as 45%, and Fannie Mae guidelines required that new developments be 70% presold to owner-occupants, not investors, before loans could be made. Now down payments of as little as 5% may be accepted by some lenders, and the presale requirement has fallen to 50%.

Greg McBride, CFA, senior vice president and chief financial analyst, Bankrate.com.

Save on Change-of-Address Service

Avoid costly change-of-address services. Many websites that look like the US Postal Service site charge high fees for an address change—which costs just $1.05 through the US Postal Service itself. Some sites take the money and never change your address.

Self-defense: Don't assume that the first results you get when searching for change-of-address sites are affiliated with the US Postal Service. Use the website USPS.com for address changes.

US Postal Inspection Service. USPS.com

To Save on College Visits...

The cost of applying to college is now about $3,500. That is the average expense for applications, testing fees and trips to schools. Schools say they favor applicants who demonstrate interest by visiting the campus and meeting admissions officers. But online exploring is fine to narrow down the list—many colleges offer virtual campus tours. When you visit schools, try to arrange the trip to include visits to two colleges a day. Ask if a school offers reduced hotel rates, free dining-hall meals or other help—some even pay for desirable students to visit.

Also: Consider tour companies that offer supervised trips by region.

Example: College-Visits.com charges approximately $2,000 for an eight-day tour of about 12 schools.

Money.com

State College Tuition Soaring—What to Do

Mark Kantrowitz, senior vice president of the college finance website Edvisors.com. He is coauthor of *Filing the FAFSA: The Edvisors Guide to Completing the Free Application for Federal Student Aid*. Edvisors.com

I n-state tuition and fees have soared over the past 10 years at many state colleges, some of which charge more than $17,000 a year for in-state students.

Example: The University of Pittsburgh costs $17,688 for 2016–2017 (up from $10,130 for 2004–2005). Although state schools still charge less than most private schools, they are not the relative bargain they used to be.

Another problem: It is getting more difficult for in-state students to get into highly rated state schools that are reserving more slots for out-of-state and international students, who pay even more.

What to do: Consider state schools in other states that offer relatively low tuition rates to certain out-of-staters. Some provide in-state or discounted rates to residents of neighboring states or residents in another state who live within a certain number of miles of the school. Some belong to "regional exchange programs" that offer in-state rates or other low rates to residents of other states within the same US region.

Example: The University of Wyoming's tuition and fees for state residents still represent a bargain—totaling $5,056. Residents of 15 states across the western US can apply to attend Wyoming state schools at 150% of the in-state tuition rate, which comes to about

$8,900 when fees are included, compared with $10,984 at Washington State University for residents of Washington (one of those 15 states), for a savings of about $2,000. Also, out-of-staters who have a parent who graduated from the University of Wyoming qualify for that 150% rate no matter where they live.

A listing of such programs is available at FinAid.org/otheraid/exchange.phtml.

File for Financial Aid Even If You Don't Need It...

Roundup of financial planners specializing in college financial aid, reported in *The Wall Street Journal*.

F amilies that can afford college without financial aid frequently do not file FAFSA, the *Free Application for Federal Student Aid*. But filing FAFSA can improve admission chances. Colleges build freshman classes that include students who do not need aid as well as ones who do—so a FAFSA showing that no aid is needed may increase the chance of admission. Also, many schools will not consider

143

merit aid—which is not based on need—unless a FAFSA has been filed.

And: Filing a FAFSA is required for students to qualify for low-interest federal student loans—some parents may want children to take out loans so that they are partly responsible for college costs...or a job loss or other occurrence might change family finances, so having a FAFSA on file could be helpful. The last day to file a FAFSA is June 30 or the final day of the academic year, whichever comes first.

Claim Your Money Now!

Do a search for unclaimed money to which you might be entitled. Funds in financial institutions or companies that have had no activity and no contact with the owner for a long time—usually three years or more—may go to state unclaimed-property offices.

To determine if any funds are being held for you, search the websites MissingMoney.com and Unclaimed.org...check the Treasury site for the state where you live and any in which you lived in the past...search under any names you have ever used, and try a first initial plus your last name as well as first and last names...and search IRS.gov for any possible unclaimed tax-refund money. In addition, The Pension Benefit Guaranty Corporation (PBGC.

gov) has a searchable database for unclaimed pensions...TreasuryHunt.gov helps in searches for unclaimed savings bonds...and websites of individual life insurers let you search for claims or payments.

Jean Chatzky, financial editor, NBC's *Today* show. Today.com

Money and Marriage for Older Couples

Getting married provides access to federal and state spousal and survivor benefits... and to Medicare if you do not qualify on your own. Marriage also makes it simpler to make health-care decisions for each other, provides better tax benefits when inheriting an IRA or HSA and sometimes saves on taxes through a joint return. But some veterans and some widows and widowers of public employees may lose pensions by remarrying...survivor benefits on a deceased spouse's Social Security account will be lost in a remarriage before age 60...and in many states, spouses—but not unmarried partners—are responsible for each other's medical bills, including long-term care. Ask your tax adviser and an elder-care attorney for details.

AARP.org.

8

Insurance Answers

Is Your Doctor Really "In"?

I t used to be pretty simple—either your doctor accepted your insurance or didn't. But all that has changed. These days, your physician may accept your insurance (from Medicare or a private insurer) only *under certain circumstances*. And if you think your doctor's services are included but they are not, you could be blindsided by a whopping out-of-pocket cost to you. Fortunately, you can avoid getting hit with a big bill—even if your doctor participates in this medical version of musical chairs.

Here's where the trouble starts: In today's world of medicine, many doctors are joining more than one group practice. A surgeon, for example, may have to join two or more group practices in order to gain treatment privileges at particular hospitals (many hospitals have exclusive agreements with certain groups). And

while one practice might accept your insurance, the other practice might *not*. In addition, some groups with multiple locations might accept your insurance only if you see the doctor at one of their particular offices! Adding to the confusion, some group practices also allow doctors within the practice to "opt out" of certain insurance plans, while other doctors in the practice accept it.

The problem—especially if you are in a plan that requires you to use "network" doctors—is that if you checked for your doctor's name on your insurance company's "network of participating doctors" roster, it may show up there. But unless you see him/her in the right practice and/or right location, your doctor might not be considered "in network"—in which case

Charles B. Inlander, a consumer advocate and healthcare consultant based in Fogelsville, Pennsylvania. He was founding president of the nonprofit People's Medical Society, a consumer advocacy organization credited with key improvements in the quality of US health care, and is author or coauthor of more than 20 consumer-health books.

145

your claim will be treated as an "out-of-network" visit or possibly denied. *How to avoid this frustrating game—and a surprise bill...*

● **Talk to the right people.** Obviously, the first thing to do is ask the person who books your appointment whether the doctor accepts your insurance. But don't stop there. Confirm with the person who is in charge of billing that your insurance will be accepted in that location and by the doctor you're seeing. This double-tiered verification is necessary, since the person who books appointments may not always know for sure if your particular insurance plan is one the practice can accept.

Special alert: If you are enrolled in a Medicare Advantage HMO or Medicare PPO and a doctor or his practice *tells you that his service is covered by your plan*, and the claim is later denied because the doctor or practice turns out not to be "participating," the law forbids the doctor or practice from billing you for the service. If you receive a bill, do not pay it and immediately call Medicare's 800-MEDICARE hotline for assistance.

● **Check with your insurer, too.** Just to make sure that the verification you got from your doctor's office is correct, call your insurance company and specifically ask if the doctor you're planning to see, at the location where the service is going to be rendered (especially important if you live near a state line and your doctor has offices in two or more states) is considered a "participating practitioner." While you're at it, also ask whether the service you will be receiving from the doctor is covered by your plan.

Warning: Do *not* rely on the insurer's online list of participating doctors, since these lists are notoriously out of date. If you're on Medicare, go to Medicare.gov and click on "Find doctors & other health professionals" to confirm that your doctor is covered. To confirm that a specific service is covered, call 800-MEDICARE.

Straight Answers on Health Care

Charles B. Inlander, a consumer advocate and health-care consultant based in Fogelsville, Pennsylvania. He was founding president of the nonprofit People's Medical Society, a consumer advocacy organization credited with key improvements in the quality of US health care, and is author or coauthor of more than 20 consumer-health books.

L et's face it—most of what makes health care so challenging these days is trying to get a straight answer to all the questions that come up—whether it's a billing matter, for example, a treatment issue or a clarification on follow-up care after a hospitalization. Now there's help available! Primarily thanks to financial incentives built into the Affordable Care Act, insurers, hospitals and doctors are being rewarded for keeping you healthier, preventing unnecessary hospitalizations and making sure that your care is coordinated between the various professionals you may be seeing. If that sounds like a tall order, you're right. That's why many health-care providers, wanting to be sure that they reap those financial rewards, have created new positions called "care coordinators," who serve as your direct contact—at no charge to you—for any questions or concerns you may have about your health care.

Care coordinators (sometimes called "care navigators") are catching on fast. Most private insurers provide care-coordination services to their policyholders, and just about all Medicare Advantage Plans have care coordinators. Most large health-care systems, such as Banner Health, UCLA Health, Bon Secours and Kaiser, now employ coordinators, and so do many large hospitals and group medical practices, including the Mayo Clinic, the Cleveland Clinic and local practices such as oncology and cardiac groups.

What you need to know about health-care coordinators...

● **Training is emphasized.** Most care coordinators are either nurses or social workers. Because of the growing demand for care coordinators, other personnel, such as patients' advocates with knowledge of health-care issues,

GOOD TO KNOW...

Little-Known Health Insurance Benefits

What is covered by health insurance can be confusing. *Here are some less known but often covered health-care benefits...*

● **Diet counseling and obesity treatment** are covered in various ways—for example, 33 states require coverage of bariatric surgery.

● **Smoking cessation**—four sessions of counseling and 90 days of medication usually are covered.

● **Prenatal folic acid supplements and breastfeeding supplies** usually are covered.

● **Autism screening and treatment** for children is covered in 43 states.

● **Psychiatric therapy** is covered, including treatment for substance abuse.

● **Health clubs and weight-loss programs** are covered by some plans.

● **Certain services may or may not be covered,** including wigs for chemotherapy patients, chiropractic treatment and acupuncture or massage therapy. Check with your insurer.

Roundup of experts on health-care coverage under the Affordable Care Act, reported at GoBankingRates.com.

---

are now being recruited. No matter what their background, care coordinators are specially trained to understand the full scope of their organization's services and how to cut through the red tape to get answers. Once trained, care coordinators can take charge of all aspects of your care and make sure your needs are being met and questions are being answered.

● **Services are wide-ranging.** Care coordinators provide a wealth of services for patients and their families. For example, a care coordinator can set up rides for medical appointments or arrange for medication delivery. Most hospitals provide very little follow-up after a patient is discharged. Care coordinators not only follow up on your status but can also directly arrange for services, such as home-care nursing or Meals on Wheels services, that might prevent you from being rehospitalized. Care coordinators also communicate with all your health-care providers to truly "coordinate" your care.

● **It's easy to get started.** To find a care coordinator, start with your insurance provider (including your Medicare Advantage Plan sponsor if you have one). Ask if care coordinators are available. If so, check out their range of services and how you can use them. If you are going to be hospitalized, call the hospital in advance and ask about care-coordination services. Because of federal incentives, your doctors are likely to be members of what are called Accountable Care Organizations (ACO), which are specifically designed to coordinate care. Ask your doctor if he/she belongs to one and how you can use these services.

Wellness Incentives Offer Big Savings

Millions of dollars go unclaimed because employees don't take advantage of wellness incentives. Only 47% of employees took advantage of their firms' wellness incentives last year. Companies may offer cash, gift cards and reduced health-care premiums to get employees into health-improvement programs.

Survey by Fidelity Investments and the National Business Group on Health.

Simple Way to Get a Discount on Health Insurance

Kiplinger.com

Fitness bands may get you a discount on health insurance or life insurance. Some employers are giving out these bands or subsidizing their expense—then rewarding employees who meet specified activity goals, such as an average of 10,000 steps a day, with discounts, gift cards and other awards. Most programs require annual requalification based on the number of steps taken in the previous year. Some insurers are making discounts available directly.

Example: John Hancock rewards eligible policyholders with up to 15% discounts on life insurance premiums if they average a specified number of steps daily and take care of their health in other ways—for instance, by getting an annual flu shot.

Caution: Fitness bands may collect data such as your heart rate and sleep patterns. If you have privacy concerns, ask before enrolling whether this information is collected and how it is used.

Free End-of-Life Planning

Some private insurers and a few state Medicaid programs have paid for patient appointments to discuss the care they want at the end of life.

Example: If a person is healthy but is in an accident, he/she may want to be resuscitated no matter what his condition...but the same person might make a different decision if he is diagnosed with terminal cancer.

As of January 1, 2016, Medicare pays for appointments to discuss such matters and does not limit how often such counseling can take place.

Rule announced by Centers for Medicare and Medicaid Services, reported in *The Wall Street Journal.*

You Don't Have to Die to Get These Life Insurance Benefits

Tony Steuer, CLU, founder of Insurance Literacy Institute, which provides insurance information for consumers, and Insurance Quality Mark, an insurance agent certification. Steuer is also a former insurance company executive and author of *Questions and Answers on Life Insurance.* InsuranceLiteracy.org

Vast amounts of life insurance benefits are left on the table each year by policyholders. Many policyholders allow their

---

BETTER WAYS...

For Better Results When Calling Health Insurers...

To get better service when contacting health insurers...

● **Avoid calling on Mondays,** their busiest days.

● **Have your insurance card and Summary of Benefits ready.**

● **Ask to be transferred to a nurse**—they often are highly knowledgeable about medical matters, and many case managers at insurance companies are nurses.

● **If you are calling for a relative, have the person there to give permission** for you to discuss his/her case.

● **Get any promises in writing,** especially if a representative agrees to make an exception to written policies.

● **Take careful notes,** including the date and time of the call, the name of the person you spoke to and what the person said.

● **Consider corresponding by e-mail** if that is an option so that you have a record of the conversation that you can reference for further issues.

Prevention.com

---

life insurance coverage to lapse because they can no longer afford the premiums or they feel that they no longer need life insurance.

But there often are better options than simply allowing a policy to lapse. You are most likely to have these options with whole and universal life policies, which have investment components as well as death benefits, but you might have some options with term policies as well. For instance, it might be possible to turn a "convertible term" policy into a universal or whole life policy. The conversion generally must be completed by a certain age, however—often 65. Contact your insurer for details. *Four possibilities...*

● **You could cancel your whole or universal policy** (rather than allowing it to lapse) and claim its cash surrender value. That's the amount your insurance contract promises you if you voluntarily terminate the policy prior to its maturity. This usually is an option with whole and universal life policies, but not with term policies.

Before choosing this option, call your insurance company and request an "in force illustration"—a projection of the policy's value based on current interest rates and dividend assumptions. Does this report show that the policy's "accumulated value" is higher than its "surrender value"? If so, you still are in your policy's "surrender charge period" and must pay a fee to claim its surrender value. Skim the report to find the date when accumulated value matches surrender value—if it's soon, consider keeping the policy in effect until this date arrives.

Tax implications: Although an insurance policy's death benefit usually is not taxable, any cash surrender value you receive in excess of the amount that you paid in premiums will be taxed as income.

• **A "life settlement" company might be willing to buy your whole or universal life insurance policy** from you for more than its cash surrender value. This company will continue paying your premiums so that it can eventually claim the death benefit. (Or it might sell your policy to a different company, which would then take over the payments and claim the death benefit.) These companies are most interested in policies belonging to people age 70 and up, though some will buy policies from people in their 60s, too.

Warnings…

• **Regulation and oversight of the life settlement industry have improved** over the past decade, but proceed with caution—there still are shady operators. There's something to be said for working with one of the well-established financial companies that has entered the business, such as Goldman Sachs or Credit Suisse.

• **There is a creepy element to life settlement**—the company that purchases your policy can contact you from time to time to ask about your health. If that company later sells your policy, these calls might come from a company that you don't even know.

• **Selling a policy to a life settlement company is not technically permitted** under the terms of most life insurance contracts. No life insurance issuer is known to have taken action against a policyholder for doing this, however.

Tax implications: The IRS has not made a final ruling about the taxability of life settlements, but the guidance it has offered suggests that any amount received in excess of the policy's cash surrender value is taxable as capital gain.

• **An accelerated death benefit might be available from your insurer.** This is very similar to a life settlement, but it's paid by your insurance policy issuer, so there's no concern about the legitimacy of the company…no potential legal complications…and no creepy calls about your health. This option exists for certain whole and universal life policies.

Strategy: Speak with a life settlement company or two before calling your insurer to ask about an accelerated death benefit. Then tell the insurer, "I've heard from a life settlement company, and it says it can offer me $X for my policy. I would like to know if you, instead, could offer me an accelerated death benefit." Cite the largest amount offered to you. This conversation sends a message to your insurer that you know what your policy is worth, which might inspire it to make a competitive offer.

Tax implications: Accelerated death benefits generally can be excluded from taxable income if the policyholder has a terminal illness and is not expected to live more than 24 months…or has a chronic condition that requires long-term care (consult your tax or financial adviser for details). Otherwise these benefits might be taxable as income.

• **Your beneficiaries might be willing to pay your insurance premiums for you.** They eventually will benefit from your policy, so it is perfectly reasonable to ask them if they would like to help you keep it in effect. These payments by your heirs could potentially be subject to gift taxes, but only if the payments exceed the annual gift tax exclusion—up to $14,000 paid by each heir.

CHOOSING AN EXPERT

If you ask an insurance agent or broker for help choosing among the options detailed above, be aware that his/her recommendation might not be truly impartial—he might receive a commission for steering you in a particular direction. A fee-only financial planner can provide an unbiased opinion, but planners often are not insurance experts.

The best way to get unbiased guidance from a true expert is to consult with a fee-based life insurance consultant. Some examples include David Barkhausen (LifeInsuranceAdvisorsInc. com)…and Glenn S. Daily (GlennDaily.com), who is a member of the *Bottom Line Personal* Panel of Experts. (Neither of these consultants has any financial arrangement with *Bottom Line Personal*.)

Some Life Insurers Are Rewarding Healthier Living

They are offering 10% or higher premium reductions or rewards from retailers to policyholders who have annual health screenings, lose weight, get annual flu shots, take online health courses and/or do regular physical activity. Offerings, requirements and prices vary and change often.

Shop around using comparison-pricing sites including Term4Sale.com…FindMyInsurance. com…and IntelliQuote.com, and also check with direct sellers such as TIAA.org and USAA. com to make sure that the premium rates being offered are competitive.

The Wall Street Journal. WSJ.com

Your Life Insurance May Be Terminated…

Tony Steuer, CLU, founder of Insurance Literacy Institute, which provides insurance information for consumers, and Insurance Quality Mark, an insurance agent certification. Steuer is also a former insurance company executive and author of *Questions and Answers on Life Insurance.* InsuranceLiteracy.org

Tens of thousands of universal life insurance policyholders are in danger of having their policies terminated early.

AXA, Transamerica and Voya are among the insurance companies that are beginning to drain accounts of these policies to make up for a shortfall in their investment returns, and other insurers are expected to follow.

Insurers say it is necessary because in recent years, market interest rates have been much lower than anticipated and are expected to continue to be fairly low. Policies issued as far back as the 1980s and up to 2007 are at greatest risk.

Universal life insurance policies include a tax-advantaged savings component in addition to a death benefit. Insurers typically do not raise the premiums throughout the life of the policy, and the cash value of the account typically increases. But because investment returns for the insurers have been falling short, the fine print allows them to increase fees, which reduces the cash value—in effect draining the account. That could mean that policies—which typically are written to expire when the policyholder reaches an age somewhere between 87 and 121—will terminate 10 or more years early if policyholders do not pay more in premiums.

The insurers are not necessarily informing policyholders that this is happening or may do so in language that is hard to interpret.

Steps you can take…

•**Ask your insurer for an "in-force illustration"** of higher premiums you could pay to avoid having your policy terminate early.

•**Alternatively, consider accepting a lower death benefit.**

For a free guide on how to get details from the insurer and a form letter to send to your insurer asking for the information, you can go to InsuranceLiteracy.org/insurance-annual-review-guides.

Credit Scores Can Raise Car Insurance Rates

Jill Gonzalez, "Wallet Guru" for WalletHub, a financial website operated by Evolution Finance, Washington, DC. CardHub.com

If you don't want to pay extra for car insurance, you must think about your credit score—because it can affect your car insurance rates dramatically and very differently with different insurance companies.

For instance, drivers who have excellent credit scores—say, 720 or above—may save money with Farmers Insurance and Progressive. These insurance companies place particular emphasis on credit scores, according to research by the financial website WalletHub.com.

A driver who has an excellent credit score might be quoted a rate 60% below the rate offered to someone who has a similar driving record but a poor credit score. These quotes for high-credit-score drivers will often—though not always—be the lowest rates available.

Those drivers who have poor credit scores—say, 620 or below—might benefit from getting quotes at Geico, which tends to place far less emphasis on credit scores.

For drivers with midlevel credit scores—above 620 but below 720—the scores generally have less effect on the rates that insurers quote.

Auto insurers are not allowed to consider credit scores in California, Hawaii or Massachusetts, and they tend not to put much emphasis on credit scores in certain other states, including Connecticut and Iowa.

The states where auto insurers generally put the greatest emphasis on credit scores include Maine, Michigan, New Jersey, Pennsylvania, South Carolina, Tennessee and Virginia.

For more details about insurers' credit-score habits, take a look at WalletHub's "2016 Car Insurance & Credit Scores Report." You can review the full report at WalletHub.com/edu/car-insurance.

TAKE NOTE...

Avoid Steep Hike When Adding Teen to Auto Policy

Auto insurers are increasing premiums by 80%, on average, when a married couple adds a teen to their policy. To reduce the increase, ask your insurer about "good student" discounts, which can cut your premium by up to 25%. Some insurers offer discounts when students attend schools far from home and do not have a vehicle on campus. Shop around.

Laura Adams, senior insurance analyst, insuranceQuotes.com, which commissioned a study of how teens affect auto insurance premiums.

Cheaper Cars That Are *Expensive* to Insure

Small sedans are the most expensive vehicles to insure relative to their prices. A recent national survey found that the worst deals in car insurance, based on likely damage, injuries and theft rates, were on the Ford Focus...Toyota Corolla...Hyundai Elantra...Honda Civic... and Chevrolet Cruze sedans. The best insurance values were SUVs or trucks—Ford Explorer and Chevrolet Equinox SUVs...and GMC Sierra, Chevrolet Silverado and Dodge Ram 1500 trucks.

Consider all long-term costs when choosing a vehicle.

Laura Adams, senior insurance analyst, insuranceQuotes.com, where you can see the full survey it commissioned on insurance rates.

If You're a Widow or Widower...

Widows and widowers are charged higher auto insurance premiums than married people—14% higher, on average. Among major insurers, only State Farm seems not to consider marital status when setting premiums. Insurers explain the disparity by saying that married people are more likely to be safer drivers than single people. Widows and widowers should inform their insurance agents that they are single because a spouse has passed away and ask for any discount given to married people. Insurers sometimes are willing to be flexible.

Stephen Brobeck, executive director, Consumer Federation of America, a nonprofit association of nearly 300 consumer groups, Washington, DC. ConsumerFed.org

5 Myths About Homeowner's Insurance: They Could Cost You Big

J. Robert Hunter, director of insurance for the Consumer Federation of America, a nonprofit consumer advocacy organization, Washington, DC. He is a former commissioner of insurance for Texas and former federal insurance administrator for the US Department of Housing and Urban Development. ConsumerFed.org

Few home owners completely understand their homeowner's insurance. The policies are written in dense legalese…and many policyholders do not even try to wade through them. As a result, many people are mistaken about their rights when dealing with insurers and are unaware of gaps in their coverage, some of which could cause financial ruin.

This problem is becoming worse—insurers have made crucial changes to policies that have escaped the notice of many customers. *Five common and potentially costly insurance myths…*

MYTH: If my home is destroyed, my insurance will pay what it costs to rebuild. Prior to Hurricane Andrew, which devastated parts of coastal Florida in 1992, most policies provided "guaranteed replacement cost coverage" that financed reconstruction whatever it cost. But this guarantee is no longer included in the vast majority of policies. These days, most policies cover only up to the dollar figure specifically listed as the coverage amount or occasionally a bit more.

Example: State Farm policies typically cover up to 20% above this amount.

Even home owners who are aware of this change tend to assume that they are safe as long as the coverage amount listed in their policy is in line with the typical cost of rebuilding a home such as theirs. Unfortunately, because of a phenomenon called "demand surge," that might not be sufficient if your home is destroyed in a major disaster. When many homes in an area require repairs, the cost of building supplies and labor tend to skyrocket—sometimes by more than 50%.

Insurers also have been eliminating "building code coverage" from their policies. When a home is more than 50% destroyed, it must be rebuilt according to current building codes, not the codes that were in effect when that home was originally constructed. Without building code coverage, a policy will not pay any added costs that are involved with upgrading to stricter codes.

What to do: Ask your insurer whether it offers a "demand surge" rider, especially if your home is in an area where hurricanes or wildfires are common—these are the disasters that most often cause sharp spikes in building costs.

Ask at your town office whether any building code changes have taken effect since your home was built that would make it much pricier to rebuild the home today. If so, ask your insurer if it offers a code coverage rider.

MYTH: Home owners must hire a contractor willing to do repairs for the amount the insurer says it will cover. Your insurer says a repair can be done for a certain amount, but the contractor you want to use says it will cost more. Policyholders often assume that their only option is to work with the low-cost contractor recommended by the insurer…or to hire a lawyer and take the insurer to court, an expensive and uncertain proposition that most people prefer to avoid. However, it sometimes is possible to convince an insurer to pay the amount a contractor wants without resorting to lawyers.

What to do: Contact your insurer's claims department. Explain that your contractor is quoting a higher figure, and ask to have this amount covered. If the insurer refuses, ask to speak to a claims department manager and repeat the request. If the answer still is no, call your contractor and ask if he/she can contact your insurer on your behalf. Veteran contractors often have experience negotiating with insurers.

Meanwhile, keep careful notes whenever you speak to your insurer's adjuster, other insurance company employees, your contractor and anyone else involved. If your contractor cannot work things out for you, mail a letter to the claims department manager explaining unemotionally why you don't believe you are being treated fairly. Include a detailed record of what you believe to be missteps by the insurer, such as dramatically underestimating the cost of specific building supplies or even times the adjuster missed appointments. Insurance executives often back down when they receive letters showing that the policyholder is too savvy to be pushed around.

MYTH: Homeowner's insurance protects against losses from most types of disaster except for floods and earthquakes. Home owners who live in or near flood zones or earthquake-prone areas generally are aware that they are not financially protected against these types of disasters (unless they pay extra for flood insurance or an earthquake rider). And they may be aware that insurance doesn't protect against such unlikely cataclysms as nuclear explosions or war. But many home owners are unaware that damage caused by other, more mundane types of disasters, such as mud slides, landslides, sinkholes and riots (germane to some urban areas), is excluded as well.

What to do: Many insurers offer sinkhole, landslide/mud slide and riot riders for an added charge, generally well under $1 per $100 of coverage.

MYTH: My homeowner's insurance will pay the bills if someone is injured on my property. Not always—there are some big gaps in the liability component of homeowner's insurance. Your policy does not cover injuries to members of your household, for example. Policies generally do not cover injuries

to people who visit your property for business purposes, either. And policies increasingly exclude injuries related to trampolines, tree houses and zip lines—some insurers won't cover home owners who have these things at all. Other potential backyard hazards including swimming pools, hot tubs and climbing structures generally are covered—if they are disclosed to the insurance company and higher premiums are paid.

What to do: If you have a home business, purchase commercial liability coverage or add a home business rider to your homeowner's insurance policy. This is particularly important if clients, employees or delivery people visit the property for business reasons. (Adding a rider to an existing homeowner's insurance policy usually is the less expensive option, but these riders sometimes have low coverage limits.)

If you intend to rent out your home, contact your insurer to ask if your liability protection extends to paying guests. If not, you could rent out the property through a service such as Airbnb that provides liability protection to property owners...or purchase coverage specifically for rental properties from a company such as CBIZ (CBIZ.com) or Peers Marketplace (Peers.org).

MYTH: Since I never bothered to make a record of my possessions, now that I've had a fire there's no way for me to get compensated for all of the things I lost. It certainly is wise to document your possessions before you ever suffer a fire (or burglary or flood or other disaster). It is much less likely that you will obtain the full amount you are entitled to for your lost property if you cannot remember everything you lost...or you cannot prove what you lost to the insurance company, opening the door for it to question your claims. The easiest way to document your possessions is to simply walk through every room of your home with a digital camera, or even a smartphone, and record video. But all is not necessarily lost if you neglected to do this before suffering a big loss.

What to do: If you have extensive damage to your home, go through the digital snapshots and videos you have taken in your home and uploaded to social-media accounts, shared with family members or backed up to the cloud. Ask family and friends who have come to your house for parties to forward to you any pictures or videos they took.

Create a Visual Home Inventory

Jeff Wignall, a professional photographer who has photographed home, municipal and estate collections for home owners, municipalities and insurance companies. He is author of more than 15 books, including *The Photographer's Master Guide to Color*. He is a contributing editor to *Popular Photography* magazine. JeffWignall.com

As your insurance company will tell you, having a comprehensive visual record of your home's contents in the event of a fire, natural disaster or someone burglarizing your home is one of the best ways to prove that those things were in your home. A visual inventory will speed payment on your insurance claims and likely result in higher payment because you have a more detailed and comprehensive tally.

You can use any still camera or video camera, including your cell phone camera, shooting a mix of video and stills. It is a good weekend project, working a few hours per day.

• **Shoot exterior views,** either still or video, to demonstrate the "before" condition of your home and your landscaping. First take an "establishing" shot that shows the home and surroundings. Then take individual shots of expensive items such as barbecue grills, lawn furniture and exterior lighting fixtures. Then head into your garage or shed to shoot yard tools and equipment such as mowers, snowblowers and generators. Anything you can move to the driveway, such as your car or bicycles, can be shot there.

• **Shoot an overall shot of each room on video,** and then create a record of items with still photos.

• **Document individual items.** Any expensive items, including electronics, jewelry and collectibles/antiques, should be photographed individually and from various angles. With electronics, be sure to show brand and model. Open drawers (your silverware drawer, for instance) and jewelry boxes to show the contents. If you collect books, shoot wide views of each bookshelf, then take individual shots of rare volumes. Stamp and coin collections can be scanned on a flatbed scanner—the same one that you use to scan documents for your computer (a simple flatbed scanner sells for between $50 and $100, but many all-in-one printers have a scanning function built in).

• **Put together a simple studio.** To speed the shooting of small items, make a simple studio space using a sheet of white poster board as a background. I simply tape the poster board to a wall and curve it down to the surface of a card table to make a seamless background. Use light from a nearby window or simple desk lights or your camera's built-in flash.

• **Don't forget closets.** Take wide views but also include individual shots of designer items (and labels). To get a good shot, hang an item on the back of a closet door or lay it on a bed.

• **Make copies.** Once your record is complete, download all of the videos and photos to your computer and then burn multiple DVD copies (and/or save to the cloud) and store your discs off premises.

For free online help: The Insurance Information Institute provides free software (and apps for iPhones, iPads and Android devices) that will guide you through creating and updating a visual inventory at KnowYourStuff.org/iii/login.html.

9

Tax Hotline

7 Things You Didn't Know Are Taxable

uried treasure…generous gifts from your employer …and that iPad you got as a gift for opening up a bank account—they all have something in common. The IRS defines them as income and expects you to pay federal tax on their cash value.

Americans underreport an estimated $68 billion in personal income annually, sometimes intentionally but often because they don't realize it counts as taxable income. Many establishments such as casinos aren't even required to notify the IRS that you have received income unless the income tops a certain threshold. But in some cases, failing to report taxable income can trigger an audit and/or result in civil penalties ranging from "failure to file" penalties (up to $135 if you are more than 60 days late) to "failure to pay"

penalties (0.5% of the amount of unpaid tax per month).

Surprising things that are taxable…

BANK OR CREDIT CARD GIFTS

Many financial institutions offer incentives for opening new accounts, ranging from cash and electronic gadgets to frequent-flier miles. These generally are considered taxable income unless you must spend a certain amount on a credit card or debit card within a limited time period.

Important: Frequent-flier miles and cash back that you receive when you use a credit or debit card are *not* taxable because they are rebates.

CANCELED CREDIT CARD DEBT

When someone negotiates a settlement with a credit card issuer to pay less than the full amount owed, the IRS treats the forgiven debt

Greg Rosica, CPA, CFA, partner with Ernst & Young LLP in the private client services practice in Tampa. He is also a contributing author for the *EY Tax Guide 2016.* EY.com/eytaxguide as income. So if you owe, say, a balance of $25,000 and the issuer settles for $18,500, the $6,500 difference counts as taxable income.

Exceptions: Credit card debt discharged in a Chapter 11 bankruptcy does not count as income. And in cases of *insolvency*, you may not have to pay tax on all or possibly any of your forgiven credit card debt. Just before any of the debt is forgiven, if your total debt exceeds your total assets (excluding assets that creditors can't seize, such as 401(k) accounts), you are insolvent by that excess amount. You subtract the insolvency amount from the forgiven debt to get the amount of taxable income. So if your total debt exceeds your assets by $5,000 and your credit card issuer forgives $6,500, you report $1,500 of the forgiven debt as income.

ILL-GOTTEN GAINS

Whether you rob a bank or win an illegal football betting pool at the office, the IRS expects you to pay tax on any ill-gotten gains, although few lawbreakers choose to do so. Although the IRS tech1nically must keep the contents of your tax returns confidential, there are enough legal loopholes that law-enforcement agencies are likely to find out if you are including ill-gotten gains as part of your income. For instance, if the IRS audits you, it is allowed to reveal certain information to law-enforcement authorities that it gathers from outside sources, such as witnesses to your illegal activities.

There is a better way to gain from illegal profits—report other individuals who are tax evaders. The IRS Whistleblower Office paid out more than $103 million in awards in 2015 to tipsters—they typically get 15% to 30% of the amount the government eventually collects. And yes, any money you get as a whistleblower is regarded as taxable income on your own return.

Get more information from: IRS.gov/uac/Whistleblower-Office-at-a-Glance.

EMPLOYER PERKS

Generally, you aren't required to pay tax on gifts you receive from family and friends no matter how much they're worth. But most sizable gifts from your boss or company are regarded as taxable compensation subject to federal and state income tax withholding as well as FICA taxes. This includes everything from golf clubs to the use of a company-owned apartment for a vacation.

Two exceptions: "De minimis" fringe benefits—gifts of minimal value, which some employers define as $75 or less but which the IRS has not defined—generally are not taxable. That includes, for example, a holiday gift basket, group meals and picnics, and local transportation after hours if it is required because of security concerns. Cash and gift cards generally are not included under the de minimis rule—they typically are taxable—but cash and gifts awarded to employees to recognize their achievements for "length of service" are not taxable if you have been with the company for at least five years and the value of the award is $1,600 or less.

GAMBLING PROCEEDS

The IRS expects you to report all "gambling" winnings, no matter how small, whether they come from church bingo games, raffles, sweepstakes, lotteries, casinos or online sports fantasy betting sites. If you win more than a certain amount, ranging from $1,200 (bingo and slot machines) to $5,000 (poker tournaments and lotteries), the gambling establishment typically withholds a 25% flat tax and must notify the IRS...and then you adjust that for your tax bracket when you file tax forms.

The good news: If you itemize, gambling losses are deductible up to the amount of winnings you report as income. You must be able to prove your losses through documentation such as receipts, tickets, payment slips and/or a gambling diary with specific dates, the type of gambling, and the names and addresses of the establishments and the names of other people accompanying you at the establishments.

RENTING OUT YOUR HOME

Services such as Airbnb.com that enable you to rent out available rooms in your house or apartment to travelers have allowed hundreds of thousands of home owners to earn extra income. The IRS considers any short-term rental income taxable if you rent out space for 15 or more days a year. Be aware that additional taxes imposed by your local and state government also may apply.

Example: Chicago, Philadelphia, San Diego and San Francisco are among cities that impose a "transient occupancy" or hotel tax on every short-term rental stay.

You can reduce the taxes you owe on rental income by taking related deductions. In addition to a portion of your own rent or mortgage payments, utilities and insurance expenses, you can deduct items such as the cost of sheets and linens that you designate for the exclusive use of your guests...toiletries for guests...and cleaning fees.

Helpful: Get more strategies at the websites of the major online lodging services, LearnAir bnb.com and Community.HomeAway.com.

A TREASURE TROVE

"Treasure Trove" is a fanciful term used by the IRS to categorize any lost or abandoned cash and/or valuables that you find. Precedent for taxing treasure troves dates back to a famous 1964 case in which an Ohio couple bought a used piano for $15 and found $4,467 in cash inside while cleaning it. Recent cases involve fans who have caught historic home run baseballs in stadiums. The balls are taxable based on "fair market value."

Tax Savers for You

Greg Rosica, CPA, CFA, partner with Ernst & Young LLP in the private client services practice in Tampa. He is also a contributing author for the *EY Tax Guide 2016.* EY.com/eytaxguide

Planning now can reduce your tax bill for 2016 outright and—if you have overpaid income tax so far this year and are employed—let you scale back your wage withholding for the rest of the year instead of continuing to overpay and then waiting for a refund.

Estimating your year-end tax bill now is especially important because volatile investment markets could complicate the calculation of gains...the Affordable Care Act could add

---

DID YOU KNOW THAT...

Nearly Half of Americans Pay *No* Income Tax

More than 45% of American adults pay no income tax. That means 77.5 million US households owe nothing to the IRS—half because they have no taxable income, and half because they have tax breaks that eliminate their tax liability. The richest 20% of Americans pay 87% of all income tax collected by the IRS.

Tax Policy Center data for the 2015 tax year, reported at MarketWatch.com.

---

surprising charges to your tax bill...and the recent increases of the top capital gains rate to 20% and ordinary tax rate to 39.6% can make mistakes in tax projections extra costly.

Helpful: Use your 2015 tax return as your guide. It will remind you of items to focus on and may contain information that affects your 2016 planning. For instance, if you applied an overpayment in 2015 to this year's taxes, add it to your wage withholding and estimated taxes when figuring out whether you have already paid enough tax for 2016 so that you don't overpay again.

Special planning areas...

INVESTMENTS

The up-and-down investment markets of 2016 create potential tax savings in the form of unrealized gains and losses. *Here's how to use them...*

First, add up all your "realized" capital gains and losses—those that you've taken by cashing in investments this year or that your mutual funds have declared. Then look at the investment holdings still in your portfolio to find capital gains and losses that you could still take, which are "unrealized." Consider realizing additional losses before year-end to offset more of your taxable gains. Moreover, a net capital loss of up to $3,000 is deductible against ordinary income, such as wages.

Helpful: Under "wash-sale" rules, if you want to sell a stock or fund at a loss to offset investment gains and then buy the same stock or fund again, you must wait until at least 30 days pass. Or you can buy very similar but not identical securities at anytime. Also, because short-term gains and losses are fully counted in income, while tax-favored long-term gains and losses (on investments held over one year) are only partially counted, it is most efficient to take long-term losses to offset long-term gains and short-term losses against short-term gains. For more information on how the rules apply to particular investments, see IRS Publication 550, *Investment Income and Expenses*, available at IRS.gov.

TIMING INCOME AND DEDUCTIONS

Compare your tax bracket for this year with what you expect it to be next year. If your 2016 tax bracket will be higher or the two will be about the same, take as many deductions as possible this year while deferring income until after year-end.

If instead you expect your 2016 tax bracket to be significantly lower than that for 2017, consider the reverse—accelerating income into this year at the lower tax rate and saving some deductions for later when they will be more valuable.

Examples of timing possibilities…

•**Voluntary taxable withdrawals from IRAs** and other retirement plans can be taken before or after year-end.

•**Stock options,** US Savings Bonds and other investments can be cashed in before or after year-end.

•**State and local income and property taxes** are deductible in the year that they are paid. You can choose whether to make the payments that you still owe for 2016 before or after year-end, picking the year that's best for your federal return. Some states also allow you to prepay property taxes owed for 2017 during 2016. Check your state's rules.

•**If you have your own small business that you report on your personal tax return, you can time billing** and sending out invoices to receive income in the most opportune year…while timing payments made for supplies, equipment and various other expenses before or after year-end to deduct them in the best year.

158

TAKE NOTE…

Perks from Charities

Perks offered by charities may induce you to choose one over another—but can reduce the tax deduction you receive. An art museum may offer a tour of artists' studios for a donation of a certain size…service groups may offer meetings or conference calls with senior executives…environmental groups may provide perks such as backpacks, free conservation lectures, holiday cards, photographic prints and similar items… zoos may give personal tours that let donors interact with animals. The IRS reduces tax deductions based on value received in return, so if you want a full tax break, choose perks that are experience-based and hard to value…or ones the IRS considers insubstantial, such as a free mug or a tote bag.

Roundup of experts on charitable giving, reported in Money.com.

•**Charitable contributions** can be made before or after year-end.

MEDICAL DEDUCTIONS

Medical expenses are deductible only to the extent that they exceed 10% of adjusted gross income (AGI) or 7.5% on a return filed by a taxpayer age 65 or older, while miscellaneous itemized deductions are allowed only to the extent that their total exceeds 2% of AGI. (These include employee business expenses, investment expenses, legal fees and various other items.) Look at your total for each to see if it will be over the AGI threshold in 2016. If so, accelerate deductible expense payments into 2016. If not, defer as many as possible to help you get over the threshold in 2017.

Also, many employers offer medical benefit flexible spending accounts with "use it or lose it" provisions, meaning that the tax-favored contributions to the account are forfeited if the money is not spent by year-end. Some allow grace periods into the following year. Check with your plan's administrator.

AFFORDABLE CARE ACT

Under this law, if you fail to obtain required health-care insurance coverage, the penalty for 2016 is 2.5% of household income or $695 per adult, whichever is higher.

If you received a subsidy for health insurance that was too large because your final income in 2016 is more than you expected when obtaining insurance, you will have to make up the difference on your 2016 tax return.

These Taxpayers Fought the IRS—and Won!

James Glass, Esq., an attorney with 30 years of experience. He specializes in taxation and related matters.

These recent victories by taxpayers over the IRS highlight tax-saving strategies that you might use to reduce your own taxes…

•**Get a tax break on your "hobby" expenses.** Henry Metz owned and operated a baking business in Sioux City, Iowa, that he sold for a multimillion-dollar gain in 2000, after which he and his wife lived on the income from their investments.

Metz and his wife enjoyed raising Arabian horses and operated a breeding farm, which they moved from near their Sioux City home to Naples, Florida, in 1995, and then to the Santa Ynez Valley in California in 2003. From 1999 to 2009, the farm had losses averaging more than $1 million per year and totaling nearly $15 million, which the Metzes deducted against their overall income.

IRS Objection: Losses so large over so long a time indicated that the Metzes could not possibly have been operating the horse farm with a profit motive—it instead must be just a hobby that they were using as a tax shelter, so their losses were disallowed.

Tax Court Ruling: Many legitimate attempts to start a business never earn a profit, so a string of losses does not prove that a person does not intend to earn a profit. Instead, intent should be judged by how the activity is managed. The Metzes had a business plan that they revised as they gained experience. They kept good books and records, consulted with experts, invested in marketing their business, relocated their farm to improve its financial results and took other steps in an attempt to make it successful. All this indicated the required intent to earn a profit. Their intent may have been unrealistic—but long-shot attempts to start profitable businesses sometimes succeed. Since there was an intent to earn a profit, even though the attempt was unsuccessful, their loss deductions were allowed.

Lesson: A money-losing hobbylike sideline may later turn into a money-maker or even a second career, and you can take deductions for the initial losses, in effect using them as a subsidy for start-up costs, if you intend to make a profit from the activity. This can apply even to activities such as stamp collecting, composing music and auto racing, and you can deduct normal business-related expenses such as auto use, equipment costs, travel, meals and even a home office. But you must demonstrate a profit motive, which establishes the activity as a business, to be able to deduct any loss. The IRS and Tax Court can't read your mind to judge your intent, so they will judge it by whether you manage your sideline in a fully businesslike manner.

Henry J. Metz, Tax Court Memo 2015-54

•**A barking dog can produce a home office expense.** Denise McMillan was self-employed in the information technology business and worked from a home office located in a condominium unit in California that she owned and lived in.

McMillan was unhappy with the condominium's managing homeowner's association and filed a lawsuit against it. In the lawsuit, she complained about construction defects that caused mold in her bathroom and noise problems…and dogs running wild, barking and defecating around the property. Complicating matters, she ended up facing criminal misdemeanor charges as a result of her attempts to gain evidence for her lawsuit. The charges were dropped after she paid a total of $26,312 in legal costs, including $5,000 to a lawyer to defend her in the criminal case and $212 in sheriff's department and court costs. Because she treated half of her apartment as a home office, she deducted half of the $26,312 as a business expense.

IRS Objection: McMillan's lawsuit against the homeowner's association had no relation at all to her information technology business and involved entirely personal matters, so the related legal costs were not tax deductible.

Tax Court Ruling: The home office is a business property, and the IRS had not explained how the noise and other problems that McMillan had complained of would fail to affect her business use of it. Therefore, the expenses that she claimed were related to her business and the deductions she claimed were fully allowed—including her criminal defense fees.

Lesson: Having a home office may enable you to claim unexpected deductions for otherwise nondeductible personal home-ownership costs not directly related to your business but related to the part of your home used in the business. You also may be able to deduct a portion of the costs of insurance, maintenance, utilities and rent or depreciation on the home you own.

Denise Celeste McMillan, Tax Court Memo 2015-109

• **Unmarried individuals can take multiple maximum mortgage deductions on the same home.** Bruce Voss and Charles Sophy were unmarried domestic partners living in California. In 2006 and 2007, they jointly owned two homes, using one as a principal residence and the other as a second home. They were jointly liable for each of the two mortgages, which amounted to more than $2 million on the primary residence and $200,000 on the second home. Voss and Sophy each claimed deductions on interest for the maximum allowable mortgage amounts—$1 million on a mortgage for a principal residence plus $100,000 of home-equity borrowing, for a total of $2.2 million in mortgages.

IRS Objection: The deduction limit should be applied per residence, not per individual, so the deductions should be cut in half.

Tax Court Ruling: The Tax Court upheld the IRS interpretation of the law.

US Court of Appeals Ruling: The law allows the maximum deduction on a per-taxpayer basis, which means that multiples of the maximum mortgage deduction can be claimed on a single residence by unmarried separate taxpayers who jointly own it. However, married individuals are treated as a single taxpayer subject to the $1.1 million limit (or $550,000 for each spouse filing a separate return).

Lesson: There is no limit on the number of maximum mortgage interest deductions that can be claimed on a single home as long as the owners are not a married couple. If family members (other than a married couple), friends or even strangers buy a home, whether it is a primary residence or vacation home, that expands the overall allowable deduction amount.

Bruce H. Voss, US Court of Appeals for the Ninth Circuit, No. 12-73257

Surprising Medical Deductions

Lawrence K.Y. Pon, CPA/PFS, CFP of Pon & Associates, Redwood City, California. He is a US Tax Court practitioner, authorized to represent clients in Tax Court. LarryPonCPA.com

Family medical costs continue to increase, with more than half the respondents in a recent national survey reporting that medical costs "seriously" or "very much" impact their household budgets—and two-thirds saying they had been surprised by medical bills in the past 12 months.

But surprising tax deductions for medical expenses exist, too—ranging from big-dollar home improvements that help people deal with medical conditions to many small items that you might not expect to be deductible, such as clarinet lessons to help remedy a child's overbite.

Here's a guide to dozens of possible medical deductions—many of them surprising...

HOME IMPROVEMENTS AND MODIFICATIONS

A client of mine was able to deduct the cost of an elevator that he installed in his multistory house for $17,000 to help him go from floor to floor after a leg injury.

Deductions also have been allowed for…

•**Swimming pools,** when swimming is prescribed as medical treatment and no suitable public facility is available.

•**New siding on a home when old siding had become infested with mold,** contributing to a medical problem.

•**Central air-conditioning** to help a respiratory condition.

Operating and maintenance costs for such improvements are deductible, too, such as the service cost for maintaining a pool or elevator.

When an improvement increases the value of your home, the deductible amount is the improvement's cost minus the increase in value. So if a $20,000 expense increases your home's value by $5,000, the deductible amount is $15,000. Document any increase in value by obtaining an appraisal. The cost of the appraisal is deductible, too, not as a medical expense but among your miscellaneous itemized deductions.

Many home modifications are assumed by the IRS not to increase the value of a home and so are fully deductible when made to meet the needs of a family member with a limiting physical condition. *These may include…*

•**Relocating or modifying kitchen cabinets.**

•**Grading the ground around a house** to provide easier access.

•**Widening doorways and hallways.**

•**Installing railings and support bars** anywhere in the house.

•**Shifting the location of or otherwise altering electrical outlets and fixtures.**

VEHICLE MODIFICATIONS

Another client of mine was able to deduct $20,000 of changes made to a minivan to meet the needs of a family member with disabilities. Smaller modifications such as special hand controls or pedals to help deal with a physical disability also are deductible. If you buy a new vehicle customized to meet the physical needs of a family member, the extra cost over a standard model is deductible.

TRAVEL AND TRANSPORTATION

Local transportation to medical appointments and treatments is deductible, including the cost of transport by taxi, bus, train and car. And despite general IRS limits on long-distance travel deductions, you can deduct the cost of long-distance travel undertaken for medical reasons, such as travel to…

•**A doctor in a distant city who has special knowledge of your medical condition** or your medical history (such as your former doctor in a location from which you've moved).

•**A conference where you can find out about a condition** that afflicts you or a family member.

Ask for and keep receipts. If you drive your own car, you can deduct either your expenses for gas, oil changes and the like or, to keep things simple, 19 cents per mile (for 2016), plus parking and tolls. Lodging and meals generally are not deductible on such trips.

COSTS PAID FOR NONDEPENDENTS

You can, of course, deduct medical expenses for your dependents—and sometimes you can deduct costs paid for nondependents, too. *These include…*

•**People who do not qualify as your dependents** only because their income is too high (more than $4,050 in 2016).

Example: A retired parent who doesn't live with you but gets more than half of his/her support from you—such as when the parent is in a nursing home. Medical costs may be very high in such cases.

•**A child who is claimed as a dependent by your ex-spouse.**

Rule: When either divorced spouse claims a dependency exemption for a child, each spouse can deduct medical expenses that the spouse actually pays for the child.

INSURANCE

As health insurance costs continue to rise, make the most of deducting premiums. *Some examples…*

●**Health insurance premiums for self-employed people** are deductible to the extent that you have earned income.

●**Long-term-care insurance** is a defense against the risk of potentially huge costs for nursing home care. Premiums are deductible in an amount that rises with age—ranging in 2016 from $390 annually for people age 40 or younger to $4,870 for people over 70.

●**Medicare Part B and Part D premiums are deductible,** as are Medigap policy premiums.

Your share of premiums for an employer's group plan generally is not deductible because premiums usually are deducted from wages before taxes.

VARIOUS ADDITIONAL SURPRISING DEDUCTIONS

●**Medical services that are included in a tuition bill**—you may have to ask the school to itemize the bill.

●**Legal expenses necessary to obtain authorization for medical treatment.**

●**Equipment used to alleviate a medical condition,** such as portable air conditioners, humidifiers and dehumidifiers—and their operating cost. (It helps if the doctor is specific about brands and specifications.)

●**Service animals with special training** used to alleviate disabilities.

Examples: Cats trained to react to sound for the deaf...Seeing Eye dogs for the blind.

●**Weight-loss programs to remedy a specific medically diagnosed condition,** such as hypertension or diabetes (but not for simply being overweight).

●**A diet prescribed by a doctor** to the extent that its cost exceeds that of standard meals.

●**Fees paid to a note taker for a deaf person.**

●**The cost of a wig prescribed for mental health reasons** following hair loss due to disease.

●**A musical-instrument remedy,** such as clarinet lessons prescribed to help treat a child's dental bite problem.

●**Pregnancy test kits.**

TAKE NOTE...

How to Maximize Medical Deductions

Medical expenses are deductible on an itemized federal tax return to the extent that the total of these expenses exceeds 10% of adjusted gross income (AGI), or in 2016 only 7.5% of AGI for taxpayers age 65 or older and joint returns where the older spouse is 65 or older. So if a return reports $50,000 of AGI, expenses exceeding $5,000, or $3,750 for a taxpayer age 65 or older, are deductible.

By claiming all the deductions that you are entitled to—and timing them wisely—you can minimize your medical costs in after-tax dollars. Time a deduction by choosing to pay an expense before or after year-end.

Examples...

●**If you expect your medical expenses to be over the 10% of AGI limit** for the current year or next year but not both, you will want to take as many deductions as you can in that one year.

●**If you will be over the limit in consecutive years,** take as many deductions as you can in the year in which you expect to be in the highest tax bracket if that will vary between the two years.

Lawrence K.Y. Pon, CPA/PFS, CFP of Pon & Associates, Redwood City, California.

●**Batteries for hearing aids.**

You may discover new surprising deductions of your own for many activities incurred primarily for the "diagnosis, cure, mitigation, treatment or prevention" of disease or a medical or physical condition.

However, having a prescription or a doctor recommendation is not necessarily going to make any expense a medical expense. Vacations and pianos, for instance, sound dubious even if prescribed. The IRS may hire medical experts to review diagnoses and treatments. Don't get carried away or too creative.

For more on deductible and non-deductible expenses, see IRS Publication 502, *Medical and Dental Expenses*, at IRS.gov/pub/irs-pdf/p502.pdf.

5 Tax Mistakes for Widows and Widowers

Amy Wang, CPA, senior technical manager of tax advocacy with the American Institute of CPAs, an accounting industry professional organization that has more than 400,000 members, Washington, DC. AICPA.org

Taxes are not the first thing on someone's mind after the death of a spouse, but they are something that cannot be ignored for long. The recently widowed face special tax considerations, some of which may need to be dealt with well before the next tax-filing deadline.

Five things you need to know about taxes if your spouse recently passed away...or if you are helping a family member or friend whose spouse recently passed away...

●**You might face massive tax penalties if you don't withdraw money from your spouse's IRA by the end of the year.** If your spouse was age 70½ or older at the time of his/her death and had a tax-deferred retirement account, such as a traditional IRA, 401(k) or 403(b), your spouse was obliged to take a required minimum distribution (RMD) from the account each year. (This does not apply to Roth IRAs.) If your spouse had not yet taken the current year's required distribution in the year of his death, then the account's beneficiary—that's often the surviving spouse—must do so on his behalf. The tax penalty for not doing so is a staggering 50% of the amount that was supposed to be withdrawn. That means thousands of dollars could be lost.

Unfortunately, many surviving spouses are unaware of this requirement...uncertain whether the deceased partner made the withdrawal...and/or not aware that the deadline for this withdrawal is the end of the calendar year in which your spouse died, not the April 15 tax-filing deadline.

Exception: The deadine is extended to April 1 of the year following the year in which the account holder turns 70½.

The financial institution that holds your spouse's retirement account can help you determine whether RMDs are up-to-date and, if not, the size of the withdrawal required.

What to do: If the year-end deadline was missed, make the withdrawal as soon as possible. Then file IRS Form 5329, *Additional Taxes on Qualified Plans (Including IRAs) and Other Tax-Favored Accounts*, along with a brief letter explaining what happened and requesting a waiver of the penalty. The IRS sometimes will waive this penalty, particularly if the account owner died late in the year and the beneficiary makes the withdrawal early the following year.

●**You have just nine months to preserve your deceased spouse's estate tax exemption.** Estate tax law offers a way for surviving spouses to preserve their deceased spouses' estate tax exemptions. This essentially doubles the exemption available upon the second spouse's death from $5.45 million to $10.9 million. (These figures will increase in the years ahead to keep pace with inflation.)

But there's an often-overlooked deadline that must be met if you wish to do this—IRS Form 706, *United States Estate (and Generation-Skipping Transfer) Tax Return*, must be filed within nine months of the date of death. This nine-month deadline often lands before the next tax-filing deadline, so even people who work with professional tax preparers might not learn about it until it is too late.

Some widows and widowers don't bother preserving the exemption of the first spouse to die because the couple's combined estate is less than the basic current exemption. But that's a gamble—your assets could expand to exceed this exemption amount later.

Example: A man dies, leaving a $2 million estate to his wife. The wife does not bother preserving her husband's estate tax exemption—but she lives another 20 years, during which time the couple's assets climb in value to $8 million. Millions of dollars of the family's wealth face federal estate taxes of as much as 40% that could have been avoided by a one-time filing.

●**The timing of real estate sales can have major tax consequences following the death of a spouse.** Some widows and widowers find it emotionally difficult to sell the family home even when it makes little sense to live there alone. If the home's value has climbed significantly since you purchased it, there could be a tax reason not to wait too long. Married couples typically can exclude up to $500,000 of the profits from the sale of a principal residence from their capital gains taxes...while single people can exclude only up to $250,000. Unmarried widows and widowers still can qualify for the full $500,000 exclusion—but only if the home is sold within two years of the date of the spouse's death. Don't cut it too close to this two-year deadline—it might take months to find a buyer and weeks more for a home sale to close.

Other widows and widowers want to sell their homes quickly after the loss of their spouses because it is painful to live in their homes without their life partners...because they need the money...or because they cannot maintain the properties on their own. But selling too quickly sometimes can lead to unnecessary taxes, too. The capital gains tax exclusion can be claimed only if you have used the property as a primary residence for at least two of the past five years...and it has been at least two years since you last claimed this exclusion on the sale of a property. If you do not quite qualify under these rules, it might be worth delaying the sale until you do.

• **You still might qualify for joint tax rates during the years following your spouse's death.** Married couples who file their taxes jointly receive a higher standard tax deduction than single people, plus more favorable tax brackets and higher income limits on many tax deductions and credits. *The death of your spouse does not necessarily mean you no longer qualify...*

• Widows and widowers can file jointly for the year of the spouse's death even if the spouse died very early in the year.

• If there are one or more dependent children in your household, you can file as a "qualifying widow or widower" for two tax years beyond the year in which you were widowed, assuming that you have not remarried. (This provides the same rates and brackets as filing jointly.) After that, you might be eligible to file as a "head of household" if you still are support-ing a dependent. The tax brackets are not as favorable with head-of-household status as they are for qualifying widows and widowers, but they are better than for single filers.

• **You generally do not have to pay income taxes on life insurance benefits—with one exception.** If the insurer pays you interest on a policy's death benefits—say, because you agree to a deferred payout or an installment payout—that interest probably is taxable at your income tax rate. Ask your adviser or see IRS publication 525, *Taxable and Nontaxable Income*, for details.

How to Make Sure Your Will Doesn't Backfire

Robert Carlson, managing member of Carlson Wealth Advisors, LLC, Chantilly, Virginia, and chairman of the board of trustees of the Fairfax County (VA) Employees' Retirement System. Carlson is also editor and publisher of *Retirement Watch*, a monthly newsletter. Retirement Watch.com.

The playwright George Bernard Shaw bequeathed a small fortune to anyone who would create a new, improved alphabet. Portuguese aristocrat Luis Carlos de Noronha Cabral da Camara divided up his estate among 70 people selected at random from the Lisbon phone book. Hotel owner Leona Helmsley left $12 million to her dog. Talk about unusual wills that result in major complications.

Chances are your will is not quite as eccentric as any of these wills are. But what you may not realize is that even a seemingly minor detail hidden in your will could subvert your planning, resulting in an unexpected allocation of your assets or other unintended consequences.

To increase the odds that your hard-earned assets will end up where you want them to...

• **Work with an attorney who really tries to understand your situation before he/she attempts to write your will.** Some estate-planning attorneys try to fit nearly every client into a cookie-cutter estate plan rather than customizing documents to fit each client. The best way to make sure you choose a good attorney is to pay attention to how much time and effort a candidate spends trying to comprehend your situation before drafting any documents. Asking one or two quick questions about your assets is not enough.

Examples: The attorney should ask if all your heirs are good at handling money...how well they get along with one another...whether any of their marriages are struggling...whether any of them has major health problems or other special needs...and whether you have any particular goals in mind for your money, such as financing your grandchildren's college educations.

These detailed questions will make for a longer meeting and, possibly, a higher bill from the attorney—an extra 30 minutes of discussion might increase a lawyer's bill by perhaps $100 to $200—but it's an excellent way to determine whether this attorney intends to create a will that truly fits your situation, greatly increasing the odds that the will ends up doing what you intended it to do.

Strategy: If a friend (or relative) recommends an attorney, ask this friend how deeply the attorney dug into your friend's family and financial situation. Check whether you can have an initial consultation without a fee.

● **Outline your ideas before you meet with an attorney.** Many people don't put much thought into what they want their wills to do until they sit down in an attorney's office. That forces them to make decisions on the fly, increasing the odds of oversights and ill-considered choices. Thinking things through in advance can be a money saver, too—it means that you won't have to ponder every issue during a meeting with an attorney who likely bills by the hour.

Strategy: Several days before meeting with your attorney, jot down thoughts about which people and/or institutions you hope to leave your money to (include heirs and charities)... how you want your assets divided...concerns you have about any heirs' ability to handle money responsibly...and any conditions you might wish to place on any of these gifts.

BEWARE...

Tax Scam Alert

The IRS will start using private debt collectors to pursue unpaid taxes, which could lead to scams.

What to do: Never provide Social Security numbers or credit card details. The debt collectors are not authorized to take payments. Be especially suspicious if you did not receive an official letter about a debt beforehand. If you get a call, contact the IRS directly at 800-829-1040.

Adam Levin, JD, founder of the cyber-security company Identity Theft 911 and author of *Swiped*. IDT911.com

---

Do not delay this step until the day before the meeting or, worse, the day of the meeting. You want to give yourself time to reflect on what you've written.

● **Draft a will that avoids conflict among your children.** Rivalries and discord among grown siblings often flare up over a parent's will—even in families where the children have gotten along well in the past. The will forces adult children to confront three emotionally difficult topics—their finances...their childhood memories...and their own mortality—at a time when they already are dealing with the emotions surrounding the parent's death. Still, a properly constructed will can reduce the odds of running into these problems.

Strategy: Name someone other than one of your children as executor of your will. If you have more than one child, naming one of the children as executor sets this child apart from the others, inflaming resentments. Also, think up a distribution strategy for your personal possessions that is unquestionably equitable. This applies even to assets that have no monetary value.

Example: If all of your children have fond memories of your countertop cookie jar that they used to run to after school but you leave it to the child who happened to ask for it first, this simple cookie jar might become a source of family strife. Instead, you could set up a lottery in which each heir chooses from among your possessions in turn...or instruct your executor to sell off all of your personal possessions at an estate auction—your heirs can bid at the auction if they wish to.

• **Take extreme care with specific bequests you make.** Bequests—special listings in wills that name particular beneficiaries for specific items or assets—often lead to undesired outcomes. If an item listed among your bequests is sold or given away before you pass away, it could create confusion or conflict among your heirs. Rising or falling asset or estate values could make any particular bequest much more substantial—or less substantial—than you intended it to be.

Example: A man has a $1 million estate at the time he writes his will. In it, he leaves a bequest of $50,000 to a favorite niece, with the remainder divided among the man's three children. But living expenses, medical bills and investment losses reduce the value of this man's estate to just $100,000 by the time of his death. Because of the bequest, this niece now gets half of his estate, with his children sharing the other half, which is very far from what he intended.

Strategy: Avoid bequeathing specific dollar amounts if possible. If you do include them in your will, work with your attorney to create a formula that minimizes the odds that they will bring unintended consequences.

Example: Rather than leaving "$50,000," you might leave "$50,000 or 5% of my estate, whichever is less." Review your will periodically, and remove any bequests of possessions that you no longer own.

• **Know what won't be distributed by your will.** Your will probably won't determine who gets your share of jointly held property—that generally passes to the property's co-owner. It probably won't determine who receives assets from retirement accounts…US Savings Bonds that name a co-owner or beneficiary…proceeds of any life insurance policies—these generally pass to whomever is designated in the account, bond or policy.

Strategy: Review account beneficiary designations every year or two to confirm that these assets will be distributed according to your current wishes. Confirm that the overall distribution of your assets is what you intend

after jointly held property and beneficiary designations are taken into account.

• **Pay a second attorney to review your will.** This is a great way to catch potential problems. For most wills, it will take only an hour or two of an attorney's time to read the document and weigh in with any concerns. It's worth the price for the peace of mind.

Alternative: If you don't want to pay extra for a second opinion, hire a different attorney when the time comes to update your will. Wills should be reviewed and updated every few years and after any major family status change—a marriage…divorce…the death of a spouse…or birth of a child, for example. You would have had to pay your original attorney to do this update anyway, so you might as well hire someone different and turn that into a second opinion.

Posthumous Protection for Your Digital Assets

ConsumerReports.org

To protect your digital assets after you die, make a list—on paper—of all user names, passwords and other login access codes for all your physical devices and every website you use. Include answers to all secret questions that each site may require you to answer before changing a password. Designate a trusted third party—such as an attorney, executor or estate administrator—to handle digital material after your death, and have an estate attorney draw up a digital-assets power of attorney to authorize your designated third party to gain access to your devices and accounts. Keep the paper inventory in a safe-deposit box. Maintain a digital version to note changed passwords or new services, and store that version on an encrypted flash drive, transferring the data to the paper inventory as often as possible. Be sure to visit each website you use to find out if it has policies for a user's death, and follow those procedures.

Example: Google's Inactive Account Manager or Facebook Legacy Contact.

10

Investment Watch

5 Stocks Insiders Love... Maybe You Should, Too

There are plenty of reasons for investors to be scared now—or at least very cautious—ranging from disappointing economic growth in many parts of the world to the prospect of rising interest rates in the US.

But the investors who tend to be most knowledgeable about certain companies have been bullish on the stocks of some of those companies. Those investors—the corporate officers and directors known collectively as "insiders"—have been buying shares in their own companies' stocks. That could be a positive signal for small investors who wonder whether the market still has attractive opportunities or has become too pricey.

We asked Jonathan Moreland, who analyzes insider-buying and selling patterns in search of appealing stocks, to explain how investors can use these insights to choose investments, and which stocks look most appealing...

INSIDERS REALLY KNOW BEST

Insiders typically have the best understanding of a company's inner workings and long-term prospects. When they use their own money to buy company stock, it can be a valuable signal that the stock is undervalued and poised to rise.

Most investors don't track trades made by insiders because they assume that such trades are illegal. But insiders legally buy and sell stock in their own companies all the time. According to the Securities and Exchange Commission, a company's insiders are permitted to buy and sell its stock as long as the action is not based on specific information unavailable to the general public.

Jonathan Moreland, director of research at Insider Insights.com, which offers corporate-insider data and analytics to institutions and high-net-worth individuals. He is editor and publisher of *InsiderInsights*.

Of course, there are various times when insiders can't do this. For instance, a CEO can't sell all his shares just before the company releases a poor quarterly earnings report. Also, insiders are prevented from buying and then selling shares within a six-month period, and that means they tend to buy when they believe the company will perform well for longer periods of time. You can view recent insider trades and insider-trade track records for any company at my website, InsiderInsights.com (click on the Free Insider Data tab, and enter the ticker symbol in the search box). *How to analyze insider purchases...*

• **Make sure the purchases are "significant."** I'm most confident about a stock when I see that the most knowledgeable insiders at a company—the chief executive officer, chief financial officer and high-ranking board members—make purchases equal to 5% or more of what they already own. I also look for three or more insiders buying their company stock at the same time, which indicates a shared belief that the stock is undervalued...insiders with a successful track record in past purchases making new purchases...insiders using their own cash to buy stock rather than just exercising stock options that their companies have awarded them.

• **Check whether the stock is undervalued.** I never buy a stock based solely on insider data. There also must be attractive fundamental valuation measures, such as a low price-to-earnings ratio and steady or increasing earnings growth. I also look for a specific catalyst that can improve a company's earnings, such as an exciting new product, an acquisition, new management or a positive change in its industry.

• **Think small.** Smaller companies often have just a handful of insiders, which makes their purchases easier to track. These companies also attract little coverage from Wall Street analysts, which leaves more room for you to discover hidden opportunities.

MY FAVORITE INSIDER STOCKS

The following five stocks have had significant insider buying recently and have been selling at bargain prices relative to their potential for appreciation...

• **Agree Realty (ADC).** The stock price of this tiny real estate investment trust (REIT) has been dropping because of Wall Street's fears that rising interest rates will increase the cost for REITs to borrow money. While that's true, Agree's ability to raise its rental rates as the economy improves and its stock's recent 4.0% dividend yield* should attract investors. The company focuses on retail properties such as shopping centers whose tenants are resistant to Internet competition—for instance, mattress stores and fitness clubs.

Insider activity: Chairman Richard Agree and longtime director William Rubenfaer have increased holdings significantly since early in 2015.

Recent share price: $47.40.

• **Amgen (AMGN).** With sales of $19 billion annually, Amgen is one of the biggest biotech companies in the US. Its stock performance this year has lagged the industry because investors are concerned that its blockbuster drugs, such as Neupogen (for cancer) and Enbrel (rheumatoid arthritis), are facing heavy generic competition. Amgen insiders are betting that the launch of a new type of cholesterol-lowering drug, Repatha, will excite investors.

Insider activity: Although I typically prefer smaller companies, the insider stock buying here is convincing. Amgen's chairman, Robert Bradway, and several directors have substantially increased the overall amount of shares they own in 2016.

Recent share price: $171.97.

• **Avid Technology (AVID).** This is a technology pick for more aggressive investors. Avid provides software for filmmakers, studios and musicians to digitally edit video and audio content. Its products have helped create TV shows, songs and movies that have won Emmys, Grammys and Oscars. But the company stumbled in recent years, and in February 2014, its stock was delisted from the Nasdaq because the company failed to file timely fi-

*Rates and prices as of August 26, 2016.

nancial statements. Now insiders think that Avid, which was relisted in December 2014, is ripe for a turnaround. Its new product line is marketed toward the much larger, lower-end, nonprofessional market.

Insider activity: Most compelling is chairman Louis Hernandez Jr.'s buy of nearly $2 million in May 2016.

Recent share price: $9.31.

• **Cross Country Healthcare (CCRN).** This leader in health-care recruiting and staffing has approximately 4,000 contracts with hospitals to provide temporary and permanent nurses and physicians. The stock has returned five percentage points less than the Standard & Poor's 500 stock index over the past five years, but new management is planning to make acquisitions to increase market share in this fragmented industry.

Insider activity: CEO William Grubbs purchased $500,000 worth of stock over the past year and a half.

Recent share price: $12.21.

• **Sotheby's (BID).** The stock price of this global auctioneer of art, jewelry and other items has been sluggish the past few years. Even though art prices have soared, which benefits Sotheby's, the company has faced fierce competition and tighter profit margins, and Sotheby's has been heavily resistant to change. But a new CEO is aggressively pursuing opportunities, including auctions for collectors who aren't multimillionaires but still want investment-grade art...and licensing the renowned brand name for wider use in real estate.

Insider activity: CFO Michael Goss made a $1.4 million buy in May 2016.

Recent share price: $40.02.

WHEN A CEO SELLS, SHOULD YOU?

If insiders know the best time to buy their company stock, they also should have good instincts for when to sell. But I've found that selling is not a reliable predictor of where a stock's price is heading or whether you should avoid it or sell if you already own it. Insiders sell their shares for many legitimate reasons

---

MONEYMAKER...

Healthy Stocks

Stocks of firms with wellness programs significantly outperform the market as a whole. A portfolio of 26 public companies that won the C. Everett Koop award—which goes to firms that can document how their wellness programs improve health and save money—had 89% higher returns, on average, than the S&P 500 Index from 1999 to 2014. Companies on the list had to provide evidence that their employees did better on 10 health measures than similar workers at companies without wellness programs. Among companies on the list were once-troubled firms such as BP America, Dow Chemical, Citigroup and Fannie Mae.

Barron's, reporting on a study in Journal of Occupational and Environmental Medicine.

---

that have nothing to do with the stock being overvalued or about to drop in price. For example, they may need the cash for personal expenses or the sales might be part of planned programs to diversify their portfolios.

Exception: When a stock price is falling and multiple insiders start selling large amounts of their holdings, that often does send a strong signal that a stock has a grim future. If insiders don't believe the sell-off will be short-lived and the stock price will soon rebound, neither should you.

Examples: Stock in the cloud storage company Box, which lets you store your digital photos, documents and videos securely online, plunged by about 20% from May 2015 through early August 2015, accompanied by heavy selling from executives and investors who owned more than 10% of the total shares in the company. Scripps Networks Interactive, which owns the cable networks HGTV and Food Network fell by more than 40% from late 2014 through September 2015, while members of the Scripps family sold more than $50 million worth of their shares.

Great Stocks You Can Buy with a $10 Bill (Most Are Less Than $5)

Hilary Kramer, editor in chief of the three newsletters *GameChangers, Breakout Stocks Under $10* and *High Octane Trader.* Formerly, she was chief investment officer at a $5 billion global private equity fund. Based in New York City, she is author of *Ahead of the Curve: Nine Simple Ways to Create Wealth by Spotting Stock Trends.* GameChangers.InvestorPlace.com

After more than doubling in the past six years, do US stock markets still offer any screaming bargains? Yes!, says stock-picking expert Hilary Kramer. She says some of the best bargains are priced around $10 or less per share. The stocks are so cheap because many investors don't recognize how much profit potential the companies have… don't realize that they are managing to overcome setbacks that pushed their stock prices down so low…and/or fear that the stocks are just too risky.

Here is how Kramer finds the best stock bargains…and what some of her favorites are now…

HIDDEN GROWTH STOCKS

Despite the large amounts of financial information available, investors often don't realize the potential that some companies have for increased revenue and profits. This is especially true of companies with low-priced stocks, which tend to draw less interest from analysts. The companies often operate in industries that aren't very exciting or in market niches where the trend toward strong growth is not yet apparent. I look for companies that can achieve 15% annual growth in revenue over the next few years. *Examples…*

•**MGIC Investment Corp. (MTG)** is one of the leading private mortgage insurers in the US, issuing policies covering more than $165 billion in loans. Mortgage insurance enables borrowers to buy homes with low down payments by protecting lenders against losses in the event of defaults by borrowers. Many mortgage insurers, including MGIC, were crushed by the real estate meltdown that be-

gan in 2007. MGIC has slowly turned around its fortunes as the US housing market has rebounded. As one of the industry's few survivors, MGIC has been able to focus on writing policies for buyers with higher-quality credit.

Recent share price: $8.04.*

•**Lionbridge Technologies (LIOX),** based in Waltham, Massachusetts, provides translation services in more than 100 languages for companies and institutions around the world. Clients include Microsoft, Google, Pfizer, Samsung and the US Department of Homeland Security. Lionbridge's growth has been inconsistent over the past few years, held back by the weak global economy. But the company is finding ways to grow, including aggressively acquiring rival translation services. One of Lionbridge's fastest-growing divisions offers a sophisticated Internet translation service in which specialists tailor clients' online marketing and advertising programs to appeal to different cultures. That's in contrast to standard services that use automated software and that often are wildly inaccurate.

Recent share price: $4.85.

FALLEN ANGELS

For these formerly thriving companies, various misfortunes and declining revenues have dragged down stock prices. In some cases, the problems were caused by management gaffes…in others, their industries were in flux. These companies are addressing their problems effectively, and they have begun to resuscitate their businesses even though many investors still don't have faith in them. *Examples…*

•**Cincinnati Bell (CBB)** is a telecommunications company operating in the Cincinnati and Dayton metropolitan areas. Wall Street has written off the 142-year-old firm as part of a dying breed because it provides traditional land-based telephone lines, a market that is eroding because of competition from cable and wireless providers. What investors have overlooked is that for the past several years, the company has made a dramatic bet, selling off its data-storage and wireless-phone divisions in order to fund its transformation into

*Prices as of August 26, 2016.

a fiber-optic-cable communications provider. Fiber-optic cable transmits signals through thin strands of glass. It can offer homes and small businesses high-speed Internet that is 100 times faster than conventional copper cable lines. This transformation is starting to pay off. Cincinnati Bell's fiber-related business had $310 million in sales last year, about one-third of total sales. The company's fiber-optic network currently is available in only about 40% of its potential market, but that should double by the end of 2016.

Recent share price: $4.17.

•**Genworth Financial (GNW)** is a top US provider of long-term-care insurance, which is meant to protect customers against the high costs of nursing home or home-health-aide care. The stock has dropped 55% over the past year.

Reason: The unexpected surge in Alzheimer's and dementia cases among policyholders who bought coverage a decade or two ago left the company with staggering losses. But Genworth's management acted quickly to shore up cash reserves to cover future losses on these policies. The company has won approval for rate hikes on premiums for customers in 47 states, and it has tightened terms on new policies, limiting benefits to no more than three to five years. That should produce strong returns in the future.

Recent share price: $4.62.

TRASH-HEAP STOCKS

These are struggling companies that are so out-of-favor with investors that their price-to-book ratios are less than one. That means the physical assets of the business including cash, equipment, inventory and properties are worth more than the market value of the company's outstanding stock shares. Expectations for these companies are so low now that any bit of positive news could lift their share prices. This is the riskiest type of low-priced stock that I own, but stocks like these have been my biggest gainers over the years. *Examples...*

•**First Bancorp (FBP) is the second-largest bank in Puerto Rico,** operating nearly 150 branches and serving 600,000 customers in Puerto Rico, the Virgin Islands and south-ern Florida. Investors are rightfully wary of any company based in Puerto Rico, given the ongoing recession there and the island's struggle to avoid defaulting on its municipal debt. But First Bancorp is financially healthy and received a recent windfall when it took over the deposits and branches of its failed rival Doral Bank. Housing prices have stabilized in Puerto Rico, and the government has taken tough measures to reform its public pension plan, decrease expenses and jump-start the economy. Any improvement in real estate values and business conditions will drive up the bank's share price, which is nearly 50% below its three-year high.

Recent share price: $4.87.

Best Stocks for the Next Bear Market

Kelley Wright, chief investment officer at IQ Trends Private Client Asset Management, Carlsbad, California. Wright also is managing editor of *Investment Quality Trends*, which ranks among the top five investment newsletters for risk-adjusted performance over the past 25 years, according to *The Hulbert Financial Digest*. IQTrends.com

---

I s it time for stock investors to become more cautious? After all, the bull market, which is more than six years old now, has seen the Standard & Poor's 500 stock index more than triple—while over the past 60 years, previous bull markets have lasted an average of only about four years and seen gains averaging 137%.

Some financial analysts claim that once the Federal Reserve resumes raising interest rates, this bull market will come to an end and a bear market will begin, while others say interest rates and inflation will remain low enough—and the economy strong enough—that the bull will continue to push ahead.

Investment expert Kelley Wright says he can't predict exactly when a bear market will debut—but when we spoke with him recently, he told us that cautious investors should start shifting their stock portfolios into stocks that can limit declines in a downturn...or investors should at least identify those defensive stocks now. *We asked Wright to tell us how he picks great bear market stocks and to name his favorites...*

CHECK DIVIDENDS AND PAST PERFORMANCE

Investors are far better off sticking with their long-term allocations to stocks through bear markets rather than trying to jump out of the market to avoid downturns and then back in to catch the next big rally. That strategy rarely works because it is too hard to time the market. However, in rough times, you don't have to take unnecessary risks by investing in low-quality or aggressive growth stocks that are likely to suffer the worst losses. Over the past three decades, I have found that companies with certain characteristics can help protect your portfolio in bear markets. Their shares typically lose 30% to 50% less than the S&P 500, making it easier for investors to recover. *Look for...*

•**Large-cap blue chips in defensive sectors such as health care, consumer staples and discount retailing.** The best of these companies have long histories of earnings growth no matter what's going on in the economy or market.

•**Solid dividends payouts.** Since 1972, dividend payers in the S&P 500 have outperformed nonpayers by 12.5 percentage points, on average, in bear markets.

•**Strong relative performance in past bear markets,** including the bursting of the tech bubble from 2000 to 2002, when the S&P 500 lost 47%, and the 2007–2009 bear, when it fell 55%.

•**Cheap stock prices.** Many bear market stalwarts that I have relied on in the past, such as Johnson & Johnson and Clorox, have done so well recently that their stocks are overvalued. So they may not provide the same protection in a down market as in the past. I want blue chips that are selling cheaply, even if it means that the companies have some problems. That may seem counterintuitive for stocks that are supposed to hold up in a bear market, but it's OK as long as the companies' problems are short term and are being addressed by management.

SOME OF MY FAVORITES

If you can't accept the possibility that your stock holdings could lose one-third of their value in the next few years (the average drop in a bear market), consider selling your most aggressive and/or overvalued stocks now and moving into the following...

•**Wal-Mart Stores (WMT).** Low-cost retailers tend to thrive in uncertain economic times. And few competitors are able to undercut the prices at Walmart. The company is facing plenty of challenges right now, including sluggish growth and public criticism that it doesn't pay adequate wages. But new CEO Doug McMillon has agreed to raise wages for 500,000 employees, about 40% of the chain's US workforce, as a way to drive productivity. He also is moving into big cities and urban markets by creating hundreds of Walmart Neighborhood Markets, just one-fifth the size of its supercenters.

Recent yield: 2.8%.*

Past bear market performance: +7.4% in 2007–2009...–20% in 2000–2002.**

Recent share price: $71.14.

•**CVS Health (CVS).** The health-care industry has years of steady growth ahead of it, thanks to an aging population and wider US insurance coverage available due to the Affordable Care Act. Most investors think of CVS as a retail pharmacy chain, but it's taking major steps to become a full-service health-care provider. Recently, CVS rolled out Minute Clinics in more than 900 of its stores, where customers can see nurse practitioners for chronic conditions such as diabetes and high blood pressure. And the company has become the second-largest pharmacy benefits manager in the US, negotiating with drug companies and paying drug claims on behalf of private and government health plans.

Recent yield: 1.8%.

Past bear market performance: –38% in 2007–2009...–30% in 2000–2002.

Recent share price: $93.26.

*Rates and prices as of August 26, 2016.

**Performance for the bear markets covers January 4, 2000 to October 9, 2002 and October 9, 2007 to March 9, 2009.

• **The TJX Companies (TJX).** The largest off-price merchant for brand-name apparel and home goods in the US operates more than 3,400 stores (including some in Canada and Europe) under names including T.J. Maxx, Marshalls and HomeGoods. TJX's business has thrived even in recessions. When department stores and other traditional retailers struggle, TJX gains access to more designer-name clothing at better prices.

The result: Same-store sales have increased in every year but one during the past three decades.

Recent yield: 1.3%.

Past bear market performance: –25% in 2007–2009…+75% in 2000–2002.

Recent share price: $78.69.

• **Philip Morris International (PM).** Many investors are opposed to owning shares in a tobacco company, but for those who are interested, it is hard to ignore the stability of Philip Morris International, the world's largest cigarette manufacturer outside of China, with seven of the world's 15 top-selling brands, including Marlboro and L&M. For growth, Philip Morris relies largely on Asia, where its profits are expected to double to more than $10 billion by the year 2020. The company is struggling with the effects of the powerful US dollar right now. Since all its revenue comes from overseas, profits are translating into fewer US dollars. However, I don't see this as a major issue in a market decline, because bear markets typically are caused by falling corporate earnings and recessions, conditions in which the US dollar weakens.

Recent yield: 4.1%.

Past bear market performance: –31% in 2007–2009.

Recent share price: $99.10. (Philip Morris International was spun off from Altria—which sells Philip Morris brands in the US—as a separate company on March 28, 2008. From its inception date to the end of the 2007–2009 bear market, the stock fell 31%, compared with a decline of 48.5% for the S&P 500 over the same period.)

• **Union Pacific Corp.** (UNP). This is the largest publicly traded railroad in North America, hauling cargo ranging from coal to agricultural products to automobiles through 23 states. The company has few direct competitors and an enduring cost advantage over every other form of shipping, especially on cross-country hauls, and it performs a vital service to hundreds of industries even in weak economies. The company produces more than $3 billion a year in free cash flow and has paid stock dividends for 116 consecutive years.

Recent yield: 2.3%.

Past bear market performance: –41.6% in 2007–2009…+34% in 2000–2002.

Recent share price: $95.12.

GOOD TO KNOW...

Expect Smaller Stock Gains

Smaller stock gains are forecast for the coming decades. Average annual returns will likely be 6% to 8% for the next 10 to 30 years—down from the 10% average since 1926.

Reasons: The S&P 500 stock index, recently trading for 18 times estimated year-ahead earnings, likely will revert to the long-term ratio of 15 times earnings. Low inflation, likely around 2%, will push stock market returns down—inflation has averaged 3% a year since 1926 and has been responsible for almost three percentage points of market returns.

The Kiplinger Letter. Kiplinger.com

Surprising Help from Your Financial Adviser

Career advice: Discuss your financial goals and career priorities with a trusted adviser to help pin down what direction you want to go in—and how you can plan for retirement while pursuing career aims. *Relationship help*: An adviser can help you and your partner create a financial plan that you both agree on—and can offer you impartial guidance during money disagreements. *Help with difficult times in life*: An adviser can make it easier to deal with unexpected life changes, such as a layoff, by putting in place strategies to help you protect yourself financially while under stress.

Phil Simonides, CFP, group vice president at McAdam Financial Group in Washington, DC, writing at Kiplinger.com.

The LESS Is More Portfolio: Why Now Is the Time to Invest in a Focused Fund

Todd Rosenbluth, senior director overseeing mutual funds for S&P Capital IQ, which provides investment research and analytical tools to more than 4,000 investment banks, private-equity firms and financial-services clients, New York City. SPCapitalIQ.com

This is the right time for investors to focus on mutual funds that do "less"—meaning they invest in a relatively small number of stocks. That's the view of fund expert Todd Rosenbluth and many other investment strategists. *Here's why so-called "focused funds" are attractive now…*

THE BENEFITS OF CONCENTRATING

Most stock mutual fund managers create portfolios with many dozens or even hundreds of stocks with the aim of controlling volatility and avoiding disaster in case one stock or industry really craters. Overall, "active" fund managers (those who pick and choose stocks rather than just tracking an index) hold an average of 144 stocks in their fund portfolios and limit how much of the assets they devote to any single holding. But in many cases, that limits their ability to outperform the overall market.

This limitation may be acceptable at times when the overall market is achieving powerful gains, as it has for several years. When the market does great and you have invested in a fund that closely reflects the market, then you're going to do great, too (even if you slightly trail the market, as many active fund managers have done in recent years).

Actively managed funds often lag behind index funds. But as overall stock market gains slow down and bargains become scarcer, active managers have more room to outperform.

And the likely prospect of rising interest rates could provide an additional boost. In past periods when interest rates were rising, actively managed funds outperformed the S&P 500 by an average of more than three percentage points a year.

These trends can be especially beneficial to the daring managers who drastically limit the number of stocks that their funds bet on. Managers of focused funds invest only in stocks in which they have the greatest conviction. They do not have to dilute their fund portfolios for the sake of diversification.

These managers also can dig more deeply into the limited number of companies they focus on, gaining a better understanding of the management and finances. However, because focused funds rely more heavily on the stock-picking skills of their particular managers, you must evaluate the managers very carefully.

HOW TO CHOOSE A FUND

Before putting money into a focused fund, make sure that you are comfortable with the fund manager's strategy and that it has resulted in market-beating long-term returns.

Some focused funds hunt for deeply undervalued stocks, rarely buying or selling and often holding high levels of cash. Others aggressively trade in and out of growth stocks and leave little in cash. Neither approach is guaranteed to succeed, but it's important to understand the approach because it sheds light on how the fund performs at various times and how volatile it may be.

To benefit from a focused fund, you need to be patient and ready to stick with the fund for at least two years. These funds can be way out of sync with other funds and with the overall market for extended periods.

MY FAVORITE FOCUSED FUNDS

Some focused funds hold only a couple of dozen stocks, but to allow for more flexibility in creating this list, I have selected no-load funds that hold up to 45 stocks…that are highly ranked by my research firm, S&P Capital IQ, based on such factors as risk-adjusted performance…that are able to invest in multiple sectors of the market (which excludes single-sector funds)…that are open to new investors…and whose managers have well-defined strategies…

• **Ariel Appreciation (CAAPX).** Lead fund manager John Rogers invests like Warren Buffett invests. He looks for high-quality companies with strong brands that generate heavy cash flow. The fund can be very volatile because Rogers keeps two-thirds of the portfolio in mid- and small-cap stocks and is willing to put more than half of the assets in just a few sectors.

Number of stocks: 40.
Performance: 8.8%.*

• **Baron Partners (BPTRX).** This aggressive mid-cap growth-stock fund hunts for innovative companies in fast-growing areas of the economy that fund manager Ron Baron believes can double their share prices in the next five years. He keeps about 70% of the portfolio in 10 holdings.

Number of stocks: 26.
Performance: 8.0%.

• **Brown Advisory Growth Equity (BIAGX).** This large-cap growth-stock fund looks for companies with annualized earnings growth rates of at least 14% over five years, much greater than the long-term earnings growth rate of the S&P 500. Manager Kenneth Stuzin relies on what he calls "Darwinian Capitalism"—for every new stock the fund adds, an existing holding must be sold.

Number of stocks: 34.
Performance: 9.25%.

• **Hennessy Focus (HFCSX).** David Rainey and two other comanagers run one of the most compact portfolios of any focused fund. They look for undervalued growth stocks of companies of any size whose annual earnings they can reasonably predict for the next decade. The managers temper volatility by holding large amounts of cash in the fund (10% or more of assets).

Number of stocks: 21.
Performance: 10.3%.

• **Janus Forty (JDCRX).** Like many Janus funds, this large-cap growth fund focuses on

*Performance figures are annualized returns for the 10 years through August 26, 2016, as calculated by Morningstar, Inc. The number of stocks is based on the most recent fund company filings.

companies that are dominating and changing their industries through disruptive technologies, products and/or business models. But fund manager Douglas Rao also mixes in various troubled companies that are in turnaround mode as well as some foreign stocks. The result has been big ups and downs from year to year but strong long-term performance.

Number of stocks: 37.
Performance: 9.1%.

• **Nicholas Fund (NICSX).** Albert Nicholas has run this growth-stock fund for more than 40 years, beating the S&P 500 by an average of two percentage points a year. He avoids volatile sectors and seeks companies of various sizes with strong balance sheets that can grow steadily despite the ups and downs of the economy.

Number of stocks: 42.
Performance: 9.1%.

• **Parnassus Endeavor (PARWX).** A large-cap growth-stock fund, PARWX practices so-called socially responsible investing, excluding any stocks that derive significant revenue from tobacco, alcohol, gambling and weapons contracting. Manager Jerome Dodson also favors companies that treat workers well. He reasons that such companies are able to recruit and retain better employees and perform at higher levels than competitors in terms of innovation, productivity and profitability.

Number of stocks: 25.
Performance: 12.5%.

The Portfolio That Pays and Pays: Stocks for Income-Hungry Investors

Charles B. Carlson, CFA, CEO of Horizon Investment Services, a financial advisory firm in Hammond, Indiana, and Chicago. He is author of nine books, including *The Little Book of Big Dividends.* Horizon Investment.com

W hat's an income-hungry investor supposed to do? Banks are paying next to nothing on deposits. The yields on bonds are paltry, and as interest rates for new bonds rise over the next few years, existing bonds are expected to lose value.

Top investment expert Charles B. Carlson, CFA, says the solution is a portfolio of carefully chosen dividend-paying stocks. These stocks can provide a stream of income that historically has grown much faster than the annual rate of inflation. The trick, however, is to choose stocks whose share prices won't be severely hurt when interest rates rise and whose dividends will grow.

Here, Carlson tells how to incorporate dividend stocks into an income-producing portfolio and how to choose the right ones...

A PORTFOLIO STRATEGY

It's true that even the best dividend-paying stocks are riskier than high-quality bonds. You can't be sure that their share prices won't suffer setbacks. But if you are able to hold the shares for at least a few years, many of them are worth the moderate risk. Keep in mind that a high-quality company can continue to pay a predictable, growing dividend in good times and bad. That ability often is a strong sign that profits are rising and will continue to do so...and that the stock's total returns (dividends plus capital appreciation) over the next decade have a good chance of beating what high-quality bonds could provide.

Try to assemble a portfolio of dividend-paying stocks with an average yield higher than that of 10-year US Treasury bonds, which was recently around 1.68%. I'm not advocating that you abandon all your bonds, because they do provide more stability and certainty than stocks. You need to decide how much volatility you are comfortable with and then determine what mix of dividend-paying stocks and bonds you want in your income-centered portfolio. For example, some of my clients have income-centered portfolios that consist of as much as 60% in dividend-paying stocks and 40% in short- and intermediate-term bonds and cash.

If your portfolio doesn't produce enough income to fund your lifestyle in certain years, you can use a "total return" strategy to supplement your income. In addition to drawing on dividends and bond interest, the principal from maturing bonds can contribute to your income rather than being reinvested in new bonds. Also, you can sell shares of stock to meet your cash-flow needs.

HOW TO CHOOSE

Investors often focus too much on how high the yields on dividends are...

• **Don't be blinded by yield.** The highest-yielding stocks often are a dangerous bet for long-term investors because the yields tend to be unreliable. The stocks typically are from troubled companies whose yields have soared as their stock prices have been beaten down, usually for good reason. These companies may not have the cash to sustain their dividend payouts.

• **Focus on "dividend growers" instead.** I like to invest in a company that has increased dividends by at least 5% annually for the past five to 10 years and that has enough cash flow to maintain that pace for the foreseeable future. This tells me that it has strong business fundamentals that are able to support a stable, reliable payout each year and that it likely will increase the payout even if the share price is stagnant or falls for a number of years. In past periods of rising interest rates, large-cap stocks with growing dividends have, on average, outperformed the Standard & Poor's 500 stock index.

MY FAVORITE DIVIDEND STOCKS

Here are nine high-quality companies with attractively priced shares that meet my criteria listed above and that you could easily hold for the next decade or more. Recently, their yields averaged 3%, and overall they have been much less volatile than the S&P 500. Over time, I expect their total returns to keep pace with the performance of that stock index. I typically hold equal dollar amounts of each stock in the portfolio and rebalance once a year.

MASTER LIMITED PARTNERSHIPS (MLPs)

MLPs operate like regular corporations but distribute most of their cash flow to shareholders in exchange for tax-advantaged status...

• **Spectra Energy Partners (SEP)** has 22,000 miles of pipeline stretching from the Gulf Coast to the Marcellus Shale basin in Ohio and Pennsylvania.

Recent yield: 5.6%.*

Five-year annualized performance: 15.3%.**

• **Star Gas Partners (SGU)** is one of the nation's largest distributors of heating oil and propane. It serves customers in 16 states from Georgia to Maine.

Recent yield: 4.5%.

Performance: 16.2%.

UTILITIES

• **Atmos Energy (ATO)** distributes natural gas to three million customers in eight states with favorable regulatory environments for rate increases stretching from Colorado to Virginia.

Recent yield: 2.3%.

Performance: 20.3%.

• **Public Service Enterprise Group (PEG)** provides electricity to four million New Jersey customers and sells excess power to metro areas in and around New York City and Connecticut.

Recent yield: 3.8%.

Performance: 8.6%.

• **Scana Corp. (SCG)** generates and distributes electricity to 1.5 million customers in Georgia, North Carolina and South Carolina. To meet rising demand, it is building the first new nuclear power plant in the US in three decades.

Recent yield: 3.2%.

Performance: 15.7%.

FINANCIAL SERVICES

• **JPMorgan Chase (JPM)** is one of the most undervalued major banks. The stock was hurt by the company's billions of dollars in settlements for questionable mortgage underwriting and other issues. But its balance sheet is in excellent shape, and earnings from its massive branch network and its investment bank and asset-management operations continue to improve.

Recent yield: 2.7%.

Performance: 15.2%.

*Yields as of August 26, 2016.

**Performance figures are 10-year-annualized returns through August 26, 2016, unless otherwise noted.

BETTER WAY...

Trading Trick

Do not trade stocks when the market first opens. This is the most volatile time of the day, when the gap between what sellers want for shares (the ask price) and what buyers are offering (the bid) generally is much larger than it is as the day progresses. One survey found a bid-ask gap of 0.84 percentage points in the first minute of trading, but only 0.08 percentage points 15 minutes later and less than 0.03 percentage points in the final minutes of the trading day. The difference may be pennies per share, but it adds up if you trade often or buy and sell many stocks.

The smaller the gap, the less the chance of buying for too much or selling below the prevailing price. The tendency was especially harmful to small investors on the morning of August 24, 2015, when the market plummeted within the first six minutes of trading—and then half of the losses were erased within minutes after that.

The Wall Street Journal. WSJ.com

• **Wells Fargo (WFC),** the largest US bank in terms of deposits, will benefit greatly from interest rate increases, widening the margin between what it charges borrowers for loans and what it pays account holders for deposits.

Recent yield: 3.1%.

Performance: 17.3%.

COMMUNICATION SERVICES

• **Comcast Corp. (CMCSA)** is the largest operator in the cable-TV industry, serving 55 million households with video, phone and/or Internet access. The company's stock was hurt when its bid to merge with Time Warner Cable ended in the face of regulatory opposition. But investors should view that as a buying opportunity for a company that will continue to dominate its cable-TV markets, as well as create its own media content through its NBCUniversal operations, which include TV networks, theme parks and a film studio.

Recent yield: 1.6%.

Performance: 27.6%.

•**Apple (AAPL).** Even though the company waited until 2012 to reinstitute its dividends, the potential for dividend growth is enormous.

Recent yield: 2%.

Performance: 16%.

When a Stock Buyback Is *Not* a Good Sign

David Fried, president and CEO of Fried Asset Management, Pacific Palisades, California. He is also editor and publisher of *The Buyback Letter*, which has been on *The Hulbert Financial Digest*'s Honor Roll for six years in a row. BuybackLetter.com

---

When a company buys back lots of its own stock from shareholders, that's often a compelling reason to invest because it reduces the overall number of outstanding shares, thereby boosting earnings per share. And it's a signal that management believes the stock price will rise. In 2015, buybacks among S&P 500 companies totaled $569 billion, helping to sustain the aging bull market. But when a big buyback program is announced or executed, it doesn't always result in higher stock prices. *Before you consider any buyback as a reason to buy shares yourself, do the following…*

•**Wait for the company to actually start buying.** Nearly 25% of companies announcing a buyback program do not follow through, often because the business ends up not doing as well as had been expected. Sometimes companies reduce the level of buybacks, which means that you should reevaluate whether to invest.

•**Determine whether the buybacks will actually reduce total shares outstanding.** This isn't always the case.

Example: The wireless-communications-equipment supplier Qualcomm has spent more than $13 billion in buybacks over the past five years, but the number of outstanding shares has increased by 2% because the company has issued nearly 100 million new shares to management. To represent an investor advantage, buybacks should be large enough to reduce outstanding shares by at least 5%.

•**Do your own research.** Just the fact that a company is buying back shares doesn't make the stock a bargain or mean that the company has strong growth prospects. It may be buying back shares as a way to please shareholders and attract investors despite a disappointing financial outlook. And sometimes a company chooses to buy shares that turn out to be overpriced. Research the company thoroughly, including measures of the stock's valuation in relation to the company's outlook.

Generate Cash After Stocks Have Plunged

Paul Merriman, founder of Merriman LLC, a fee-only investment advisory firm in Seattle that manages $1.5 billion in client assets. He is author of the free e-book *101 Investment Decisions Guaranteed to Change Your Financial Future*. PaulMerriman.com

---

Many people depend on their investments not only for long-term gains but also as a steady source of cash. But when stock prices plunge—as they did in August 2015—selling off shares of stock to meet expenses starts to decimate your holdings at an alarming rate. I know investors who panicked during the August market plunge and dumped their riskiest holdings to raise cash. In doing so, they locked in steep losses so they could feel momentarily safer—but probably damaged their long-term portfolio returns unnecessarily.

Here is the four-step strategy I recommend for investors who find themselves forced to sell something right away…

1. Clean up your past mistakes. Most people own one or more investments that they probably should never have bought and that don't fit in with their goals…risk tolerance… and/or time horizon. This may include not only investments that may be too aggressive for you, such as gold, which can be very volatile...but also ones that may be too conservative, such as money-market funds. Determine which investments don't really fit in with your overall needs and sell those first.

2. Rebalance your long-term allocations. Sell from the portion of your portfolio that has grown large enough that it has exceeded your allocation targets. For more on determining stock and bond allocations, go to SEC.gov/investor/pubs/assetallocation.htm.

3. Determine whether each investment you currently own would be attractive to buy today. Too often, investors focus on whether an investment has had a big loss or a big gain since they bought it, rather than whether it's likely to do well in the future. If you wouldn't buy one of your current investments at its current value, that's a strong signal that it is a candidate for selling if you need cash.

4. Consider tax consequences last. Taxes should never be the dominant factor in choosing investments to sell, but they should not be ignored either. Consider how big a capital gain or capital loss would be generated by the sale of an investment in a taxable account. And consider whether it makes most sense to tap into a taxable account...a tax-deferred account such as a traditional IRA or 401(k)...or a Roth IRA or Roth 401(k), whose withdrawals are tax-free.

Keep in mind that selling stocks in a taxable account could mean paying taxes on capital gains at a rate that may be lower than your income tax rate, unless you have held the investment for just a year or less. Withdrawals from a traditional IRA or 401(k) are taxed at your ordinary income tax rate. And if you are younger than 59½, the IRS may charge you a 10% penalty for withdrawals from traditional and Roth IRAs unless you qualify for one of the exceptions that apply. Penalties also may apply for withdrawals from a 401(k).

For more details on tax consequences, go to IRS.gov and search for Publication 590-B for IRAs or 560 for 401(k)s.

GOOD TO KNOW...

Mutual Fund Smarts

Make regular "contact" with your mutual funds to ensure that your account is not deemed abandoned and turned over to your state as unclaimed property. States and mutual fund companies have different rules about what constitutes account abandonment. States used to require that mail sent to the owner be returned as undeliverable and the financial institution be unable to find the owner. But many states are finding easier ways to seize assets—even if mail gets to the account owner—by saying that the owner has not been in contact, however the state defines that.

Self-defense: Phone your mutual funds at least once a year...log onto a password-protected account...or stay in touch by e-mail or letter.

Caution: Automated deposits and withdrawals are not considered contact in many states.

Roundup of experts on state treatment of mutual fund investors, reported in *The Wall Street Journal*.

How to Check on Your Broker

Dan Brecher, JD, head of the securities and investment banking group in New York City at the law firm Scarinci Hollenbeck. He specializes in claims against brokerages. SH-Law.com

---

Although the new Labor Department fiduciary rule mandates that your financial adviser act in your best interest, it doesn't guarantee that he/she will be honest and/or competent. For greater assurance, check on your adviser's background.

Self-defense: Type your financial adviser's name and firm into the regulatory databases listed below to view his disciplinary records. The types of information shown include customer complaints, personal bankruptcies, unpaid tax liens and court judgments, disciplinary actions taken by regulators and employment terminations.

Negative information isn't always a serious concern. Pay particular attention to red flags such as complaints involving misappropriation of funds and "churning," which involves urging investors to buy and sell securities to generate commissions. Address any concerns you have with your broker and with his firm before you decide to move your money.

If your adviser is a broker: BrokerCheck. FINRA.org.

If your adviser is a certified financial planner: CFP.net.

If your adviser is an insurance agent: NAIC.org/state_web_map.htm links you to the Department of Insurance in your state, where you can find licensing and disciplinary records.

If your adviser is a registered investment adviser (RIA): AdviserInfo.sec.gov. RIAs already are required by the SEC to abide by fiduciary standards. Look for two documents under the adviser's name called Form ADV Parts 1 and 2, which contain the same kind of disciplinary information found in the databases above. RIAs also are required to give you these documents upon request. Firms that manage less than $25 million in assets are required to register with their state securities regulators and provide the same documents. Find links to your state regulator at NASAA.org.

Choosing Better Benchmarks

David John Marotta, CFP, president, Marotta Wealth Management, Charlottesville, Virginia. His website is MarottaOnMoney.com.

How is your investment portfolio doing? You might answer this question by comparing its returns to a popular stock market index such as the Standard & Poor's 500. For most investors, however, using the S&P 500 as a "benchmark" isn't appropriate and can lead to investment mistakes.

Reason: The index is dominated by large-cap US stocks, while many portfolios are, or should be, widely diversified. Your portfolio might include various asset classes such as small-cap and foreign stocks as well as bonds. Since US large-caps have outperformed most other asset classes over the past three years, it's likely that your own portfolio's performance has trailed that of the S&P 500, tempting you to adjust your asset allocations and/or investment choices.

A better way to judge your investment performance quickly and conveniently...

First, determine what percentage of your portfolio is in stocks, what percentage is in bonds and what period of time you are using to evaluate your returns.

As a benchmark for the stock portion of your portfolio, use an index more widely diversified than the S&P 500. The FTSE Global All Cap Index tracks 98% of the world's total investable stocks by market capitalization. For the bond portion, the Barclays US Aggregate Bond Index tracks most types of US government and corporate bonds. Both indexes can be easily found through a search engine.

If your portfolio has, for example, a 60% stock and 40% bond allocation, to evaluate its relative performance, choose a time period, multiply the performance of the FTSE index over that period by 60% and the performance of the Barclays index by 40%, and add the two results together. Although your portfolio may not be as diversified as these two indexes, using them likely gives you a more valid comparison than using the S&P 500.

11

More for Your Money

How to Shop Smarter Online

Acolleague recently ordered flowers over the phone from a very well-known seller. She purchased two arrangements, each listed at $36 plus a delivery fee. But when the sales rep totaled up her bill, it was higher than expected. The retailer was tacking on a "service fee" of $14 per arrangement ($28 total) on top of the delivery charge.

Sneaky fees are nothing new—banks, airlines and car dealers are masters of the sneaky fee. However, the rapid growth of Internet and phone-order shopping has increased our odds of encountering them.

The best way for Internet- and phone-based businesses to attract more buyers in this competitive environment is to advertise very low prices. But these companies often can't turn a profit by charging ultralow prices, so they

sometimes tack extra fees onto the final bill. "It's a huge problem," warns Edgar Dworsky, former Massachusetts assistant attorney general and founder of the consumer-protection website ConsumerWorld.org. "Companies are advertising one price and then adding fees that really should have been included in the basic price." When you buy online, double-check your order before confirming it. If an extra fee has been added, contact the company online or by phone before hitting "submit." That way, you can complain to a company rep who might be empowered to waive the charge. That flower company waived the service fee for my colleague. If the first person you contact can't help you, ask for a supervisor. If you're willing to walk away from the order, say you'll cancel it if the fee isn't waived—and then do it!

Note: Prices, rates and offers throughout this chapter and book are subject to change.

Edgar Dworsky, former Massachusetts assistant attorney general and founder of the consumer-protection websites, ConsumerWorld.org and MousePrint.org, reported by Karen Larson, editor, *Bottom Line Personal.*

Super Easy Discounts

Below are some easy-to-get discounts that often are overlooked...

●**Store receipts** often have coupons on the back. Invitations to take part in customer surveys also appear frequently on receipts—participants may get prizes or be entered in sweepstakes.

●**Ticket stubs** from sporting events and concerts often have coupons on the back.

●**Work discounts** may be available—your company or your spouse's company may have arrangements with cell phone providers, fitness clubs and other businesses.

●**Product packaging** sometimes has coupons printed on it.

●**Deal sites** such as Groupon and Living Social may offer special rewards for referring new members.

●**Check-in discounts** are available at some stores if you simply walk in and then check in via Facebook and other websites.

Cheapism.com

How to Save at Amazon

To save at Amazon.com—use the "Camelizer" browser extension, available for Chrome, Firefox and Safari. It shows an item's price history, and you can set up e-mail notifications when the item drops to a price that you have specified. Go to CamelCamelCamel.com/camelizer for more information.

This works for items you are not in a hurry to buy. If you need something immediately, scroll down to the middle of the product's Amazon page and look for a section called "Special Offers and Product Promotions"—visible only on computers, not with the mobile Amazon app, and available only for some products.

The-Gadgeteer.com

Price-Matching Rules

Price-matching rules vary widely at major retailers...

●**Amazon.com** matches prices on certain TVs and cell phones if you find lower prices at select retailers within 14 days of shipping. Best Buy matches local competitors, certain online stores, including Amazon, and its own online prices.

●**Home Depot and Lowe's** will beat local competitors' prices by 10%.

●**Staples** price-matches identical products from competitors, including online retailers, if you find a lower price within 14 days.

●**Target** price-matches any item in stock at its stores if you find a cheaper price within seven days or in a competitor's next weekly ad.

●**Walmart** matches any competitor's ad featuring a specific price for a specific item and honors competitors' buy-one-get-one-free offers if they include prices.

Roundup of experts on price-matching policies, reported at GoBankingRates.com.

Coupon Stacking

Redeem multiple online coupons at once at retail sites that allow coupon stacking.

Example: Redeem a coupon for 10% off and another for free shipping.

Sites where stacking is sometimes allowed: Banana Republic, Gap and Old Navy... CVS...Kohl's...Target...Victoria's Secret.

Try stacking at any site that does not state that it limits coupon-code use. Simply enter one coupon code at checkout and, after it is accepted, enter another. To find additional coupon codes—sometimes called promo codes—enter the retailer's name and "coupon code" or "promo code" into a search engine.

Roundup of experts on coupon-code use, reported at MoneyTalksNews.com.

When to Ask for a Discount…

Ask politely for a discount if your reasonable expectations as a consumer are not met.

Examples: You recieve shoddy service at a restaurant, such as food arriving cold or a server being rude…you get poor seats at an event…an item is mislabeled, such as a tool set promising 25 tools but containing only 23…something is a floor model—that means it is used and should be discounted.

You also should ask for a discount anytime you pay cash—merchants pay fees when consumers use credit cards, so cash buyers should request discounts…when an item is scratched or dented…when a seller is in a hurry—for example, when flea-market sellers are packing up at the end of the day…and when a store is closing or going out of business.

Money.com

Little-Known Ways to Save More at Costco

Here are six ways to save at Costco that you may not know about…

• **Get discounts even if you are not a member**—anyone can use the Costco pharmacy and take advantage of hearing and eye exams and immunization services, and nonmembers can buy alcohol in certain states.

• **Try the food court for an inexpensive lunch**—you can eat there without being a member.

• **Keep receipts**—Costco offers 30-day price protection and 90-day returns.

• **Consider booking a vacation through Costco Travel,** which offers flight and hotel packages, cruises, rental cars and more at low prices.

• **Check pricing codes**—prices ending in $0.97 have been marked down from original prices, which end in $0.99, and an asterisk in the upper right of the sign means the item will not be reordered.

• **Shop end-of-season deals**—large summer items are marked down before summer ends.

GoBankingRates.com

Products Worth Spending More On

• **House paint**—a $40 can may cover an area in one coat, while a $10 can may require multiple applications.

• **Blu-ray players**—a $20 one may last less than a year.

• **Vacuum cleaners**—a $50 model typically does not clean well.

• **Fire extinguishers**—for safety, it is worth spending $25 for a real one, rather than $7 for an aerosol can.

• **Black Friday tablets**—the ones sold for $79 right after Thanksgiving often fail in six months.

ConsumerReports.org

DID YOU KNOW THAT…
Outlets Aren't Always a Bargain…

Outlet prices often are higher than store prices. Traditional stores often run sales that bring prices below those charged at their own outlets.

Examples: Prices at regular American Eagle stores were recently lower than those at its outlet stores 43% of the time—on one weekend in Philadelphia, women's jeans cost 20% less at regular stores than similar jeans in outlets. And at one point, the cheapest sweater at Ann Taylor's traditional stores in Houston cost $10 less than the same $22.50 sweaters in its outlets.

Prices change and vary substantially by market and time of year.

The Wall Street Journal. WSJ.com

Key to Better Deals on Craigslist

For better deals, use these words to search on Craigslist...

• **Moving or end of lease** often connects you with low-price offers on lots of items because people who are moving may have to get rid of things fast.

• **Divorce** often means a seller is clearing out possessions because of bad memories or to avoid splitting everything with a former spouse—so prices tend to be low.

• **Everything must go** may connect you not only with individual sellers but also with stores and companies that are going out of business.

Kim Komando, host of The Kim Komando Show, *a weekly national radio program, writing in* USA Today.

Great Buys at Dollar Stores

Party supplies—they can cost 70% less than at other stores. *Gift bags and boxes and wrapping paper*—they cost two to three times less. *Greeting cards*—the fanciest ones may not be available, but selection is wide. *Reading glasses*—they are as good as the ones found elsewhere at much higher prices. *Hair accessories*—elastic bands, bobby pins, headbands, combs and brushes are all good buys. *Pregnancy tests*—these $1 tests are as accurate as ones selling for $10 to $15 in other stores. *Vases, bowls, mugs, glasses and dishes*—quality is as good as at other stores, and you do not have to buy sets.

Also worth considering: Storage containers, picture frames, bagged or boxed candy, socks, washcloths and dish towels.

Roundup of experts on bargain shopping, reported at DailyFinance.com.

Danger in New Clothes

Steven R. Feldman, MD, PhD, professor of dermatology at Wake Forest University School of Medicine and director of the university's Center for Dermatology Research, reported by Karen Larson, editor, *Bottom Line Personal*.

I have never bothered to wash new clothes before wearing them, but after talking to Steven R. Feldman, MD, PhD, I'm going to start.

Dr. Feldman is professor of dermatology at Wake Forest University School of Medicine and director of the university's Center for Dermatology Research. He pointed out that new clothes are not always unworn clothes—other shoppers might have tried them on in the store or even taken them home, then returned them. And that means these clothes can be infested with all sorts of things. Lice, scabies and bedbugs have been transferred this way, but Dr. Feldman points out that the likelihood is small.

What's more, dyes and resins that manufacturers sometimes apply to new clothing to give it a wrinkle-free or crisp finish can cause allergic reactions, potentially producing an itchy rash wherever a garment comes in contact with the skin. I have never exhibited these symptoms, but that doesn't guarantee I never will—different clothing manufacturers use different chemicals and concentrations.

So I will wash washable clothes. But what if the new clothes are dry-clean only, such as a wool jacket? I asked Dr. Feldman.

"Dry cleaning could get rid of infestations and some chemicals," said Dr. Feldman. "But it can introduce formaldehyde, another chemical that some people are allergic to." Even "organic" or "green" dry cleaners may be using chemicals that can cause allergic reactions. Put new clothes in a sealed plastic bag for two weeks. This won't get rid of chemicals, but it will kill bugs.

When Cotton Isn't Cotton...and Other Clothing Lies

Edgar Dworsky, former Massachusetts assistant attorney general and founder of the consumer-protection websites ConsumerWorld.org and MousePrint.org.

Clothing companies sometimes use confusing product names, hard-to-locate labels or even outright lies to make it difficult to tell what fabrics their garments actually are made from...

• **"Heavy cotton" and "ultra cotton" shirts** might not be 100% cotton. Clothing maker Gildan uses these names even for some shirts made from a cotton/polyester blend.

What to do: Search garments for a label indicating fiber content by percentage.

• **"Genuine leather" garments** and accessories may be made from low-quality leather, though the term "genuine" implies legitimacy and reliability. Garments labeled "bonded leather" are made from shredded scraps of leather and fiber, mixed with a bonding agent, and spread over a backing material. There also are many faux-leather products on the market that seem to be leather but actually are made from synthetic materials. If what you really want is high-quality traditional leather, look for the term "top-grain leather" or "full-grain leather" on products or labels. (Full-grain leather tends to be especially durable.)

• **"Cashmere" sweaters,** coats and other garments sometimes aren't cashmere at all—disreputable companies have been known to pass off fakes as the real thing. In 2014, for example, Italian authorities seized more than a million "cashmere" garments actually made from lower-end fibers—including rat fur.

What to do: Steer clear of cashmere garments made by obscure companies and sold at low-end stores.

• **"Fake fur" could be real fur.** It costs apparel makers less to buy real skins of certain animals, including rabbits, coyotes and raccoon dogs (a canine family member, but neither a dog nor a raccoon), than it does to manufacture very high-quality fake fur. As a result, "fake fake furs" secretly made from real animals turn up—even in stores such as Neiman Marcus and Nordstrom Rack.

What to do: Examine the tips of the fur's hairs—real animal hairs taper to a point, while fake fur generally does not.

Make Money on Clothing You Don't Want Anymore

Tradesy charges only 9% commission on clothes they sell, but sellers do a lot of the work. You take your own photos, describe the items, upload the pictures to the Tradesy website, set prices and ship to buyers using a Tradesy-supplied shipping kit. The site does not accept men's clothing.

DailyFinance.com

The Best Sunglasses for You

What those extra features on sunglasses do...

Polarized lenses reduce reflected glare—but can make it harder to see cell phone, ATM and dashboard displays. *Mirrored lenses* can be good for very bright conditions, but they

185

scratch easily. *Photochromic lenses* darken and lighten automatically—it takes about 30 seconds for them to darken in bright light and five minutes to lighten when you go indoors. (*Note:* Windshields block most UV rays, so the lenses typically won't get as dark inside a vehicle as they do outside.) *Gradient lenses* are darker at the top and lighter at the bottom—reducing light from the sky but letting you see the car dashboard and the horizon. *Ultra-impact-resistant* lenses may be helpful for people who play certain sports or are in certain occupations.

University of California, Berkeley Wellness Letter. BerkeleyWellness.com

---

TAKE NOTE...

Sunscreen Savvy

Sunscreens may not deliver the promised SPF. Eleven of 34 tested were below their stated SPF value by 16% to 70%. But some of the products that did deliver the promised SPF were among the lowest-cost ones, including Coppertone Water Babies SPF 50 lotion, Walmart's Equate Ultra Protection SPF 50 lotion and Banana Boat SunComfort SPF 50+.

ConsumerReports.org

Best Hose Nozzles and Sprinklers

Monica Hemingway, editor, of GardeningProducts Review.com, licensed arborist and a graduate of the School of Professional Horticulture at the New York Botanical Garden. She is based in Tuscon, Arizona.

H ose nozzles and sprinklers can have a big impact on how effectively you water your lawn...

BEST HOSE NOZZLES

• **Dial nozzles** typically have a pistol grip and a round, plastic rotating head that lets you choose from a variety of spray patterns—

they suit most people because they allow for many different types of watering.

Features to look for: At least six spray patterns, including cone, flat, flood, jet, mist and shower...and a heavy-duty metal screw that adjusts the grip tension when you spray water (plastic screws crack easily).

Recommended: Dramm 9-Pattern Revolver Spray Nozzle, $12.

• **Pistol-grip metal nozzles** with a single set spray pattern are best if you mainly do cleanup jobs such as rinsing walkways, decks and patios. These provide a more concentrated stream than the "jet" setting on dial nozzles, are less expensive and last longer because they have fewer moving parts. They also are easier to use than the traditional brass cylindrical single-stream nozzles that you adjust by twisting the end.

Features to look for: All-brass or die-cast zinc parts, because the water pressure creates so much wear and tear.

Recommended: Gilmour 573TF Zinc Pistol Grip Nozzle, $7.

• **Watering wands** are elongated nozzles that extend your reach for watering close-by-but-hard-to-reach spots such as hanging baskets.

Recommended: Dramm OneTouch Rain Wand, starting at $20.

Helpful: Mineral deposits can build up over time, making nozzles tough to unscrew from the hose. Smear petroleum jelly on the threads of the hose coupling before you screw on the nozzle.

BEST SPRINKLERS

• **For small lawns that are square or rectangular,** use an oscillating sprinkler that arcs water back and forth in a fan-shaped pattern.

Features to look for: A heavier metal base instead of a plastic one to prevent tipping...at least 15 spray jet holes to avoid gaps...easy adjustment settings to manage the degree of swing.

Recommended: Melnor Metal Oscillating Sprinkler, starting at $16.

• **For larger lawns and irregularly shaped areas,** get an impulse sprinkler. It shoots water in pulses and distributes it farther and more precisely than oscillating sprinklers.

Features to look for: All-metal design, which is more durable than plastic…a throw capability of at least a 100-foot diameter…a spike-shaped base to help keep the sprinkler in place and make it easy to install in hard soil.

Drawback: These require time to set up because you have to adjust levers and screws to set part- or full-circle operation, the fineness of the spray and the distance that the water is thrown. Consider buying several so that you can leave each one customized for different areas of your property.

Recommended: Melnor 9580 Metal Pulsating Sprinkler with Step Spike, $29.

Why You're Paying More for Contact Lenses

Clark Howard, host of *The Clark Howard Show*, a syndicated radio program about saving money. He also is a consumer reporter for Atlanta's WSB-TV. His latest book is *Clark Howard's Living Large for the Long Haul.* Howard.com

The four major contact lens makers—Alcon, Bausch & Lomb, CooperVision and Johnson & Johnson—have implemented "price floor" policies that block sellers from offering discounts on their most popular lenses. As a result, some consumers now must pay more than twice as much for their lenses as they did two years ago.

Lens manufacturers are setting these price floors to stop discounters such as Costco, 1-800 Contacts and Vision Direct from undercutting prices charged by eye doctors. The lens manufacturers are eager to please eye doctors because these doctors write prescriptions for specific brands of contacts, giving them power over which lenses are successful.

Several class-action lawsuits have been filed challenging the legality of contact lens price floors, but as of May 2016, most remain in effect. (Johnson & Johnson recently dropped its price floor policy, and Utah recently passed legislation designed to end lens price fixing for residents of that state.)

Two potential ways to save money…

• **Order lenses not covered by price-floor policies.** The manufacturers have set price floors on their most popular brands, but not on all of their brands. The brands not affected typically are not the latest offerings, but they should be perfectly fine for most people. Ask a lens discounter such as 1-800 Contacts (1800Contacts.com) or Costco which lenses they still can offer at a discount.

• **Buy lenses at Costco.** The manufacturers have agreed to let Costco provide gift cards worth 10% of the price of lenses to consumers affected by price-floor policies. Costco is not allowed to advertise these gift cards, and the cards cannot be used to purchase the contact lenses themselves.

Sample savings: 10% off $320 (one year's supply of Acuvue Oasys for Astigmatism) is $32.

Pillow Talk

Replace your synthetic pillow every two to three years…and a down or feather pillow every five to six years. An allergen-barrier cover can extend the life of a pillow by protecting it from sweat and dust mites. If you fold your synthetic pillow and it stays folded…or if you fluff your feather pillow and it does not return to a good height…it is time to replace it.

Editor's note: You can wash synthetic and down or feather pillows—not foam pillows—in your washer in warm water on the gentle cycle. But you should buy a new pillow when you fold the pillow in half and it doesn't spring back into shape.

Ana C. Krieger, MD, MPH, medical director, Center for Sleep Medicine at New York-Presbyterian/Weill Cornell Medical Center, New York City, reported in *The Wall Street Journal.*

For a Better Mattress...

What's the best mattress for someone with lots of aches and pains? It really comes down to individual comfort and preference. To find one that's right for you, lie on any mattress you're considering (in the position in which you will most likely be sleeping) for at least 10 to 15 minutes in the showroom. Does it give good back support? Do your knees feel comfortable when you lie on your side? Does it support your weight without sagging?

Helpful: Bring someone along. He/she can make sure your spine is straight if you tend to sleep on your side (if your hips hurt after lying on your side, the mattress is probably too firm)...and confirm that there's no gap between your lower back and the mattress if you sleep on your back (if someone can easily slide a hand under your lower back, the mattress is likely too firm).

William J. Lauretti, DC, associate professor of chiropractic clinical sciences, New York Chiropractic College, Seneca Falls, New York.

Top-Rated Grocery Chains

The highest-rated grocery chains in five different categories...

• **Freshest**—Wegmans was rated highest, followed by Publix and Raley's.

• **Cleanest**—Wegmans, followed by Publix and Trader Joe's.

• **Best bakeries**—Wegmans, then Publix.

• **Least expensive organics**—Trader Joe's, followed by Wegmans, Costco and Sprouts.

Grocery chains with the lowest scores for overall satisfaction were Walmart Supercenter, Waldbaum's and A&P.

Consumer Reports. ConsumerReports.org

Meat Lovers: No Need to Pay Up for Prime Rib

Stanley Lobel, partner of M. Lobel & Sons, which operates Lobel's Prime Meats, a butcher shop on Madison Avenue in New York City, and Lobel's of New York, which sells meat nationwide over the Internet. The Lobel family has been in the butchering business since the 1840s, and Stanley Lobel has worked for Lobel's since 1954. He is a Fellow of the Culinary Institute of America and is one of the authors of *Lobel's Meat Bible.* Lobels.com

Meat lovers don't have to spend a lot to enjoy a wonderful meal. Inexpensive cuts of beef, pork and chicken can be delicious, too—if you know how to select and prepare them. Some of the most delicious preparation options come from foreign cultures, where cuts of meat that are somewhat overlooked in the US receive more respect. *Here, three reasonably priced cuts of meat, plus a recipe for each...*

BEEF

Chuck steak costs 40% to 50% less than prime rib, yet it can be just as tender and delicious...if you buy the right piece of chuck. Simply ask your butcher to point out the "first cut" of chuck. This is the section of the chuck that was immediately next to the prime rib before the animal was butchered—and it has almost exactly the same flavor and texture as prime rib. It is wonderful grilled...in pot roast...in beef stew...and cut into strips for stir-fry.

Quick and easy preparation: Cut the steak into slices around one-quarter-inch thick, and season with salt and pepper. Heat a pan over very high heat, then cook the slices of meat for 30 to 40 seconds on each side.

BETTER WAY...

Best Way to Send Flowers

You will pay less and get a better bouquet of flowers if you order directly from a local florist near the recipient's home or office. According to a recent J.D. Power survey, one in five customers of the major online flower-delivery services reported a problem.

Kiplinger.com

BEEF, BLACK BEAN AND GINGER STIR-FRY

1 pound first-cut chuck steak, well-trimmed, sliced across the grain into strips ⅛-to-¼-inch thick

2 generous Tablespoons fermented black beans, rinsed (available in Asian grocery stores)

1 Tablespoon soy sauce

¼ cup chicken broth or beef stock

1 teaspoon kosher salt

1 teaspoon sugar

1 teaspoon Asian sesame oil

1 piece fresh ginger, around ½-inch long, crushed with skin on

3 Tablespoons peanut oil

2 teaspoons minced fresh ginger

2 large garlic cloves, minced

3 scallions, thinly sliced crosswise

2 teaspoons cornstarch dissolved in 1 Tablespoon cold water

Mash the black beans coarsely with a fork in a mixing bowl. Add the soy sauce, broth/stock, salt and sugar. Whisk until the solids dissolve, then whisk in the sesame oil and crushed ginger. Let sit for 30 minutes, then remove the ginger.

Heat a 14-inch wok or pan over high heat. Coat the cooking surface with the peanut oil. Add the minced ginger and garlic as soon as the oil begins to smoke. Stir for five to 10 seconds until fragrant, then arrange the steak slices in a single layer on the cooking surface. Let these cook undisturbed until lightly browned, perhaps 45 to 60 seconds. Add the scallions, and flip the beef slices to cook on the other side.

Add the ginger/bean sauce and dissolved cornstarch to the wok, stirring well. Cook, stirring regularly, for an additional minute or so, until the beef is cooked through and the sauce has thickened but still is somewhat fluid. Garnish with fresh cilantro, if desired. Serves two.

PORK

Picnic shoulder roast and Boston butt are delicious cuts from the shoulder of the pig. (Picnic shoulder roast is sometimes called upper-arm roast.) You can buy one large enough to feed four people for $10, much cheaper than a pork loin roast.

Easy preparation: Preheat the oven to 325°F. Use a pastry brush to spread a mixture of olive oil, garlic salt and pepper on the roast. Set it in a roasting pan, then roast until a meat thermometer shows an internal temperature of 160°F to 170°F, which should take around four-and-a-half hours.

CUBAN-STYLE ROAST PORK

1 6-to-8-lb. bone-in, skin-on pork picnic shoulder or Boston butt

2 large heads garlic, cloves peeled—1 head sliced, the other minced

1 teaspoon dried oregano

1 teaspoon dried thyme

2 teaspoons ground cumin seed

Finely grated zest of 1 orange

Finely grated zest of 1 lime

1½ teaspoons ground black pepper

2½ Tablespoons kosher salt

10 bay leaves—five ground, five whole

1 cup olive oil

1 medium onion, sliced

5 cups fresh orange juice

1½ cups fresh lime juice

In a mixing bowl, combine the sliced garlic, oregano, thyme, cumin seed, orange and lime zests, one teaspoon of the pepper, one-and-a-half tablespoons of the salt and the five bay leaves that have been ground or finely crumbled.

Heat one-half cup of the olive oil to a gentle simmer. Pour this over the mixing bowl ingredients. Transfer to a food processor, and process for around 30 seconds, until it forms a loose paste.

Use a sharp knife to score through the skin, fat and one-quarter inch of the flesh of the pork at one-and-a-half-inch intervals to form a diamond crisscross pattern across the entire skin side of the meat. Rub the mixture from the food processor all over the meat, working it into the slits. Place the pork in a dish, cover with foil, and leave to marinate in the refrigerator overnight.

Remove the pork from the fridge, and let it return to room temperature. Preheat the oven to 325°F. Place the pork skin-side down on a rack in a roasting pan, and roast for three hours, basting occasionally. Turn it skin-side up, and roast for another one-and-a-half to two-and-a-half hours, until the temperature at the middle is 160°F to 170°F. (Cover with foil if the pork is browning too quickly.)

While the meat is roasting, combine the remaining one-half cup of olive oil, the minced garlic and the five whole bay leaves in a small saucepan over medium heat. Simmer for around one minute, stirring occasionally, without browning the garlic. Stir in the onion…the remaining one tablespoon of kosher salt…and the remaining one-half teaspoon of freshly ground black pepper. Return to a simmer, and cook for another minute. Combine the orange and lime juices, then whisk the mixture from the small saucepan into this juice. Salt to taste.

Transfer the pork to a cutting board, and let rest for 45 minutes, then slice. Douse with a portion of the juice mixture, and serve the remaining juice mixture alongside. Serves six to eight.

CHICKEN

Chicken legs and thighs, the dark meat of the bird, are moister and more flavorful than the white meat—and less expensive. Keep the skin on and remove after cooking, if desired, to reduce the odds that the meat will dry out.

Quick and easy preparation: Butterfly the legs or thighs by running a knife along the bone, cutting through the meat and taking the bone out. Heat a pan over medium heat, then add a little olive oil. Cook the chicken for three to four minutes per side.

MALAYSIAN-SPICE FRIED CHICKEN

3 lbs. chicken thighs (16 to 18 pieces), cut in half along the bone
1 cup thinly sliced shallots
1 piece fresh ginger, around 1-inch long, peeled and thinly sliced
1 Tablespoon ground coriander seed
2 teaspoons each turmeric, cinnamon and ground fennel seed
1 teaspoon each ground cumin seed and ground black pepper

½ teaspoon cayenne pepper
¼ teaspoon ground cloves
1 Tablespoon kosher salt
2 Tablespoons sugar
½ cup unsweetened coconut milk
Peanut or vegetable oil, for frying
6 Tablespoons Worcestershire sauce
2 Tablespoons fresh lime juice
1 Tablespoon + 1 teaspoon soy sauce
1½ teaspoons powdered mustard
1 or more hot red chilis, thinly sliced

Use a food processor to make a paste from the shallots, ginger, coriander, turmeric, cinnamon, fennel, cumin, black pepper, cayenne pepper, cloves, salt and two teaspoons of the sugar. Add the coconut milk, and process to incorporate.

Place the chicken in a large bowl, and mix with this spice paste until the chicken is thoroughly covered. Refrigerate for three to 24 hours, then remove from the fridge and let sit at room temperature for around 45 minutes.

Fill a 12-inch, straight-sided skillet to a depth of one-half to one inch with peanut or vegetable oil. Bring the oil to 365°F over high heat. Preheat your oven to 200°F. Place half of the coated chicken pieces into the hot oil, skin-side down. Fry for four to five minutes, until the chicken is a deep reddish brown where the spice paste has adhered to it. Turn the chicken over, and cook for four minutes more or until cooked through.

Drain the chicken, and keep warm in the oven while frying the second batch.

Make a dipping sauce with Worcestershire sauce, lime juice, soy sauce, mustard, chili(s) and one tablespoon plus one teaspoon sugar. Serves four.

The Big Olive Oil Hoax

Janet Bond Brill, PhD, RDN, FAND, a registered dietitian nutritionist, a fellow of the Academy of Nutrition and Dietetics and a nationally recognized nutrition, health and fitness expert who specializes in cardiovascular disease prevention. Based in Allentown, Pennsylvania, Dr. Brill is author of *Blood Pressure DOWN* and *Prevent a Second Heart Attack*. DrJanet.com

---

Olive oil has long been among the top go-to items for a heart-healthy diet. But you need to be smart when shopping for this health food. There are now plenty of mislabeled olive oil products that have insufficient amounts of the ingredients that help keep your arteries clean...are cut with cheaper oils...contain chemical additives...and/or come from a country other than what's highlighted on the label. So, how do you know that the bottle of olive oil in your shopping cart is not some adulterated, inferior oil? *To avoid being tricked by these deceptive practices, here's what to look for when shopping for olive oil...*

• **Single country of origin.** An olive oil label may say that it is produced in a particular country when, in fact, it was only bottled there. For example, "Product of Italy" does not necessarily indicate that the olives are grown or pressed in Italy—only that it was bottled there. Look for the phrase "Produced and Bottled," which means that the oil is actually produced and bottled in the place of origin listed on the label. For olive oil with the very highest levels of anti-inflammatory plant chemicals known as polyphenols, look for these olive varieties: Coratina and Moraiolo from Italy...Cornicabra

and Picual from Spain...and Koroneiki from Greece.

• **Certification seals.** The following governing bodies guarantee that the oil has passed extensive quality checks, so look for a product that includes one of these seals to identify a trustworthy, authentic olive oil.

  • International Olive Council (IOC)
  • North American Olive Oil Association (NAOOA)
  • California Olive Oil Council (COOC)
  • Denominazione d'Origine Protetta (DOP)
  • Protected Designation of Origin (PDO)

• **"Extra virgin."** This term is given by governing bodies (see above) to only the purest and best of olive oils. With extra virgin, the oil is "cold pressed," which means that it has been extracted mechanically from the olives without the use of excess heat or chemicals—processes that would damage the fragile polyphenols. Extra virgin also has the most natural olive flavor, antioxidants, vitamins, minerals and other heart-healthy components of the ripe olive fruit. In general, extra-virgin oils have up to 10 times higher polyphenol content levels than lower-grade oils.

• **A dark bottle or can.** The anti-inflammatory plant chemicals in olive oil are fragile and highly susceptible to deterioration by light, heat and air. To keep the heart-healthy ingredients stable, buy olive oil in dark bottles or cans.

• **Expiration date.** Unlike fine wines, olive oil does not age well, so the fresher, the better. The expiration or "best-by" date should be no more than 18 months from the date of purchase. If the harvest date is given, it should be less than one year ago. To ensure freshness and the greatest health benefits, you should use olive oil as soon as possible after the container is opened.

• **Price.** A good olive oil is time-consuming to produce, so a quality product will cost up to $35 for a 17-ounce bottle. But if you want an olive oil that will help keep your ticker beating strong, it's worth it! You can find such olive oils online at OliveandGourmet.com or high-end specialty food stores.

Frozen Produce vs. Fresh

Lisa R. Young, PhD, RD, a nutritionist in private practice and an adjunct professor in the department of nutrition and food sciences at New York University in New York City, reported by Rebecca Shannonhouse, editor, *Bottom Line Health*.

Let's be honest. No matter how much you enjoy fresh fruits and veggies, you have to admit that they can be a bit of a hassle. They require frequent trips to the grocery store or farmers' market. Then there's the prepping. And the cost—have you checked the price of fresh berries lately?

Don't get me wrong. I love in-season produce, but I have also come to appreciate the ready-to-go bounty of frozen produce. Processed foods get a deservedly bad rap these days, but frozen fruits and veggies really are good—and good for you.

"There are a lot of great arguments for using frozen produce," says Lisa R. Young, PhD, RD, a nutritionist in private practice in New York City…

•**Locked-in nutrition.** Fresh produce is often picked early (so that it will look good when it reaches the store). But frozen produce is harvested at the peak of ripeness—when nutrient levels are highest. Studies have shown that some frozen produce has more vitamins than fresh.

•**Good price.** At my favorite discount store, organic frozen blueberries cost about $3.50 a pound—better, on average, than the price for fresh berries.

•**Superconvenient.** Frozen produce comes prepped and ready to go. You can go straight from the bag into a sauté pan or microwave dish—or into the blender for a "berry-good" smoothie.

Maybe it's time for experts to quit emphasizing "fresh" quite so much. The most healthful fruits and vegetables are the ones that we actually eat—and the freezer section sure makes it easier.

Everyday Items Not Worth Buying in Bulk

Canned vegetables—supermarket sales on small cans usually are better. *Cereal*—sale prices at supermarkets often are less per ounce than the price of large quantities. *Cooking oil*—it has a shelf life of about six months, so buying more may mean more goes bad. *Eggs* tend to cost less at supermarkets than at warehouse clubs and are good for only three to five weeks, so stocking up may not be a good idea. *Liquid bleach*—its shelf life is six months, so if you don't use much, small bottles are better buys. *Paper goods*—sales at supermarkets usually bring better prices than you get on big packages at warehouse clubs. *Produce*—some items cost more in bulk than in smaller quantities, and produce spoils quickly. *Soda*—supermarkets often sell it below cost to bring in customers. *Spices*—they lose flavor in about a year.

Kiplinger.com.

Stop Wasting Food…

Wasted food costs Americans about $640 a year per household. *Here's how to reduce waste…*

•**Do not throw away food based on sell-by dates**—those may show when an item is at peak quality, but it usually is good for a while afterward unless it smells bad or develops mold.

•**Cook at home on the weekend,** and eat leftovers for lunch at the start of the week—plan lunch and dinner dates for later weekdays.

•**To make herbs more useful,** cut them up and freeze them in ice-cube trays that have been filled halfway with water. Use the cubes in soups and stews.

•**Freeze meat, vegetables and fruits** before they go bad.

• **Avoid any recipe that calls for an ingredient that you don't expect to use again.**

USAToday.com

Easy Ways to Spend Less on Food and Drink

Make up double portions of dinners, and store one in the freezer to reheat on a busy night so that you're not tempted to order in. *Eat less meat*—use eggs and beans for protein. *Visit food blogs* such as "Smitten Kitchen" and "Cooking with Amy" for suggestions on low-cost recipes. *When making fish*, use less expensive varieties, such as tilapia, instead of costly salmon or tuna. *Make store-bought treats yourself*—hummus, for example, is easily made in a blender. *Buy appliances that encourage you not to go out for food and drinks*—such as a slow cooker and a coffee-maker.

Roundup of experts on frugal cooking, reported at USNews.com.

Don't Let Medical Bills Ruin You

Charles B. Inlander, a consumer advocate and health-care consultant based in Fogelsville, Pennsylvania. He was founding president of the nonprofit People's Medical Society, a consumer advocacy organization credited with key improvements in the quality of US health care, and is author or coauthor of more than 20 consumer-health books.

While it's a well-known fact that medical expenses are the number-one reason that people file for personal bankruptcy, one especially troubling recent study shows just how dire the consequences can be for one's health. According to this research, cancer patients who file for bankruptcy have a significantly higher risk of dying earlier than those who have less financial distress. Other studies show that people tend to not im-

prove or get sicker when they have personal financial problems.

What you may not know: Even if you are fully insured, with either private insurance, Medicare and/or Medicaid, the cost of premiums, deductibles, co-payments and noncovered services could put your financial well-being at great risk...even leading to bankruptcy. In most cases, however, there are ways to get the health care you need—without going broke. *Here's how...* *

• **Federally provided low-cost or free health care.** Let's say you need a checkup, dental care or a pricey prescription drug at little or no cost. You can get these services through a national network of health-care clinics administered by the federal Health Resources and Services Administration (HRSA), the prime agency responsible for helping uninsured, underinsured and medically vulnerable people with chronic and/or debilitating conditions get care based on their income.

To find a clinic near you: Go to HRSA.gov or call 877-464-4772.

• **Your local nonprofit hospital.** About 80% of US hospitals are nonprofit, and in order to retain their nonprofit status, they must provide a certain amount of charity care (the amount varies). That means nonprofit hospitals cannot deny you emergency room services or care for a serious illness if you cannot afford it. In addition, these hospitals have many free services such as nutrition counseling for diabetics and mental health counseling.

To learn what's available: Call hospitals in your area to find out which ones are nonprofit. Then check those hospitals' websites and/or call their social service departments and ask what they can do to meet your needs.

• **Free or low-cost medications.** Many new advanced medications that aren't available as generics can have monthly retail prices of up to $10,000 or more. Even with medication insurance, your co-pay may run up to 50% of that or more each month until you reach your insurance plan's out-of-pocket limits. What's more, many insurers don't include these high-

*Financial eligibility criteria may vary by program.

cost drugs on their list of covered medications. Fortunately, most major pharmaceutical companies have patient-assistance programs that can help by discounting the drug if you can't afford it…or even providing the medication for free.

For additional information: Search online to find out what company manufactures the drug you need, and check its website or call the company for more details. Not all of these drug programs are based on income.

• **Other ways to get help.** You may also qualify for non-health-related programs that will help offset medical costs. For example, most states have programs that will help pay your utility bills, mortgage or rent. If you need cash for medical bills and have equity in your house, you may qualify for a reverse mortgage.

For more details: Contact your local Area Agency on Aging.

Outsmart High Drug Costs

Rebecca Shannonhouse, editor, *Bottom Line Health*, Bottom Line Inc., 3 Landmark Square, Stamford, Connecticut 06901. BottomLineInc.com

Just when you thought that drug-company greed couldn't get any worse, entrepreneur Martin Shkreli smirked and grinned as he pled the Fifth when being grilled by lawmakers at a recent congressional hearing. Shkreli, as you may recall, became the human face of mind-bending drug prices when his previous company raised the price of a lifesaving toxoplasmosis medication from $13.50 to $750 per pill!

No one has to be reminded that even if you have insurance, your share of drug costs—in the form of high co-payments or deductibles—can add up to thousands of dollars a year.

A secret I wish everyone knew: Use the Internet before you order your prescription. The latest resource is a new online company called Blink Health, which offers steep discounts—with the added convenience of ordering and paying for your drugs online…all you do is pick them up at your local pharmacy. (Check first to make sure your drugstore participates.) *Other cost-saving sites:* GoodRx.com and NeedyMeds.org.

Another little-known fact: Pharmacies in the same town—and even in the same zip code—can charge wildly different prices. In one town, for example, a month's supply of the generic statin drug *atorvastatin* (Lipitor) cost $61 at Kroger and $196 at Kmart. At Blink Health, the same drug is priced less than $10. That's a huge savings.

Drug Discount Plans with No Annual Fee

Kroger offers hundreds of generic drugs at $4 for a 30-day supply or $10 for a 90-day supply. *Kmart's* plan charges $5 for a 30-day supply or $10 for 90 days on selected generics, with higher rates on others, and discounts some brand-name drugs by 20%. *Rite Aid* discounts many generics to $10 for a 30-day supply or $16 for 90 days…and discounts some brand-name drugs by 15%. *Walmart* offers generics for $4 for a 30-day supply and $10 for 90 days.

ConsumerReports.org

The Generic-Drug Rip-Off

David Belk, MD, a physician based in Alameda, California, specializing in internal medicine. He is founder of the *True Cost of Healthcare* blog, which provides information about health-care cost and billing issues. TrueCostofHealthCare.net

Using health insurance to fill a prescription for a generic drug could dramatically increase your out-of-pocket costs, particularly if you have not yet reached your policy's annual deductible. That is because people who use health insurance have to pay the price that the insurance company has set for the drug, and with generic drugs, these prices often are much higher than the prices you might pay when no insurance is used—sometimes hundreds of dollars higher for a 90-day supply.

Here's what happens behind the scenes: Many generic drugs cost pharmacies 10 cents a pill or less. A value-oriented pharmacy, such as those at Costco, Walmart and Kroger, or a reputable online pharmacy, such as GoodRx.com and HealthWarehouse.com, might charge as little as $4 for a 30-day supply or $10 for a 90-day supply—if you don't use insurance. What's more, even after you reach your deductible, many insurance policies require a co-pay that is higher than what these types of pharmacies charge for generic drugs.

Among the many widely used medications that can be purchased without insurance as generics for as little as $10 for a 90-day supply are the blood pressure drugs *atenolol, carvedilol, clonidine* and *furosemide*…blood-clot-prevention med *warfarin*…diabetes drugs *glimepiride, glipizide, glyburide* and *metformin*…cholesterol drug *lovastatin*…antibiotic *amoxicillin*…and pain medication *naproxen.*

What to do: When filling a prescription for a generic drug, check whether it's cheaper to fill the prescription without using your cover-age. Also, ask pharmacies whether they have a membership or rewards program that can further reduce the cost.

On the other hand, if you expect to spend a lot more than your deductible for medical costs in a given year, it might make sense to pay the higher prices so that you get past the deductible period more quickly. In some cases, depending on the specifics of your coverage, that might result in greater overall savings.

Why Buy When You Can Rent!

Did you know that you can rent college textbooks? *Well, you can…and many other helpful items as well…*

•**Smartphones**—look for short-term rentals at PhoneBum.com. The website offers many models for most carriers.

•**College textbooks**—CampusBookRentals.com rents texts, which must be returned after use to avoid a buyout fee. Students can save 50% to 85% versus the cost of buying a new or used textbook.

•**Drones**—multiple websites offer them for as little as $20/day.

•**Wearable technology**—Lumoid.com rents fitness trackers, such as Fitbit and Moov and other items.

•**Arcade equipment**—many firms rent it for company parties and special events, but a few, such as AllYouCanArcade.com in California, rent to individuals.

•**Miscellany**—HeyNay.com rents just about anything, including blenders, car hitches, patio chairs and more.

DailyFinance.com

Ways to Save on Apple Products

The Apple store will give a discount of up to 10% if you show that one of its products costs less at another physical store—but online merchants such as Amazon and eBay do not count. Student discounts on new computers are available year-round, not just during Apple's back-to-school promotion. Discounts also are available for educators, government employees and members of the military.

Caution: Third-party repairs of Apple devices may cost less, but they invalidate Apple's warranty—which could cost you more in the long run.

Kiplinger's Personal Finance. Kiplinger.com

Best Ways to Lower Your Cable Bill

To lower your cable bill, start by calling your provider and asking for a better rate—companies offer multiple rates to different kinds of customers, and you may be able to get a reduction. But if that fails, BillCutterz and BillFixers will negotiate with cable and satellite providers—as well as cell phone companies—to lower your costs. These companies typically collect 50% of the first year's savings as their fee. BillCutterz says it also negotiates gym memberships, landscaping, pest control, and alarm and security bills, saving customers an average of 30% or more. If you currently spend $100/month for TV service—$1,200/year—a 35% reduction would be $35/month or $420/year...saving you $210 the first year after payment of 50% to the negotiating company. Visit the firms' websites for details.

USNews.com

How to Go Solar Without Getting Burned: Save Big on Energy Bills

Bill Keith, president of SunRise Solar Inc., manufacturer of solar-powered attic fans, St. John, Indiana, and a founding member of the Indiana Renewable Energy Association. SunRiseSolar.net

These are sunny days for solar power. A decade ago, solar panels were still a rare sight outside the Sun Belt, but now they are popping up on residential rooftops across the US. A new solar power system was installed every 2.5 minutes, on average, in 2014, thanks in part to rapidly falling prices for the equipment. Trouble is, few home owners have any experience with solar power, leaving them vulnerable to costly mistakes.

Seven things you need to know before you get solar power...

YOUR POWER COMPANY MAY PENALIZE YOU

Some power companies now impose special fees and minimum charges on solar homes, in effect "taking back" some of the savings of having solar. Various other power companies are lobbying state officials for the right to do the same thing...or for the right to reduce the amount home owners earn when their solar systems feed electricity back into the nation's "power grid," something that happens when a home's solar panels provide more power than the home is using. (Most solar homes remain connected to the power grid.) The power companies complain that solar homes take advantage of the nation's electricity infrastructure without paying their fair share for its upkeep. But these new charges and related changes make owning a solar system less economically attractive.

Examples: An Arizona utility recently changed its fee structure in a way that could increase the monthly bills of customers who install solar systems by $50 a month on average. Wisconsin regulators have approved fees that will add more than $180 a year to the bill of a typical solar power customer.

What to do: To see whether this is a serious issue in your state, check websites of organizations that keep tabs on utility company efforts to increase solar bills. Utility Dive (UtilityDive.com, then select "Solar" from the Topics menu) is a good general site for news about the electricity industry...and the Database of State Incentives for Renewables & Efficiency (DSIREUSA.org, select your state, then scan for listings identified as "Regulatory Policy") is a great resource. These two lobbying groups cover regional news about solar legislation—Tell Utilities Solar Won't Be Killed (DontKillSolar.com)...and The Alliance for Solar Choice (AllianceforSolarChoice.com).

Don't install a solar system that produces more power than your home regularly uses. (Talk to your utility company for an estimate.) Home owners may do this to generate a profit by selling power to the grid, but homes with solar panels that generate more power than they consume on an ongoing basis are especially likely to be targeted by new rules designed to reduce their earnings potential.

DON'T INSTALL ON OLD ROOFING

If your roof must be replaced after solar panels are installed, you probably will have to pay $2,000 to $3,000 to have the panels temporarily removed and then put back in place after the new roof goes on.

What to do: If you have an older roof, replace it before solar panels are installed. If your roof is not new but still has a lot of years left in it, at least replace the section of roofing underneath where the panels will be installed. Replacing this section of roofing beforehand is very likely to save you money, compared with removing the solar panels to replace the roofing later, even though it means replacing something that still works. An experienced solar installer or roofer can help you evaluate your roof's condition. Make sure that the service contract you sign with a solar installer or solar leasing company includes coverage for repairs if water leaks in through the section of roof under the solar panels as a result of the installation.

DON'T DWELL ON CLIMATE

There's a common misconception that home solar power makes great economic sense in the Sun Belt but much less anywhere else. That reasoning places too much emphasis on sunlight. In fact, the amount of sunshine in your area often is less important than the cost of electricity in your region...and less important than the state and utility solar incentives available to you.

Example: A recent report by North Carolina State University researchers found that home owners in the New York and Boston metro areas stood to benefit the most from solar power, due largely to high electricity rates.

What to do: Give solar serious thought even if you live in a northern state if you are paying a high rate for electricity—the national average is around 13 cents per kilowatt hour (kWh). Check where your area ranks in the North Carolina State University report (enter "going solar in America" and "NC clean energy" into a search engine to find this report). Also visit DSIREUSA.org to see whether any significant state or local solar incentives are offered in your state.

DON'T LOSE THE TAX CREDIT

Home owners who have solar systems installed are eligible for a federal investment tax credit worth 30% of the cost of both parts and labor if the system is installed by December 31, 2019. After that, the credit shrinks to 22% for systems installed between 2020 and 2022. (If you lease a system, the leasing company gets the tax breaks.) The typical rooftop residential solar system costs around $20,000, so that's a savings of $6,000.

What to do: If you do plan to install a solar system eventually, do so before the credit is reduced. Do not put this off until late next summer, either—reliable solar system installers might be booked solid as home owners try to beat the deadline.

CONSIDER THE EFFECT ON THE HOME'S VALUE

Companies that lease solar systems make it sound as though you have nothing to lose—there are no upfront costs, and the amount you pay each month on the lease likely is less than you would have paid your local utility for the same amount of power. (The same goes for companies that offer solar "purchase power agreements," where solar panels are installed at no cost, then the home owner pays the solar company a lower rate than the local power company charges for the electricity provided.)

Unfortunately, you do have something to lose—if you try to sell your home during the 15- or 20-year length of your lease contract, you will have to find a buyer who is willing to assume that lease—and many prospective buyers won't want to do that. (Lease contracts usually do have an early payoff option, but the payoff terms tend to be unfavorable for home owners.)

What to do: Don't lease. If you want a solar system but cannot afford to pay for one out of pocket, investigate whether taking out a home-equity loan—or a "solar loan" available through some major solar installers—makes sense for you. If you qualify for reasonable loan terms, you are likely to come out ahead, in part because you will get the 30% tax credit if you act soon.

INVESTIGATE THE INSTALLER

There are lots of unqualified solar installers. Some point to their membership in the Solar Energy Industries Association (SEIA) to prove that they are experts—but anyone can become a member of SEIA simply by paying its dues.

What to do: Work only with installers who have at least five and preferably 10-plus years of experience installing solar systems...and who have been certified by the North American Board of Certified Energy Practitioners (at NABCEP.org). These installers have passed a challenging examination. Also, ask installers what brand of *inverter* they use. The inverter is the part of the system that converts the solar power to the 120-volt power used in the home. It's a good sign if an installer uses one of the sector's two most respected and established brands—Fronius or Sunny Boy. It's also fine if the installer recommends using solar collection panels that contain micro-inverters rather than use a single inverter for the entire system.

This new technology costs a bit more, but it's more efficient, particularly in cloudy areas.

TREES CAN HURT

Even trees that do not currently block solar panels could grow tall enough to do so during the 20 to 30 years that these panels are in use. Removing large trees can cost thousands of dollars.

What to do: Before you have solar panels installed, have an arborist or other tree-care professional evaluate the growth potential of any trees that could later block your sunlight. It might be wise to remove these trees now before they grow.

Who Needs a Lawyer? Pros and Cons of Do-It-Yourself Legal Forms

Steven J. Weisman, Esq., attorney and senior lecturer in the department of law, tax and financial planning at Bentley University in Waltham, Massachusetts. He is founder of the scam-information website Scamicide.com and author of *The Truth About Avoiding Scams*.

It can cost you thousands of dollars to have a lawyer draft your will or a divorce settlement. Even paperwork to rent out a property or to grant someone the power to make your health-care decisions can cost hundreds of dollars. You could save most or all of that money by downloading a form online and filling it out yourself. But there is, of course, a catch—if you make mistakes, the do-it-yourself (DIY) route can backfire in a big way.

Examples: Make a mistake with your will, and you might accidentally disinherit an heir. Make a mistake with a lease agreement, and you could set yourself up for a lawsuit from a tenant.

Filling out your own legal forms makes sense only when the odds are extremely high that you can do so correctly and/or the downside for making a mistake is very limited. *Here are some legal forms offered by DIY sites—and whether it's wise to use each of them...*

WHEN DIY TYPICALLY WORKS

Websites such as Nolo.com and LegalZoom.com sell DIY legal forms for modest amounts, and some forms can be found online for free. The following forms generally are so straightforward that the DIY option is unlikely to create problems.

•**Health-care proxy,** also called a *durable medical power of attorney for health care,* lets you appoint someone as a proxy to make health-care decisions on your behalf should you become unable to make them yourself. It's usually perfectly fine to fill out this form on your own because health-care proxies are best when they're simple—just name someone to act on your behalf and leave it at that. As long as the person is someone whose judgment you trust, your health-care proxy should be effective. Check whether you need a different form if you move to a different state.

Caution: Some people try to provide detailed instructions in their health-care proxies, explaining what should be done in specific medical situations. But these details are more likely to create problems than solve them—you cannot predict every potential medical situation, and if you explain what you want in certain situations but not others, it could have unwanted consequences. Your proxy might feel that he/she has to act according to the most similar situation that you describe (or someone might sue to force him to do so) even if this option is not appropriate for someone in your situation. It is reasonable to provide general guidelines to your proxy, but this need not be done in the health-care proxy document.

Helpful: If you do your health-care proxy on your own, include a *HIPAA release form,* too. This form grants your doctors permission to share details of your health condition with the person you named to act as your health-care proxy—details that this person needs to make intelligent decisions on your behalf.

•**Bill of sale** legally transfers ownership of a vehicle or some other piece of property. Assuming that the payment arrangement is straightforward, this should be a very simple form, so no attorney is needed. There are subtle differences in state laws that can come into play with the transfer of vehicles, however, so it's best to seek out a bill of sale that is designed specifically for use in your state. Enter "bill of sale" and your state's name into a search engine—you might discover that this form is available for free on the website of your state's department of motor vehicles.

•**Promissory note** is a legal agreement to pay a specified amount to a particular person (or to the bearer of the note) by a specified date. Promissory notes usually are fairly easy to complete without an attorney or even a notary.

WHEN DIY MIGHT BE OK

The following legal form might be easy to complete—but there are reasons why the DIY route might not be ideal for you…

•**Lease agreement** is a contract used by a landlord to rent out a home, apartment or other property.

Residential leases tend to be fairly easy to complete without an attorney, although you need to read them very carefully to understand your responsibilities. Unfortunately, it is not uncommon for leases to be challenged in court when tenants become dissatisfied, so many landlords conclude that it's worth paying an attorney to draft a lease agreement just to be safe. The attorney will almost certainly start with a standard form that can be completed in a matter of minutes, but certain sections of this form might have to be reviewed, modified or removed to make it appropriate for a specific lease.

Example: The section of the lease dealing with maintenance responsibilities often must be modified. This lays out which maintenance matters are the responsibility of the property owner and which are the responsibility of the person leasing the property. But an out-of-town property owner might reasonably need the lessee to accept additional maintenance responsibilities…or the leased property might have components that require maintenance beyond what is mentioned in the standard document.

Commercial leases, unlike residential ones, always require an attorney because they tend to be more complex, often are customized and will likely face close scrutiny by the tenant's attorney.

WHEN DIY IS TOO DANGEROUS

Wills, trusts, divorce settlements, powers of attorney and prenuptial agreements can be quite complicated—and they often should be complicated, especially because significant amounts of money and family relationships may be at stake. Hiring an attorney is recommended here—even if your estate is modest... your estate plan ideas are simple...or your divorce is amicable.

Still, DIY forms can serve a purpose even here. If you are willing to make the effort, go ahead and fill out these forms to the best of your ability (or use a DIY computer program such as *Quicken WillMaker*), then take the completed documents to an attorney for re-

view. Most attorneys are willing to review DIY legal forms.

Best-case scenario: Few or no changes to your draft will be required, and you will have to pay for only an hour or two of the attorney's time.

Worst case: The attorney will have to completely redo your documents. But even if this occurs, filling out the DIY forms will help you think through the issues.

4 Warning Signs of a Subpar Home Inspector

The inspector wants to work without you present—he/she should want you there so that you can learn about your home purchase. He is not licensed in your state—a possible issue if you live close to a state border, leading to a risk that the seller will say your repair request is invalid because the inspector was not licensed in the state. He does not clearly explain building codes—for instance, showing that a home was built to the correct code decades ago, even though today's codes are different. He tells you everything is fine—all homes have issues of some sort, and the job of an inspector is to find and report them.

Roundup of experts on home inspection, reported at USNews.com.

12

Retirement Guide

Turn Your Retirement Dreams into Reality

ome people dream of playing golf every day in retirement, while others plan to travel the world, work part-time, take up a hobby, see grandchildren or just relax. The trouble is, no matter what they envisioned, many retirees discover that it's very difficult to turn their dreams of retirement into a satisfying reality.

There are lots of reasons why the reality of your retirement might not match your dream. *But there also are many ways to improve things—if you know some important truths about retirement…*

•**Leisure activities must provide much more than just relaxation in retirement.** If you ask people who are not yet retired what they expect to do with their free time in retirement, many will say that they'll do the same types of things they currently do on weekends—but do them on weekdays, too. Many discover, however, that their weekend pastimes are much less satisfying as full-time pursuits.

Example: Golf or tennis might be very enjoyable and relaxing when you play once or twice a week during the years when you still are working, but it could begin to feel boring—or even stressful—if you play most days in retirement.

What to do: Engage in a variety of leisure activities that collectively supply the following six needs—relaxation…physical exercise…social interaction…intellectual stimulation…cultural enrichment…and creative expression. Yes, you actually should make a list of your

---

Joanne Waldman, director of training for Retirement Options, which certifies retirement coaches, and founder of New Perspective Coaching, a nationwide retirement-planning practice located in Chesterfield, Missouri. She is a professional certified coach (PCC), a board-certified coach (BCC), a licensed professional counselor and a certified gerontological counselor. RetirementOptions.com

leisure activities, and then write down which needs are met by each. If retired life ever starts to feel empty and unenjoyable, review this list…determine which of these six needs are missing from your retirement…then explore activities that fill this niche until you find one you enjoy.

Example: A retired entrepreneur who had no creative outlet in retirement discovered that he loved glassblowing.

•**The single best way to make your retirement better is to make someone else's life better.** If you're like most people, a career isn't just a way to earn a paycheck. It also provides purpose—your clients, coworkers, employees and/or employers depend on you. Life in retirement can feel empty without this sense that you are doing things that are useful to other people.

What to do: Consult…or take a part-time job in a field that interests you…or volunteer with a nonprofit organization. If you don't already have a favorite nonprofit, check whether your local library has a "community service directory" or some other list of local nonprofits. Leaf through this until you find a few that seem appealing, then arrange meetings with these groups or volunteer with different ones until you find one that makes you feel truly useful.

Examples: A retired teacher who had survived cancer found meaning by volunteering at a cancer education center. A former high-level executive who discovered that making children laugh made his life feel meaningful went to clown school and then volunteered to entertain at children's hospitals.

Alternatives: Feeling useful generally is the most effective way for retirees to find meaning in life, but it is not the only way. Some people find meaning in tracing their heritage—research your family tree and/or travel to places that have a connection to your family history or ethnicity. Other people find meaning in going back to school to study something of deep interest.

•**The retirement you're planning may not be the retirement your partner is planning.** Most people approaching retirement think that they are on the same page as their spouses when it comes to retirement plans. Many will discover how far from the truth that is. Spouses often have different ideas about when to retire…where to live during retirement…and/or how to spend time and money during retirement. That's true even when couples believe they have hashed these things out—because one or both partners might not have fully communicated priorities…or simply might have had a change of heart.

What to do: Do not just chat informally with your spouse about retirement—hold a retirement-planning meeting to put a plan down on paper. Don't be surprised if your spouse's ideas are different from your own, and try not to get angry. If certain differences cannot be immediately resolved, schedule additional meetings.

Example: A husband did not realize that his younger wife would not be ready to retire when he was, and he feared that he might be too old to travel by the time she concluded her career. The couple agreed that the wife would cut back on her work hours, providing sufficient time for travel, while the husband continued working part-time as a consultant. Then they set a full retirement date roughly halfway between the dates each originally had in mind.

•**Your dream retirement destination might not be so dreamy in reality.** Some people dream of retiring where it's warm… others of living near the kids and grandkids… or in an exciting city. But if your retirement destination is not somewhere you have spent lots of time in recent years, living there might be quite different from what you imagine.

Example: A retired couple dreamed of returning to their long-ago hometown in retirement—but they hadn't lived there in 30 years. When they moved back, they discovered the people they knew were gone and the town no longer felt like the home they remembered.

What to do: Rent homes in possible retirement destinations before finalizing a move there. If your goal is to live near your children or other family members, chat with them about their long-term plans—are they planning to stay where they currently live? If moving close to young grandchildren, consider whether you will enjoy being an always-on-call baby-sitter…and whether your grandkids are likely to have time for you as they get older.

•**You're not going to hear from your old work friends as much as you expect.** Loss of socialization is not just a problem for older retirees who cannot easily get out of the house. It's also a problem for recent retirees whose friends still are working. Office friends are particularly likely to lose touch with you.

What to do: Join new groups and form new friendships when you retire.

•**One more thing you are likely to lose in retirement—status.** You may have worked for decades to reach a respected position in your profession. When you leave that profession, it's natural to feel diminished. In fact, people who retire from management positions sometimes try to fill this void by treating their spouses like employees. They might not even realize they are doing it—and it really can strain a marriage.

GOOD TO KNOW...

Where to Retire That's *Not* Florida or Arizona...

Knoxville, Tennessee, home to the University of Tennessee, has a symphony orchestra, opera and art galleries. Two-bed, two-bath condos average $300,000. *Blacksburg, Virginia*, home of Virginia Tech, is in the Blue Ridge Mountains and features lots of sports and a new arts center. Homes of 2,500 square feet cost $300,000 to $350,000. *Bella Vista, Arkansas,* 30 minutes from Fayetteville, where the University of Arkansas is located, has minor league baseball as well as college sports and 126 holes of golf. Homes of 2,200 square feet go for about $192,000. And *Traverse City, Michigan*, has golf, boating, fishing, wineries and an annual cherry festival. Median price for a 1,700-square-foot non-waterfront home is $160,000.

Roundup of real estate agents and experts on retirement planning, reported in *USA Today*.

What to do: If you owned a small business, worked for a Fortune 500 company or simply would enjoy helping small-business owners succeed, volunteer with the nonprofit association SCORE, which helps owners of small businesses, and serve as a mentor. Or volunteer to take a leadership role on projects for nonprofit organizations.

•**Your travel plans might be cut short.** People who plan to travel extensively in retirement almost always travel much less than they expect—around half as much, on average. They discover that frequent travel is tiring…that health issues can make travel a challenge…and/or that travel is more expensive than they thought. For couples, retirement travel tends to decrease as soon as *either* partner grows disenchanted with it.

What to do: If you plan to spend much of your retirement traveling, develop some contingency plans, too.

Example: A wife became frustrated when her husband did not want to travel in retirement as much as the couple had anticipated. She solved this by taking trips with a group of female friends while her husband stayed home.

Retirement-Friendly Cities

These tax-friendly cities have low or no income tax and reasonable sales, personal-property and estate taxes, and they tend to have small-to-moderate-sized populations…

Granbury, Texas, 70 miles southwest of Dallas, population 9,052…Greeley, Colorado, 60 miles north of Denver, population 98,596…Lake Havasu City, Arizona, 200 miles northwest of Phoenix, population 53,103…Pensacola, Florida, far west on the Florida panhandle, population 53,068…Rome, Georgia, 70 miles northwest of Atlanta, population 35,997…San Juan Islands, Washington, 100 miles northwest of Seattle, population 16,015…Summerville, South Carolina, 25 miles northwest of Charleston, population 46,974…West Feliciana Parish,

Louisiana, 30 miles northwest of Baton Rouge, population 15,406.

Note: Be sure to consider climate, health care, proximity to family and availability of cultural and outdoor activities that are important to you—in addition to taxes and other costs—when choosing a retirement location.

Where to Retire. WheretoRetire.com

Less-Known Costs of Moving in Retirement

If you're planning to move to a southern state with little or no state income tax for retirement, there are several things to consider...

State residency laws require you to be there physically to say that you are a resident (or not be there to say that you are not a resident) for a specific number of days per year—and this must be documented. You may also have to change your address...mailing, voting and driving status...and establish local bank accounts. Additionally, states that are popular for not having income tax may have high property or sales taxes, which may increase your living expenses in the new home. Finally, there are emotional costs of a move, such as being far from family as well as creating a new network of health professionals for your medical needs.

MarketWatch.com

90 Is the New 70

Rebecca Shannonhouse, editor, *Bottom Line Health*, Bottom Line Inc., 3 Landmark Square, Stamford, Connecticut 06901. BottomLineInc.com

In the not-too-distant past, you might have thought that once you hit your 70s you were edging toward "old age." That's just not true anymore!

INTERESTING FINDING...

US Centenarians Are Living Even Longer

Death rates for Americans age 100 and older fell steadily between 2008 and 2014 (latest data available). There are more than 72,000 Americans who have celebrated 100 birthdays or more.

Study by researchers at US National Center for Health Statistics, Centers for Disease Control and Prevention, Atlanta, published in *NCHS Data Brief*.

Recently, I've been following the activities of some pretty amazing nonagenarians (people in their 90s).

Some of my favorites...

• **Betty White,** who continues to unleash verbal zingers, won her first Grammy at the age of 90.

• **Jimmy Carter,** who at age 92 recently helped build a house for Habitat for Humanity—while undergoing treatment for melanoma.

• **Evelyn M. Witkin,** age 95, a geneticist who recently won a Lasker Award for her research on DNA.

• **Tao Porchon-Lynch,** a 98-year-old master yoga teacher who still teaches!

• **Gloria Tramontin Struck,** a 91-year-old woman who has ridden a motorcycle for decades and aims to make a cross-country trek when she hits 100!

Life expectancy has been increasing in the US for quite some time.

Now: More than half of people born today will live to 100. And medical advances are only part of the reason. Research is uncovering some surprising secrets.

For example, even though a bit of extra weight is discouraged in middle age and younger, it's believed to be protective when you are in your 80s or older.

If you'd like to get an estimate of your life expectancy, use the calculator at Livingto100. com.

10 Tricks to Look 10 Years Younger!

Lauren Rothman, style and trend expert who has appeared on *Entertainment Tonight, CNN, E! News* and *ABC News,* among other news outlets. She is a style consultant for individuals and corporations in the greater Washington, DC, area and author of *Style Bible: What to Wear to Work.* StyleAuteur.com

Most of us want to look as youthful and vital on the outside as we feel on the inside. But without realizing it, we may be appearing older than we need to.

Here are 10 simple things you can do that will make you look younger…

CLOTHING AND ACCESSORIES

• **Cut back on the black.** Wearing all black is certainly stylish, but as you age, it can make dark circles under the eyes and facial wrinkles appear even more pronounced. It's better to wear bright colors, which instead convey a sense of youth and vibrancy. You don't have to cover yourself from head to toe in loud colors to accomplish this. Just add a dash of color, ideally near the face or neck where it will draw people's attention up toward your eyes. People are more likely to consider you as an individual—and less likely to judge you based on your age—if they make eye contact with you. A brightly colored scarf or necklace is a good choice for women…a brightly colored tie, pocket square or polo shirt for men.

Alternative: If you prefer to wear muted colors, not bright ones, at least replace black garments with navy, cranberry, charcoal, brown and olive.

• **Stop wearing worn garments.** Teens and 20-somethings can get away with wearing threadbare or vintage clothing. But when older people wear past-its-prime clothing, it makes them seem old and past their prime, too. Once an item of clothing goes out of style or starts to show wear, it's time to stop wearing it, at least in public.

• **Buy clothes that fit the body you have today.** Some people are so used to wearing clothes of a certain size that they go right on purchasing that size even as they age and their bodies change shape. Other people intentionally buy baggy clothing because they think it will hide the physical imperfections that inevitably come with age. In reality, wearing clothes that do not fit properly only calls additional attention to physical imperfections.

When you try on clothes in a store, take your usual size along with one size larger and one size smaller into the fitting room, then purchase whichever fits best, regardless of what size you thought you were. If you're not great at gauging fit, shop with a friend who knows a lot about clothes…or ask a store employee for assistance.

Also: Women should get a bra fitting—and purchase new bras if necessary—at least once a year. Women's bra sizes often change as they age.

• **Take a look at your eyeglasses.** These days, wire-frame glasses seem old and dated, which can make their wearers seem old and dated, too. Consider switching to more fashionable plastic frames, either black or colored. If that doesn't fit your personality, switch to rimless glasses.

Also: If you wear bifocals (or trifocals), try switching to progressive lenses. These serve the same purpose but without that line across the lens that often is associated with old age.

• **Avoid being too "matchy."** Carrying a handbag that matches one's shoes was once considered stylish. These days it is associated with older women—young women tend to prefer a more casual, unmatched look. If you own sweater sets, break them up.

• **Skip the turtleneck.** Some people think wearing a turtleneck will hide the sagging neck that often comes with age. But turtlenecks actually call attention to the portion of the saggy neck and jowls that still can be seen.

Instead, women should consider wearing V-necked or scoop-necked shirts that visually extend the length of the neck—then add a brightly colored necklace, scarf or high-collared jacket. Men should opt for collared shirts.

SKIN AND BODY

• **Apply sunscreen to your hands.** You probably already know that using sunscreen regularly on your face can help you look younger. The moisture in the sunscreen gives older, dry skin a moist, younger look, and the UV protection limits age spots and other skin damage that is associated with age.

Also, sunscreen prevents a deep-tan look, which appears old and out-of-touch in today's skin cancer–conscious society—a light tan is fine…too dark is dated.

What many people do not consider is that sunscreen should be applied to the backs of the hands in addition to the face. Wrinkled, dry, heavily tanned or age-spotted hands can make people appear old even if the skin on their faces still looks young. Spots on the hands are one of the first signs of aging.

Men who are losing their hair or are already bald should apply sunscreen to the scalp…or they can wear a baseball cap or a straw fedora, which are stylish and youthful options. Sunburn, flaking or overall redness will draw attention to your head and make you look old.

GOOD TO KNOW...

Better Brain-Building Activities

Retired adults age 75 and older who held demanding jobs that required strategic thinking, verbal skills and some advanced-level education scored higher on cognitive tests over an eight-year period than adults whose jobs did not.

Explanation: These skills use areas of the brain that build a cognitive reserve, which helps protect memory and thinking abilities.

Even if you didn't have this type of job, you can still develop cognitive skills after retirement by doing volunteer work that involves organization and planning.

Francisca S. Then, PhD, research fellow, Institute for Social Medicine, Occupational Health and Public Health, University of Leipzig, Germany.

Helpful: Recent research suggests that "broad spectrum" sunscreens that protect against UVA light, in addition to the UVB associated with sunburns, are particularly effective in combating the aging effects of the sun.

Also: Stay hydrated. Drinking eight eight-ounce glasses of water each day can help your skin maintain the moist, dewy glow that is associated with youth.

• **Strong arm yourself.** Toned arm muscles can help you look younger—but which muscles you should target varies by gender. Consider working with a trainer to learn the best exercises for you.

Women: Sagging biceps and triceps in the upper arm can make women look old. Exercising with dumbbells is the best way to tone these. Start with very light dumbbells if necessary—even two-pound weights can make a difference. Do bicep curls, hammer curls and tricep exercises several times a week.

Men: Broad shoulders help men continue to look young and powerful as they age. Bench presses and/or push-ups help here.

• **Stand up straight.** Hunching over makes people seem old and wizened. Sitting or standing with your back straight and your shoulders back conveys an air of youthful strength and confidence.

Tip: If you find it difficult to maintain proper posture, take a Pilates class. Pilates is an exercise regimen that focuses on core strength, which is crucial for good posture.

• **Trim facial hair.** Women should be on the lookout for long, stray hairs and pluck them.

Having a beard doesn't make a man look old—even if the beard is gray—but having an unkempt beard does. Trim your beard at least once a week, and shave your neck and around the other edges of the beard every day.

Also: Trim nose hair, ear hair and bushy eyebrows frequently. Excess hair in these areas doesn't just look sloppy, it is associated with old age. Ask your barber to trim your eyebrows when you get a haircut if you're not confident in your ability to trim your own brows properly.

More Older Americans Are Using Social Media

Social-media use tripled among those 65-plus since 2010. Now 35% of Americans age 65 or older report using social media—compared with only 11% in 2010. Among adults in that age group with Internet connections, 56% reported using Facebook in 2014, compared with 45% in 2013...and 10% said that they used Twitter, compared with 5% the year before.

Studies and analyses by Pew Research Center, reported at MarketWatch.com.

Better Sleep During Retirement...

Michael Breus, PhD, sleep specialist in private practice in Los Angeles and author of *The Power of When: Discover Your Chronotype*. TheSleepDoctor.com

It is very common for people to get "off schedule" when they begin retirement (for example, staying up all night and sleeping all day). But this can have some significant effects on their quality of sleep and overall health. Restorative sleep can help ward off anxiety, depression, weakened immunity, weight gain and even diabetes and heart disease.

In general, the most restorative overnight sleep begins before midnight. During sleep, 90-minute cycles of light, deep and dreaming sleep repeat four to six times overnight. The amount of time you spend in each stage of sleep changes as the night progresses. You spend more time in the lighter stages as the night begins and more time in the deep, restorative stages before awakening in the morning. People who go to bed very late may not spend enough time in the deeper sleep stages.

If your sleep schedule in retirement is out of whack, the best thing you can do is go to bed and wake up at the same time *every day*. Since you no longer have to wake up to get to work, you could create a new morning routine, such as meeting friends at the gym or a local coffee shop.

If you have trouble sticking to a sleep schedule, you should consult a sleep specialist. Some adults and teens who are unable to fall asleep until the wee hours of the morning suffer from a sleep disorder known as *delayed sleep phase syndrome*. A sleep specialist can help the patient reset his/her circadian rhythm with treatments such as light therapy and the hormone melatonin.

Debt Is Good! Unconventional Financial Advice for Retirees

Thomas J. Anderson, a wealth-management executive and author of *The Value of Debt in Retirement*. He is a certified investment management analyst and was named one of the top 1,200 financial advisers by *Barron's* in 2014. ValueofDebtinRetirement.com

The debt load for older Americans is growing bigger. According to the Employee Benefit Research Institute, about two-thirds of US households headed by someone age 55 or older had debt in 2013, up from about half in 1992. But that's not necessarily a bad thing, and in many cases, it may be a good thing.

Conventional wisdom holds that debt drags people down, especially approaching retirement or in retirement when monthly payments on loans might seem like a particular burden for people on fixed incomes. Of course, loans with high interest rates, such as credit card debt, should be paid down as soon as possible. But certain types of debt can be beneficial—assuming that a retiree understands the risks and takes certain precautions.

Two smart ways you might be able to put debt to very good use in your retirement...

KEEP THE MORTGAGE

Paying off a mortgage as you approach or enter retirement may seem like a positive step—but for many home owners, it can instead prove to be a negative move.

Reason: Paying off your mortgage reduces your liquidity. If you pay it off before you are required to, you may unnecessarily shrink the pool of assets that you have for other purposes. That might leave you in a more precarious—or at least restrictive—financial position than you realize. True, you could take out a home-equity line of credit (HELOC) and plan to borrow against the equity in your home if you ever need cash fast—but home equity sometimes dries up when it's needed most. Many lenders suddenly canceled or significantly reduced HELOCs during the last economic downturn, for example.

There also are potential tax disadvantages to paying off a mortgage and then, at some point, borrowing against the value of the home. While interest on a primary mortgage is almost always tax-deductible, the interest on a home-equity loan or line of credit sometimes is not. If you are subject to the Alternative Minimum Tax, for example, the money you borrow is deductible only if the money is spent on home improvements.

Furthermore, having a mortgage costs less than you might think, especially when you include tax breaks.

Consider this: Most mortgages have an interest rate of 3.5% to 5% these days. You might think that paying off the mortgage, and so no longer having to pay interest on it, is the equivalent of putting the same amount of money in an investment that generates the same amount of interest income. But the interest you pay on the mortgage is tax-deductible. As a result, if your mortgage rate is between 3.5% and 5%, you likely are paying just 2% to 3% on an after-tax basis, assuming that your federal tax bracket is 25% or higher and that you pay significant state income taxes.

Helpful: If your mortgage rate is above 5%, consider refinancing. If you still are working and expect to retire soon, try to refinance before you leave the workforce. That's because retirees often lack sufficient income to qualify for attractive mortgage terms.

Another tax advantage of keeping a mortgage: If you are not paying mortgage interest, there's a good chance it will not make sense for you to itemize your tax deductions—which means that you might not be able to deduct things such as gifts to charity and medical expenses either.

Exceptions: Paying down your mortgage could be a smart move if your mortgage rate is well above 5% and you do not qualify for attractive refinance terms…or if your rate is well above 5% and your mortgage balance is below $50,000—with small loan balances, refinancing does not provide enough upside to justify its fees and hassles.

BORROW AGAINST INVESTMENTS

Do you plan to buy an RV and roam the country in retirement? Or maybe you would like to take an entire summer and tour Europe. Most retirees would either dip into their savings to finance large expenses such as these or perhaps take out a bank loan (or, worse, use credit card debt). You might be better off obtaining a "securities-based loan" instead. This type of loan uses your investment portfolio as collateral.

Securities-based loans are similar to the better-known margin loans, but…

•**Unlike with margin loans,** the money borrowed can be used for purposes other than increasing your investments.

•**You might choose to obtain this type of loan from a financial institution** other than one that handles your investments, perhaps to get a better rate or because yours does not even offer it.

•**The interest rate can be very low—** sometimes just 2% to 4% on amounts above $500,000. With rates that low, retirees could reasonably conclude that they are better off taking out the loan rather than withdrawing money from their savings. As long as investments return more than the 2% to 4% paid on the loan, the borrower comes out ahead.

Financing a major purchase with a securities-based loan can help with tax planning—it might mean that you can put off selling those securities and being hit with a capital gains tax bill until a year in which you are in a lower tax bracket. It also preserves your financial flexibility—unlike most car loans and personal loans, these have no required monthly loan payments.

Helpful: Lenders frequently specify that securities-based loans not be used to purchase additional securities, but there's a way around this—use the loan to pay other expenses, then use the money you would have used to pay those expenses to purchase additional securities. But take care—borrowing money to increase the amount you invest also increases the amount you could lose.

Caution: Securities-based loans are subject to "collateral calls" similar to the margin calls you might face with margin loans. That means that if the value of the assets used as collateral falls significantly due to losses or withdrawals, the borrower might be required to quickly add cash or other assets to the account. If the borrower cannot do this, shares might be liquidated to cover the cost of the loan. The best way to avoid this risk is to borrow no more than half of the amount the lender says you can borrow based on the size and composition of your portfolio—ideally even less.

Beware Reverse-Mortgage Ads

Stacy Canan, deputy assistant director of the Consumer Financial Protection Bureau's Office for Older Americans, Washington, DC. ConsumerFinance.gov

Reverse mortgages allow home owners age 62 and older to borrow against the value of their homes without any repayment being required until they move out, sell the home or die. Unfortunately, some companies that offer reverse mortgages put confusing, incomplete or inaccurate statements in their ads, making these already complex financial instruments even more difficult to understand…

•**Ads often refer to reverse mortgages as "government-backed" or "government-insured."** The ads might cite government agencies such as the Federal Housing Ad-

ministration (FHA) or prominently feature US government symbols, creating the impression that reverse mortgages are a government program. In reality, reverse mortgages are offered by private companies, and consumers should proceed with great caution. The government's involvement is quite limited.

•**Ads often gloss over the fact that reverse mortgages are loans that charge interest and fees just like other loans.** Instead, these ads might make these mortgages seem like bank accounts—an asset you own that can be easily tapped. Some ads stress that reverse mortgages have no fixed monthly payments, fostering the impression that the home owner need not make any housing-related payments. In reality, the borrower must maintain the home in good repair and pay real estate taxes and insurance premiums.

•**Ads often refer to reverse mortgages as "tax-free."** This makes some consumers think that they won't have to pay property taxes. But "tax-free" just means income taxes are not due on money borrowed. That's not really much of a selling point—income taxes generally are not due on money received from other types of loans, either.

•**Ads often claim that "you can stay in your home as long as you want" or even that "you cannot lose your home."** In truth, you could lose your home if you fail to pay your property taxes or fail to comply with reverse-mortgage terms that might be buried in the contract's small print.

The 3-in-1 Retirement Portfolio: It Makes Your Money Last!

Robert Carlson, managing member of Carlson Wealth Advisors, LLC, Chantilly, Virginia, and chairman of the board of trustees of the Fairfax County (VA) Employees' Retirement System. He is editor and publisher of *Retirement Watch*, a monthly newsletter. RetirementWatch.com

Picking the best mix of mutual funds for your investment portfolio gets even trickier when you are near or in retirement.

Biggest challenge: You will stop having income (or much income) from a job. That means you need investments that will help generate income and withstand periods of sharp market losses. But you may also need to invest in a way that makes sure your assets keep growing enough to help see you through your entire retirement and offset the effects of inflation.

Retirement expert Robert Carlson says that what works is combining three mutual fund portfolios that he has designed and adjusting them over the course of your retirement. *Here's how his approach works…*

DON'T INVEST BACKWARDS

The biggest mistake that I see retirees make is that they *invest backwards.* They start by choosing funds that have delivered high yields and/or strong performance in the past, rather than starting by figuring out what their needs are now and for the future.

Smarter approach: Use my three-step process, described in detail below. You will start by assessing the major risks that you will face in retirement…then you will select a variety of funds that you can rely on to address those risks…and then you will decide how to allocate your assets among the different funds depending on your individual circumstances.

THE REAL RISKS YOU FACE

I have advised thousands of retirees, and most face the same three major financial risks—and you probably do, too…

Income risk: Your fund portfolio may not generate enough spending money. To estimate your retirement living expenses, use the cash-flow calculators at FinCalc.com, a website recommended by the American Association of Individual Investors.

Inflation risk: Your investment returns may not keep pace with the cost of living. Over time, the cash that you pull from your portfolio needs to increase if you are to maintain the same standard of living.

Longevity risk: You may outlive your assets. The average 65-year-old man can expect to live to more than 84 years old…the average 65-year-old woman to nearly 87 years old. That means that many of us will live even longer.

Solution: Don't think of your retirement assets as one overall portfolio, as most people do. Instead, think of your assets as divided into three separate portfolios, with each designed to address one of the three risks. *Here are the three portfolios of no-load mutual funds that let you do this…*

RETIREMENT PAYCHECK PORTFOLIO

This portfolio typically generates a 5%-to-6% annual yield without much risk of large drops in value (principal). The funds have different approaches to generating income, which include investing in dividend-paying stocks…preferred securities, which are stocks with some bondlike qualities including high fixed dividends…and master limited partnerships (MLPs), which trade like ordinary stocks but distribute most of their taxable income to shareholders annually in a form similar to dividends. *Current allocations…*

•**40% in DoubleLine Total Return Bond (DLTNX)**—which is an intermediate-term fixed-income fund that focuses on mortgage-related bonds.

•**20% in DNP Select Income (DNP)**—a closed-end fund that invests in utility stocks and master limited partnerships.

•**10% in Cohen & Steers Global Income Builder (INB)**—a closed-end fund with five types of investments, which include large-cap stocks and other closed-end funds.

•**10% in Cohen & Steers Infrastructure (UTF)**—a closed-end fund that invests in dividend-paying stocks of airports, railroads and telecom firms.

•**10% in Cohen & Steers Preferred Securities & Income (CPRRX)**—invests in preferred securities.

•**10% in Eaton Vance Municipal Bond II (EIV)**—a closed-end fund that owns long-term tax-exempt bonds.

Important: Most of the funds in this portfolio will be able to weather expected mild increases in short-term interest rates by the Federal Reserve. But some of these investments, such as the DNP and Eaton Vance funds, are more interest rate–sensitive. When it seems that the Fed is close to raising rates, I will drop those funds and shift to other investments less likely to be hurt by rising rates, perhaps MLPs and short-term bond funds.

INCOME/GROWTH PORTFOLIO

This portfolio provides less income (it yields about 3% annually) but more growth. About 40% of the portfolio is in stocks, but there also is exposure to investments that can do well in inflationary periods, including commodities. *Current allocations…*

TAKE NOTE...

Putting the Portfolios Together

Here is how any retiree (or near retiree) can decide how to use the retirement portfolios described in the main article…

•**Most retirees will need a combination of the portfolios.** While there is significant overlap in the kinds of funds held in my three portfolios, that's OK because each separate portfolio works to address a particular risk that retirees face. The percentage of overall assets that you allocate to each will depend on several factors—the size of your nest egg…when and how much you will need to withdraw annually to meet living expenses…your risk tolerance…and how much income you receive from such sources as Social Security and pensions. As a broad starting point, a 65-year-old who plans to start drawing down the standard 4% of his portfolio annually for living expenses may want to begin with a one-third allocation to each portfolio. If you need more income, then shift toward the Paycheck Portfolio, and if you need more growth, shift toward the Longevity Portfolio.

•**Some of the investments,** such as bond funds, are best kept in tax-deferred accounts and some in taxable accounts. Try to steer taxable money into the Longevity Portfolio or any of the stock funds.

Reason: These generate the least taxes on income and capital gains.

•**Convert from your existing investments gradually.** If you decide that one or more of my portfolios make sense for you, in order to shift existing assets over, begin by drawing on cash that you can spare and by selling any investments that have had poor long-term performance.

Robert Carlson, managing member, Carlson Wealth Advisors, LLC, Chantilly, Virginia.

•**29% in DoubleLine Total Return Bond (DLTNX).**

•**25% in Nicholas Fund (NICSX)**—focuses on about 40 US growth stocks.

•**21% in Cohen & Steers Realty Shares (CSRSX)**—focuses on REITs.

•**10% in Bridgeway Managed Volatility (BRBPX)**—aims to match the returns of the Standard & Poor's 500 stock index with just 40% of its volatility.

•**10% in Pimco All Asset (PASDX)**—invests in about 40 different Pimco funds and can include US and foreign stocks and bonds, commodities, futures and options.

•**5% in Tweedy, Browne Global Value (TBGVX)**—a large-cap value fund.

LONGEVITY PORTFOLIO

This portfolio stresses asset growth and diversification. It is designed to match the returns of the S&P 500 over the long run, but without its steep periodic declines. It uses funds that can perform well in a variety of stock- and bond-market environments. For instance, some of the funds can short (bet against) stocks. Others invest in dividend-paying stocks that are less volatile than the overall stock market. *Permanent allocations…*

•**23% in MainStay Marketfield Investor (MFLDX)**—a global fund that can buy or short stocks of any size.

•**22% in FPA Crescent (FPACX)**—mixes stocks, bonds and cash to minimize losses.

•**16% in Pimco All Asset All Authority (PAUDX)**—can use borrowed money to invest and can short stocks.

•**13% in Berwyn Income (BERIX)**—can invest up to 30% of assets in dividend-paying stocks.

•**11%, Harbor High-Yield Bond (HYFIX).**

•**5% in Cohen & Steers Realty Shares (CSRSX).**

•**5% in Pimco Real Return (PRRDX)**—it buys mostly Treasury Inflation-Protected Securities (TIPS), which are bonds whose principal increases when inflation rises.

•**5% in Oakmark Fund (OAKMX)**—buys stocks that are selling at least 40% below the manager's estimate of their actual worth.

Best Ways Now to Boost Your Social Security

Michael Kitces, CFP, director of planning research for Pinnacle Advisory Group, Inc., a wealth-management firm based in Columbia, Maryland. He is also publisher of the financial-planning blog *Nerd's Eye View*. His website is Kitces.com.

Since Congress voted in 2015 to end two Social Security loopholes, many married couples have been searching for other strategies to maximize their benefits.

For some couples, there still is time to take advantage of the loopholes—which have boosted retirement income for many couples by tens of thousands of dollars—before they disappear. And couples who already started taking advantage of the loopholes can continue to do so.

For people who *can't* start using the loopholes before they disappear, here are the best alternative strategies…

Best option for most couples: The spouse with the higher earnings history postpones claiming benefits, while the spouse with the lower earnings history starts collecting benefits as early as age 62. Your level of Social Security benefits depends, in part, on your earnings history and the age at which you start collecting benefits. Postponing the start of the higher earner's benefits increases the size of that spouse's future monthly benefits by 6% to 8% for each year of postponement, up to age 70. (There is no advantage to postponing the start of benefits past 70.)

Whether it pays to do this depends in part on how long the higher earner expects to live, making the choice difficult. But keep in mind that by postponing the start of the higher earner's benefits, you also can increase the amount that the spouse with the lower earnings history ends up receiving—that's because of "survivor benefits." When one spouse dies, the surviving spouse can, in effect, opt to claim the deceased partner's benefits. Because of that option, delaying the start of the higher earner's benefits until age 70 typically will produce the highest total benefits for a married couple if *either* spouse lives to at least

83. Based on actuarial tables, it's likely that for the typical married couple, if both reach age 65, at least one will live past 90. (Be aware that benefits claimed before full retirement age are subject to a Social Security earnings test, which could reduce or even eliminate benefits if the lower earner still is working and earning $15,720 or more.)

Example: Say a husband is entitled to monthly benefits of $2,000 if he starts collecting at age 62…or around $3,500 if he waits until age 70.* And say he decides to start collecting at age 70 and dies at 80, so he receives just $420,000 in total benefits, less than the $432,000 he would have received if he had started his benefits at age 62. But his wife lives to 90, so the combined benefits they receive from his account, including her survivor benefits, total $840,000—much more (a difference of $168,000) than the $672,000 they would have received if he had started at age 62.

Meanwhile, the wife started collecting Social Security benefits at age 62 based on her own earnings history and kept on collecting those benefits until she switched to survivor benefits. That way, the couple receives at least some benefits while waiting for the higher earner to start collecting at age 70. (Of course, if the wife had not earned much at all, these benefits might be very small. If her benefits are much less than half the husband's benefits, it might make sense for the husband to start collecting before age 70—more on that below.)

A possible alternative when the lower earner has an extremely low earnings history or no earnings history: Rather than waiting until age 70, the higher earner starts collecting benefits when the lower earner reaches "full" retirement age. One downside to waiting until age 70 to claim benefits, as the husband in the previous example did, is that under the new rules, the wife in the example could not claim spousal benefits based on the husband's earnings unless the husband is collecting his benefits. (Under the old rules, the husband could file for benefits to allow his

---

*Social Security amounts cited in this article are based on current levels. Actual benefits may increase each year based on a measure of inflation.

wife to claim spousal benefits, and then he could immediately suspend his own benefits, allowing his eventual monthly benefits to continue to increase in size.)

The new barrier to claiming spousal benefits is not a major problem if the wife has a significant earnings history of her own, but for couples where one spouse earned virtually all the income, it could mean that the low-earning spouse loses out on substantial benefits for many years. And be aware that although most Social Security benefits increase in size for each month you wait to claim them up to age 70, spousal benefits stop increasing once the spouse reaches what the government refers to as "full" retirement age, which is 66 for people born between 1943 and 1954.

That means it might make sense for the higher earner to start collecting his benefits when the low earner reaches full retirement age so that the low earner can start collecting spousal benefits at that point.

Example: Say the husband is the higher earner and is eligible to start collecting monthly benefits of $2,500 when he reaches full retirement age of 66...or $3,300 if he waits until age 70. Say his wife, who is the same age, did not have significant earned income during her working years. The husband chooses to start collecting his benefits at age 66...the wife starts collecting spousal benefits at age 66...and both live to 80. The couple receives a combined $630,000 versus just $594,000 if they had waited until age 70 to start collecting benefits.

However, in some cases, it might make more sense for the high earner to wait, possibly until age 70, even though that means the low earner sacrifices some spousal benefits. The correct choice depends on such factors as whether the couple has enough assets to tide them over and their expectations about their life spans. (If the high earner is at least four years older than the low earner, this is a nonissue—by the time the low earner reaches full retirement age, the high earner will have started his benefits anyway.)

Example: Say the wife in the example above lives to 90 rather than 80. As a result, the couple would have been better off waiting until age 70 to start collecting benefits, which would have meant the couple earned a total of $990,000 versus a total of $930,000 if the husband started at age 66.

Possible alternative when both partners are in poor health: Claim benefits as soon as possible. If health and/or family history strongly suggest that neither spouse is likely to live past his/her early 80s, the best way to maximize total benefits is for both partners to start their benefits as soon as possible, meaning at age 62 or immediately if they already are past age 62.

IF YOU HAVE DEPENDENT CHILDREN

When a Social Security recipient has children who are unmarried and not yet 18, each of those children might be eligible to receive dependent benefits equal to as much as 50% of a parent's full retirement age benefit. But under new rules that were part of legislation passed by Congress last year, the child can receive these "auxiliary" benefits only if a parent is receiving his/her own benefits. So the question is, should the parent claim at age 62 or as soon as possible after that to take advantage of these auxiliary benefits...or postpone benefits to age 70 based on considerations discussed above?

The answer depends in part on how many auxiliary benefit payments the family is likely to receive. If there is one child in the household who is just months away from 18 when the older parent turns 62, it almost certainly isn't worth claiming early. But if there are multiple children in the household who will be eligible for benefits for many years, it very often makes sense. (A parent or other designated adult receives and controls the payments.)

Key details: The 18-year-old age limit is extended to 19 and two months if the child still is in high school. There is no age limit if the child is disabled, but the disability must have begun before age 22. If the child is younger than 16 and the spouse who is not starting his/her own benefits is providing child care, that spouse might be eligible to receive a spousal benefit. This is possible even if the spouse is not yet old enough to receive spousal benefits under normal circumstances. (Dependent grandchildren also may be eligible to qualify for dependent benefits, but there are extensive rules that restrict this eligibility.)

The 5 Worst Social Security Scams

Steven J. Weisman, Esq., attorney and senior lecturer in the department of law, tax and financial planning at Bentley University in Waltham, Massachusetts. He is founder of the scam-information website Scamicide. com and author of *The Truth About Avoiding Scams.*

Your Social Security account is a tempting target for scammers whether you are already collecting benefits or will be in the future. Few people understand all the ins and outs of this complex government program, and the bad guys have developed ways to exploit this confusion. *Watch out for these five scams…*

SCAMS THAT APPLY TO EVERYONE

•**Online account hijacking.** The Social Security Administration is encouraging beneficiaries and future beneficiaries to set up "My Social Security" accounts on its website, SSA. gov. If you set up an account, you can check on the size of future Social Security benefits or make changes to your account, such as altering your mailing address or bank information, without visiting an office or waiting on hold for a phone rep. Unfortunately, this system is proving convenient for scammers, too. They have been setting up accounts in the names of benefit recipients (and people who are eligible to receive benefits but have not yet done so)…and then routing benefits to the scammers' bank accounts or debit cards.

Scammers can do this only if they know a victim's Social Security number, date of birth and other personal information, but thanks to recent data breaches, that information often is easily accessible. If a scammer hijacks your benefits, Social Security will reimburse you, but it could take months to sort this out, during which time you could have financial trouble if you depend on your benefits.

MONEYMAKER…

To Maximize Your Social Security…

Most people get lower Social Security benefits than they could because they take them as soon as they are eligible—generally at age 62. More than 75% of women and 70.3% of men recipients take benefits before full retirement age. The best way to maximize benefits is to take them as late as possible. Someone due to get $1,000/month at the full retirement age of 66 would receive $750 at age 62 but would get $1,320 at age 70.

MarketWatch.com

What to do: Set up an account at SSA.gov/ myaccount before a scammer sets up a bogus account in your name—the sooner, the better. You can set up an account even if you have not yet reached retirement age and/or do not yet wish to start receiving your benefits (accounts may be set up only for people who are at least 18 years old). When you set up your account, click "Yes" under the "Add Extra Security" heading on the online form. That way, a new security code will be texted to your cell phone each time you try to log onto your account. Access to the account will be allowed only if you enter this code, making it extremely unlikely that a hacker would be able to hijack your account.

•**Fake data-breach scam.** There have been so many data breaches in recent years that it would hardly come as a surprise if the Social Security Administration's database were hacked. Scammers use this fear of data breaches to their advantage.

It works like this: The scammer contacts a victim, claims to work for the Social Security Administration and says that its computers have been breached. The scammer says that in order to find out which accounts have been hacked and altered, he/she must check whether he has the correct bank and account number for the beneficiary. He gives account information that he knows does not pertain to the victim. When victims say the account mentioned is not theirs, they are asked to provide the correct bank information and perhaps other information as well. In reality, victims who provide the requested information might have their bank accounts robbed and their benefits and/or identity stolen as well.

What to do: Always ignore calls and e-mail messages about Social Security data breaches—the Social Security Administration never initiates contact with recipients via phone or e-mail. If you receive a letter claiming you must take action because of a data breach, this, too, could be a scam—call the Social Security Administration at 800-772-1213 (not at a number provided in the letter) to ask whether the letter is legitimate. Be extremely wary if someone who contacts you about a Social Security data breach asks you to provide sensitive information, such as bank account details—the real Social Security Administration would never ask for this.

SCAMS THAT APPLY ONLY TO CURRENT BENEFICIARIES

•**Cost-of-living adjustment scam.** Social Security benefits increase in most years to keep pace with inflation. 2016 was an exception—falling energy prices kept inflation down in 2015, so there was no 2016 cost-of-living adjustment. To scammers, this exceptional situation represents an opportunity.

Victims receive an e-mail, a text, a letter or a phone call explaining that the Social Security Administration has noticed that they did not apply for their cost-of-living increase this year. Apply soon, these victims are warned, or this benefit boost will be forfeited. An application form might be provided or possibly a link to a website. In reality, victims who supply the requested information will have their identities and/or Social Security benefits stolen.

What to do: Ignore any notices or calls suggesting that you must apply for a Social Security cost-of-living adjustment. These adjustments are made automatically in years when they occur. And never assume that a phone call is legitimate because your phone's caller ID says that it is coming from the Social Security Administration—scammers have ways to fool caller-ID systems.

•**Social Security card scam.** It seems perfectly reasonable that the old paper Social Security cards might be due for an upgrade—after all, the latest credit cards contain computer chips. In fact, Social Security card modernization is a scam.

Scammers contact benefits recipients, claim to work for the Social Security Administration and say that no further benefits can be issued until the beneficiary's old, out-of-date paper card is replaced with a modern, chip-enabled card. These scammers offer to expedite replacement-card requests if the beneficiary will provide some identification details. If this information is provided, the victim's benefits and/or identity will be stolen.

What to do: Ignore anyone who says you need a new, high-tech Social Security card. There is no such thing.

•**Fake-scam scam.** Scammers have come up with a way to steal Social Security benefits by exploiting people's fear of being scammed.

The scammer contacts victims, claims to be an employee of the Social Security Administration, and says the Administration's scam-spotting software noticed a suspicious change to the victim's account—did the victim recently reroute his benefits to a bank account in a different state? When the victim says no, the helpful Social Security "employee" warns that a scammer must have hijacked the victim's account. The scammer says that he will help the victim fix the problem, but the person must act fast.

As part of the process, this fake government employee will request information such as Social Security number and bank account details that will allow him to steal the victim's benefits and/or identity.

What to do: Never provide any information to anyone who contacts you with a warning that you might be the victim of a Social Security benefits scam. Instead, contact the real Social Security Administration at 800-772-1213, describe the warning you received and ask if your account is truly at risk.

Better Way to Plan for Retirement Health Expenses

Sudipto Banerjee, PhD, research associate at EBRI, Washington, DC. Dr. Banerjee is author of the study "Utilization Patterns and Out-of-Pocket Expenses for Different Health Care Services Among American Retirees." EBRI.org

Soaring health-care costs can wallop consumers as they grow older, even though some expenses remain stable. A recent study done by the nonprofit Employee Benefit Research Institute (EBRI) suggests that the best way to plan for retirement health-care expenses is to divide them into two separate categories...

•**Recurring expenses** include doctor and dentist visits and prescription medications. These generally are consistent throughout a person's retirement.

Exception: Prescription drug costs can spike with certain medical problems, adding $1,000 to $2,000 to annual costs for possibly 10% of retirees.

Strategy: If you already are covered by Medicare, add up your yearly out-of-pocket expenditures for these recurring medical costs over the past year, then build this amount into your annual budget allowing for a 2% rate of inflation and a 3% return on savings. If you are not yet Medicare eligible, budget around $1,885 a year.

•**Nonrecurring expenses** include nursing home stays, outpatient surgery, hospital stays and treatments, and special facilities such as rehabilitation programs.

Strategy: Create an investment account specifically to pay for these expenses. Earmarking a separate account this way, rather than keeping health-care money in a general account, is the best way to ensure that it is not misspent.

Another EBRI study found that to have a 90% chance of covering retirement health costs, a man should plan for $116,000 in costs...a woman $131,000. The good news is that because nonrecurring health costs tend to occur mainly late in retirement, people still in their 60s can invest this money in a relatively aggressive portfolio of investments.

13

Bon Voyage!

The World's Smartest Traveler Busts 5 Myths About Flying

Some of the things people think they know about airline travel are not actually true. Widely followed strategies for finding affordable airfares turn out not to save money…while widely held beliefs about avoiding airport delays turn out not to save time. *The truth about five air travel myths…*

MYTH: Stopovers save travelers money. Conventional wisdom holds that travelers pay significantly less for connecting flights than for nonstop flights. This might be true on certain routes, but in general, stopovers save air travelers far less than they likely expect. A recent study of more than 57 million tickets sold in 2014 found that nonstop flights, when available, cost only $1.03 more, on average, than connecting flights between the same airports.

What to do: When you use an airfare website to search for flights, do a search specifically for nonstop flights in addition to a search for lowest-priced flights. Even if nonstop flights do cost more, you often will discover that the price difference is small enough that it's worth paying a premium to avoid the potential complications of a stopover.

MYTH: Booking your tickets early usually will save you money. Actually, history suggests that ticket prices are as likely to fall as they are to climb during the months leading up to the flight—and if you buy a ticket many months before a flight, you essentially are giving the airline an interest-free loan. Besides, the earlier you book your ticket, the greater the odds your travel plans will change, which

Note: Prices, rates and offers throughout this chapter and book are subject to change.

Christopher Elliott, author of the *Washington Post* travel section's "Navigator" column and cofounder of Travelers United, which advocates for travelers' rights. He is author of *How to Be the World's Smartest Traveler.* Elliott.org

217

might mean that you must pay a hefty fee to change your flight.

What to do: It is reasonable to book a ticket months in advance if your travel plans are very unlikely to change and you spot a fare that is well below normal for the route—websites including Google Flights let you compare the fare you've found to other fares being offered for the route over the coming months. (On Google.com/flights, enter your departure and destination cities, then click the tiny calendar icon located beneath the departure city to see a chart of daily low fares.) In general, there is no great savings to be had by booking months early. Do try to buy tickets at least seven and preferably 14 days before the travel date—fares tend to trend upward in the week or two before departure, sometimes significantly.

Exception: It occasionally is possible to obtain great last-minute deals by buying tickets a week or less before flight time, but you cannot depend on this, so it is advisable only if your travel plans are very flexible.

MYTH: Flying into or out of major hubs costs more than using smaller airports. In reality, major hubs generally offer lower fares than you would find flying into or out of smaller airports in the area. Massive airports such as JFK in New York, LAX in Los Angeles and O'Hare in Chicago have huge numbers of flights, and that added competition tends to hold fares down.

What to do: Include smaller airports in your search when you look for a flight to or from a metro area that has multiple airports—on occasion, these secondary airports offer attractive fares—but never search exclusively for flights to or from these smaller airports.

MYTH: Summer air travel is more reliable than winter air travel because bad weather is less likely to interfere. Surprisingly, flight delays and cancellations due to weather are more common in summer than winter. Winter blizzards get lots of media attention, but summer thunderstorms and tropical storms are much more common and just as capable of wreaking havoc on airline schedules. Airlines are not required to compensate travelers

whose flights are delayed or canceled because of bad weather.

What to do: Monitor weather reports and watch for flight status updates if you have an upcoming flight—or are picking someone up from the airport—even if it's summer. Websites and apps such as *FlightAware* make it easy to monitor flight status (FlightAware.com, the app is free for Android or iOS).

MYTH: Every flight is packed these days, and the lines are almost always endless in the airport. Yes, airports and planes generally have been crowded—but there still are flights with plenty of open seats and times when the lines are not very long.

What to do: If you want to avoid the crowds, choose flights that depart before 8 am or after 11 pm. Even the largest, busiest airports and most heavily traveled routes tend to be fairly quiet during these hours.

Joining the TSA Pre-Check program can help you to speed through airport security checkpoints. This lets you skip the normal airport security line in favor of a special line that tends to move much faster. The Pre-Check program generally makes sense only for fairly frequent fliers, however—there is an $85 application fee, and the application process itself takes time (TSA.gov/tsa-precheck).

Sneaky Ways Airlines Are Tricking You Now

George Hobica, founder of AirfareWatchdog.com, a website that reports on airfare bargains including unannounced, unadvertised rates. He previously was a travel writer for magazines including *Travel + Leisure* and *National Geographic Traveler.*

What's a bigger hassle these days than traveling on an airplane? Trying to get a good deal and accurate pricing information from the airline in the first place.

Airlines have become adept at using complicated fee schemes to maximize the amount of money they get from passengers while filling up every seat on the plane. But you can improve your chances of getting a good deal and a flight that meets your needs if you know what to watch out for.

Six things that the airlines are *not* telling you...

•**Fuel prices are down—but our fuel surcharges are as high as ever.** The "fuel surcharges" that many airlines tack onto ticket prices for foreign trips really took off in 2008, when jet fuel approached $4 a gallon. Jet fuel recently cost well under $2 a gallon, but only a few airlines, including Qantas and Virgin Australia, have eliminated the surcharges. (Some airlines have renamed them.)

Many airlines even tack fuel surcharges onto "free" awards tickets earned through frequent-flier programs. Some "free" round-trip international tickets cost more than $800 because of "fuel surcharges."

What to do: For tickets booked with frequent-flier miles, proceed through the airline's online booking system far enough to determine what the total price is, including all fees and fuel surcharges. Whether you are using money or frequent-flier miles, shop around. A partner airline or a competing airline might charge a lot less because of different surcharges.

TAKE NOTE...

How to Get the Best Airline Seats

To get the best airline seats without paying heavily for an upgrade...

•**Compare planes and seats online** at websites such as SeatGuru.com, SeatExpert.com and SeatPlans.com.

•**Join an airline's frequent-flier program.**

•**Book early** to have the widest selection of seats.

•**Use a travel agent**—he/she sometimes has access to better seats and may charge only $20 to $30 for simple bookings.

•**If you must book a middle seat,** sign up with a notification site such as ExpertFlyer.com to be notified immediately if a better seat opens up—you may be able to change seats without cost.

Roundup of experts on airline seating, reported at MoneyTalksNews.com.

•**Didn't get the upgrade?** We're still keeping your payment. Airlines often neglect to refund prepaid fees when passengers don't actually get what they paid for.

Example: You can prepay for an upgrade to "premium economy," a class of seat above standard economy but below business class. But if you get bumped back to a regular economy seat when the airline substitutes a plane that has fewer premium-economy seats, the upgrade fee likely will still be charged.

What to do: Call the airline, explain that you did not get the upgrade you paid for, and ask that your fee be refunded to you. Airlines typically back down when confronted about this. Trouble is, some passengers never notice that the fees were not automatically refunded.

•**We are improving our on-time arrival record—by giving ourselves an extension.** Airlines have found a way to boost their on-time arrival statistics without actually getting passengers to their destinations in a more timely manner. They simply list later flight-arrival times, building in a cushion that allows them to be officially on time even when there's a delay.

Unfortunately, that means many flights now are arriving *earlier* than they are expected, in many cases leaving passengers sitting around airports waiting for a long time for connections or rides.

What to do: If someone is picking you up at the airport, ask the person to use the free flight-tracking service known as FlightAware (FlightAware.com), which will enable them to determine when your plane actually will land, rather than trust official airline arrival times. In addition to the website, there are apps for iOS, Android and Windows Phone.

•**You have options if you have a nonrefundable ticket and your flight is delayed or canceled, but we're not telling you what they are.** Airlines are required by their "contract of carriage" to let passengers skip the trip and receive a refund if their flights are canceled or significantly delayed—even if they are flying on nonrefundable tickets.

But airlines rarely mention this. Instead, they act as though the only option is to wait for the next available flight on the same airline. (The length of delay required to trigger this rule varies by airline, but generally it is 90 or 120 minutes.)

What to do: If your flight is canceled or delayed so long that the trip no longer makes sense—or if you are able to obtain a better flight from a competing airline—you might want to tell an airline representative that you want a refund, not a later flight. This advice applies even if you booked your flight through a travel website, but you may not get back any service fee that you paid to that site.

In years past, airlines were required to put passengers on any available flight to their destinations—even a different airline's flight—if the original flight was delayed or canceled for non-weather–related reasons. Now, because of changes to their contract of carriage, airlines can make passengers wait for the next available seats on their own flights—although they may sometimes still choose to follow the old rules, so it's worth checking. (The old rules still apply at Alaska Airlines, for example.)

•**Want a basic economy seat? Our website might make it seem, falsely, as though that isn't an option.** You purchase an economy ticket through an airline's website…but when you try to select your seat, only pricier premium-economy seats might be shown as available. It appears that the only option is to pay extra for an upgrade.

What to do: You do not have to upgrade to premium economy if you don't want to. If you don't select any seat, the airline will assign you one prior to flight time. If no economy seats remain, you even might be assigned a premium-economy seat for no additional charge.

•**The passenger in the seat next to you is flying on a completely different airline**—at a much lower price. Because of airline partnerships and mergers, a single airplane trip might be listed as two different flights on two different airlines—and the fares charged by these airlines could differ by hundreds of dollars.

Examples: Some US Airways and American Airlines flights are listed separately as flights on each of those airlines…a Delta flight to Europe might also be listed as an Air France

or Alitalia flight…a United flight to Canada might also be listed as an Air Canada flight.

What to do: Before booking any flight, use a fare-comparison site such as Orbitz.com, Cheaptickets.com or Kayak.com to scan for a flight on other airlines that feature exactly the same airport, departure time and arrival time—there's a good chance that it's the same plane.

You often can opt to earn miles in a particular airline's frequent-flier program even if you purchase your ticket through one of its partner airlines, though in some cases you might earn miles at a lower rate. Check the airline websites for how to do this.

Save on Airfare with Google Flights

Kim Komando, host of *The Kim Komando Show*, a weekly national radio program focusing on consumer technology issues. Komando.com

---

G oogle's airfare-finder website Google Flights offers some money-saving features that better-known sites such as Expedia, Orbitz and Kayak either don't offer or don't do as well.

To save with Google.com/flights, use it to…

•**Find the least expensive travel dates.** If you are flexible about when you fly, enter departure and destination cities into Google Flights, then click the calendar icon located below the departure city (the calendar icon is the small square containing the number 31). A calendar will pop up displaying the lowest fares available each day during a two-month window. A bar chart that accompanies this calendar makes it easy to spot the departure days that have the lowest fares. Click the arrows below this bar chart to adjust the length of your trip…click the arrows to the sides of the calendar to see day-by-day low fares for additional months.

Recent example: If you planned to travel from Portland, Maine, to Portland, Oregon, for a week in early August, the least expensive round-trip ticket would have cost $725. But if you used this calendar feature, you would have seen that you could cut that price to $390 by delaying the trip until August 25 (saving $335 over the $725 flight).

When you are ready to purchase a ticket, you're typically connected to an airline booking website.

• **Find the best fares to a broad region in a single search.** Most airfare-finder sites require that you enter a specific airport or city as your destination with perhaps an "include nearby airports" option. With Google Flights, you have the option of entering a state, country or even a continent (along with specific travel dates).

When you do this, a map appears displaying the lowest fares available to each of the major airports in or near the specified region. You might be able to save money by flying into a different airport than you originally intended. This is especially useful when you intend to tour a wide area and are not concerned where this trip begins...or when you haven't decided precisely where you want to visit.

Recent example: Imagine that you want to see both France and Germany on a 14-day August trip departing from Washington, DC. The least expensive round-trip tickets available to most airports in these countries cost more than $1,100. But this Google Flights feature would have pointed you to a savings opportunity—flights to Frankfurt, Germany, costing as little as $925.

• **Get bonus tips.** If the site identifies an opportunity to save money or get a better travel experience, it will supply a "Tip" to this effect in a bar among the flight listings.

Recent example: Included among the listings in a search for flights from Los Angeles to Rome was "Tip: Fly in Premium Economy"—a premium-economy seat with extra legroom was available for less than many airlines were charging for standard economy seats on the route.

Other Google Flight tips might point out that you could save money by flying into or out of a nearby airport...or by adjusting your travel dates.

Fake First-Class

First class on airlines isn't necessarily first class. The first-class experience for the same-priced tickets can vary drastically within a particular airline.

Example: Some United flights have first-class lie-flat beds and personal video screens. Other flights have first-class seats that are two inches narrower with limited recline and no seat-back entertainment.

Helpful: Enter your flight number and date at SeatGuru.com. It gives seat amenities and dimensions plus passenger reviews.

George Hobica, founder of AirfareWatchdog.com, a website that reports on airfare bargains.

Animal Allergy? Alert the Airline

Tell the airline if you are allergic to animals as far in advance as possible. Airlines are required to accommodate passengers with service animals, and ordinary pets now are traveling in passenger cabins as well. Airlines can make arrangements for passengers who are highly allergic by rearranging seating or moving you to a different flight. If you are only mildly allergic, take allergy medicine such as Benadryl with you—and bring a dose of epinephrine in your carry-on bag if you might need it.

Roundup of experts on airline travel involving animals, reported in *USA Today.*

Is It Safe to Fly Now?

Mary Schiavo, former inspector general of the US Department of Transportation. She is a licensed pilot and CNN aviation analyst, heads the aviation litigation team for Motley Rice, a law firm in Mount Pleasant, South Carolina, and is author of *Flying Blind, Flying Safe.*

Is enough being done to make passenger flights safe? Last year, a pilot for the airline Germanwings deliberately crashed an Air-

221

bus passenger jet into a mountain, killing 150 people. And that's not the first time a pilot has deliberately crashed a plane.

Below, former US Department of Transportation Inspector General Mary Schiavo answers questions about air safety...

•**Following the Germanwings disaster, we learned that US carriers are required to have two crew members in the cockpit at all times. Is this an effective safety measure?** Yes, it's very, very valuable—and not just because it could prevent pilots from intentionally crashing planes. I do believe that having a second person in the cockpit would have prevented the Germanwings crash. But there also have been cases where pilots have passed out or died in the cockpit or struggled to put on their oxygen masks in an emergency. Following the Germanwings crash, Canadian, Australian and European Union carriers have adopted the US policy of requiring at least two crew members in the cockpit.

•**How significant is the threat of terrorism to air travelers these days?** Terrorism is probably the single greatest threat to air travelers today—and it requires extensive security measures. Sooner or later, terrorists will attempt an attack on a plane involving an electronic device, which will lead to new restrictions on our laptop computers and smartphones...or they will try to get a bomb in a checked bag, and we will face additional luggage restrictions.

•**How well is the TSA protecting air travelers against terrorism?** Before 9/11, security was handled by the airlines, and they were terrible at it. So viewed that way, the TSA is a vast improvement. But there has been a tendency to focus on the most recent terrorist attack and forget about other threat vectors. While the passenger side of airport security has been substantially improved, there have been hundreds of breaches through the fences and gates around runways at US airports...and almost no US airports subject airline and airport employees to daily security screening, such as metal detectors. (Miami International Airport does, to its credit.) If these gaps are not corrected, terrorists will find a way to exploit them, such as recruiting employees.

•**We sometimes hear that Israel does the best job with airline screening. Why can't we match them?** Israel is far ahead of us in this area, but there currently is no realistic way for us to do what Israeli security does. There's less air traffic in all of Israel than in a single large US airport. If we tried to implement Israel's level of individual screening and interviewing, our air-transit system would grind to a halt. The only feasible way for the US to dramatically improve airport screening is through technology such as next-generation facial-recognition software and better detection of weapons and explosives. Expect much more of this in US airports in the coming years.

•**Should airline passengers attempt to subdue a passenger or crew member who seems dangerous?** Absolutely they should. And what's more, they have. Americans have shown an impressive willingness to team up and take action in these situations. Passengers helped stop the shoe bomber in 2001 and the underwear bomber in 2009...and they were coming up with plans to take on the terrorists on all four of the 9/11 flights, though only the passengers on Flight 93 had time to put their plan into action.

Passengers are shielded by law from liability if they accidentally injure or kill someone they reasonably believe poses a threat to an aircraft.

•**Are any airlines so unsafe that they are best avoided?** Don't fly on any airline that is on the European Union's Air Safety List (for the list, go to EC.Europa.eu and put "Air Safety

List" in the search box). This list is dominated by carriers based in Africa, Southeast Asia and the Middle East. There is no US list.

•Is it especially risky to fly into or out of certain airports? Three factors can make an airport dangerous. The first is weather—there is a huge correlation between snowy, icy weather and plane crashes. Avoid winter flights with connections in northern cities when possible. Second is geography—some airports, including Friedman Memorial Airport in Hailey, Idaho, and Pitkin County Airport in Aspen, Colorado, require pilots to land on short runways surrounded by mountains. Third is an old-style layout where runways intersect one another and taxiways cross active runways, such as at Chicago's Midway, New York's LaGuardia and Washington's Reagan National. LaGuardia and Reagan National also have water at the end of certain runways, increasing the danger if a pilot overshoots.

Also avoid flying into or out of airports in countries that have a "Significant Safety Concern," according to the International Civil Aviation Organization (ICAO.int/safety/Pages/USOAP-Results.aspx).

•Are certain commercial aircraft more dangerous than others? I avoid flying on aircraft manufactured by the French-Italian company ATR because it has a long history of crashes in various countries, including an American Eagle crash in Indiana in 1994 that was blamed on icing. I also try to avoid "tired irons," such as old Boeing 757s or McDonnell Douglas MD-88s, and propeller planes because they don't handle icing conditions well. I never fly on any airplane made in Russia.

It's generally safer to fly on large planes than small ones—they are tougher, and larger planes tend to get the most experienced pilots.

•A government report warned that hackers might use Wi-Fi to crash a plane. Is this a real danger? It is a legitimate concern, but no one has yet proved that you can really do it. And only the very latest planes—the Boeing 787 and Airbus A350 and A380—are potentially vulnerable.

The FAA's new NextGen air-traffic control system has an even more pressing problem. This multibillion-dollar system, which already

is being slowly phased in, puts most of the air-traffic control workload in the hands of computers—yet amazingly the FAA did not bother to put in a firewall to keep hackers out. It definitely is vulnerable.

•How dangerous are bird strikes? Bird strikes have grown far more common in the US in the past two decades because of increasing Canada geese populations that are big enough to destroy the engines of commercial airlines. They are most likely to cause problems at airports near water, landfills or wildlife preserves. LaGuardia Airport is near water and a landfill.

•Is it safer to fly at certain times? Earlier in the day is safer. Pilots and air-traffic controllers are more likely to be fatigued by late afternoon, and delays and frustration might have piled up that could divert their attention.

The Safest Seats on a Plane

Edwin R. Galea, PhD, director of the Fire Safety Engineering Group at University of Greenwich in London. He studied more than 100 plane crashes to determine who survives plane crashes and why.

Did you know that some seats on an airplane are safer than others? *Smart advice from a crash expert...*

•Get a seat near an exit. The closer your seat is to an exit, the better your odds of getting out alive if the plane crashes. Passengers who are within six rows of the nearest viable exit have a greater chance of surviving than dying if they survive the initial impact.

Warning: On many aircraft, including the Boeing 737 and Airbus A320, the exit hatch over the wing is significantly smaller than the exits to the front and rear of the plane. Sit near a large exit if possible—the smaller the opening, the longer it will take each passenger to get through. If you are seated a similar distance from a large exit and a small one, head for the large one in an accident.

•Favor the aisle. Passengers sitting in aisle seats have a slightly higher chance of evacuating the aircraft than those seated in most window seats—though window seats in exit rows are best of all.

Warning: Keep your shoes on for takeoffs and landings, which is when most crashes occur. Shoeless passengers have a more difficult time escaping through the debris of a crashed plane.

For information, go to FSEG.gre.ac.uk (put "Surviving an aviation crash" in the search box, and scroll down).

Destroy That Boarding Pass After a Flight

Boarding passes, which travelers often carelessly leave behind on planes or in hotels, contain information that thieves can use to break into your frequent-flier account and steal your miles...or to learn details of your flight—as well as future flights—then break into your house while you are away. Some information might be hidden in a bar code that thieves can read.

John Sileo, CEO of The Sileo Group, an identity-theft-prevention consulting firm in Denver, a keynote speaker on cybersecurity and author of *Privacy Means Profit*. Sileo.com

Safer Train Travel

The safest seats on a train are one or two cars back from the middle of the train. That's because trains are more likely to derail than be involved in collisions with other trains or cars, and derailments usually happen near the front of the train. There were about 13,200 derailments from 2005 to 2014 and about 1,450 collisions. The last car is less safe if the train is rear-ended. Aisle seats are safer than window seats, where a passenger can get hit more easily by broken glass or be thrown from the train. Rear-facing seats may be safer because riders are less likely to be

thrown forward. Avoid the café car, which has rigid tables that can be dangerous if the train suddenly brakes.

Federal Railroad Administration. FRA.dot.gov

Highest-Rated Car-Rental Firm

Enterprise scored 831 out of a possible 1,000 points in the latest JD Power survey of car renters. National scored 818, and Alamo scored 807. All other firms were below the industry average of 798. At the bottom were Thrifty, which scored 733, and Dollar, at 768.

Also: Millennials, who make up 34% of all renters, are more satisfied with rental firms than baby boomers or members of Generation X.

JDPower.com

The Top Hotel Loyalty Programs

The top two hotel loyalty programs, out of 15 ranked and based on customer satisfaction, are Delta Privilege and Hilton HHonors. They scored 727 points out of a possible 1,000. Delta serves only the Canadian chain Delta Hotels and is not affiliated with Delta Air Lines. Hilton covers all Hilton brands, including Homewood Suites and Waldorf Astoria.

Lowest-rated loyalty programs: Red Roof Inn Redicard, Omni Hotels Select Guest and Starwood Preferred Guest.

J.D. Power 2015 Hotel Loyalty/Rewards Program Satisfaction Report, JDPower.com.

Ask for These Travel Perks...

The following travel perks and services are worth asking for...

• **Waivers of hotel fees—**some hotels will remove parking fees, resort fees and various other extra charges from the bill if you ask, especially if you have had any issues with hotel services.

• **Increased award availability—**phoning a hotel's central reservation line and asking the representative to contact the specific hotel where you want to stay can sometimes get that hotel to make some extra award nights available to you.

• **Airline phone-booking fees** sometimes will be waived if you are booking an award ticket that cannot be booked online.

• **Elite rental car status** can speed up car pickup and is available directly from major auto-rental firms and through some credit cards.

• **Compensation for poor service** is sometimes offered by airlines, usually in the form of frequent-flier miles.

ThePointsGuy.com

Vacation Rental Scams

Vacation rental scams target both renters and owners. Some crooks use photos and descriptions of properties that have been listed for sale, advertise them as rentals, make deals with renters, then ask for payment upfront—which they steal. Other thieves book rentals and send a check for the deposit—but the check is too large. The thief claims that the bank made an error and asks the property owner to refund the difference. The thief steals the money, and the crook's original check turns out to be phony.

Self-defense: Paste descriptive text about a rental in a search engine to see if it was copied from a sale listing. Use a search engine to map the location to be sure it exists. Ask the supposed landlord for proof of identity and ownership, such as a driver's license. Deal by phone, not e-mail—e-mail addresses can be made to look like they are coming from anyone you like. Pay with a credit card, not in cash or by check.

Sid Kirchheimer, author of *Scam-Proof Your Life,* writing at AARP.org.

Annoying Fees for Vacation Rentals on the Rise

Some rental managers charge booking fees, change fees, cleaning fees, parking fees and even so-called convenience fees. Rental managers get commissions only on the rental part of a transaction but usually keep all fee revenue—so they are adding more fees.

Self-defense: Review booking policies on the management company's website. Ask questions about fees before booking. Ask if a quoted price is all-inclusive or will have added fees. Consider buying travel insurance to protect against change fees if you must alter vacation plans. If an unreasonable fee is charged, ask for it to be waived.

Example: One renter was charged a $25 check-in fee—disclosed only in the fine print of her contract.

Roundup of experts on vacation travel, reported in *USA Today.*

EASY-TO-DO...

Trick to Make Travel Easier

Put your hotel phone number in your phone's list of contacts before you leave home. If your arrival is delayed, you can easily alert the hotel. And once you're there, if you get lost sightseeing, need help finding a restaurant or have any other questions about the area, help is just a touch away.

To Save on a Cruise...

If you're planning to pay for upper-tier suites on mainstream and premium cruise lines and for specialty dining and other extras, consider switching to a luxury cruise line—your overall cost may be lower.

Other ways to save on cruises: Book close to the sail date—three to six weeks before departure—and be willing to settle for whatever cabins are left...sail during a slower travel time or during hurricane season in the Caribbean...sign up for e-mail services that track cruise pricing... take a cruise from a location close to home— most people live within a five-hour drive of a cruise port and need not pay for airfare (cruises set sail from New York, Boston, Baltimore, Houston, Los Angeles and other port cities)...or book your next cruise during the current one—

this may get you $25 to $100 in onboard credit to use on the current or future cruise.

Roundup of experts on cruise pricing, reported at HuffingtonPost.com.

Cruising Solo? How to Save Up to 75%!

Solo travelers can now save 25% to 75% on cruises. In the past, solo passengers had to pay for a double cabin...or agree to share a cabin with a stranger to avoid the "single supplement." Now cruise lines sometimes don't charge the entire or possibly even any of the single supplement...and many new ships offer single-occupancy cabins.

Examples: Royal Caribbean International's Quantum of the Seas...Norwegian Cruise Line's Norwegian Escape.

Dori Saltzman, an editor with Cruise Critic, which offers cruise reviews and information. CruiseCritic.com

---

Ultralow Fares to Europe

Inexpensive travel to Europe is possible on Norwegian Air and Iceland's Wow Air, which offer ultralow fares to Europe from US cities including Boston and Los Angeles. These are no-frills carriers flying limited schedules and charging for all amenities.

Example: One recent nonstop Norwegian Air flight from Los Angeles to London was priced at $546 round-trip, but cost $708 when checked baggage, a seat reservation and meals were included. However, that compares with a typical carrier's nonstop LA-to-London charge of $928 recently, so the no-frills flight could still save $220.

Prices vary widely and change constantly— always shop around.

Kiplinger.com

More Savings on Flights to Europe

Big savings on flights to Europe are available by using secondary airports as well as lesser known airlines. Flights leaving from Providence…Baltimore…Portland, Oregon…Austin, Texas…Oakland, California…and the Florida cities of Tampa, Fort Myers and Fort Lauderdale may cost significantly less than ones departing from the airports that are the usual jumping-off points to Europe, such as Boston or New York. Carriers such as Condor, Norwegian Air Shuttle and AirBerlin use the smaller airports and may charge significantly less than better known carriers.

Example: One Boston-to-Frankfurt round-trip coach ticket recently sold for $1,743, while a Providence-to-Frankfurt ticket sold for $700—a savings of $1,043.

Flight availability varies widely, and prices change constantly—shop around.

The Wall Street Journal. WSJ.com

Bargains to Warm Locations Off the Beaten Track

The travel industry is cutting prices in places such as the Azores islands, off the coast of Portugal, and Panama, to lure tourists away from popular Caribbean and southern European destinations.

Examples: Round-trip airfare from Boston to the Azores plus six nights at the four-star Pousada de São Sebastião hotel for $699 per person (go to AzoresGetaways.com)…round-trip airfare from New York City to Panama City plus four nights at the Hard Rock Hotel for $699 per person (see GreatValueVacations.com)…four nights at the Pelican Eyes Hotel in Nicaragua for $599 per person, excluding airfare (PelicanEyesResort.com).

Gabe Saglie, a senior editor at Travelzoo, which tracks travel and entertainment deals.

See Broadway Shows Cheap

Claudia Stuart, founder of BroadwayforBrokePeople.com. She also is a general manager of a children's theater company.

You can save big on Broadway shows and have fun doing it. Many shows, including the hits *Hamilton, Aladdin* and *The Book of Mormon,* offer a small number of great seats for just $10 to $40, a massive markdown from the $100 to $300 ordinarily charged. However, to snag these savings, you must enter a lottery held in the hours prior to showtime.

Details about specific lotteries can be found at Playbill.com (under "Popular Links," click on "Broadway Rush, Lotto & SRO")…and on my site, BroadwayforBrokePeople.com (lotteries are listed under "Cheapest Tickets").

Some theaters in other cities have lotteries, too. Visit their websites to check, or enter the words "theater"…"lottery"…and the city name into a search engine.

Twenty or so seats might be offered through a Broadway show's lottery for each performance, though this varies. Each winner generally can claim no more than two seats, so entering makes more sense for couples and singles than for larger groups. The quality of seats provided varies—some may be in the first two rows, while others may have obstructed views. Several Off-Broadway shows have similar programs.

Lotteries fall into two categories…

GOOD TO KNOW...

Quick Fix for Sandy Hands

Baby powder is perfect for removing sand from your hands, feet, legs and more. Sprinkle on a generous amount, and the powder will remove moisture from your skin, allowing you to easily shake or wipe the sand off. Cornstarch also works well.

DayTrippingMom.com

•**In-person lotteries** must be entered at the box office. In most cases, they open for entries two-and-a-half hours before showtime and close 30 minutes later, with winners drawn soon after. Winners must be present when their names are drawn. The odds of winning can be bad for the newest and biggest hits but reasonably good for some shows that attract just a few dozen entries, particularly with midweek shows...when the weather is cold or rainy...and with older or less popular shows. Occasionally turnout is so low that everyone who enters wins.

If you hope to attend the play as a couple, both of you can enter the lottery. (It's not a problem if you both win—lottery winners are not required to buy tickets.) If your plan is to attend alone, try to find someone else in the crowd waiting for the drawing who also is alone and offer to team up—if either of you wins, buy two tickets and split the cost.

Warning: Many in-person lotteries, including those for *Aladdin, Hamilton* and *Wicked,* require that winners pay for their tickets in cash, so make sure you have enough money.

•**Online lotteries** are entered through websites or smartphone apps on the day of the show or, in some cases, as early as curtain time of the previous performance. But many more people tend to enter online lotteries than in-person lotteries, reducing your odds of winning. Winners receive a text or e-mail notification. Read this message carefully—you might be required to pay for and/or pick up your tickets well before showtime.

Most Accurate Weather Sites and Apps

Tiffany Means, meteorologist and weather expert at About.com.

Where you get your weather forecast can make a big difference. Although most weather websites start with the same data from the US National Weather Service and the National Oceanic and Atmospheric Administration (NOAA), they differ in the

---

TAKE NOTE...

When to Tip—and How Much

Taxi drivers, hairstylists, manicurists and masseuses—15% up to 20%. Buffet servers—10%. Bartenders—$1 to $2 per drink. Skycaps and bellhops—$2 for first bag...$1 per each additional. Doormen who carry luggage or acquire transportation for you—$1 to $2. Hotel housekeeping staff and valets—$2 to $5 nightly.

Advice from The Emily Post Institute, reported in USA Today.

---

additional analysis they do and how accurate they are. (For track records on the accuracy of various sites, go to ForecastAdvisor.com.)

The best sites...

•**Best site for a quick summary**—Yahoo Weather (Weather.Yahoo.com) includes on its first page a quick five-day local forecast including current high and low temperatures for the day...a graph of monthly trends for the year... visibility...humidity...a graph of the rising and setting sun and moon...wind speed...and barometric pressure. The app is free for Apple and Android mobile devices.

•**Best all-around site**—Accuweather (Accu Weather.com), drawing on more than 100 staff meteorologists, is indeed very accurate as well as easy to navigate and packed with a big variety of data and useful graphics, such as various radar maps...hourly forecasts for three days... extended forecasts for up to 45 days...and enhanced satellite images. The app is free for Apple and Android mobile devices.

•**Best for local accuracy across the US**—Weather Underground (Wunderground.com) incorporates constantly updated reports provided by more than 140,000 weather stations run by amateur weather observers located in homes and schools around the US. This can be very valuable if, for example, you are planning an outdoor event or snow is on the way. However, unless you are a weather enthusiast, the site can overwhelm you with information, including highly technical data that you probably don't need, such as buoy-based surface-water temperature readings. The app is free for Apple and Android mobile devices.

• **Best to get up-to-the-minute forecasts about precipitation at your precise location**—Dark Sky (DarkSkyApp.com), available through an app for Apple mobile devices, features "Nowcasting" that incorporates data from barometers on hundreds of thousands of individuals' iPhones. It pinpoints the forecast to where your phone's GPS indicates you are to tell you, for instance, that a light rain will start in six minutes on the corner where you are. Dark Sky's largely short-term focus might make it impractical to use as your only source for weather, but golfers and dog walkers will love it. There is a onetime $3.99 fee.

Cell Phone Savvy When Overseas

When traveling overseas, leave your cell phone in airplane mode to avoid sky-high international rates for calls and messages. Leaving it on its regular setting means that you will be billed each time someone leaves you a voice mail or sends you a text. In airplane mode, you still can use the phone to take photographs.

Alternative: Before traveling, set up an international plan with your carrier for the time you will be out of the US—you can cancel it when you return. Costs vary.

AARP Bulletin. AARP.org/bulletin

Get Insured Before Your Trip

Charles B. Inlander, a consumer advocate and health-care consultant based in Fogelsville, Pennsylvania. He was founding president of the nonprofit People's Medical Society, a consumer advocacy organization credited with key improvements in the quality of US health care, and is author or coauthor of more than 20 consumer-health books.

Even the best-laid plans for a weekend jaunt to a neighboring state can get derailed by an illness or a medical emer-gency. If you're going on an overseas cruise or tour, the stakes are much higher. Let's say that some medical problem forces you to cancel your journey…or you get sick or injured while you're away. You stand to lose a lot of money in prepaid tour costs or medical expenses while you're abroad.

What to consider when looking for overseas travel insurance…

• **Find out what you have—and if you need more.** If you're planning an overseas trip, call your current health insurer to see if your policy covers any overseas medical costs. Some do, including a few Medicare supplement policies (Medicare itself does not). But even if your carrier does provide some coverage, it will usually be limited and almost never pay the overseas hospital or doctor directly—you must pay first and then submit your bills for reimbursement when you return.

Rule of thumb: If you're prepaying all or part of an overseas trip and/or if you have a medical condition that could flare up before or during your travels, it's wise to consider getting travel medical insurance.

Good news: If you have health insurance, medical travel insurance is usually not needed for domestic travel.

FREEBIES...

Handy Free Travel Apps and Sites

Free apps and sites make travel easier, cheaper and more fun. *Free Wi-Fi Finder* (for iOS) and *Wi-Fi Finder* (for Android) find free wireless hot spots. *Hotels.com* offers good last-minute deals. *Vayable* (iOS only) lets you buy excursions with local residents as guides. *FindGravy.com* shows where you are and what events are nearby—search by date and type of activity. *SitorSquat* locates clean bathrooms—and steers you away from those you want to avoid. *OandACurrency Converter* works quickly and allows you to factor in the typical ATM or credit card rate for conversions. *Google Translate* rapidly translates text and the spoken word.

DailyFinance.com

• **Know your options.** Most people don't realize what types of travel insurance are available for medical issues.

The main ones include: Flight insurance, which is simply a life insurance policy that pays if the plane crashes. *Evacuation coverage* kicks in if you are injured or become ill while traveling and need to be moved to a distant hospital or even brought home for appropriate care—this type of evacuation is expensive (possibly running as much as $100,000 or more). *Cancellation and interruption insurance* pays you back if your trip is cancelled by the tour company (some travel or tour companies go bankrupt and don't offer refunds) or if you or a traveling companion (who is also insured) gets sick or injured and cannot start or continue your trip. *Medical travel insurance,* depending on the type of policy you buy, either pays all or part of any medical expenses you incur while traveling.

Insider tip: In recent years, some of the biggest travel insurance companies, such as Travel Guard (TravelGuard.com) and Travelex (TravelexInsurance.com), began offering comprehensive plans that act as your primary insurer while traveling. Such plans may also include medical evacuation and cancellation/interruption coverage.

• **Learn the going rates.** You can expect to spend from 5% to 10% of the total cost of your trip for insurance premiums.

Insider tip: Be sure that the insurer is licensed to sell in your state. If not, any claims you later submit will not be honored. And steer clear of insurance offered by travel agents—they usually offer only one company's plans from whom they receive a hefty commission. Instead, search online for a travel insurance broker, such as InsureMyTrip.com, which represents more than 20 companies.

Important: If you are traveling to a country on the US State Department's at-risk list (Travel.State.gov), your policy will likely not be honored. Check that list before you buy any type of medical travel insurance.

Get Vaccinated Before Going Overseas

Many US travelers fail to get vaccinations before going overseas. Outbreaks of infections such as measles and hepatitis A could be prevented if more people were vaccinated against the diseases. Many people do not realize how prevalent these diseases are outside the US. Measles outbreaks occur in developed countries, including Europe, and while hepatitis A is rare in the US, it is common in places with poor sanitation and limited access to clean water.

Self-defense: Visit a travel clinic four to six weeks before an international trip, or see your doctor to get recommended shots.

Study of more than 40,000 US travelers by researchers at Harvard Medical School and Massachusetts General Hospital, both in Boston, reported at a recent meeting of specialists in infectious illness during Infectious Diseases Week in San Diego.

Zika Self-Defense

Individuals who are immunocompromised should stay away from Puerto Rico, the US Virgin Islands, Mexico and other Zika-affected areas. The Zika virus, now rampant in Central and South America and the Caribbean, is transmitted by mosquitoes. Most media reports have focused on its danger to pregnant women—it is linked to birth defects. However, people whose immune systems are compromised, including those taking high-dose steroids or undergoing chemotherapy, are at risk for serious illness from Zika. If you do go to (or live in) an infected area, wear insect-repellent all the time—the Aedes mosquito, which carries Zika, bites at any time of day.

More information: CDC.gov/zika/geo.

Phyllis Kozarsky, MD, professor of medicine at Emory University School of Medicine, Atlanta.

14

Having Some Fun

Fun Games for Grown-Ups to Play on a Smartphone, Tablet or Computer

Teenagers are not the only ones who can have a lot of fun playing games on their smartphones and tablets. A recent study found that two of the 10 most popular apps among people age 55 and older are games, including *Words With Friends* (see next page).

Six other exciting and mentally stimulating smartphone and tablet game apps*—some of them can be played on computers, too…

*Prices reflect the cost of the app itself and are subject to change. Many games also encourage players to make in-game purchases, but these are not required. Apps for iOS devices can be downloaded at the Apple App Store (or through iTunes)…for Android devices at Google Play (Play. Google.com)…and for Windows phones at the Windows Phone Store (WindowsPhone.com, then click "Games").

•**A crossword puzzle/jigsaw puzzle hybrid.** The game *Bonza Word Puzzle* looks a lot like a crossword puzzle, except there are no clues. Players instead are given a puzzle theme, plus jigsaw-puzzle-piece-like letter groupings. These letter groupings must be assembled together to form crossword-like interlocking words that fit the theme.

The first few puzzles in the starter pack are easy, but puzzles soon become more challenging. A new free puzzle is available every day. Free for Android and iOS.

•**A truly addictive game of trivia.** *Trivia Crack* is similar to the board game *Trivial Pursuit*. Players compete against friends or strangers answering multiple-choice questions in six categories—art, entertainment, geography, history, science and sports. Question difficulty is greatly varied.

Jason Parker, senior editor with CNET, a leading consumer technology website owned by CBS Interactive. He specializes in reviewing software and third-party apps. CNET.com

Trivia Crack games can move slowly, however—your opponent gets several days, if he/she wants them, to take his turn each time you get an answer wrong. For faster play, choose *Trivia Crack*'s "Challenge" option. With this, there are no alternating turns—all participating players try to answer the same series of questions in just a few minutes. Free for iOS, Android or Windows. Upgrading to an ad-free version for iOS or Android costs $2.99. Or play through Facebook (free, Facebook.com/triviacrack).

● **A captivating game of connect the dots.** Colored dots are arrayed on a grid in the engaging single-player game *Flow Free: Bridges*. The player's task is to trace lines connecting each dot to the dots of the same color—but these connecting lines can cross one another only where a "bridge" is provided on the grid. More than 1,000 different puzzles are included, each with a different pattern of dots and bridges. Free for Android, Windows and iOS.

Helpful: If you like *Flow Free: Bridges*, also try *Flow Free*, an earlier version of the game that does not include bridges. It's free for iOS, Android and Windows.

● **A beautiful, mind-bending maze game.** Players navigate through three-dimensional mazes in the visually striking game *Monument Valley*. The award-winning graphics are not the only reason it stands out—players must think their way through clever obstacles, such as M.C. Escher–like optical illusions. The app costs $3.99 for iOS, Android and Windows.

● **A Mahjong tile-matching game.** In *Mahjong Solitaire*, 144 tiles are arranged face up in a four-layer stack. Locate matching pairs of tiles, and they can be removed from the stack, exposing tiles previously hidden below. Remove all of the tiles to win. Several software companies have developed *Mahjong Solitaire* apps, but *Mahjong Solitaire Epic* is perhaps the best. It features attractive graphics and hundreds of different starting boards. An app simply called *MahJong* by software company ByteRun is very good, too. *Mahjong Solitaire Epic* is free for iOS, Android, Windows, Mac or PC. (A free trial of Mac and PC versions can be downloaded at Kristanix.com. $4.95 for the full version.) *MahJong* by ByteRun is for iOS only and is free.

● **A numbers game that makes addition addictive.** *Threes* is fun, fast and mentally challenging. Numbered tiles appear on a simple four-by-four grid. Players slide 1s and 2s together to create 3s…and slide 3s and multiples of 3 into matching numbers to double them—slide two 3s together to make a 6…two 6s to make a 12…and so on. But each time you slide a number, new numbers slide onto the board…and any other tile on the board that has room to slide that direction does so,

---

TAKE NOTE…

Words With Friends vs. Scrabble

Words With Friends is extremely similar to the classic game *Scrabble*. Both games are available on Apple and Android phones, while *Words With Friends* also is available on Windows phones. You can play either game on a computer through Facebook (Facebook.com/WordsWithFriends or Facebook.com/Scrabble).

So if you have an Apple or Android phone, which of these two games should you play? *That depends on…*

● **How well you spell.** In *Scrabble*, you lose your turn if your opponent challenges and it turns out that your word is not actually a word. Words With Friends is more forgiving—the app simply tells you that your word is not acceptable and lets you try again.

● **Which of these games your friends play.** The *Words With Friends* and *Scrabble* apps both let players challenge their Facebook friends—but you can challenge a friend only if that friend plays the same game.

● **Whether you also play the board game Scrabble.** The differences between these games are relatively minor—most notably, the board layout, points system and acceptable words lists differ slightly. But those minor differences could lead to costly mistakes if you try to jump back and forth between the games.

Example: You might lose a turn in *Scrabble* if you accidentally play a word that is permitted in *Words With Friends* but not *Scrabble*.

Jason Parker, senior editor with CNET.

too. Sliding tiles is easy at first, but as the numbers climb and the board fills with tiles, it becomes increasingly difficult to avoid getting stuck in a situation where there are no more moves that can be made, ending the game. The goal is to build the numbers on the board as high as you can.

It is free for iOS, Android and Windows. You can also play for free through Facebook (Facebook.com/threes-game).

---

9 Useful Things You Didn't Know Your Smartphone Could Do

Edward C. Baig, personal-tech columnist for *USA Today*, who reviews new devices and writes about consumer technology trends. He is coauthor of *iPhone for Dummies*.

Some individuals build their entire lives around their smartphones. Others use them just to make calls. But no matter where you fall on the spectrum of tech users, there are new apps as well as hidden features built into the phones that can make your life easier and more enjoyable…

SMARTPHONE APPS

1. Monitor your heart. Many people check their heart rates often for signs of a medical problem or to help determine fitness levels. The app *Instant Heart Rate* has more than 25 million users. You place your fingertip over your phone camera lens for 10 seconds. Using the camera sensor and flash, the app detects a color change in your finger from blood flow each time your heart beats and then calculates your pulse rate. *Instant Heart Rate* keeps a record of your tests so that you can share them with medical professionals and/or monitor the effects of your physical workouts.

Available for iPhone, Android and Windows Phone for $1.99.* (*Note:* Some Android phones, such as the Samsung Galaxy S5, come with a built-in heart-rate sensor on the back of the phone.)

*Prices subject to change.

2. Find dropped screws and other metal objects. These apps use the phone's built-in magnetic sensor to detect metals such as steel and iron. The apps are effective only within a few feet of the object, but that may be enough to avoid stepping on a nail that you dropped.

Free for iPhone (*Metal Detector*) and Android (*Metal Detector*)…99 cents for Windows Phone (*Magnetic Field Detector*).

3. Measure height and distance. These apps are useful if you need to check the dimensions of a room or the distance across your yard…or determine whether a piece of furniture will fit through your door.

Free for iPhone (*Dot Measure*)…$1.50 for Android (*Smart Measure Pro*)…99 cents for Windows Phone (*Measure Tools 8*).

4. Translate foreign languages. Point your phone's video camera at any printed material such as a road sign. The app replaces the words in the live picture on your screen with its English translation. It covers major languages including French, German, Italian, Portuguese, Russian and Spanish. The Android and Windows versions even work without an Internet connection.

This is a free feature in the *Google Translate* app for Android and iPhone. Windows Phone users can download a similar visual translator that is part of the free *Bing Translator* app.

5. Digitize documents. *CamScanner* allows you to take a picture of any document, receipt or photo and instantly convert it to a high-quality PDF or JPG file format. The ability to "scan" on the go without a cumbersome office scanner can be very useful. Features allow you to enhance scanned images, adjusting for low lighting and for documents with light print or handwriting. Free for all three major phone operating systems.

BUILT-IN FEATURES

Here are other things your phone can do for you without your having to download any apps…

6. Allow you to create a high-security password. Instead of using a simple four-digit code to unlock your phone, you can create a more complex password with a mix of letters, numbers and special characters.

iPhone: In the Settings menu, tap Touch ID and Passcode (or just Passcode on older phones), then Turn Passcode On. Turn off the switch that reads "Simple Passcode."

Android: In Settings, tap Screen Security, then Screen Lock. Select Password, then type in the password you want.

Windows: In Settings, tap Lock Screen, then Password. Type your password.

7. Take a screenshot. There may be times when you want your phone to capture a picture of what appears on your screen and save it—for example, detailed information on a web page that has constantly changing content.

iPhone: Press and hold the Home button, along with the Sleep/Wake button. The screenshot will appear in your Camera Roll section. If you have an operating system earlier than iOS 6, consult Apple.com for directions.

Android: Hold down the Power and Volume buttons at the same time. The image is saved to the Screenshots folder in your Gallery app.

Note: This works only for Android OS 4 or later. If you have an earlier version, you'll need to download the free app, *AirDroid*.

Windows: In Windows Phone 8.1, press the Power and Volume Up buttons at the same time. The screenshot is stored in the Screenshots album in Photos Hub. For Windows Phone 8, press and hold the Start button and Power button at the same time. The shot also is stored in your Screenshots album. Earlier Windows Phone versions do not have screenshot capability.

8. Enable you to see text more easily. If you're having a difficult time reading from your phone's small screen, you can change the size of the text.

iPhone: In the Settings menu, tap General, then Accessibility, then Larger Text and/or Bold Text.

Android: In Settings, tap Display, then Font Size.

Windows: In Settings, type Ease of Access. Under Text Size, move the slider to change the size of the text. This works only in Windows Phone 8 or later. Earlier versions do not allow you to change the text size.

9. Let you customize vibration mode patterns. With iPhones and Android phones, you can set your phone to vibrate in a different pattern depending on who is calling you—so you can tell, say, that your spouse is trying to reach you, even if your phone is not set to ring.

iPhone: Go to Contacts. Tap on a contact name. Tap Edit, then Vibration to choose or create a pattern.

Android: Go to Contacts, and tap on a contact name. Under Vibration Pattern, tap Default and choose a preset pattern.

Make Facebook Do Much More for You

Carolyn Abram, author of *Facebook for Dummies* and a former Facebook product manager. Dummies.com

---

The search bar located near the top of the screen when you sign into your Facebook account can do more than you might realize. *Not only does it let you enter keywords to locate your old Facebook posts— it's also a good way to…*

• **Find friends who share your interests.** You could search for "my friends in [your town] who like the ballet" to find an acquaintance interested in attending with you…or "my friends in [your town] who play poker."

• **Uncover new professional opportunities.** Search "my friends who work for [a company you would like to work for or do business with]" to find acquaintances who could help you get a foot in the door there. Or search for people in your field with whom you have something in common, such as "Queens College graduates who are CPAs."

Helpful: Entering "my friends who worked at GE" rather than "my friends who work at GE" will also list friends who have GE listed among prior employers.

• **Get recommendations from friends.** You could search "dentists in New Jersey liked by my friends" or "bed and breakfasts in Vermont liked by my friends."

• **Track down old posts by friends.** If you would like to go apple-picking, for example, and you recall that one of your friends posted about doing so in the past, search "apple-picking posts by my friends."

TIPS FOR BETTER SEARCHES

• **Use phrases.** Facebook is more likely to track down what you're looking for if you enter a complete phrase, such as "Italian restaurants in Chicago liked by my friends," rather than individual words, such as "Italian," "restaurant" and "friends."

Results are divided into subcategories, such as "Posts," "People" and "Photos." Posts will appear first. If you are trying to find a person, place or picture, click on one of the other headings near the top of the results page.

Example: If you search "my friends who like ice hockey," the first results that appear probably will be posts related to ice hockey written by your friends. Click on the "People" tab near the top of the page to instead get a list of your Facebook friends interested in the sport.

• **Expand the search parameters if the first search comes up empty.** If an initial Facebook search produces no useful results, try replacing "my friends who…" with "friends of my friends who…" Or expand the geographic area of the search by searching neighboring towns…or your entire state.

Example: If "my friends in [your town] who like ballroom dancing" does not turn up anyone, try "friends of my friends in [your state] who like ballroom dancing."

• **Add search criteria to cull long lists.** You can combine multiple factors to locate people with whom you have a lot in common.

Examples: You could search "friends of my friends who like knitting and yoga."

INTERESTING FINDING…

Facebook Fact

Facebook users spend 50 minutes/day on facebook, Instagram and Messenger on average. That is about one-sixteenth of all their waking hours.

US Bureau of Labor Statistics data, reported in *The New York Times*.

---

6 Blackjack Mistakes Most Players Make

Thomas Gallagher, former Las Vegas casino pit boss who now serves as a gambling coach and consultant. He is also author of numerous gambling workbooks, including *Blackjack Magic*, available through his website, TheGamblingSchool.com.

Blackjack is one of the best bets in the casino—*if* you play it well. Make smart decisions, and the house's edge on each hand can be well under 1%. Trouble is, most blackjack players make mistakes that significantly decrease their odds of winning.

One way to avoid these mistakes is to purchase a blackjack basic strategy card in the casino's gift shop—these typically cost just a dollar or two—then follow its instructions. Most casinos even allow players to refer to these cards at the table, particularly if the player requests permission to do so…is not playing for particularly high stakes…and doesn't take too long studying the card before each decision.

But if your pride prevents you from playing with a strategy card in front of you, at least avoid the following common blackjack mistakes…

MISTAKE: Taking insurance. This is almost never worth doing. When the dealer's up card is an Ace, he/she will ask if any player wants to take insurance. Players who wish to do so put out an additional bet that is worth half the amount of their original bet. If the dealer then reveals a blackjack, he will pay off these insurance bets at 2:1, covering players' losses on the hand.

But while insurance pays 2:1, the odds that a dealer showing an Ace has a blackjack are even steeper—approximately 9:4 against. That means declining the insurance is the better move in the long run. This is true regardless of what cards you have been dealt.

MISTAKE: Standing on 12 when the dealer shows a 2 or 3. The smart move is to hit. The cards 2, 3, 4, 5 and 6 are sometimes called "dealer bust cards" because the dealer is particularly likely to go over 21 when one of these is his up card. Thus players often stand on 12 when the dealer has one of these—that way the player avoids the possibility that he will bust before the dealer has a chance to do so. But not all dealer bust cards are created equal—while the odds of a dealer bust are high enough that it makes mathematical sense to stand on 12 when the dealer shows a 4, 5 or 6, you're better off hitting 12 when the dealer has a 2 or 3.

MISTAKE: Hitting a pair of 4s when the dealer shows a 5 or 6. The smart move is to split the 4s—that is, divide them into two separate hands, doubling your bet. It can be tempting to hit a pair of 4s because doing so feels safe—you won't bust even if you are dealt a 10. But when the dealer shows a 5 or 6, the odds that he will bust are so high that it actually makes more sense to split your 4s. That lets you get an extra bet on the table and doubles your payout if the dealer does indeed go over 21.

MISTAKE: Standing on a 16 when the dealer shows an Ace. The smart move is to hit. (Or split, if your 16 is a pair of 8s—see below.) It might seem counterintuitive to hit on 16—you will bust if you draw any card above five. But if you have a 16 and the dealer is showing an Ace, the odds are against you no matter what you do, and it turns out that hitting makes you slightly less likely to lose. In fact, it generally is worth hitting on 16 if the dealer is showing any card 7 or above.

Alternative: Some casinos offer a "surrender" option, which lets the player give up his hand after the initial cards are dealt and recover half the money he has bet (assuming that the dealer does not have a natural blackjack). Surrender usually is not offered at the low-minimum tables, but there is no harm in asking the dealer. If surrender is available, take advantage when holding a "hard" 16—that is, one that does not include an Ace—and faced with a dealer showing a 9, 10 or Ace...or when holding a hard 15 and faced by a dealer showing a 10.

MISTAKE: Splitting 10s.* The smart move is to stand on a pair of 10s, regardless of what the dealer is showing. Some players split 10s

*When blackjack players refer to a "10," they mean any card worth 10, which includes both 10s and face cards.

when the dealer is showing a bust card such as a 5 or 6. But while this might seem like a great opportunity to double your bet while the dealer is in a tough spot, it turns out you'll win more over time by just playing the two 10s as a hand of 20.

Also: Never split a pair of 5s either—double down (see below) if the dealer is showing anything less than 10, or hit if the dealer is showing a 10 or an Ace. Conversely, it is always worth splitting Aces or 8s regardless of what the dealer is showing.

MISTAKE: Doubling down on 11 when the dealer shows an Ace. When a player "doubles down," he doubles his initial bet and receives exactly one more card for his hand. Doubling down is almost always wise when your initial two cards total 11. After all, there's a solid chance that you will be dealt a 10, giving you a total of 21.

But contrary to the conventional wisdom, there is a time when doubling down is *not* the smart move with an 11. If the dealer is showing an Ace, you are better off just hitting...usually. *The wrinkle*—this advice assumes that the dealer will stand on "soft 17"—that is, he will not draw another card if he holds an Ace and a 6, which total 17. At some casinos, the dealer hits on a soft 17, in which case doubling down on 11 is the right move. (What the dealer does with a soft 17 can vary even from table to table within a single casino. Look for a sign on the table listing this and other rules. When possible, play at a table where the dealer stands on a soft 17—this slightly improves players' odds.)

If remembering what to do with an 11 against an Ace gets too confusing, at least remember that at any table it is worth doubling down on 11 against all non-Ace dealer cards... on 10 if the dealer is showing a 4, 5 or 6...or on 9 if the dealer is showing a 5 or 6.

To double down, simply place chips equal in value to your original bet next to that first bet. (If you have a pair, say "double down" as you do this so that the dealer doesn't mistake your bet for an attempt to split the pair.)

CHOOSE THE RIGHT BLACKJACK TABLE

There is one costly mistake that many blackjack players make before they are even dealt a card—they sit down to play at the wrong table. In the past several years, casinos have quietly reduced the payout on blackjacks at some tables. Traditionally, when a player hits a blackjack—that is, when his initial two-card hand adds up to 21—he receives 3:2 on his bet, such as $7.50 on a $5 bet. But some tables now pay just 6:5, which is just $6 on a $5 bet. Do not play blackjack at a 6:5 table—this one rule change makes it nearly impossible to beat the house even if you play very well. Usually there is a placard at the table that lists this and other table rules. If you do not see one, ask the dealer, "Is this 6 to 5 or 3 to 2 blackjack?" If all of the blackjack tables with stakes that you consider affordable at a casino are 6:5 tables, choose a different casino or do not play blackjack at all.

Save Big Bucks on Baseball Tickets

Jon Greenberg, former columnist for ESPN Chicago.

The average ticket to a Major League Baseball game now costs close to $30. A "premium" ticket for a seat close to the infield can cost $100 or more. But a day at the ballpark does not have to be a budget buster. It often is possible to obtain tickets for less than $15 apiece—occasionally less than $5. *Premium seats often can be had for less than $40. To find these deals...*

Where to buy: If your goal is to save money, the best place to purchase baseball tickets is on secondary-market websites, where tickets already purchased from the team are resold. These might be tickets owned by season ticket holders who cannot attend a particular game... or tickets purchased in bulk by brokers. Most baseball games do not sell out, so these sellers must price their tickets significantly below the amount the team charges to attract buyers.

Exception: Tickets can sell for above face value on the secondary market if a game does sell out. Baseball games especially likely to sell out include post-season games...opening-day

games...Fourth of July games...games during tight pennant races...and games between rivals played in relatively small stadiums, such as Yankees/Red Sox games in Boston's Fenway Park.

There are many different ticket-resale websites, but two stand out...

•**SeatGeek.com is not technically a resale site**—it's a consolidator site that displays tickets available from most of the major reliable online resellers in one place for easy comparison.

•**StubHub.com is the largest ticket-resale marketplace**—and the only major marketplace that does not currently list its tickets through SeatGeek.

When to buy: The longer you wait to buy tickets on the secondary market, the lower the price—up to a point. According to SeatGeek's research, baseball tickets are 37% cheaper on game day than 30 days earlier. But while it often is worth waiting, do not wait until the last minute. Many baseball teams require that secondary sites stop selling tickets to their games a few hours before the first pitch. With most teams, this cutoff is two to three hours before game time, according to SeatGeek, but with the Chicago Cubs, it's six hours before.

Helpful: To determine when your local team cuts off secondary sales, call the team's ticket department. Or visit StubHub or Seat-Geek repeatedly in the hours before a few of the team's games. Take note of when the tickets offered for the game suddenly disappear. If you miss this cutoff on game day, you can either buy tickets directly from the club at face value...or buy from scalpers outside the stadium if this is legal in your area. One way to get a good deal from scalpers is to wait until after the first pitch has been thrown, then drive a very hard bargain.

Bargain games: Bargains on the secondary market tend to be greatest for weeknight games...spring and September games (though prices can remain high in September if the team is in a pennant race)...and games against bad teams and/or teams from small markets.

The Best Motorcycles for Grown-Ups

Marc Cook, editor in chief of *Motorcyclist* magazine. He has been working for motorcycle publications and reviewing motorcycles since 1982. MotorcyclistOnline.com

Today's motorcycles are much more advanced than those sold just 15 years ago. Many include safety features you may be familiar with from cars. They're also more reliable—riding a motorcycle no longer requires mastering roadside repairs. And they're more powerful—the fastest sport bikes can top 200 miles per hour (mph). Many motorcycles now even have high-tech infotainment systems similar to those found in cars—and a few come with comfort features such as heated seats and handgrips.

But not every motorcycle makes sense for middle-aged and older riders. A bike that has a firm suspension, awkward seating position or so much power that it is touchy to control could quickly become uncomfortable for many riders. If you choose the right bike for your needs and preferences, though, it can be a great source of pleasure.

Great bikes for riders who want power and style as well as comfort and safety…

• **The big, powerful Harley you wanted when you were young—only better.** Harley-Davidson has long been known for muscular, heavily chromed, visually appealing cruisers that announce their presence with a low rumble. Most of today's Harleys still fit this classic Harley mold. But these days, hidden beneath that classic styling is cutting-edge motorcycle technology and much better reliability than the Harleys of the past—no more puddles of oil in the garage.

Harley-Davidson Dyna Low Rider stands out as a very well-made bike that combines classic 1970s Harley styling, a powerful 1690-cubic-centimeter (cc) engine and a reasonable sticker price. Its adjustable ergonomics make it suitable for even smaller bike buyers in search of a comfortable ride—this bike's handlebars and seat can be easily modified to fit the rider. Antilock brakes are a $795 option.

Base price: $14,399.*

• **A big touring bike for long trips.** In 2014, the *Harley-Davidson Electra Glide Ultra Classic* was substantially redesigned. It now combines classic Harley styling and power—like the Dyna Low Rider, it has a big 1,690-cc engine—with some refinements to to make this bike a great choice for extended journeys.

While most Harleys are air-cooled, this new Electra Glide features partial liquid cooling to prevent engine overheating even when laden with luggage on hot summer days. Harley added an unobtrusive radiator that does not interfere with the bike's attractive air-cooled style. It also comes with standard electronic cruise control…antilock brakes…an excellent infotainment system…and well-designed luggage that has an easy-to-use latching system.

The seats are low, deep and comfortable. The suspension's firmness can be adjusted to the rider's preferences, and the bike's fairing (the shell in front) does a very nice job of shielding riders from wind and rain. The only downside is the high price.

Base price: $23,549.

Helpful: This bike is available in an *Electra Glide Ultra Classic Low* model with a seat that's 27 inches off the ground, compared with more than 29 inches for the base model. It's a good choice for shorter riders, though it does boost the already steep sticker price by $1,150.

• **A comfortable, refined ride even on bumpy roads.** "Adventure touring" bikes are designed to go anywhere—around town…on long road trips…or even off-roading.

BMW R1200GS Adventure is the gold standard of adventure touring motorcycles. Its excellent adjustable suspension is designed to handle rocky trails, so it provides a very smooth ride on paved roads—even bumpy ones. Its seating position is upright and easy on the back. Its fairing does an effective job of keeping the wind and rain out of the rider's face…and it has less engine vibration than most bikes. Antilock brakes and stability control come standard. The R1200GS Adventure is a fairly large bike with a powerful 1,170-cc

*All prices and descriptions refer to 2016 model-year motorcycles, except as noted.

engine—but to BMW's credit, it feels remarkably light and nimble once in motion.

Base price: $18,695.

Alternative: *KTM 1290 Super Adventure* is a worthy competitor for this BMW in the adventure touring class. It is a bit lighter with a more powerful engine. Its base price is $20,499.

Warning: Like most of the adventure touring bikes, these have high seats—more height provides better ground clearance on uneven terrain but makes them challenging for shorter riders. Comparable bikes appropriate for shorter riders include the *Triumph Tiger 800* and *BMW G650GS*.

• **A great bike at a very nice price.** Arguably no new bike offers more for the money than the *Star Bolt*. This is a cruiser—its seating position designed for long rides, not breakneck speeds—made by Yamaha subsidiary Star Motorcycles and sold by Yamaha dealers. It offers clean, attractive styling, excellent reliability and a comfortable ride. It is light and easy to handle, and its 942-cc air-cooled engine provides ample power. The Bolt is small compared with some of today's big, beefy cruisers, but its size will seem more than adequate to riders who remember the slimmer bikes of the 1970s and 1980s. This is a really good motorcycle and a really, really good deal.

Base price: $7,990.

• **An even less expensive bike that is still enjoyable and reliable.** If even the $8,000 price tag of the Star Bolt is more than you want to spend on a motorcycle, consider the *Honda CB500* series. You might think of these as the Honda Civics of motorcycles—they're very reliable and reasonably priced…but not as exciting, distinctive, powerful or feature-laden as some of the other bikes on the road. That said, a CB500 still is a blast to ride—light, low and easy to maneuver—and it can provide plenty of pleasure for anyone new to motorcycling (or who hasn't ridden in decades). Its 471-cc engine is on the small side by today's standards, but this bike still will get off the line faster than the vast majority of cars on the road.

Honda offers several different models in the CB500 series, including the CB500F, which is somewhat sporty…and the CB500X, which is a scaled-down version of go-anywhere adventure touring bikes such as the BMW mentioned earlier. Both CB500s have a comfortable, upright seating position. Antilock brakes are available as a $300 option.

Base price: $5,999 for the CB500F…$6,499 for the CB500X.

Alternative: If you want a bike that's as well-made as the CB500 and nearly as inexpensive—only with a bit more personality—try the *Yamaha FZ-07*. It's a light, manageable bike with a comfortable upright seating position like the CB500F, but while the CB500 is fun for beginners, the FZ-07 is just flat-out fun for anyone. It has the responsive steering and driving feedback of a true sports bike and a larger engine. The base price for the FZ-07 is $6,990.

How to Grow Delicious Tomatoes…Problem-Free

Teri Dunn Chace, a gardening expert who has written more than 30 books, including *The Anxious Gardener's Book of Answers*. She lives in a small village in upstate New York. TeriChaceWriter.com

---

Homegrown tomatoes are typically better than store-bought. But sometimes things go awry just when you're looking forward to that wonderful flavor. *How to diagnose and address common tomato woes…*

• **Splitting fruit.** The reason? Inconsistent watering. Soak your plant roots thoroughly every few days (more often in hot, dry spells). Either run the hose at a trickle for a while or use soaker hoses. Apply an inch or two of mulch (straw is ideal) around your plants.

Small cherry tomatoes often split despite your best efforts. This is a case of the flesh outgrowing the thin skin. If it bothers you, pick them early.

• **Yellow or whitish blotches.** This is most likely due to *sunscald*. Insufficient coverage from the leaves often is to blame. Not only does it mar the look of the fruit, it spoils the flavor.

Tomato leaves dry and drop off when the weather is hot and you've neglected watering.

To prevent this, follow the watering recommendations above.

Pests and disease also cause leaf loss, which can lead to sunscald. Tomato hornworms—green caterpillars with a hornlike tail—can strip a plant. Keep a lookout, and the moment they appear, handpick them, then drop the worms into a bucket of soapy water. Soil nematodes (root-infesting worms), tiny flea beetles and various fungal diseases can damage leaves. In the future, look for resistant plants labeled VFNT (for verticillium wilt, fusarium wilt, nematodes, tobacco mosaic virus).

When tomato leaves become dried or tattered, remove them. They aren't going to recover. Dispose of them in the trash, not the compost pile, which won't get hot enough to kill pathogens or pests. You can then try to rescue tomatoes on already partially defoliated plants by providing shade, such as a strategically placed board, tarp or lawn chair.

• **Puckering at the blossom end.** This is called catfacing, and the tomato may go on to develop crevices, holes and scars. This malady usually is caused by cold weather. High nitrogen levels in the soil also can cause it.

Avoid it by waiting to plant your seedlings until danger of frost is past. If an unseasonable cold spell is predicted, protect plants with cloches (bell-shaped clear glass or plastic covers) or row covers—available wherever gardening supplies are sold.

If you suspect high nitrogen, don't grow tomatoes near grass if you use high-nitrogen lawn fertilizer, or you can withhold plant food in the vegetable garden until fruit starts to form.

• **A disappointingly small crop.** The most and best tomatoes are produced when daytime temperatures are in the 80s and drop to the 50s or 60s at night. If your summer is hotter or cooler, quality can suffer and the plants may produce less. Dry soil, too, discourages fruit set. See watering instructions above. Insufficient sunshine is a problem as well—tomato plants produce plentiful crops when they receive eight hours of sun a day.

Get Out of Your Wine Rut! Deliciously Different Wines for About $10

Jeff Siegel, the Wine Curmudgeon, a wine writer, wine critic and wine judge who specializes in inexpensive wine. He is author of *The Wine Curmudgeon's Guide to Cheap Wine* and oversees the award-winning Wine Curmudgeon.com website. He also teaches courses on wine, spirits and beer at El Centro College, Dallas.

Buying wine can be difficult, what with all the choices and too much "winespeak." How do you know whether you want to buy a wine with "aromas of wildflowers and a touch of spice?"

Is it any wonder, then, that it's easier to drink the same kind of wine—even the exact same wine—every time, even if it gets a little boring?

Fortunately, there are choices that are enjoyably different but that still have some of the same qualities of the wine you usually drink. With the information here, you can try something new with a good chance you will enjoy it—and expand your wine horizons during the process...

WHITE WINES

• **If you like chardonnay, try chenin blanc.** Chardonnay is one of the most popular white wines in the world, which means it's the white wine most people buy when they can't think of anything else to buy. If you want to try something new, a California or South African chenin blanc is an excellent alternative. These wines have many of the same fruit flavors as chardonnay, such as green apple, and the same sort of rich mouth feel, but without oak aging and the vanilla taste that often comes with it.

Ken Forrester Petit Chenin Blanc ($10), from South Africa, has the fruit flavors of chardonnay plus a touch of honey in the middle and some minerality on the finish. *Dry Creek Chenin Blanc* ($10), from California, has white fruit aromas, a taste of lemon peel and a sort of slatelike, fruit pit finish. Both of these wines are served chilled and are terrific with cheeses, salads and grilled chicken.

• **If you like sauvignon blanc, try albariño.** Sauvignon blanc drinkers are a loyal bunch, if only because they always have to defend their decision not to drink chardonnay. But even the most loyal of adherents can tire of the same thing glass after glass—which brings us to albariño, a Spanish grape. It has some of the same freshly acidic citrus flavors as sauvignon blanc, but they aren't as pronounced, and the wines can be almost spicy, a welcome change from sauvignon blanc.

Columna Rías Baixas ($10)—Rías Baixas is the region in Spain where the wine is from—has all of that, while *Bodegas La Cana Rías Baixas* ($10) has even more—citrus and tropical fruit, a long finish and even a bit of a salty tang. These, like sauvignon blanc, are great with seafood—grilled shrimp, fried oysters and the like—as well as poultry and salads.

• **If you like Champagne, try cava.** Champagne—the real stuff, which comes only from the Champagne region of France—is some of the most expensive wine in the world. It's almost impossible to find anything labeled Champagne for less than $30 a bottle, and Champagne that costs less than that doesn't taste much like it should.

Cava, the sparkling wine made in Spain, rarely costs more than $20 a bottle, and almost every cava around $10 offers value and quality. Know that it's made with different grapes than Champagne, so it doesn't taste as rich or as sophisticated. But it has the tight, firm bubbles that great sparkling wine should have.

Cavas such as *Dibon Brut Reserve* ($10) and *Perelada Brut Reserva* ($9) demonstrate this. The Dibon is creamy and caramel-like, with candied pineapple in the back and not as much tart apple as other cavas. The Perelada is impossibly well-done for the price, very crisp and with apple and lemon fruit. Both are tremendous values whether for toasting a birthday or the New Year or to enjoy with dinner, be it pasta with cream sauce or roast chicken.

RED WINES

• **If you like cabernet sauvignon, try a red blend.** Wine drinkers who like cabernet sauvignon like the assertive black and red fruit flavors, as well as the wine's tannins—which give a puckery feeling in the back of the mouth. The problem with finding an alternative is that cabernet is unique, and there aren't too many other grapes like it.

The solution? Look for red blends made with cabernet, a common winemaking practice and done especially well in France's Bordeaux region and much of California and Washington State. These wines still have cabernet's manly characteristics but are a little more subtle.

Château Bonnet Rouge ($10), from Bordeaux, is one of the world's great cheap wines, with red fruit, some earthiness and tannins that aren't overwhelming. California's *Josh Cellars Legacy* ($12) has sweet blueberry fruit, smooth-ish tannins and an almost cabernet-like heft.

Be aware that some red blends, such as Apothic and 14 Hands, are sweet—not as sweet as white zinfandel, but noticeably sweet—and taste very little like cabernet.

• **If you like merlot, try red Rhône-style blends.** Merlot is most people's cabernet alternative—it's fruitier and softer. As such, it's everywhere, a familiarity that can breed contempt and also accounts for the market being flooded with too much one-note merlot—with gobs of sweet fruit and nothing else. But red Rhône-style wines, made with the grapes popularized in France's Rhône region such as syrah and grenache, can offer appealing fruit flavor and merlot's softness, but they can be more interesting in the process.

One of the best examples is *Little James' Basket Press* ($10), a blend from the Rhône region that includes grenache, a red grape known for its juicy fruit. It also has some peppery notes, making it a good wine with beef, especially for everyday dinners such as hamburgers and meat loaf.

Also from France: *Le Coq Rouge* ($10), also mostly grenache, with enough red fruit to be pleasant, plus soft tannins and a bit of a finish—a pleasant taste that lasts in your mouth after you have swallowed the wine.

• **If you like Chianti, try nero d'avola.** Chianti from the Tuscany region of Italy is made from the sangiovese grape and is one of the great wines of the world. Nero d'avola, a grape common to Sicily, the island off the southern Italian coast, is one of the least-known grapes

241

in the world. What these grapes have in common is the ability to make fine wine.

A nero d'avola wine has some of the dark, earthy aromas that a Chianti has, though its fruit isn't as sour cherry—more black plum. But like its better-known cousin, it is fresh and approachable, making it a red wine to pair with the same sorts of dishes—sausages, red sauces and pot roasts.

Cusumano Nero d'Avola ($10) was one of the first successful Sicilian wines in the US. It is a little less dark and plummy than it used to be. But it is earthy and interesting, perfect for pizza night. *Cantine Colosi Rosso* ($10), a blend made with nero d'avola, is more Chianti-like, with juicy cherry fruit.

Marvelous Mocktails

Linda Gassenheimer, an award-winning author of numerous cookbooks, including *Delicious One-Pot Dishes* and *Quick and Easy Chicken*. She also writes the syndicated newspaper column called "Dinner in Minutes." DinnerinMinutes.com. Recipes in this article are from *Delicious One-Pot Dishes*.

S ometimes you want a festive cocktail but don't want the alcohol. These fun "mocktails" have no booze but lots of flavor.

POMEGRANATE MOJITO

A good Mojito has mint and lime muddled together. A muddler is a wooden or metal stick with a round end used to press against the fruit and herbs to release their juice and oils. In a pinch, you can use the handle of an unvarnished rolling pin or press the ingredients against a sturdy glass or shaker with a spoon.

1   cup unsweetened pomegranate juice
¾   cup sugar, plus 1 Tablespoon
12 mint leaves, plus 2 small sprigs for garnish
½   lime
1   cup club soda

Add the pomegranate juice and three-quarter cup of the sugar to a small saucepan over low heat. Stir to completely dissolve the sugar. Cut the half lime into two pieces, and add it to a pitcher with the mint leaves and pomegranate juice. Muddle the lime and mint. Place the

remaining one tablespoon of sugar on a plate. Remove two tablespoons of the pomegranate mixture to a bowl. Dip the rims of two 12-ounce glasses into the liquid in the bowl, and then dip them into the tablespoon of sugar to coat the rim. Half-fill the glasses with ice, and divide the pomegranate mixture between them. Divide the club soda between the two glasses. Place a sprig of mint on the side of each glass as a garnish. Two servings.

BITTERS AND TONIC

Serve this drink to guests who don't want to drink alcohol but who want something that looks like a "real" drink.

1 cup cold tonic water
5 dashes nonalcoholic bitters*
¼ fresh lime

Half-fill a lowball (about six-to-eight-ounce) glass with ice cubes. Add the tonic water and bitters, and squeeze in the lime juice. Stir. Drop a lime peel into the glass. One serving.

MOCK COSMO

This is a colorful drink to add to a fall or winter menu.

½ cup cranberry juice
1 Tablespoon lime juice
1 to 2 teaspoons sugar
¼ cup lemonade
Slice of lime, for garnish

Fill a cocktail shaker three-quarters full of ice. Add the cranberry juice, lime juice, sugar and lemonade. Shake well, about 20 to 30 seconds. (If you don't have a cocktail shaker, fill

*Regular bitters can have more than 40% alcohol, so opt for nonalcoholic.

a 12-ounce glass with ice and stir well.) Strain into a cocktail glass. Place a slice of lime on the rim of the glass as a garnish. One serving.

PEAR SPARKLER

Sweet pear flavor marries well with mint for this special drink.

12 mint leaves, plus sprig for garnish
1 cup pear nectar
¼ cup club soda

Add the mint leaves to a sturdy glass or bowl. Add the pear nectar, and stir well. Mash the mint with a muddler or against the sides of the glass with a spoon to release their oil. Half-fill an eight-ounce glass with ice. Strain the pear mixture into the glass. Pour in the club soda. Garnish the rim of the glass with a sprig of mint. One serving.

Dating: A Surprising Way to Boost Your Health

Judith Sills, PhD, a Philadelphia-based clinical psychologist and a contributing editor at *Psychology Today.* She is also author of *Getting Naked Again: Dating, Romance, Sex, and Love When You've Been Divorced, Widowed, Dumped, or Distracted.*

If you're not in a committed relationship, maybe it's time to consider dating again. And if you're age 50 or older—the point at which most of us become *much* more focused on staying healthy—then it is an especially good time to give dating a chance.

While the prospect of dating as a mature adult can seem overwhelming or downright scary, *here's some compelling motivation*—the latest research indicates that being in a relationship can improve your health in a variety of ways.

And take heart: There are specific tips for daters who are 50+ that can make getting out there again much easier.

HEALTH BENEFITS GALORE

Plenty of singles age 50 or older say they don't need a relationship to be happy. But those who are in committed relationships seem to have significant health advantages over those who fly solo.

Case in point: An analysis of data from more than 300,000 adults found that those without strong relationships were 50% more likely to die from *all* causes over a seven-year period—a risk that's the equivalent to daily smoking! Additionally, men and women who live alone and have a heart attack are twice as likely to have a second heart attack within a few months.

The list goes on. Married people are less likely to get pneumonia than singles, and those who are married or live together in midlife are less likely to develop dementia.

HOW TO GET BACK OUT THERE

You might not be sure that you want to get back in the dating game.

But one thing is certain: Humans have a deep need for intimacy and companionship.

And while some people are perfectly satisfied with their close friends and family, a healthy committed relationship generally offers a greater level of stability and support. After all, if your best friend moved to a different state, you wouldn't follow that person, but you likely would if it were your partner.

The advantage of later-life dating is that you've been through it all before. And you probably have some idea of what you're looking for. Also, while you may be a bit insecure in how you look as you age, you may have more confidence in your personality and social skills.

Advice for dating after age 50…

•**Get online.** The Internet is a fantastic way to meet people. The number of potential partners vastly exceeds those you'll meet any other way. If you're willing to put in the time—writing an interesting profile, putting up an attractive photo and wading through the possibilities—you *will* get dates. (They won't all be fabulous, but you'll start to meet people.)

There are hundreds of dating websites for you to choose from. The most popular sites, like Match ($42/one month*) and eHarmony ($59.95/one month), have the most members (and potential partners), but they tend to attract younger users.

Helpful: Try sites that target older adults, such as OurTime ($24/one month) or Senior-PeopleMeet ($29.95/one month). Monthly pric-

*Prices subject to change.

TAKE NOTE...
Dating Deal Breakers

Top 10 deal breakers for dating...

Disheveled or unclean appearance, cited by 63% of men surveyed and 71% of women...being lazy, 60% of men, 72% women...being too needy, 57% men, 69% women...lacking a sense of humor, 50% men, 58% women...living three or more hours away, 51% men, 47% women...bad sex, 44% men, 50% women...lacking self-confidence, 33% men, 47% women...watching too much TV or playing too many video games, 25% men, 41% women...having a low sex drive, 39% men, 27% women...and being stubborn, 32% men, 34% women.

Collection of six relationship studies published in *Personality and Social Psychology Bulletin*.

---

es are lower if you sign up for a longer time. Plenty of Fish is a free dating site for all age groups, although some features are only free if you "upgrade."

•**Don't waste time.** A survey by the Pew Research Center found that one-third of those who connect online never take the next step and meet face-to-face. Unless your only goal is Internet flirting, pin down a time to meet. You don't want to rush it, of course, but don't wait too long. If you like the person after exchanging three or four e-mails, it's time for a phone call or a meeting (in a low-key public place like a coffee shop). If someone you're interested in doesn't ask you out first, take the plunge and do it yourself.

•**Set aside your preconceptions.** Dating sites have analyzed what their members want—or think they want. Women, for example, tend to respond to men of certain ages, or with particular jobs or education levels. Men tend to reach out to women who are blond. Give other types of people a chance!

•**Give yourself (and your date) some slack.** When dating, you will no doubt have some anxious and awkward moments. What do you do when every attempt at conversation withers and dies? Or when your date doesn't laugh at any of your jokes? Give yourself and your companion a break. First dates are hard, but it does get easier with practice.

Helpful: Forget the traditional dinner date. It's too much for a first meeting, particularly if the chemistry isn't there—or when you discover between the first and second courses that you do not seem to have a whole lot in common. Meeting for coffee, a drink or lunch is easier and less expensive—and you can quickly cut your losses when it just isn't clicking.

•**Keep your insecurities in check.** No, you're not the same person you were 30 years ago. You might have a few extra pounds or a little less hair. Just do not let the nagging negative voice in your head—"I'm not good enough"..."She is way out of my league"...or "What if he doesn't ask me out again"—ruin what could be a perfectly pleasant time.

Your date saw *something* in you before you met. Relax and enjoy yourself. Besides, *everyone* is insecure on first dates. The person sitting across from you is probably having his/her own insecure thoughts.

•**It's not a job interview.** An unfortunate first-date strategy is to ask a lot of questions. Granted, asking questions and showing interest will keep the conversation going. But it can also be intimidating—or simply off-putting.

Some women tell me that they "interview" potential partners to save time. They ask things like, "Are you looking for something serious?" "Do you own or rent?" "What kind of relationship do you have with your ex?" Men do their own interviewing but tend to take their cue from the workplace, posing questions such as, "So tell me...where would you like to be in five years?" None of this is friendly give-and-take—it feels more like interrogation.

My advice: Be a little less efficient. A date is a chance to get to know someone...to reveal a little about yourself...and have some fun. *Keep it light.*

•**Aim for a full stomach.** There may be some truth to the old cliché—the way to a man's (or woman's) heart is through the stomach. A study in the journal *Appetite* found that women who were shown romantic pictures after they'd eaten had more brain activation than women who looked at the same pictures on an empty stomach!

15

On the Road

6 Things Car Dealers Don't Want You to Know

Today's car shoppers are harder to trick. Many know to refuse overpriced add-ons such as rust-proofing and fabric protection. They even may know they can get price quotes from multiple dealerships online and detailed information on dealer costs, rebates and financing.

But that doesn't mean customers—even those who think they have learned many of the standard tricks—can withstand all the tactics that a car salesperson can throw at them. That's especially true when they face some new twists on the classic sales techniques.

Of course, not all salespeople are out to trick you, but here are the things that a car salesperson might say that could signal he/she intends to try to get you to pay more than you should...

• **"I'm selling it to you for just $300 over cost.** Look up the invoice price yourself— you'll see I can't go any lower." Salespeople know shoppers have become used to looking up the so-called "invoice price" of a new vehicle online. So rather than try to hide this information, they sometimes encourage buyers to look up invoice prices...and encourage them to believe that these prices are what dealers actually pay for cars. They aren't. Invoice prices are sometimes referred to as "dealer cost," but in fact, automakers typically use "dealer holdbacks" and "dealer incentives" that reduce the amount dealerships pay to hundreds of dollars below invoice price— sometimes thousands.

What to do: Do not let a salesperson convince you that you are getting an incredible

Karl Brauer, senior director for insights into automotive trends at Kelley Blue Book, which provides information about new and used cars. He has more than 15 years of experience as an automotive journalist and was the first web-based journalist to be named to the jury of the prestigious North American Car and Truck of the Year award. KBB.com deal just because the price you are paying is fairly close to the invoice price. A better sign you're getting a good deal is if you are paying less than the typical buyer in your area paid for the same vehicle. Several major car-shopping websites provide this information, including my company's site, KBB.com.

• **"You have to decide today."** Car buyers can easily get quotes online from multiple dealerships, even dealerships hundreds of miles away. That gives salespeople more incentive to convince shoppers to buy the first time they set foot on a dealership lot—if they walk away, there's a strong chance they'll buy somewhere else. To encourage a quick purchase, a salesperson might claim a price is available only today...that supplies of a model are very limited...or that the dealership has only one vehicle with the desired colors and options and that another buyer is interested in it, too.

What to do: Ignore these classic high-pressure tactics. Buyers who move slowly and shop around almost always get better deals than those who rush. Any "today only" price you are offered is likely to be offered in the future, too.

Exception: It is possible that a "today only" price is available only today if it is the last day of a month and the dealership needs to make some final, quick sales to meet its quota and earn a bonus from the manufacturer. Even so, do not rush to buy unless you have researched the prices other buyers have paid for this vehicle and you are confident you are being offered a competitive price.

• **"We're a different kind of dealership—we offer no-haggle pricing."** No-haggle pricing, also called "guaranteed pricing," has been tried on and off for decades and is becoming increasingly common as dealerships try to attract buyers who dread the difficult, protracted negotiation process. It sounds sensible—almost everything we buy has a fixed price, so why not cars?

Trouble is, at many dealerships, the no-haggle guaranteed price is guaranteed to not be a very good deal. In fact, it often is not much different from the opening price the salesperson would have offered to a buyer who did negotiate. Choosing the no-haggle option just might mean you don't get to make a counteroffer.

What to do: Use a car-shopping website to check how the no-haggle price that you are offered compares with the price the typical buyer in your area is paying for the car. (You even can do this right at the dealership using your smartphone, tablet or laptop.) While some no-haggle prices are fair, in many cases you can save perhaps up to $500—potentially much more on a high-end vehicle—by haggling just a little at a no-haggle dealership.

Exception: If you buy a car from Tesla, the luxury electric-car maker, there is a fixed price and no haggling.

• **"Bad news—you didn't qualify for that interest rate."** Unscrupulous salespeople will sometimes offer an attractive deal...then make up an excuse for changing the terms when the deal is nearly finalized. Even smart buyers often fall for this—the buyer has invested so much time and mental energy in the purchase by this point that it would be psychologically difficult to walk away.

Increasing the interest rate charged for an auto loan is perhaps the most common way to do this. The dealership claims the buyer did not qualify for the low interest rate originally quoted. This lets the dealership pretend it's the buyer's fault that the original deal fell through—he/she didn't have a good enough credit rating.

What to do: Have a financing offer in place from a credit union, bank or some other third-party lender before you shop for a car. If the dealership tries to charge a steeper interest rate, use this financing instead.

Variation: The salesman offers a very appealing price for a buyer's trade-in in addition to a competitive price on a new car. When the deal is nearly done, the salesperson apologetically says he cannot offer nearly as much for the trade-in as promised because the dealership's service department discovered the vehicle had a hidden mechanical problem. Either walk away from the deal or pull the trade-in out of the deal and sell this used car through the classifieds or Craigslist.com.

• **"But everyone pays the vehicle-prep fee."** If a savvy car buyer won't pay a steep purchase price, the salesperson might move to plan B—agree to a fair price, then tack on hundreds of dollars in extra fees at the last minute when you are about to sign the papers. If the buyer protests, the salesperson will act surprised and claim that these fees are standard and unavoidable.

What to do: Well before you are about to sign the final papers, ask the dealership to quote you an "out-the-door price" that includes absolutely all charges. Some fees, including destination charges and tax, title and licensing fees, are truly unavoidable. Many dealerships also refuse to budge on a "documentation" fee, which covers processing the paperwork for the title and registration, although it is worth at least trying to negotiate this fee if it is significantly above $50. Many other fees, however, are negotiable, especially if you threaten to walk away. This includes dealer prep fees...delivery fees in excess of factory destination charges...and charges for add-ons you did not request and that are not necessary, such as vehicle identification number (VIN) etching on the windshield. Any fees that are charged should have been included in the out-the-door price you were quoted.

• **"If you buy a car, we'll pay off your loan on your trade-in."** The dealership might try to roll your current loan into your new one. Or it might delay paying off your loan, sticking you with late-payment penalties while it enjoys what amounts to an interest-free loan.

What to do: Check the total amount being financed in the new loan contract to confirm that the balance on your existing loan has not been rolled into it. Confirm that the contract stipulates that the dealership will pay off your loan by your next payment deadline.

USED-CAR SALES TACTIC

In a tactic that applies only to used cars, the car salesperson says...

"This used car is in great shape—I'll even show you the Carfax." Salespeople know that sophisticated used-car buyers are likely to check a vehicle's Carfax report before buying. This report lists the vehicle's accident rec-

ords and certain other aspects of its history. So salespeople steer sophisticated buyers to vehicles that have clean Carfax reports, then offer to provide these reports for free. This creates the impression that the salesperson is honest and that the car is problem-free. In reality, the salesperson might be using the buyer's faith in the Carfax report to trick him/her into failing to take prudent steps to uncover other significant issues. Automotive problems that do not result in insurance claims often do not find their way onto Carfax reports.

What to do: Pay an independent mechanic $200 to $400 to give a used car a prepurchase inspection before buying even if it has a clean Carfax report.

A Very Popular Car...

The most popular car to keep for 10 years is the Honda CR-V. Owners like its roomy interior and high safety and reliability ratings.

The rest of the top 10: Toyota Prius, Toyota Rav4, Toyota Highlander, Honda Odyssey, Toyota Sienna, Toyota Camry, Toyota Avalon, Honda Pilot, Subaru Forester. All these vehicles had 23% of owners or more owning them for 10 years.

On average, 13.5% of owners keep a vehicle for a decade.

Study by auto research site iSeeCars.com, reported at CBSNews.com.

Pros and Cons of Certified Used Cars

Certified used cars may be almost as good as new ones, at lower prices, but they sell for premiums over other used cars—sometimes less than $500, but sometimes $1,400 or more. Not all certified programs are the same—look for ones backed by manufacturers, not dealers. Programs run by manufacturers typically have higher standards. But even the manufacturer-backed programs can vary widely. Shop around for good deals and special offers—for example, Lexus may provide a loaner when your certified car is in for service.

Roundup of experts on certified used cars, reported at CBSNews.com.

Hazards of Car Backup Cameras

Karl Brauer, senior director for insights into automotive trends with Kelley Blue Book, which provides information about new and used cars. KBB.com

Backup-camera systems that give drivers a view behind the car are becoming increasingly common on new cars, and studies suggest that they do indeed reduce the odds of accidentally backing into things. But paradoxically, they can present their own dangers. *What you need to know to use your car's backup camera safely...*

• **A glance is not enough.** The display screen—in the dashboard or rearview mirror—usually is small, so you must pay close attention to spot all but the largest obstacles. And don't neglect to also look back over your shoulder to check whether there is anything just out of the viewing area of the camera.

• **The view varies greatly from vehicle to vehicle.** Some backup cameras show a full 180-degree span behind the vehicle...others

as little as 130 degrees. The narrower field of view could miss an obstacle...but the wider view distorts the image, making things look farther away than they really are. Take special care when driving a vehicle, such as a rental car, that has a different field of view than your own vehicle.

• **You can become too dependent.** Once you drive a car with a backup camera for a while, it's easy to forget how to safely back up if, say, your car's camera is covered by dirt or snow. Clean an obstructed lens as soon as possible.

• **"Around View" systems are available in some new vehicles,** especially Infiniti and Nissan models, with more on the way. They have cameras arrayed all around the vehicle, showing potential hazards on all sides. Consider choosing a vehicle equipped with this sort of system.

Driver Distraction Alert

Voice-controlled car systems distract drivers. Drivers who use hands-free systems to dial phone numbers, change music, send texts and do other tasks remain distracted for up to 27 seconds after talking to the systems. At a slow speed—25 miles per hour—a driver distracted for 27 seconds travels nearly the length of three football fields before returning full attention to the road.

Self-defense: Use the systems for as short a time as possible while driving and only to support elements of driving, such as navigation or climate control—not for entertainment purposes such as e-mail and web access.

Two studies of voice-activated car systems by researchers at University of Utah, Salt Lake City, done for the AAA Foundation for Traffic Safety, a nonprofit charitable organization based in Washington, DC.

A Hidden Danger for Drivers

Warren Brodsky, PhD, a professor at Ben-Gurion University of the Negev, Beer Sheva, Israel, and author of *Driving with Music,* reported by Rebecca Shannonhouse, editor, *Bottom Line Health.*

We all know that driving while gabbing on your cell phone (or, even worse, texting) is dangerous. What you might not realize is that merely listening to music—and your choice of music—can also result in unsafe driving. The CDC reports that nearly one in five injury-involved crashes is caused by distracted drivers. And listening to your favorite music can be distracting.

One study, for example, found that young drivers who listened to their favorite tunes (such as pop, hip-hop or rap) committed more traffic violations, drove more aggressively and made more miscalculations than those choosing "easy listening" tracks.

But no matter what your age, your music choices can affect your driving style, says Warren Brodsky, PhD, a professor at Ben-Gurion University of the Negev in Beer Sheva, Israel, and the author of *Driving with Music. Possible dangers...*

TAKE NOTE...

Safest Seat in the Car

Rear seats in cars are now less safe than front passenger seats. In cars made after 2006, someone sitting in the rear seat—even wearing a seat belt—has a 46% greater chance of dying in a crash than someone in the front passenger seat.

Reason: Automakers have focused on front-seat safety because there always is someone sitting in at least one of the front seats, and rear seats have not been similarly upgraded.

Caution: That does not mean front seats are better for kids—the rear seat is safer for children under nine years old and still recommended for all children under age 13.

ConsumerReports.org

• **High-volume music** can disrupt vestibulo-ocular reflexes and slow reaction times.

• **Fast-paced music.** In driving simulations, people who listened to fast-paced music committed more driving violations (such as disregarding red lights) than those who listened to slower-paced tunes.

• **Favorite music.** Actively listening to a favorite song uses cognitive space and can take your mind off the road.

Also, beware of "car"-aoke. If you're drumming on the steering wheel and passionately singing along, you're not driving safely.

So what's the safest music in the car? Low-volume easy listening or light jazz is probably your best bet!

You Don't Have to Give Up Those Car Keys

Patrick Baker, an occupational therapist, certified low-vision therapist and certified driver-rehabilitation specialist at the Cleveland Clinic in Cleveland, Ohio. Baker, also a clinical specialist in chronic pain and neurological and cognitive issues, works in an outpatient setting advising patients with all types of medical conditions. He has written textbook chapters focusing on driver rehabilitation and functional performance in older adults.

Driving may just be the most hazardous thing that most of us do each day, but simply growing older—or having a chronic medical condition, no matter what your age, that affects your vision, thought process or physical abilities—doesn't mean that you can't continue to be independent.

To drive safely as long as possible: It's crucial to proactively avoid problems that can limit your car-handling competence. *Here is how...*

PREEMPT PROBLEMS

Beyond commonsense imperatives such as getting regular medical, vision and hearing checkups, a few simple steps will help ensure that your driving abilities are intact.

At your checkup with your primary care physician, have a candid talk to discuss any medical conditions you may have that could affect your driving now or in the future.

For example, a stroke may result in lingering visual or movement problems...diabetes might be causing neuropathy in your feet, making it difficult to feel the gas or brake pedals...and cataracts, macular degeneration or glaucoma may limit vision if it's not carefully treated. A conversation with your doctor can help you minimize these issues and prevent them from becoming a bigger problem down the road. *Also...*

MANAGE YOUR MEDS

Some prescription or over-the-counter medications can impair your ability to drive by triggering drowsiness, cutting concentration, inducing shakiness or uncoordinated movements, or increasing your reaction time. Taking multiple drugs—a common practice among older adults and those coping with chronic medical problems—can make matters even worse by amplifying medication side effects. Certain dietary supplements, such as melatonin or valerian, may also have an effect.

What to find out: Show your doctor or pharmacist a list of *all* the medications (prescription and over-the-counter) and dietary supplements you take and ask how they interact and may affect your driving abilities. *Also:* Ask if the timing of when you take any drugs or supplements that may affect cognition or coordination can be altered—for example, taken before bedtime instead of in the morning.

Important: If you are on painkillers or narcotics, also ask your spouse or a trusted friend if the medication makes you "loopy"—an effect that you may not notice but is perhaps obvious to another person.

CUSTOMIZE YOUR CAR

Age can compromise your eyesight and bring physical changes that make it more difficult to see the road while driving—for example, many people lose one to three inches of height due to bone loss and spinal compression. Or a stroke or eye condition (such as cataracts) may affect your peripheral vision, interfering with your ability to spot traffic alongside your car. To address these changes, it helps to customize your car. *Here's how...*

•**Set power seats at the highest level.** Also, consider adding a firm cushion (such as the durable type used for outdoor furniture) to the driver's seat so that your chin is at least three inches higher than the top of the steering wheel.

•**Use extra (or bigger) mirrors inside and/or outside your car** to increase your field of vision. For example, you can get a mirror that attaches to your rearview mirror to expand your view to the rear. Or you can get bigger mirrors or extra mirrors that can be bolted onto existing side mirrors or the side of the car itself. Check with your car dealer for details for your make and model.

•**Keep your headlights clean.** Also, consider replacing the bulbs—even before they burn out. The bulbs get dimmer before they've completely burned out.

•**Opt for automatic.** If you're buying a new car, be sure to get one with automatic transmission, power steering and power brakes, which don't require as much strength to operate. Also, consider a car with backup alert sensors, which detect objects in your blind spots.

SPRUCE UP YOUR SKILLS

A driving refresher course (ideally taken every three to five years) will keep you up to date on the newest traffic rules and can reduce road mishaps.

Good news: Some car insurance companies even lower premium rates if you take one of these courses, which usually lasts four to eight hours. *Good choice:* A course such as those offered by AAA or AARP is likely to have an instructor who is well versed in issues facing older adults—as well as classmates who are true peers. If you are interested in taking a driver course because of a medical condition, consult The Association for Driver Rehabilitation Specialists (ADED.net) to find a program near you.

FOCUS ON FOOTWEAR

When it comes to hitting the gas and brake, what's on our feet can be just as important as our ability to see and react. *Consider these important footwear-related issues...*

•**Choose the right sneaker.** Running-style sneakers with soles that are thick, chunky and/or beveled can catch on pedals as you move your foot, so opt for a flat sole, such as a tennis-style or walking sneaker.

•**Go for thin soles.** People with diabetic neuropathy or limited foot sensation should wear thinner-soled shoes while driving. Thin soles, which don't have much padding between the bottom of the feet and the car pedals, give you a better sense of how hard you are pushing the brake and accelerator.

Important: Be sure to choose a car that "fits" you well—with good sight lines to the sides and rear...controls that are easy to reach...and a model that is easy for you to get in and out of.

Crooks Have a New Way to Break into Cars

Michael Calkins, manager of technical services at AAA, Heathrow, Florida. He has more than 35 years of experience in the automotive industry...is a certified Master Automobile Technician...and has an Associated Applied Science degree in auto mechanics. AAA.com

Thieves have discovered a new high-tech way to break into certain types of cars. The vehicles that are vulnerable constantly emit a low-power signal that automatically allows entry when the car's remote key fob is within a few feet of the lock, even if the fob is in a person's pocket or purse. The person who has the fob does not need to touch the fob—he/she just pulls the door handle open to gain entry.

The thieves don't steal the key fob—instead they use a portable radio-signal booster to trick the car into thinking that the fob, which might be, say, somewhere inside the owner's house and as far as 100 feet away, is close enough to the car to release the lock. If the fob also allows the car to be started with the push of a button on the dash, as some do, the thief even can drive the car away without having a key.

What to do: If your vehicle has this type of entry system, park in a locked garage when

---

---

possible. If you park outside, do not leave valuables in view—even when the car is parked in your own driveway.

If you want to be especially cautious, store your key fobs inside a metal container when they are not in use to block any incoming radio waves. Encasing the fobs in aluminum foil or storing them in a small decorative tin also works. Don't leave them in a wooden drawer.

Do not store your key fobs inside a freezer, refrigerator or microwave oven, as some people have recommended. While these appliances can block radio waves, key fobs can be ruined by condensation when repeatedly cooled and warmed...and they definitely will be ruined if someone accidentally turns on the microwave with the fobs inside.

Make Car Rides More Pleasant for Pets

Michael W. Fox, DSc, PhD, BVet Med, a veterinarian based in the Minneapolis area and former vice president of The Humane Society of the United States. He writes the syndicated newspaper column "The Animal Doctor" and is author of several books about animals including *Dog Body, Dog Mind* and *Cat Body, Cat Mind*. DrFoxVet.net

Do you dread car rides with your pet? Does the animal pant or get physically ill in the car? Some dogs and cats

251

suffer from anxiety or motion sickness in cars. *To make car rides more enjoyable...*

OVERCOMING ANXIETY

•**Desensitize your pet to your car.** Play with the pet inside the vehicle with the engine turned off. Provide treats. Do this several times until the pet seems calm, then repeat the process with the engine on but the car stationary. Then take the pet on short drives, providing treats along the way, before attempting longer trips.

•**Try lavender oil.** Lavender has long been known to have a calming effect on humans. Studies have shown that it has a similar effect on nervous dogs. Anecdotal evidence suggests that it works for cats, too. Mix 10 drops of lavender oil into one ounce of water in a spray bottle, then spray the inside of your vehicle approximately one hour before taking the pet on a ride. Bring this spray bottle along on long drives, and give an additional spritz in the air if the animal shows signs of anxiety, such as excessive movement or barking. Or you could put drops of lavender oil on cloth strips and hang these in the car...or put a few drops on a bandanna, then tie this around the pet's neck.

Warning: Don't spray lavender oil onto a cat's fur. Licking up lavender oil can cause stomach discomfort for cats. This does not seem to be an issue for dogs.

•**Buy a pet harness or transport crate,** and use this to secure the animal in the car. Some cats and dogs do not like crates and harnesses at first, but these items generally do help pets feel more secure once they get used to them. (Crates and harnesses significantly decrease the odds that the pet will be injured in a car accident, too.) And a pet in a harness or crate cannot run around the vehicle making you anxious as you drive—your pet can sense your anxiety, and it will make the pet more anxious. Avoiding sudden starts and stops and listening to soothing music can help both driver and pet stay calm in the car.

•**If all else fails, ask your vet if he/she can prescribe an anxiety medication** such as Xanax or Valium for your pet before long trips.

COMBATING MOTION SICKNESS

•**Place a small amount of ginger**—crystalline ginger or fresh chopped gingerroot—into a small ball of a food the dog loves, such as cream cheese or peanut butter, and feed it to the pet around 30 minutes prior to a car trip. A fingertip-size piece of ginger is sufficient for a 30-pound dog. For cats, you can try shredding a tiny bit of ginger into food, but cats are notoriously finicky.

•**If the ginger does not do the trick, give your pet *Dramamine*** 30 to 60 minutes before car trips. The typical dosage is 12.5 milligrams (mg) for a cat...or two to four mg per pound for a dog.

The 12 Best Road Trips in America

Jamie Jensen, author of *Road Trip USA: Cross-Country Adventures on America's Two-Lane Highways,* which is now in its seventh edition. Based in New York City, he has been writing about roads for more than 20 years. RoadTripUSA.com

Summer travel does not have to involve airline hassles or interstate highway tedium. If you select interesting secondary highways, getting there truly can be half the fun.

America is full of roads that offer incredible views...interesting history...stops in charming towns...and/or twists and turns that make driving fun. And with the current low gas prices, this is a great year for a road trip. *Twelve great American roads...*

THE PACIFIC STATES

•**Historic Columbia River Highway** is an unforgettable drive through Oregon's majestic Columbia River Gorge in the Cascade Mountains. Multnomah Falls is the most spectacular of several different waterfalls—it drops 620 feet to the densely forested canyon floor that's below.

This historic highway has been largely replaced by nearby I-84, but several segments remain open to vehicles. If you are headed east from Portland, take exit 17 off I-84 in Troutdale. If you are headed west, take exit 35 off I-84 in Dodson. A second segment can be reached by taking Highway 30 east from I-84 exit 69 in Mosier...or west from I-84 exit 83 in The Dalles. The total driving distance is around 80 miles.

●**Oregon Coast Highway**—the Oregon section of Route 101—traces the state's rocky, forested Pacific coastline for its entire 340-mile length. Fishing and logging towns dot the route, but the real highlight is all the unpopulated space between the towns—there are numerous state parks along the Oregon coast. The ocean usually is in view from Route 101, and there are many places, such as Cannon Beach or Cape Blanco, where you can stop for a stroll along a Pacific beach that you might have completely to yourself.

●**California Highway 1 between Carmel and San Simeon** is a 90-mile stretch of road offering unforgettable views of the Pacific Ocean. Unlike most of the California coast, this area is largely undeveloped, with just one small village—Big Sur—along the way. (This road is sometimes called the Big Sur Highway.)

There's just one problem—the breathtaking beauty of this drive is no secret, and the road often is clogged with slow-moving traffic in the summer. You might want to consider driving it early in the morning or in autumn or spring when it is likely to be less crowded.

THE SOUTHWEST AND MOUNTAIN STATES

●**Highway 50 across Nevada** has been called "The Loneliest Road in America." You can travel for more than 400 miles—over mountain ranges...through forests and desolate open stretches...past Great Basin National Park—all without seeing many other cars. It's truly a unique driving experience to feel so completely alone on the road, but every 100 miles or so a town appears with at least one gas station, restaurant and motel. The road roughly follows the path once used by the Pony Express, and with so few cars around, it is easy to imagine you are back in frontier times.

●**Going-to-the-Sun Road in Montana's Glacier National Park** just might be the world's

most scenic drive. The 50-mile roadway provides awe-inspiring views of mountains and valleys as it winds over the Continental Divide. Vehicles longer than 21 feet and/or wider than eight feet are not allowed on certain sections because of the tight turns and narrow lanes. Portions of the road are closed from early fall through late spring because of snow.

The park entrance fee must be paid to drive it. A vehicle permit valid for seven days costs $30 during the summer months. (If you are 62 or older, you can purchase a lifetime Senior Pass for all national parks for $10 in person or $20 online or in the mail.)

●**Old Route 66 across western Arizona** is one of the few stretches of the legendary Route 66 that remains almost as it was back in its pre–World War II heyday. You'll see mostly the same motor courts and roadside attractions, beautiful vistas and dusty villages that you would have seen if you had driven this road decades ago.

Though it was removed from maps in 1984, Route 66 has been resurrected as an official historic route. Take exit 1 from I-40 soon after crossing the California/Arizona line. This part of old Route 66 is now the Oatman-Topock Highway (Highway 10). When you reach Kingman, follow the road now called Arizona 66 to Seligman.

●**Million Dollar Highway**—that's US-550 between Silverton and Ouray in Colorado's San Juan Mountains—climbs to more than 10,000 feet above sea level, making it among the highest-elevation highways in America. The views are spectacular—as is the danger. This narrow, 25-mile stretch of road snakes along mountain sides, often without so much as a guardrail between your car and a drop of thousands of feet.

Do not attempt this drive at night or in bad weather. Drive it northbound if you prefer to hug the side of the mountain...southbound if you want the full experience of being just a few feet from a very long drop. It can be exhilarating and is definitely memorable!

THE HEARTLAND

●**The Iowa section of the Lincoln Highway** lets drivers recapture the feel of old-time, small-town America. The Lincoln Highway might not be as famous as Route 66, but it was America's first cross-country road when it connected New York to San Francisco in 1913. The interstates rendered it obsolete by the 1950s, but you still can follow what is essentially the old Lincoln Highway by taking present-day US 30 across Iowa. Keep your eyes open for red-white-and-blue Lincoln Highway roadside markers—the route diverts from US 30 in places. While modern highways bypass towns, this one goes right through lovely little communities such as Belle Plaine and Woodbine.

• **Great River Road** follows the Mississippi River for 3,000 miles, but the roughly 450-mile stretch between Hannibal, Missouri, and La Crosse, Wisconsin, is particularly scenic. You'll see dramatic cliffs and bridges—and, of course, many wonderful views of the Mississippi River. Towns worth visiting along the way include Galena, Illinois, a nice antiquing town…and Nauvoo, Illinois, the former home of the Mormon Church before it moved to Salt Lake City. The town of Nauvoo has been restored and rebuilt to look as it did in the 1840s.

The Great River Road route is marked by white road signs featuring a green pilot's wheel logo. To pick up the route northbound from Hannibal, cross over the Mississippi on I-72, then take 1-72 north to Illinois state highway 57 north. To pick up the route southbound from La Crosse, take Wisconsin state highway 35 south. A free map of the Great River Road can be ordered at ExperienceMississippiRiver. com.

THE ATLANTIC STATES

• **Blue Ridge Parkway** is a wonderfully scenic 469-mile drive through the Blue Ridge Mountains of western Virginia and North Carolina. The parkway's high elevation provides sweeping views of the surrounding countryside. The US Park Service owns the road and surrounding land, so no billboards and few buildings block the view. This is not the road to choose if you're in a rush, however—the speed limit is a sedate 45 miles per hour most of the way. Nearby Asheville, North Carolina, boasts America's largest home, the Vanderbilt family's Biltmore Estate.

• **Overseas Highway** is a 127.5-mile stretch of US 1 connecting the Florida Keys to Miami and the mainland. For long stretches all you can see is blue sky, emerald sea and the road stretching out ahead. The exits lead to white-sand tropical isles rather than to towns or cities. It's a drive truly unlike any other in America.

• **Vermont Route 100** has 200-plus miles of forests, mountains, rivers and picturesque towns with hardly a billboard or chain restaurant in sight. Much of the southern portion of Route 100 runs inside or along the edge of the Green Mountain National Forest. The road can get congested in the fall when the leaves change color, but it's beautiful at any time of year.

16

Family Time

When Grandparents and Parents Disagree About the Kids

Do you cringe when your grown children coddle your grandchildren too much? Does your blood boil when your parents give your child a treat after you told the child he could not have it? Welcome to the club. Disagreements between grandparents and parents about child-rearing occur in the majority of families. The result can be arguments, anxiety and strained relationships—even though everyone wants only what's best for the children.

It is perfectly normal for different people to have different ideas about how best to raise a child. But this can be a difficult topic to discuss without ruffling feathers.

Parents tend to be touchy about any comments critical of their child-rearing. They are working hard to raise a family and don't want to be told that they are getting it wrong.

Grandparents, as well, have trouble accepting criticism about their way of treating their grandchildren because, after all, they've had plenty of experience raising kids and are just trying to help.

Here's how grandparents and parents can respond to this challenge...

THREE TIPS FOR GRANDPARENTS

Silence usually is the wisest response when grandparents disagree with their grown children on parenting matters. Your concerns as grandparents might be legitimate, but your child is not likely to respond well to hearing them. The best solution usually is to just let it go. Remind yourself that parenting is hard—

Nancy Samalin, founder and director of Parent Guidance Workshops, a New York City–based organization that has been working with parents and grandparents for more than three decades. She is a best-selling author of numerous books, including *Loving Without Spoiling and 100 Other Timeless Tips for Raising Terrific Kids*. Samalin.com

255

harder than grandparents tend to remember—and that your child is doing his/her best.

When you feel you absolutely must say something…

1. Speak with a person you respect who is objective before voicing your concerns to the parent. Ask your spouse or a trusted friend whether he/she agrees that something needs to be said. This person might provide helpful insight into the situation. If nothing else, expressing your concerns to this person lets you get whatever is bothering you off your chest, which often can reduce your need to confront your son or daughter.

If you know and respect a parent who has children similar in age to your grandchildren, this could be a particularly good person to chat with about your concerns. He/she might be able to help you see the matter from your own son's or daughter's perspective.

Each generation raises children very differently from the one before, so something that seems troubling to you might simply be the way things are being done these days.

Example: You are appalled that your daughter let your granddaughter dye her hair purple—something unthinkable when your own daughter was a teen—but nowadays purple hair is quite acceptable.

2. If you still feel you must say something, phrase it by commiserating about the challenges of parenting, not as criticism of your child's choices. If you begin with criticism, the parent likely will become defensive and the conversation will degenerate into an argument. Instead, start by expressing honest empathy about the difficulties of raising children, then transition gently to a nonjudgmental conversation on the subject you hope to discuss.

Example: If you think your daughter lets your grandkids spend too much time watching TV and smartphone screens, you could say, "I remember when we were trying to decide how much TV was too much for you when you were little. These days, kids carry smartphones with them wherever they go. It must be even harder to keep screen time under control."

3. Get into a habit of complimenting your children about their parenting. One way to improve the odds that your kids will listen to your parenting opinions in the future is to make the vast majority of your parenting opinions favorable. Praise them when they handle difficult parenting situations well. Mention what a good job they are doing overall. That way, when you do voice a concern, you will seem less like a nag and more like an ally offering potentially helpful advice.

THREE TIPS FOR PARENTS

For parents, these disputes can fall into two different categories—some don't like the way the grandparents handle the grandkids…while others just wish the grandparents would stop criticizing their parenting. *Strategies for both of these situations…*

1. Stifle your natural impulse to fire back when your parents (or in-laws) criticize your parenting. Your feelings might be bruised, and you might be bursting to respond…but will that really improve the situation? It's more likely to lead to an argument. In the interest of family unity, instead try to react in a neutral, nonconfrontational manner, such as, "I guess we have a different approach to that" or "I'll think about that"…then change the subject.

If you suspect that the topic might come up again, seek out an article, study or parenting authority whose position on the matter is in line with your own. Cite this when the grandparent next raises the issue. That way, if the grandparent wishes to continue the argument, he/she will be arguing with this expert source rather than with you.

Example: Your mother-in-law claims you shouldn't let your children swim right after eating. Thank her for thinking of your children's safety, then explain that researchers now say that swimming soon after eating is not actually a safety risk. If you have a smartphone handy, you could type the words "swimming after eating" into a search engine and pull up confirmation of this, ideally from a source this grandparent knows and respects.

2. Express your concerns from the grandchild's viewpoint rather than your own. If you present the information as if it came directly from your child, it's more difficult for the grandparent to argue the point with you.

TAKE NOTE...

Just One Hour of TV Is Too Much!

Children who watch even one hour a day of television are more likely to be overweight or obese when entering kindergarten than children who watch less TV or none. On average, kindergartners watch about three hours of TV daily.

Study of more than 11,000 children attending kindergarten in 2011–2012 by researchers at University of Virginia, Charlottesville.

Example: A grandfather seems to favor one grandchild over another. If you confront the grandfather about this, he probably will deny it. Instead, tell him that your child believes this to be true. "It's wonderful that you have a close bond with Sally, but Bobby asked the other day, 'Why doesn't Grampa like me as much as my sister?' What can we do to help him feel that he's as special to you as Sally is?"

3. When you trust your kids to their grandparents' care, cede at least some control to the grandparents. You get to set the rules when you hire a babysitter because that babysitter works for you. A grandparent is not an employee—he/she is a family member who is helping you by looking after your kids. It is OK to tell this grandparent how you prefer to handle certain matters, but if the grandparent chooses to do things differently, you generally should either live with it or stop leaving your child in this grandparent's care.

If the matter is important to you, you could try to modify the grandparent's behavior by making a heartfelt request rather than a demand.

Example: You believe strongly in feeding your child only organic foods...but your mother thinks you are going overboard with the dietary rules and gives your child junk food. It is acceptable to say, "I know we are never going to see eye to eye on this, and I don't expect you to do exactly what I would, but could you at least try to meet me halfway?" Even if your mother thinks you are unreasonable on this issue, the way this request is phrased is entirely reasonable.

If your child asks why different rules apply when Grandma is in charge, explain that in Grandma's house Grandma is the boss...and/or that when Grandma is visiting, it's a special occasion.

Is Your Child Getting Enough Water?

Most kids in the US are not drinking enough water. Half of children between the ages of six and 19 are not adequately hydrated. Chronic dehydration can result in kidney problems, heatstroke, headaches, irritability, poor circulation, reduced physical performance and poor mental functioning. Children are more susceptible to dehydration than adults because they adapt to heat more slowly.

Best: Encourage kids to drink plain water, not juice or sports drinks. Infuse it with fresh fruit such as oranges...vegetables such as cucumbers...or herbs such as mint to enhance the taste without adding sugar. Serve it ice-cold when possible (or use frozen water bottles in lunch bags)—cold water tastes better to children than room-temperature water.

Analysis of data from 4,134 children ages six to 19 led by researchers at Harvard T.H. Chan School of Public Health, Boston, published in American Journal of Public Health.

Surprising Autism Indicator

Reaction to smells may help with diagnosis of autism. Most people instinctively inhale pleasant smells deeply but limit breathing of unpleasant ones. Children with autism don't make this adjustment as quickly. In a small study, the researchers were able to determine which children had been diagnosed with autism 81% of the time based on how quickly the children responded to certain odors.

Study by researchers at Weizmann Institute of Science, Rehovot, Israel, published in Current Biology.

Common Pesticides Linked to ADHD

Pyrethroid pesticides, considered safer than other pesticides, are the most widely used for home and public-health pest control. But a recent study found an association between exposure to these pesticides and *attention-deficit/hyperactivity disorder* (ADHD)—although it did not find that the pesticides caused ADHD. The link was stronger in boys than girls. More research is needed, but thoroughly washing produce may help to limit pesticide exposure.

Study of almost 700 children by researchers at Cincinnati Children's Hospital Medical Center, published in *Environmental Health*.

Cell Phone Addiction

More than half of college students admit they are addicted to their cell phones. Female college students average 10 hours a day on their phones. Males average almost eight hours. Top activities include texting (94.6 minutes/day) and sending e-mail (48.5 minutes).

Study of college students led by researchers at Hankamer School of Business, Baylor University, Waco, Texas, published in *Journal of Behavioral Addictions*.

Track Your Family for *Free*

Track friends and family with free apps on an iPhone or Android phone. The apps allow users to stay in touch with elderly parents, keep track of children and find lost or stolen phones—and are used by spouses who are suspicious of their partners. These apps are becoming regular elements of divorce cases. *Connect* follows people you are connected to through social-media sites. *Find My Friends*

258

shows contacts on a map who have chosen to share their location data. *Phone Tracker* and *Glympse* combine mapping and GPS technology to let you track your phone and one other. (The PhoneTracker upgrade allowing tracking of 10 users costs 99 cents.)

Roundup of experts on tracking apps, reported at MarketWatch.com.

Don't Bite Your Tongue: What to Say When Your Adult Children Make Bad Choices

Ruth Nemzoff, EdD, resident scholar at Brandeis University's Women's Studies Research Center who lectures on topics including parenting adult children. She is the mother of four adult children and author of *Don't Bite Your Tongue: How to Foster Rewarding Relationships with Your Adult Children*. DontBiteYourTongue.com

Your grown child is spending money that he/she should be saving...making questionable career choices...or marrying the wrong person. What do you do?

Many parents think their best option is to say nothing when they disagree with their adult children's choices. Adult children are,

BETTER WAYS...

To Help a College Grad Get a Job...

Look within your company—entry-level jobs often are filled through referrals, not by postings... *talk to people you know at other companies*, including ones in other industries, on the new graduate's behalf...*get permission from your company to have the grad shadow you* so that he/she learns what work is like in your office and industry...*help him/her with mock interviews* for practice...*try setting weekly goals*—for example, reaching out to 30 companies and getting three interviews—and help him refine his approach if he does not accomplish what he wishes.

USNews.com

after all, adults who have a right to live their own lives. And speaking up could sour the parent-child relationship.

But the "bite your tongue" approach to parenting adult children is doomed to fail. Saying nothing increases the odds that your child will make poor decisions. It means that you must live with the knowledge that you did nothing to help. And it might not even protect your relationship with the child—adult children usually can deduce from their parents' tone and body language that they are not happy with a choice even when their parents don't say so.

The secret to maintaining family harmony when you disagree with your adult child is to say something but say it in a way that minimizes ruffled feathers. *Here is an eight-step plan for doing that…*

1. Seek a neutral party's opinion. Before you confront your child, ask a friend or acquaintance whether your concerns are truly justified. Select someone who has experience with the topic—your financial planner if it's a money matter, perhaps…or a level-headed member of your child's generation if you suspect that your concerns might stem from a generational divide.

Example: A mother was upset that her 20-something son was dating a woman who had several tattoos. When this mother spoke with a coworker who was also in her 20s, she learned that "body art" is extremely popular with today's young adults—even among respectable, responsible women.

Whomever you consult, make it clear that you are after honest input. If you fail to spell this out, your "consultant" might take your side out of solidarity even if he/she disagrees. You might want to check in with more than one consultant before talking with your child.

2. Find a private, low-stress moment to raise concerns. *When* you choose to speak up can matter nearly as much as *what* you say. The best time for this conversation is whenever your child tends to be most relaxed.

Examples: If your child has young children, the best moment might be when the kids are napping or at school. If he has a high-stress job, it might be on the weekend. If he

always seems busy, ask him when he has time for a phone call or a cup of coffee.

Do not voice your concerns in front of other people—that only increases the odds that your child will become defensive. If you and your spouse both take issue with the child's decision, the parent with whom the child historically has had an easier time discussing difficult topics is the one who should have this conversation.

It is acceptable for both parents to take part if both feel very strongly about the matter and both get along well with the child. But you don't want your child to feel ganged up on. One way to avoid that is for you and your spouse to be frank about the slightly different views you both most likely have.

3. Open your discussion with curiosity. If you begin this conversation by blurting out your opinion, you and your child will immediately be at odds. Instead, you could begin with, "I've been wondering about…" and ask questions that allow your child to calmly explain his thinking. You might find that your opinion will change. These questions should sound curious, not judgmental—they must not be thinly veiled attempts to express displeasure.

Examples: You disagree with your daughter's decision to "co-sleep" with your grandchild (allowing the youngster to share her parents' bed). Your questions should express curiosity about co-sleeping, such as, "That wasn't something we did. What are the advantages?" Your questions must not have an obvious negative tone, as in, "Why would anyone do such a thing?"

4. Cite your own mistakes or shortcomings. You might imagine that presenting yourself as an expert on a topic would encourage your child to heed your guidance. In fact, the opposite is more likely to be true. Adult children desperately want their parents' respect. If the tone of this conversation leans toward, "I'm your parent and I know better," the child likely will feel disrespected and tune out your advice. The child is more likely to listen to what you have to say if you instead mention a related topic that you struggle with…or reveal an occasion when you made a mistake in this area. This sends the message that you respect the child as an equal.

Example: "When your mother and I purchased our first house, we did exactly what you're thinking about doing—we stretched our budget. For the next few years, we spent a lot of nights lying awake worrying whether we could pay the mortgage. In retrospect, I wish we had bought something less expensive."

5. Compliment the child, then blame your concerns on your own shortcomings. This makes it less likely that the child will become defensive. Say that you know the child is intelligent…or cite a smart decision he made in the past. Then ask the child to discuss the decision to reduce your anxieties…or to help you understand a topic you struggle with.

Example: "I know you're right a lot more often than you're wrong, so I'm sure you've thought this through. But for my peace of mind, I was hoping we could talk about your plan for quitting your job and starting your own company. You know how I worry."

6. Offer your advice if you feel it has value. But don't expect your child to follow that advice—and don't hold it against her if she doesn't want to.

Example: "This is just my opinion, but I don't think you should let your husband make fun of you like that. In my experience, jokes at a spouse's expense lead to escalating disrespect. But I also know that there's no way I can fully understand someone else's relationship, so maybe I'm misreading the situation. Now that I've said my piece, I won't mention it again."

7. Suggest that the child speak with a third party. Many adult children find it psychologically easier to take advice from someone other than a parent.

Example: "I'm no financial expert, but your cousin Tom is a financial planner. Why don't you call him before you take such a major step?"

8. If the conversation goes poorly, apologize—even if you don't think you were wrong. You could say, "I'm sorry I upset you." You're the parent, and sometimes the

parent has to set his feelings aside for the sake of the family.

If you cannot bring yourself to actually say, "I'm sorry," send a small gift instead. Choose something your child is likely to truly appreciate, such as a gift certificate to his favorite restaurant or coffee shop. Add a little note such as, "This is a peace offering. I love you and do not want this to come between us."

How to Get Grown Kids to Move Out

Kevin Leman, PhD, a psychologist based in Tucson, Arizona, who specializes in parenting, family and marriage issues. He is author of numerous books including Making Children Mind Without Losing Yours *and* Planet Middle School: Helping Your Child Through the Peer Pressure, Awkward Moments & Emotional Drama. *DrLeman.com*

For more and more young adults, growing up no longer means moving out. About 23% of Americans between the ages of 25 and 34 are living with their parents or grandparents, compared with just 11% in 1980. Some have pressing reasons to live at home—perhaps they recently experienced a divorce or layoff and are in a period of turmoil. But many are simply *choosing* to live "at home."

This arrangement doesn't just complicate parents' lives…it prevents these young adults from truly launching their own lives. The kindest thing parents can do is not coddle these "kids" but nudge them out of the nest.

Here's how to respond if an adult child wants to move back in…and how to get an adult child currently living in your home out the door…

WHEN AN ADULT CHILD WANTS TO COME BACK

There's nothing wrong with letting an adult child live at home temporarily during times of turmoil. A child who has lost his/her job or his partner might need a safe place to lick his wounds. But it is in no one's interest for a parent's home to become a place where this adult child can hide from life. So when a child asks if he can return, say yes—but that you're concerned that he might not be happy if he does, because of the rules he would have to live by. *These rules might include...*

- **You must get a job.** If the child protests that he can't find anything better than flipping burgers, tell him he'll have to flip burgers. It's not enough for the child to promise to "look for work." This could mean nothing more than sending out a résumé every now and then. He must understand that living in your house will not help him escape or delay joining the workforce. Besides, working in an unpleasant or low-paying job could be the motivation he needs to go out and find something better.

You must contribute 25% of your take-home pay as rent. This reinforces the message that living at home is not a free ride. The adult child also should be responsible for paying his personal expenses.

Helpful: If you do not need this rent money, set it aside in an interest-bearing account. If the adult child works hard to get his life on track, present the money to him when he moves out. This return of rent must come as a surprise, however—if the child expects it, that could undermine the message that he must pay his own way.

- **You will have to do housework.** List specific chores that he will have to do such as his laundry, clean his room, take out the garbage, etc.

Also: If this adult child has young children who will be moving in, too, and you have offered to help with child care, set limits. Perhaps you will provide child care one or two days a week or you will help when the adult child is working, but he should not expect you to babysit every evening while he goes out with friends.

You will have to abide by the house schedule. This might mean guests must be out by 10 pm...the TV volume must be turned way down (or off) by 11 pm...or that there's a midnight curfew.

- **You must deal with your own debts.** Do not get sucked into your adult child's financial problems. Not only could this cripple your

retirement, it could cripple the adult child's sense of financial responsibility. It's fine to offer guidance, but don't bail him out.

- **You must move out by a specific departure date.** This could be one month, three months or six months down the road—the timetable is up to you. The important part is that there is a deadline so the adult child doesn't start to see living at home as a permanent solution.

If these rules sound severe, they're meant to be. If living in your house is unrestrictive, the adult child will have less reason to move out and get on with his own life.

When you pitch all of this to your child, explain that you understand that it probably doesn't sound very appealing and that you won't be offended if he opts to get together with some friends and split a cheap apartment—no harm in floating this idea.

If the child still wants to move in, get a handshake agreement that he will abide by the terms you laid out. If he does, treat him with respect—don't joke about the bad job he has been forced to take or tell him he's made a mess of his life. Instead, commiserate by sharing stories about your struggles as a young adult—the child might not realize that you faced challenges early on, too. Offer advice when it is requested, but do not try to run his life—that will not foster the sense of responsibility you are trying to help him develop.

IF AN ADULT CHILD ALREADY IS LIVING IN YOUR HOME

If you failed to establish strict rules and a departure date before your adult child moved in, this child might now be showing little interest in moving out. If so, tell the child these five words—"I owe you an apology." This is much more likely to get the child's attention than yet another admonition to get a job or an apartment.

When the child asks the reason for the apology, reply, "When we let you return home, we had the best of intentions, but in retrospect, it wasn't what was best for you. We should have had an agreement in place for how this would work, because without that, it clearly is not working for anyone. We realize that you're not going to like this, but if you're going to continue staying here, this is what will be required..." then list rules and deadlines such as those described earlier.

HOW TO RAISE KIDS WHO RETURN ONLY FOR VISITS

Four ways to increase the odds that young children and teens will move out when they grow up...

• **Encourage without overpraising.** By all means tell your child "good job" when he works hard and accomplishes something—but do not consistently tell your child that he is the greatest thing in the world. Overpraised children can turn into adults with an inflated sense of self-worth. They might consider entry-level jobs beneath them and end up living at home when no one offers them a six-figure salary and corner office right out of school.

• **Assign children chores.** Kids raised in households where everyone pulls his weight tend to become adults who understand that they must work hard and take responsibility to achieve anything.

• **Remind laggard teens that your home has a check-out time.** If a teen lacks drive and responsibility and doesn't want to adhere to your rules, remove a strip of 18 squares of toilet paper from a roll, then sit the child down for a talk. Count off one sheet of the toilet paper for each year this teen already has lived—16 for a 16-year-old, for example—then hold up the small number of remaining squares and say, "You have just two more years living under my roof." This is likely to earn you some teenage eye rolling, but it truly can be an effective wake-up call.

• **Let the child take the lead on college money matters.** College is supposed to prepare kids for adult life. Taking charge of college finances is a crucial part of that. Help your kids pay their tuition (or even pay for college outright) if you are in a financial position to do so—but insist that college kids take part-time or summer jobs to cover some costs. If college loans are needed, the child—not the parent—should take these out. Your role is to help the child understand loan terms and the dangers of going deeply into debt.

When Aging Parents Can't Manage Their Money

Shirley B. Whitenack, Esq., president of National Academy of Elder Law Attorneys and a partner with Schenck, Price, Smith & King, LLP, Florham Park, New Jersey. NAELA.org

Elderly parents typically don't want their adult children taking control of their finances. And most adult children don't relish the idea of taking control. Handling their own financial matters is challenging enough for those adult children. But the day might arrive when there is not much choice. As parents age, ensuring that their financial future is not threatened might require immediate intervention. Many people experience a decline in cognitive function starting in their 70s or 80s. They might seem perfectly sharp for much of the time, but their ability to manage their finances could be increasingly diminished. This causes them to make costly money mistakes and become more vulnerable to scams.

If no one steps in to help, the assets that parents spent a lifetime accumulating could be lost. Their adult children's assets might be in jeopardy, too, if those children must provide financial support for their parents as a result. *Here's what adult children need to know...*

TIME IT RIGHT

If you wait until you notice the classic signs of financial problems, there's a good chance that significant financial losses already will have occurred. Those signs include the parent cutting back sharply on activities that you know he/she enjoys...receipts pointing to reckless spending...past-due bills in the mail...and calls from collection agencies during your visits.

The time to act is when you notice the early signs of cognitive decline. These could include an increase in forgetfulness...repeating the same story to you several times during a series of visits or calls...and/or getting lost in places that the parent has been in many times before.

RAISING THE TOPIC

How you broach the subject of taking control of a parent's finances can have a tremendous effect on how the parent reacts. Many resist even when help clearly is needed because they fear losing control of their lives as well as their finances...or because they worry that the adult child is after their money—cognitive decline can trigger paranoia.

It's best to bring this up in a way that does not initially call the parent's competence into question. *For example, you could...*

• **Say that you are thinking about setting up a power of attorney for yourself,** then casually ask your parent if he/she has done so. (See below for more on power of attorney.) If the answer is yes, suggest that he let you or one of your siblings know where these documents are located. If the answer is no—or the parent doesn't want to discuss it—explain why you are having these legal documents drawn up for your finances. Offer to arrange a meeting for your parent with your estate-planning attorney or with an elder-law attorney.

• **Ask the parent for guidance on a financial topic.** If you are approaching retirement age, for example, your parent might have useful insights to share about Social Security or Medicare. Asking for advice helps balance the conversation so that the parent does not feel disrespected when you raise the possibility of participating in his finances. Rather than send the message, "You're no longer capable," it sends the message, "This entire family is working together for mutual benefit."

• **Volunteer to help the parent with a specific financial chore** that you know he does not enjoy. If the parent complains about filling out tax forms and/or paying bills, for example, say that you also hate these tasks but that they might be less onerous if you drop by to lend a hand. This seems more like a social activity than an attempt to take financial control, so it is a less jarring transition into your taking control. It also gives you a chance to examine elements of the parent's financial situation to confirm whether you need to take control. You might go a step further and offer to set up online bill payment, which you then could manage.

DRAFTING DOCUMENTS

If you find that a parent is experiencing cognitive decline, it is not enough to keep an informal eye on his finances. This might let you spot problems after they have occurred, but it is not an effective way to prevent costly missteps from happening. And if your parent later becomes fully incapacitated, you will not have a legal right to act on his behalf. Instead, establish one of the following...

• **Power of attorney** is an estate-planning document that names an adult child (or someone else) as the parent's agent to act on his behalf in financial matters. These are inexpensive to set up—expect an attorney to charge $100 to $200 to create a power of attorney (each parent will need one if both are still alive). The parent must agree to sign this document while still legally competent.

Helpful: There are two types of powers of attorney—a *durable* power of attorney goes into effect as soon as it is signed...a *springing power of attorney* takes effect only if some designated event occurs, such as a physician ruling that the parent is incapacitated. *Durable* is the better option because it does not force the agent to jump through time-consuming hoops to take charge...and it protects the parent's privacy. With a springing power of attorney, the parent's mental state might become a matter of public record.

• **Living trust** is an agreement that names someone to take control of the parent's assets.

Even though the parent often is named as the primary trustee and remains in full control as long as he is able, a "successor trustee," who might be an adult child, is named to take over when the parent is deemed no longer capable, perhaps by a doctor.

Parents often prefer living trusts to powers of attorney because these trusts do not just provide a way for an adult child to take over the management of the parent's financial affairs—they also allow assets in the trust to pass to heirs after the parent's death without dealing with the potentially costly and public probate process.

Downside: These trusts grant the successor trustee power to manage only the assets that have been transferred into the trust, which leaves gaps. For example, a parent still could sign up for a new credit card and then mismanage it...or fail to pay important bills. Trusts are more expensive to set up than powers of attorney, too—anywhere from several hundred dollars to several thousand dollars—and must be updated when new assets are acquired.

• **Guardianship,** known as a conservatorship in certain states, requires a court ruling that the parent is no longer competent to make his own financial (or health-care) decisions and appoints someone—potentially an adult child—to do so on his behalf. This arrangement is a last resort, appropriate only if the parent will not agree to the options above. It is time-consuming, unpleasant and expensive to establish and administer a guardianship, particularly if your parent disputes the need for guardianship in court. Expect to spend several thousand dollars or more on lawyers' bills and court fees. But if it is necessary, do it.

RED FLAGS IN YOUR PARENT'S FINANCES

When you take control of your parent's finances, monitor his/her mail, checkbook, credit card statements, bank statements and investment statements for...

• **Bills that seem much steeper** than they should be or that the parent cannot explain.

• **Bills for services** that your parent does not seem to have received or required.

• **Bills that have been paid repeatedly.** Disreputable service providers sometimes bill older customers multiple times to see if those customers will forget that they already paid.

Helpful: If problematic bills arrive in your parent's mail regularly, consider having his mail forwarded to your address.

• **Donations to charity that do not match your parent's priorities** or financial means. People experiencing cognitive decline sometimes give money to every nonprofit that approaches them.

• **Excessive trading in brokerage accounts** and/or inappropriately risky investments. Disreputable brokers sometimes "churn" older clients' assets, buying and selling investments with great frequency to generate numerous commissions. Or they might invest older clients' money in risky securities such as penny stocks.

Keep detailed records of every financial move you make and every dollar you spend on this parent's behalf or from his accounts. A logbook is one way to do this. That way, if your parent, a sibling or anyone else ever questions your motives, you can prove that you always have acted in the parent's best interests.

Caregiver Dementia: It's Real

Brenda Avadian, founder of The Caregiver's Voice, an organization that provides information and support to family caregivers, Los Angeles. She is author of the Finding the Joy in Alzheimer's series of books. She previously served as a caregiver for her father, who lived with Alzheimer's. TheCaregiversVoice.com

People who provide prolonged care to family members living with dementia often develop dementia symptoms themselves, including memory loss and disorientation.

This "caregiver dementia" usually is not the result of a degenerative brain condition—it stems from stress and lack of sleep. People who experience it typically recover after their caregiving duties end. But not all do—some face elevated risk for permanent dementia. A study published in *Journal of the American Geriatrics*

Society found that people who care for spouses who have dementia are six times more likely to later develop permanent dementia than people whose spouses are dementia-free. The study's authors concluded that the "chronic and often severe stresses associated with dementia caregiving" might be responsible.

Four things caregivers can do...

●**Learn as much as possible about the specific disease affecting the person you care for.** Increasing your knowledge can decrease your frustration.

●**Find moments of joy with your loved one.** Give silent thanks for a quiet moment sitting together. Share a laugh when you can.

●**Take respites.** Caregivers need time off. Sometimes this can be accomplished through assistance from professional caregivers, friends and other family members. When that is just not possible, at least give yourself five-minute respites. Step outside to take a deep breath. Walk into another room. Pet your cat or dog— research shows this is calming.

●**Replace obligation with empathy.** Reflect on how much your loved one is trying to make sense of his/her world...and how you would feel if the roles were reversed. This can help you provide care out of a sense of love rather than duty.

Why Does My Dog Do That?

Stanley Coren, PhD, professor emeritus of psychology at University of British Columbia who has studied dog behavior in addition to human psychology. He is an instructor with the Vancouver Dog Obedience Training Club and author of several books about dogs, including *Do Dogs Dream? Nearly Everything Your Dog Wants You to Know.* StanleyCoren.com

---

Dogs and humans have forged a special bond throughout thousands of years of living with each other. But occasionally our faithful companions do things that leave us wondering, *What the heck is that dog thinking?*

Here, psychologist and dog expert Stanley Coren, PhD, explains nine common—and commonly misunderstood—dog behaviors...

●**Why do dogs walk in circles before lying down?** This behavior likely is left over from when dogs slept outside. The leading theory is that walking in circles tramples down long grass, creating a smoother, more comfortable nest. That would explain why pet dogs are most likely to do this when settling down to rest on an uneven or a soft surface, such as a dog bed or carpet. Another theory holds that dogs walk in circles to scan for nearby predators.

●**Why do dogs kick at the ground after defecating?** They're trying to spread the scent of their leavings over as large an area as possible. For a dog, defecation and urination serve a purpose beyond the elimination of waste—these are ways to mark territory, the equivalent of saying, "I was here," to any other dogs in the vicinity. Some people believe dogs kick at the ground to cover their feces with dirt, but covering feces is not something a dog would want to do.

●**Why do otherwise-well-behaved dogs rip up paper products such as toilet paper and tissue boxes?** Soft paper products feel like fur and feathers in the dog's mouth, and some dogs find that sensation irresistible. It's especially common among dogs that originally were bred to catch or carry small furry or feathered creatures, such as sporting hounds and terriers.

Tip: It is very difficult to train a dog to stop ripping up paper products. The best solution is to store oft-targeted items where the dog can't get at them. You can buy covered toilet paper dispensers, for example.

●**Why do dogs bury bones (or other toys and treats) and then never retrieve them?** If you suspect your dog never goes back to dig up the bones it buries, you're probably right. The things that dogs bury typically remain buried. The leading theory is that dogs do not remember precisely where they have buried their treasures. Instead, they seem to retain only a fairly general sense of where they tend to bury things. If a dog endures lean times, it will dig in this area and hope to get lucky, but many items will inevitably go unrecovered.

Similar behavior has been observed in squirrels. Some people theorize that squirrels do not remember exactly where they have buried the precious acorns. They know the general vicinity where they have buried them and dig in that area when food is scarce.

• **Why do dogs chase their tails?** Tail chasing is a common form of play for young puppies, but it is rare among dogs older than four months. When a grown dog does chase its tail, there does not seem to be any reason deeper than that the dog suddenly noticed its tail was back there. Typically, tail chasing happens when a dog is in a brightly lit area. The light causes the dog to notice its shadow. While investigating (or chasing) that shadow, the dog suddenly notices its tail, and a brief chase ensues.

Tip: When grown dogs chase their tails, they generally do so for only a few seconds. A grown dog that frequently chases its tail for longer periods is engaging in pathological behavior and likely is in psychological distress. Ask your vet whether medication could treat this problem. The same drugs that help humans cope with obsessive-compulsive disorder can help dogs overcome pathological tail chasing.

• **Why do dogs eat grass?** The current thinking is that dogs eat grass for the same reason that dogs eat anything else—they're hungry, and it's the tastiest option available at that moment. Most dogs prefer the tops of new shoots, which have the most flavor.

The conventional wisdom used to be that dogs used grass as an emetic—they ate it when they were feeling ill and wanted to throw up. There is no evidence to support this theory. The high fiber content of grass does sometimes make dogs throw up, but vomiting seems to be less of a dog's goal when it eats grass than a price it is willing to pay for a snack.

• **Why do dogs eat their own feces?** For its nutrients. Dogs' intestinal tracts are relatively short, so they cannot always absorb all of the nutrients from food before it is expelled. Eating feces allows them to run food through their systems a second time and absorb nutri-

ents that otherwise would go to waste. That might seem gross to a human, but to a dog, nutrients are nutrients.

Tip: If you want to stop your dog from eating its feces, you may want to switch to a less expensive dog food. Less expensive food usually contains fewer nutrients, which increases the odds that your dog's digestive system will be able to absorb its nutritional content the first time through.

• **Why do some dogs bite after wagging their tails?** Because wagging does not always mean a dog is friendly and happy. When the tail is held high and the wags are short and quick, the wagging actually is meant as a warning—the dog is trying to tell you to back off. If you approach a dog that is wagging this way, a bite is a possible result. Friendly wags are long and sweeping, with the tail typically held fairly low.

• **Why do dogs roll in disgusting, smelly things?** It's actually a doggy form of camouflage. When wild dogs hunt, their odor sometimes gives them away—their prey smells the dog approaching and escapes. Rolling in something that has a very pungent odor can mask the smell of the dog.

A second possible reason: Creatures tend to be drawn to things that excite their dominant sense—and smell is a dog's dominant sense. So perhaps some dogs roll in horrible-smelling things for the same reason that some humans wear brightly colored Hawaiian shirts—it excites their dominant sense…albeit in ways that are difficult for the rest of us to understand.

GOOD TO KNOW…

What to Do If Someone's Pet Bites You…

If you are bitten by someone's pet, be sure to get the owner's name and contact information…ask for proof of rabies vaccination…clean the wound with soap and water…and check in with your doctor as soon as possible.

Family Safety & Health, published by the National Safety Council, NSC.org.

Dog and Cat Dangers at the Groomer

Debra Eldredge, DVM, a veterinarian based in Vernon, New York, and coauthor of *Dog Owner's Home Veterinary Handbook*.

Most trips to pet groomers go smoothly, but on rare occasions an animal is injured or killed. *Five dangers…*

• **Pets sometimes leap from grooming tables while wearing a hanging collar.** The result can be a snapped neck or strangulation.

What to do: Ask the groomer his/her policy about monitoring pets while they are on grooming tables. The answer should be unequivocal—someone will *always* be with your pet the entire time it is on the table. Visit the groomer to confirm that there's always a person with any pet that's on a table.

• **Pets occasionally die of heat stroke in heated dryer cages.** These devices generally are safe, but tragic mistakes sometimes occur.

What to do: Specify that you want your pet dried with cool air and/or towels only, not hot air. This is particularly important with *brachycephalic* (flat-faced) dog breeds, which can struggle to breathe in dryer cages…and with older or overweight dogs, which are especially vulnerable to heat stroke.

• **Some groomers sedate nervous pets.** The result could be an accidental overdose or a potentially fatal allergic reaction.

What to do: Never use a groomer who sedates animals. If your pet is so anxious during grooming that a sedative truly is needed, ask your vet if he can arrange grooming right in the office so that there's a medical professional on hand.

• **Pets that have a strong dislike for grooming can be injured when they struggle** with groomers.

What to do: Brush your pet and handle its paws in the weeks leading up to a trip to the groomer. This could increase your pet's comfort level with grooming.

• **Pet groomers are not licensed or regulated in most states.**

What to do: Favor groomers who are certified by the National Dog Groomers Association of America (NationalDogGroomers.com)…International Professional Groomers (ipgicmg.com)…or the National Cat Groomers Institute of America (NationalCatGroomers.com). Or ask your vet to recommend one.

How to Raise Puppies to Be Guide Dogs

Jamie Hanf, associate director of puppy development for The Seeing Eye, Inc., the world's oldest existing guide dog school. She has personally served as a Seeing Eye puppy raiser nine times. SeeingEye.org

The nonprofit organizations that train guide dogs depend on volunteer puppy raisers to prepare young dogs for their programs. It's a great way to enjoy a dog's love and companionship while also providing a valuable service for people in need.

Most guide dog programs provide financial assistance for puppy raisers, in some cases even paying for dog food and vet bills. Puppy-raising expenses not covered can be deducted as charitable gifts if you itemize your income taxes.

Approximately half of the puppies raised for guide dog programs fail to make the cut. Some programs offer these dogs back to their puppy raisers as pets for free.

To become a puppy raiser…

• **Investigate opportunities in your area.** The website of the International Guide Dog Federation is the best place to locate guide dog–training programs that work with puppy raisers in your area (IGDF.org.uk, then click on "Closest Guide Dog Providers"). There also might be organizations in your area that train dogs to assist people with other disabilities, such as hearing impairment, seizures and autism. One way to locate these is through the website of Assistance Dogs International (go to AssistanceDogsInternational.org/members/programs-search).

• **Understand the commitment.** Puppy raisers typically receive puppies at seven weeks of age and raise them to 12 to 15 months.

The demands are greatest during the first few months when the young puppies cannot be left alone for more than a few hours at a time. *Helpful:* Some employers agree to let puppy raisers bring future guide dogs into the workplace, even if pets normally are not allowed. Puppy raisers also must bring their puppies to special training sessions, which could be as frequent as once a week or as infrequent as once a month, depending on the organization.

Puppy raisers are asked to teach the puppies commands that pet dogs do not ordinarily learn, such as to relieve themselves on command. And they might be asked to bring the puppies places that pets normally cannot go, such as into stores and on public transportation. Future guide dogs must be comfortable in a wide range of locations.

Warning: Either the guide dog program or the puppy raiser must obtain permission from these businesses before the puppy can enter. Unlike certified service animals, guide-dogs-in-training do not have a legal right to enter places where pets are not allowed.

• **Attend a training session before applying.** While there, speak with other puppy raisers about their experiences to confirm that this makes sense for you.

Also ask the program organizers whether there is a puppy-sitter program you can participate in before becoming a full-fledged puppy raiser. Puppy sitters look after puppies for a few days or weeks when puppy raisers are out of town or otherwise unavailable.

Expect to be asked to fill out an application...be interviewed...and provide character references before you are accepted as a puppy raiser or puppy sitter.

Protect Your Family from Coyotes

Carol Cartaino, Ohio-based environmentalist and author of *Myths & Truths About Coyotes: What You Need to Know About America's Most Misunderstood Predator.*

Coyotes, once shy of humans, are becoming bolder. Though most active at night, they can be spotted at any time of day in many residential areas and parks across the US. *To stay safe...*

• **If you see a coyote, do not approach it.** Keep facing it as you move slowly toward a safe place. Do not run or crouch down. If the coyote approaches you, stand tall, wave your jacket or otherwise make yourself as big as possible. Throw something at it. Make loud noises. Brandish a stick.

• **If coyotes have been seen in the neighborhood, keep a very close eye on small children.** Never leave them unattended.

• **People who walk pets in places that coyotes frequent should avoid the hours between dusk and dawn.** *At other times:* Go with other people. Carry a stick, umbrella or other long object to keep coyotes at bay. Avoid areas with heavy vegetation. Carry a can of pepper spray—if a coyote gets close, spray it into its face. Pick up small pets if you spot a coyote. Keep cats and small dogs inside, especially at night, even with a fenced yard.

To keep coyotes off your property...

• **Keep garbage and compost in secure containers.**

• **Pick up fallen fruit instead of letting it stay on the ground.**

• **If pets are fed outside, remove dishes as soon as the pet is finished.** Don't store pet food outdoors.

• **Clean up scattered birdseed.** It attracts squirrels and other rodents—which in turn attract coyotes.

• **Clear out brush piles,** especially around children's play areas.

• **Never, never feed coyotes.**

Useful resources on the web: NHPTV.org/ NatureWorks/coyote.htm and Web.Extension. Illinois.edu/wildlife/directory_show.cfm.

17

Around the House

Never Do This to Your Home! Renovations That Reduce Its Value

Home-renovation projects seldom pay for themselves when the house is sold. Sometimes the financial hit is considerable. For example, if you add a sunroom…put in a swimming pool in a cold-weather state… or remodel a home office, you would be lucky to recoup half your costs when you sell. But some specific home projects are even worse financially—not only do they not pay for themselves, they actually will make your home sell for less than it would have if you hadn't done them at all. Things *not* to do to your home…

•**DO NOT expand your master bedroom if that means eliminating another bedroom.** Small master bedrooms are a common complaint, particularly in older homes. But in many cases, the only realistic way to expand a master bedroom is to sacrifice one of the home's other bedrooms, which is likely to be a costly mistake.

Fewer bedrooms means fewer potential buyers—most buyers have a specific number of bedrooms in mind and never even look at homes that fall short of this number. The buyers who remain will expect your home to be priced in line with the mostly smaller homes.

The financial hit is greatest when a home starts with three or fewer bedrooms. Dropping from three to two or two to one will greatly reduce both the potential number of interested buyers and the eventual selling price—it could cost you tens of thousands of dollars.

Exceptions: Removing a bedroom might not detract from your home's value if the home

Note: Prices, rates and offers throughout this chapter and book are subject to change.

Scott McGillivray, host of the HGTV series *Income Property.* He is also a real estate investor and contractor in Toronto, Ontario, Canada, and Fort Myers, Florida, and author of *How to Add Value to Your Home.* His website is ScottMcGillivray.com.

currently has six or more bedrooms…or if the home is in an area where a large percentage of buyers are retirees—bedroom quantity is not a major concern for many empty nesters.

•**DO NOT convert a garage into living space.** Finishing a garage can seem like a cost-effective way to enlarge a home—it is significantly less expensive than having an addition built from scratch. Trouble is, many buyers will not even look at properties that do not have garages. As a result, converting your garage into part of your home could reduce the value of the home by $10,000 or more—particularly if you convert the garage into a family room or an office rather than an extra bedroom that would at least increase the home's appeal for some larger families. Finishing part of the basement is almost always a better financial move in the long run, assuming that the ceiling is at least eight feet high.

•**DO NOT add artistic flourishes or personal touches to the home itself.** The smart way to add art and/or personality to a home is to hang art on its walls, not to alter the home in ways that can't be easily undone when it is time to sell.

Examples: Do not have a mural painted on a wall or ceiling—or if you do, paint over it before you put the home on the market. It would be relatively easy for buyers to paint over it themselves, but most buyers prefer homes that already are the way they want them, not homes that require even modest amounts of work. Do not have a large masonry fountain built in your yard. Do not incorporate a mosaic artwork into the tile of your kitchen or bathroom.

It's perfectly fine for a home to have style, but that should be a mainstream style that fits in with the neighborhood and the overall architecture of the home—a home in a rural area could have a farmhouse style, for example. If a home's style is out of character for the neighborhood…dramatically out-of-step with the size and value of the property…or reflects only your personal tastes, your home's value is likely to take a hit—even if the flourishes you added truly do look nice. Buyers want a home to be a blank slate for them to fill, not a reflection of a prior owner's tastes.

•**DO NOT paint interior walls dark colors.** Dark interior walls have become a trend—decorators will tell you that they can make rooms feel cozy and elegant. But many home buyers do not think "cozy and elegant" when they walk into a dark-walled room—they think "small and unwelcoming." Light-colored walls might not be trendy, but they make spaces feel larger and friendlier, which buyers value more than stylishness.

If you do paint walls dark colors, repaint them before putting the property on the market. You might have to apply primer before repainting to cover the dark color with a light one.

Similar: Avoid garish and unusual wall colors. Neon pink or lime green, for example, will be offputting for many potential buyers.

•**DO NOT attempt do-it-yourself home repairs if the result will look like do-it-yourself repairs.** Home owners who have the skills to do basic home repairs can save themselves thousands of dollars over the years. But when home buyers (or the home inspectors they hire) see evidence of do-it-yourself work, they often start to worry about what else the home owner might have done on his/her own that isn't so evident—such as electrical and plumbing work or foundation work—and whether this work was done properly. Potential buyers feel much more confident when it appears that a home has been professionally maintained.

Before you tackle a do-it-yourself project, consider not just whether you can do it, but whether you can make the finished job look like professional work. It might be worth paying a paint or drywall pro to expertly close up the wall or ceiling you had to open up, for example.

When you are about to sell, be sure to point out your do-it-yourself projects to your real estate agent and ask whether there is anything that should be done to make the work look more professional.

•**DO NOT texture interior walls and ceilings.** Drywall compound can add texture to interior walls and ceilings, resulting in a stucco look. This textured look goes in and out of style and might not be in vogue when you sell.

• **DO NOT install a chain-link fence in your front yard.** These look low-end and unwelcoming, giving potential buyers a negative first impression of your home. If you must have a fence, it's worth paying extra for wood (or if you don't want to deal with the ongoing upkeep that wood requires, perhaps a composite or vinyl fence designed to look like wood). These can cost twice as much as chain link, but they will not reduce the value of the home—a nice wood picket fence could even increase the value.

Exceptions: A chain-link fence is unlikely to detract from the value of your home if most of the homes in your neighborhood have one...if it is in the backyard and not easily seen from the road...or if it is hidden by tall, attractive hedges.

5 Clever Ways to Upgrade Your Bathroom: Luxury for Less

Matt Muenster, host of the DIY Network show *Bath Crashers*, which airs Mondays at 11 pm ET/10 central. He is a licensed contractor based in Minneapolis and has a degree in interior design. DIYNetwork.com

It can cost $10,000 to $20,000 to have a bathroom professionally renovated—even more when high-end components are used. Fortunately, there are ways to improve how a bathroom looks and feels that don't require a major investment.

Here's a look at five projects that can provide a lot of bang for your buck...

• **A narrow-depth vanity and quartz countertop.** Quartz is excellent for bathroom countertops, but it can be expensive, perhaps $60 to $100 per square foot. Quartz countertops, engineered from ground quartz, an extremely hard mineral, are very scratch- and stain-resistant...require very little maintenance...and look great.

To contain costs, choose a narrow depth. Countertops and vanities traditionally are 21 inches deep, but most people like an 18-inch deep countertop as much or more—the narrower unit makes the bathroom feel bigger and makes it easier to lean across the vanity for a close-up look in the mirror. Slicing three inches off the depth of a quartz countertop saves $15 to $25 per linear foot. Bathroom vanity cabinets that are 18 inches deep are increasingly available.

Savings: $100 on a four-foot-long vanity.

Helpful: If you replace your vanity and countertop, consider making it taller than standard ones, too. Instead of the traditional 31-to-32-inch height, many people prefer 36 inches when given the choice.

• **Better lighting.** In most bathrooms, all the lighting is overhead, which casts shadows and gives everyone raccoon eyes. Adding wall sconces at roughly eye level...or a bathroom mirror that has lights around its perimeter... can solve this problem and make the whole room seem brighter and more pleasant. The mirror or sconces could cost anywhere from $100 to several hundred depending on what you select.

If you decide on hardwired sconces rather than ones that plug into outlets, expect to pay an electrician between $300 and $500 to wire them into the electrical system.

Also: Consider adding LED *tape lighting*— long strips containing many small lights—in unobtrusive locations in the bathroom, such as the underside of the vanity. Choose spots where the tape itself cannot be directly seen— tape lighting can look tacky when it is directly in view. It provides an easy and inexpensive way to add a dramatic lighting highlight. Do-it-yourself plug-in or hardwired LED tape-lighting kits often sell for around $50 to $100.

• **Large floor tiles.** Porcelain or ceramic tiles are a great choice for bathroom floors. They look good and require relatively little upkeep...and quality tile can be found for just $5 to $10 a square foot. Installation can add another $4 to $10 per square foot—but choosing large 18-inch-by-18-inch tiles can keep the installation costs close to the low end of that range. It takes a tile installer much less time to put in one large tile than many smaller ones. In contrast to what you might think, big tiles make small rooms feel bigger...and they require less grout per square foot, which minimizes the amount of upkeep they'll require from you in the future.

•**Underfloor electric heat.** This may sound like an extravagance, but if you are replacing your bathroom floor anyway, it's actually not that expensive. And once you have experienced warm bathroom floors, you'll agree that it is money well-spent. The Ditra-Heat system from Schluter Systems (Schluter.com) does a wonderful job and costs around $650 for a kit that is capable of heating about 43 square feet. It's connected to your home's wiring and controlled with a wall-mounted digital thermostat. Expect to pay an electrician around $200 to $400 to have it installed.

•**Toilet with a super-slick enamel.** Toilet makers have developed enamel finishes so smooth that waste has nothing to attach itself to, even on a microscopic level. These toilets can completely flush away waste using just 1.2 gallons of water—much less than older toilets. That means that it can trim about 25% from a home's water bill (which could save you around $150 a year) and you won't have to scrub the toilet as often.

All of the major toilet makers are working on smoother enamel, but Toto's SanaGloss (TotoUSA.com) is easily the best—and it is available on some affordably priced Toto toilets, such as the Drake, which sometimes can be found in stores for less than $350.

UNUSUAL BATHROOM ADDITIONS

These bathroom features are unusual, but they can make a bathroom special...

•**Ethanol fireplaces can be a distinctive bathroom focal point.** Prices range from less than $100 for a tabletop unit...to a few hundred dollars for a small steel fireplace mounted to the wall...to several thousand dollars for a large installed steel firebox. Ethanol burns clean, so it does not require a venting system. High-quality manufacturers include Ignis (IgnisProducts.com) and EcoSmart Fire (EcoSmartFire.com).

•**Bidet toilet seats, which replace the standard seats on most toilets, offer cleansing water sprays.** The bidet concept might sound a bit foreign, but most people fall in love with it once they have tried it.

Prices range from $100 to more than $1,000 for a version with an automatically opening and closing seat, remote control, warm-air dryer, two-user memory, night-light and air deodorizer.

Example: Toto SW502 B100 Washlet includes a heated seat, adjustable water temperature and water flow control for $600.

Add Style to Your Home with Salvage Design

Joanne Palmisano, an interior designer based in Shelburne, Vermont, and contributing designer for the DIY Network. She is author of *Salvage Secrets: Transforming Reclaimed Materials into Design Concepts* and *Salvage Secrets Design Décor*. SalvageSecretsDesign.com

Vintage tiles, old doors, claw-foot tubs, fireplace mantels and a host of other items salvaged from old homes, barns, schools and more can add character and soul to even a modern home. These components can be used for their original purposes or transformed into something different—wood from an old barn could become the surface of a table, for example.

The advantages are not just aesthetic—the architectural components of the past often were built to last...reusing salvaged materials is environmentally friendly...and it creates domestic jobs—new items tend to be made overseas, but salvaged items generally are ripped out, reconditioned and resold by people right here in the US.

CREATIVE SALVAGE FINDS

Some salvage items that can add character to any home tend to be ignored by home owners when they are available. *Keep an eye open for...*

•**Old, dingy lumber.** Vintage floorboards and other wood planks that are covered with decades of grime or paint can look totally unappealing. But this old wood could be stunning when sanded down and refinished. It could be used as flooring or transformed into things like tabletops or sliding doors for pantries and closets. Lumber can go for 60 cents a linear foot to $6 a square foot, depending on the wood.

•**Light fixtures with ugly metallic finishes.** These can be worth buying despite their ugly finishes as long as they work and their form is attractive. The finish can be transformed by applying a spray paint designed to stick to metal. A local paint store can help you choose one of these. (You might have to sand the fixture's metal surface first and/or use a spray primer designed to stick to metal before applying the paint.) And because the ugly original finish turned off other buyers, you often can pick these up for $20 or less apiece.

•**Old doors.** Most homes have boring interior doors. Replacing these with old doors can add instant charm and interest. Doors featuring frosted-glass windows can be especially nice for small, under-lit spaces, such as bathrooms and laundry rooms, because they let in light without letting people see in. Heavy industrial doors and big sliding wood doors can bring visual interest to a home, too. Doors cost $10 to $250.

•**Old dressers with stained, cracked or badly worn tops.** An ugly furniture top will turn off most home owners, but it's worth looking past a damaged top if the rest of the chest or dresser is very well-made and in good shape. These can sell for $20 at a garage sale. The top could be covered or replaced by a piece of marble (or some other stone) and the piece reused as a dresser or even used as a kitchen island. Or transform the dresser into a distinctive bathroom vanity by replacing the top with a sink.

WHERE TO LOOK

The easiest way to obtain interesting salvage materials is to visit architectural salvage shops in your area...or hire an architect or designer who often works with such things. (This also is the best way to ensure that any old items you buy are in good working order.) But if you are trying to save money and/or if you enjoy hunting for distinctive salvage decorating materials yourself, there are other options...

•**Rebuild centers,** sometimes called building recycle centers, sell mostly mundane materials removed from recent renovations or tear-downs. But occasionally you can find old and interesting architectural salvage materials such as old doors, tile, banisters, pedestal sinks and claw-foot tubs.

What to do: Enter your state or city name into a search engine together with the words "used" "construction" and "building supplies" to locate these resellers. Also visit the website of Habitat for Humanity to see if it has a "ReStore" rebuild center in your area (Habitat.org/env/restores.aspx). Or ask the employees at your local dump where area contractors get rid of old but still useful building materials from renovations.

•**Colleges and high schools** sometimes sell off interesting old architectural components plus furniture and other items useful for decoration. You might be able to obtain cool vintage lighting fixtures, lab tables and stools, maps, chalkboards or lockers that could be repurposed into distinctive cabinets.

What to do: Call colleges and high schools in your area, and ask to speak to their facilities management departments. Ask whether the school ever sells off old equipment, furniture or architectural surplus.

•**Restaurant secondhand equipment resellers** are a good place to find dining room and kitchen equipment and furniture. Vintage lunch counters, banquettes and stainless steel kitchen work areas can look distinctive.

What to do: Enter your state and city and the words "restaurant equipment" and "used" into a search engine.

• **Craigslist.com, local newspaper classifieds, flea markets and yard sales** can be excellent sources of reasonably priced items. Occasionally people even list salvage items for free to anyone willing to haul them away.

What to do: Enter specific items you are looking for into Craigslist...or enter more general keywords such as "vintage," "reclaimed," "architectural salvage" or "wrought iron." Focus on yard sales and newspaper classifieds in towns that have many older homes and/or barns. When you come across a flea market, ask sellers who have architectural salvage items if they have shops or websites through which they sell similar items.

• **Some auction houses and estate sale companies** offer architectural salvage items on occasion.

What to do: Get on the e-mail lists of any of these businesses in your area, or monitor their websites.

• **Some secondhand shops and antiques stores** sell architectural salvage items.

What to do: Call or drop in on every secondhand or antiques store listed in your local phone book, and ask if they ever stock architectural salvage. Make regular visits to any that do.

The New Way to Declutter Your Home (Do It the Japanese Way)

Marie Kondo, a cleaning consultant based in Japan and author of *The Life-Changing Magic of Tidying Up: The Japanese Art of Decluttering and Organizing*, from which this article is adapted. The book has sold more than two million copies worldwide. TidyingUp.com

Tidying up your home can dramatically improve your life. Yes, dramatically. Tidying—clearing away clutter—can help you let go of the past...increase your confidence in your decision-making abilities...reduce stress...clarify what's truly important in

---

BETTER WAYS...

Smarter Downsizing

Need to do some downsizing? *Follow this good advice...*

• **Take photos of items you do not use but keep for sentimental reasons,** then donate or trash the items, keeping the photos for memories.

• **Go through items carefully before discarding them**—valuables and important papers may be tucked into unexpected places. Do not pay to store things—that just puts off the inevitable task of cleanup.

• **Put items your family members may want in a single room,** and have relatives come over to take what they would like—be sure they understand that they have to move anything they select.

• **Temporarily pack items in boxes, and see if you miss them after a few months**—if not, get rid of them.

• **Do not rush**—give yourself time to think things over before discarding anything that still has meaning.

Roundup of experts on downsizing, reported at US News.com.

---

your life...and make it easier to see where you should focus your energies in the future.

Unfortunately, tidied homes often degenerate back into clutter. But Marie Kondo, a cleaning consultant in Japan, has come up with ways to declutter a home so that it stays decluttered. In Japan, where apartments are small, tidiness is a philosophy of living. Her personal neatness education began at age five, when she learned feng shui principles from her mother. At age 18, she worked at a Shinto shrine keeping order for the shrine elder. *She has taken what she's learned and created her own life-changing method for creating order...*

• **Tidy up in one big push.** The usual advice is to tidy a very cluttered home a little at a time so that the task does not seem overwhelming. This slow-and-steady method does not work.

If you completely declutter your entire home within a short period—in perhaps a few days—the transformation is jarring and unforgettable. You feel happier and calmer...and are truly inspired to continue to live this way. If you tackle the task of tidying a little at a time, there is no jarring transformation and, likely, no fundamental change in mind-set. The bad habits that led to clutter in your past likely will recur. In fact, you might already be recluttering parts of your house before you declutter other parts.

Helpful: The best time to start decluttering is first thing in the morning. That's when the mind is clear and sharp. If you struggle to begin this big job—or struggle to see it through—visualize what it will be like to live in a clutter-free home. That will help motivate you.

• **Tidy by category rather than by room.** It seems natural to clean first one room, then the next. Trouble is, most people have similar items stored in more than one room in their homes. Clothes might be in multiple closets and in the attic…books might be spread throughout the house. If you tidy room by room, you could easily fail to notice that you have more of something than you need. Tidying category by category avoids this problem.

Start with categories that hold little sentimental value, such as clothes, books and paperwork. Leave the category of family mementos for last—these are especially challenging to give away.

• **Keep things that bring you joy, and get rid of the rest.** Hold a possession that is not in regular use in your hands. Ask yourself, *Does this spark joy?* If it does not, you're better off without it. It is cluttering your life, and that is keeping you from joy. Repeat this with every rarely used item in your home.

Warning: It can be difficult to get rid of items that still are in good condition—it feels wasteful. Thank these items for the joy they gave you in the past…or for teaching you that items like them do not truly bring you the joy you expected. These objects cannot hear you, of course, but you will hear these words. Hearing this could help your mind understand that these objects have served their purpose, so it is not wasteful to get rid of them.

• **Honor the past by discarding items that have sentimental value.** People often hang onto things from the past because they think throwing them away would dishonor a trea-sured memory. In fact, it's leaving these items untouched in boxes that dishonors memories. Discarding sentimental items—for example, family photos—involves picking them up, holding them and reliving the memories, which is likely more honor than has been bestowed upon these things in years. It also lets you identify the small percentage of your sentimental items that spark the greatest joy. These few items can then be truly treasured rather than left untouched in boxes.

• **Don't buy organizing products.** Home stores are full of storage bins, shelving systems and other organizing products that claim to contain the clutter. Do not buy these—they're a trap, especially when you are just beginning the tidying up process. No matter how many storage bins you buy, they soon will be filled to overflowing. The primary solution is not putting things away more efficiently…it's getting rid of the things that you don't need.

• **Do not badger other members of your household to tidy with you.** This will only sour them on the task. Instead, quietly go about decluttering your own spaces and your own possessions. You might find that the other people in your household start to tidy, too, as if by magic—tidying can be contagious.

• **Do not put out-of-season clothing into storage.** Organizing professionals often recommend freeing up closet space by stashing winter clothes in bins during summer and summer clothes in bins during winter. This is a mistake.

People who free up closet space this way often end up filling that space by buying more clothes—including duplicates of garments they already own, because they forget what's in storage. Packing and unpacking seasonal clothes twice a year is a time-consuming task that's often delayed until deep into a season. Clothes look wilted after months in bins. And this system makes it difficult to access warm clothes on unseasonably cold summer days and light clothes on unseasonably warm winter days.

Stash out-of-season clothes in bins only if your closet is extremely small.

SEVEN MORE THINGS TO THROW AWAY

These items almost always should be disposed of during the tidying up process…

275

• **Unwanted gifts and old greeting cards.** The purpose of gifts and greeting cards is to convey the giver's feelings. Once they are received, they have served this purpose and can be discarded if they do not spark joy.

• **Unidentified electrical cords and plugs.** These will remain unidentified. Most probably are for products that you stopped using long ago.

• **Broken appliances.** These will never be fixed.

• **Electronics packaging.** This is unlikely to ever be needed again.

• **Promotional giveaways.** Companies often give out free items bearing their logos. Most are never used.

• **Credit card statements and old check registers.** Once you have paid credit card bills and balanced your checking account, these no longer serve any purpose. If you later need to track down some spending detail, you can do so through your bank or credit card issuer's website.

• **User manuals.** Most people never refer to the manuals that come with the products they purchase, at least not after the first few days of ownership. User manuals typically are available online if they are needed.

---

5 Home-Repair Tips from the Pros

Greg Chick has been a licensed plumbing contractor for 40 years based in Ramona, California. He offers plumbing how-to videos on his website, DIYPlumbing Advice.com.

Danny Lipford has been a remodeling contractor for 36 years. He is based in Mobile, Alabama, and is host of *Today's Homeowner with Danny Lipford*, a nationally syndicated program. TodaysHomeowner.com

Eric Kleinert has more than 40 years of experience in major appliance and heating, ventilation and air-conditioning (HVAC) service and installation. He has served as program director for Fortis Colleges and Institutes in Palm Springs, Florida, and is author of *Troubleshooting and Repairing Major Appliances*.

Handling common home repairs on your own rather than bringing in expensive repair people could save you hundreds of dollars—or cost you thousands of dollars if you make a big mistake. Because of the possible pitfalls, home owners often are too scared to attempt repairs that are surprisingly doable. Before you attempt to tackle any of these, you need to know the secrets that experts rely on to avoid catastrophe.

We asked three experts to identify some low-risk home repairs that truly are worth tackling as DIY projects and to reveal the twists and turns that will help guide you to success.

PLUMBING—Greg Chick

Bungled plumbing repairs can cause costly water damage or other problems—but certain repairs are relatively simple and have limited downside…

• **Clear a clogged bathroom-sink drain.** A plunger isn't always enough. And chemical drain cleaners such as Drano and Liquid-Plumr can damage plastic pipes and other plumbing components…corrode metal pipes…and/or alter the chemistry of a septic system if used frequently.

Instead, tackle the problem without chemicals. Start by removing the stopper. If it doesn't simply lift out, remove the nut located on the back of the drain pipe just below the sink. The lever that passes through this nut is holding the stopper in place. (Some sinks have slightly different stopper systems.) You might be able to use a thin grabbing tool, such as hemostat forceps (available at medical-supply stores or online for less than $5), to remove the obstruction. If not, reattach the nut you removed when freeing the stopper (to prevent leaking and loss of suction)…then run the water…cover the sink's overflow opening with your hand…and place the nozzle of a running wet/dry vac over the clogged drain. (If you don't own a wet/dry vac, buy one—at around $60, they cost less than most plumbers charge for a single service call.) After a few seconds, move the vac nozzle to the overflow opening for a few seconds…then back to the drain (again covering the overflow). Continue moving the nozzle back and forth until the changes in pressure dislodge the clog—pulling it up to the vac or sending it down the drain—and the water flows freely down the drain.

Helpful: Dislodging the detritus from your sink drain in this manner might result in noticeable drain odor. If so, use a bottle brush to scrub the drain line. If the odor persists, put the stopper back in, close the drain, then run the hot water for three to five minutes with the water flowing down the overflow opening. This washes away the detritus that was causing the smell. Monitor the sink to make sure that water doesn't spill onto the floor.

• **Fix a running toilet the right way.** First, make sure that nothing simple has gone wrong—remove the tank lid and look inside. Is the chain that is connected to the flush handle caught under the flapper (the part lifted by the chain when you flush)? If so, shortening this chain slightly should solve the problem.

Flush the toilet. Is some part of the mechanism snagging on another part? If so, making a small adjustment to one of these parts—adding a slight bend to a float ball arm, for example—could be the solution.

If neither of these things is happening, the problem probably is a warped flapper. These fail faster than ever these days due to the chemicals put in the water by local water districts and the cleaning chemicals that some home owners put in their toilets. It isn't always easy to select the proper replacement. Shut off the water to the toilet…flush to empty the tank…disconnect the chain connecting the flapper to the flush arm…then lift out the flapper—flappers vary, but removing them usually is simple and intuitive.

The most challenging part of replacing a flapper is buying the right replacement. You could bring the old flapper to a home center or plumbing-supply store and ask for a match—but if the last person to replace this flapper chose the wrong part, this would get you the wrong part, too. A safer solution is to jot down your toilet make and model and see if one of the flappers at the parts store lists this model. Also, look under your toilet's tank lid—some provide a list of replacement-part numbers.

• **Unclog a showerhead.** Clogged spray holes in a showerhead often can be cleared without even removing the showerhead from the wall. Soak a washcloth in white vinegar, then use a rubber band to secure it around the showerhead with the cloth tight against the nozzle. The vinegar can clear clogs in as little as 20 minutes, though longer soak times improve your odds. This technique works on clogged faucet aerators, too.

If the washcloth doesn't work, fill a gallon-size plastic bag halfway with vinegar and secure it over the showerhead (rubber bands work) so that the head is immersed.

DRIVEWAYS—Danny Lipford

This is relatively easy for home owners but relatively costly if you hire a pro…

• **Seal an asphalt driveway.** Sealing an asphalt driveway can prevent cracks from becoming large holes. Pros charge $300 to $600 or more—depending on the size of the driveway—and you might not get your money's worth. There are many shady operators that do low-quality work.

Clear away encroaching grass and weeds from the edges, then clean your driveway with hot water or use a pressure washer if you have one. Next use a driveway caulk to fill small cracks… asphalt patching paste to fill large cracks…and a "tamp and set" product such as Latex-ite Super Patch (about $10 for one gallon or $17 for 3.5 gallons) to fill potholes. (Remove loose materials before filling these cracks and holes.)

Buy a good-quality sealant from a home-improvement store. Then follow the instructions on the container. Pay attention to temperature recommendations—applying sealants when it is too hot or cold can cause them to fail. If your driveway is sloped, start at the uphill end.

Caution: Sealant quality varies. It's worth it to pay extra for a product intended to be applied with a squeegee, not a paint roller. (Pulling the squeegee toward you will work better than pushing it away from you.) The best I've found is Latex-ite Optimum Driveway Filler Sealer (about $25 for a 4.75-gallon bucket sufficient for 400 to 500 square feet of driveway, Latexite.com).

APPLIANCES—Eric Kleinert

Modern appliances are computerized, which makes them very difficult for home owners to fix. *But here's a repair that's still fairly easy…*

• **Fix a washing machine that is no longer spinning or agitating.** The problem could be a snapped or dislodged drive belt—that's the rubber belt that connects the unit's motor to its drum or transmission. Unplug the washing machine, and remove its access panel. With a top loader, it typically is the front panel that detaches. You might have to remove a few screws near the base…and/or slide a putty knife along the top of this panel, releasing several clips. With a front loader, access is typically from the rear. If you cannot figure out how to get inside your washer, enter its make and model online and search for videos on gaining access.

Once you get the washer open, look for a rubber belt lying near the bottom of the unit or hanging loose from the motor or drum pulley. If it is intact but dislodged, the repair might simply require putting it back in place. If it's snapped, take it to an appliance parts store and ask for a replacement.

Helpful: Tipping the washer back and resting it against a wall can provide easier access—just make sure it is stable. If it is difficult to stretch the belt into place, first position it on the motor, then hold it in place along one side of the drum pulley. Ask someone to slowly rotate the drum, which should ease the belt the rest of the way around the pulley—be careful not to catch your fingers between the belt and pulley.

Note that some washers don't have drive belts at all—they use a "direct drive" connection between the motor and the drum. When they stop spinning, it's generally time to call a repair person or replace the washer.

Try a "Fresh Air" Cleaning

Jamison Starbuck, ND, a naturopathic physician in family practice and a guest lecturer at the University of Montana, both in Missoula. She is also a past president of the American Association of Naturopathic Physicians and a contributing editor to *The Alternative Advisor: The Complete Guide to Natural Therapies and Alternative Treatments.* DrJamisonStarbuck.com

N o doubt about it, I am a fresh air freak. My doors and windows are always open when the weather's good. And even on the coldest Montana winter night, I've got a window cracked while I sleep. One of the nicest compliments I ever received came when my sister once visited and said, "Sis, I love how your house smells—just like fresh air and trees!"

Sadly, however, fresh air can sometimes be hard to come by. Everything from forest fires to engine exhaust pollutes our air. And while it may feel like there's little you can do to avoid these pollutants, there's actually a lot that you can do to take control of your indoor air quality. Increasingly, researchers are finding health risks associated with scented everyday household items, including cleaning products, laundry detergent, shampoo, bath gel, cat litter, air fresheners, incense, dryer sheets and body lotion. Research links air contaminants in these products to nervous system disorders (such as tremors), certain types of cancer, asthma, hormone imbalance, irritability, headache and fatigue. In one study conducted at the University of Washington in Seattle, air coming from laundry machines using top-selling liquid laundry detergent and scented dryer sheets was found to contain seven hazardous air contaminants, including two chemicals—*benzene* and *acetaldehyde*—that the Environmental Protection Agency classifies as carcinogens.

Important: You may be surprised to learn that manufacturers of cleaning and laundry supplies as well as air fresheners are not required to inform consumers of the potentially harmful compounds found in their products. It's worth noting that the University of Washington study found that all of the scented products contained pollutants—even so-called "green" products.

To avoid these potentially harmful products, here's my advice…

•**Choose unscented household products.** This will not eliminate all risky compounds from these products, but it will improve your indoor air quality and reduce the related health risks. If you must use more noxious cleaning compounds, such as ammonia, do so sparingly and avoid nonessential products, including dryer sheets and air fresheners.

•**Use natural cleaning substances.** The granddaddy is vinegar (you can use equal parts of white distilled vinegar and warm water for such chores as cleaning your windows…and straight vinegar will remove soap residue from shower doors). But there are other good natural options if you use a little old-fashioned elbow grease with such products as baking soda (good for cleaning sinks and deodorizing carpets) and steel wool pads (for scouring ovens).

• **Freshen your air naturally.** Rather than the toxic air fresheners that you buy at the supermarket, add a natural scent to the air.

What to do: Put a pint of water in a saucepan on your stove, and heat until it's almost boiling. Add one-quarter teaspoon of a spice, such as cinnamon, ginger or clove. Turn down the heat, and let the water simmer for approximately 10 minutes. The gentle scent will diffuse through your home without leaving any toxins behind.

Try all these quick and easy remedies for a home that's *naturally* clean.

How to Clean Where It's Hard to Clean

Julie Edelman, known as "The Accidental Housewife," is a rich source of everyday tips to maintain your home, family, health and sanity. She is also author of *The New York Times* best-seller *The Accidental Housewife: How to Overcome Housekeeping Hysteria One Task at a Time.* JuliesTips.com

Below are some very clever tricks that will help make your home clean and fresh…

• **Freshen your mattress.** Mix three to five drops of an essential oil (such as lavender, peppermint, citrus or eucalyptus) with one cup of baking soda. Sprinkle it on your mattress, and work it in with a stiff brush. Leave for one hour so that the baking soda can absorb odors and the oils can infuse the mattress. Vacuum, using an upholstery attachment for best results.

• **Remove toilet rings with cola.** Pour a can of cola into the bowl, and let it sit overnight to get rid of rings and rust. Or use a wet, used dryer sheet.

BEWARE…

Bleach Warning

Bleach may increase the risk for respiratory infections. Children whose homes were cleaned with bleach at least once a week had a higher risk for respiratory and other types of infections—20% higher risk for flu at least once in the previous year…35% higher risk for recurrent tonsillitis…and 18% higher risk for any recurrent infection. Airborne components of bleach may irritate children's lungs, triggering inflammation and making it easier for infections to take hold.

Study of more than 9,000 children by researchers at Center for Environment and Health, University of Leuven, Leuven, the Netherlands, published in *Occupational and Environmental Medicine.*

• **Keep air vents debris-free with car wax.** If you can, remove the vent grilles for a more thorough cleaning. (If not, take the hose of your vacuum and set it on the grille to remove as much dust and other debris as possible.) If the grilles are very dirty, wash them with dishwashing soap and water. Then vacuum inside the vent as far as you can reach, and wash with soap and water as you did the grilles. Wipe away any remaining dirt with a damp cloth. Before replacing the grilles, coat them with a thin layer of car wax and buff to prevent dust from building up and to maintain better air flow.

• **Use your hair dryer to clean radiators.** Place damp newspapers or cloths between the rungs and behind the radiator. Blow with your hair dryer to dislodge debris and dust. The papers or cloths will catch the dirt.

• **Put glass light fixtures in the dishwasher on the top rack.** Make sure to leave enough space to avoid potential breakage. Run on the gentle cycle.

• **Remove dust on cloth lamp shades with a lint roller.** Roll on the inside and outside of the shade until the dust is gone.

• **Prevent mold on houseplant soil with cinnamon.** Remove any visible mold growth on the surface of the soil, and discard it in a sealed plastic bag. Replace with a layer of fresh potting soil. Sprinkle on cinnamon or an essential oil such as tea tree oil or lavender to repel future mold growth.

• **Use a "Post-it" to clean your laptop keyboard.** Slide the sticky side of a Post-it note between the keys to remove dirt, dust and crumbs.

• **Wash makeup brushes in shampoo.** Most makeup brushes are made of hair, so clean them with a little shampoo and warm water. Use baby shampoo or another gentle shampoo that does not have conditioner in it. Rinse with cool water. Then reshape and lay the tips over the edge of the sink to dry.

• **Revive potpourri with vodka.** Revitalize your potpourri by spraying it lightly with vodka.

Surprising Household Products That Go Bad

R ubbing-alcohol wipes dry up quickly even if the foil they are wrapped in is unbroken. *Child car seats* should be replaced every six to 10 years. Look for a sticker or stamp with the date of manufacture and expiration date, or check the user guide. *Sunscreen* is good for only one season. *Makeup* traps bacteria each time it is used—most products should be re-placed every three to six months. *Bleach* loses effectiveness in time and should be replaced in 12 months or less. *Flour* may contain weevils, and specialty flours may contain oils that can go rancid. *Perfume* is good for about three to five years.

Roundup of experts on household products, reported at BusinessInsider.com.

Simple Computer-Screen Cleaner

G ently swipe a coffee filter over your computer and TV screens. The filter catches dust and cuts static (which attracts dust) without leaving behind fibers as a paper towel would.

Lifehacker.com.

Quick Greasy-Floor Cleanup

T o get grease or oil off your floor, cover the spill with flour. Wait one to two minutes for the flour to absorb the grease, then clean it all up with paper towels.

Joan Wilen and Lydia Wilen, writers and researchers based in New York City who have spent decades collecting household tips and "cures from the cupboard." They are authors of the free e-letter *Household Magic Daily Tips*—sign up at BottomLineInc.com.

Spiff Up Your Fireplace

Bob Robinson, head sales manager for EvenTemp Distributing, Waco, Nebraska, a hearth-products distributor in 20 states from Colorado to Michigan. EvenTempInc.com

H ere are secrets for dealing with the messy ashes and sooty surfaces of a wood-burning fireplace...

• **Ashes.** Wait until every bit of ash is cool. Leave a small layer of ash at the bottom of the fireplace as insulation to make it easier to build and maintain the next fire. Before removing the top layers of ash, sprinkle them with damp coffee grounds to keep down dust. Gently scoop up the ash with a fireplace shovel, and place in a metal container. Wood ash has a variety of uses, including adding traction on icy walkways and lowering the acidity of garden soil.

•**Blackened glass doors.** Clean the glass facing the fire whenever you notice a buildup of soot, which comes from the carbon particles in smoke. Rub with a cloth and a commercial cleaner such as Rutland Hearth and Grill Conditioning Glass Cleaner. It leaves an invisible coat of silicone that keeps glass clean longer.

Cost: About $14 for eight ounces. For baked-on soot, you first may need to scrape the glass with a glass scraper (available in paint stores).

•**Sooty surfaces surrounding the chimney opening and mantel.** For marble, tile, stone and brick with minor stains, rub with a cloth and a mixture of one-half Tide laundry detergent and one-half water. For tougher stains, especially on brick and stone, use a nylon brush and an enzyme cleaner such as Speedy White Hearth and Stove Cleaner.

Cost: About $15 for 22 ounces.

•**Stained walls and ceiling.** Wash with dish soap and water. If the stain does not come out or the paint doesn't stand up well to washing, you may need to cover the area with a primer that blocks stains such as Kilz (available at home-improvement stores) and then repaint.

Important: If you have frequent soot buildup on your chimney surround, mantel, walls or ceiling, have a chimney professional evaluate why your chimney is not drawing up the

smoke from your fire effectively. For example, the damper (the metal flap inside the chimney flue) may not be functioning properly or the height of the fireplace opening may not be in proportion to the size of the flue.

•**Odors.** A persistent smoky odor throughout the house is due to the buildup in the chimney of creosote, the highly flammable byproduct of burning wet or newly cut wood.

Solutions: Have your chimney cleaned in the spring rather than waiting until the following autumn. In the meantime, you can absorb the odor by filling a container with kitty litter and putting it in the fireplace and changing it every few days.

Better Bug Spray for Plants

This formula gets rid of spider mites, whiteflies and aphids. In a blender, puree three cloves of garlic and two teaspoons of Tabasco sauce. Add one pint of water and two tablespoons of liquid dish detergent. Strain into a spray bottle, and spritz infested plant leaves.

Joan Wilen and Lydia Wilen, writers and researchers based in New York City who have spent decades collecting household tips and "cures from the cupboard." They are authors of the free e-letter *Household Magic Daily Tips*—sign up at BottomLineInc.com.

Natural Way to Keep Mice Away

Mice dislike the smell of peppermint. Put a few drops of oil of peppermint (available at health-food stores) on cotton balls, and place them wherever you think a mouse has visited or entered your home.

Joan Wilen and Lydia Wilen, writers and researchers based in New York City who have spent decades collecting household tips and "cures from the cupboard." They are authors of the free e-letter *Household Magic Daily Tips*—sign up at BottomLineInc.com.

GREAT IDEA...
Chemical-Free Weed Killer

Mix one gallon of vinegar, two cups of Epsom salt and one-quarter cup of dish soap. Pour into a sprayer, and spray on weeds.

Consumer Reports. ConsumerReports.org

14 Little Kitchen Miracles: Quick Fixes for Common Annoyances

Joan Wilen and Lydia Wilen, writers and researchers based in New York City who have spent decades collecting household tips and "cures from the cupboard." Their most recent book is *Bottom Line's Treasury of Home Remedies and Natural Cures*. They are authors of the free e-letter *Household Magic Daily Tips*—sign up at BottomLineInc.com.

Talk about annoying! How about buying a pineapple that never seems to fully ripen? Or having a wrestling match with a piece of Saran wrap? *Here are fixes for these and other common kitchen annoyances…*

• **Unclinging cling wrap.** Keep your roll of cling wrap in the refrigerator. It will keep it from sticking to itself, making it much easier to use. But it still will stick to whatever you put it on.

• **Prolonging the life of uncut lemons and limes.** Lemons will stay fresh for weeks if you place them in a glass jar, fill it with water and cover tightly.

Limes just need to be placed in a jar, covered and kept in the refrigerator.

• **Corn-shucking magic.** Microwave an ear of corn, with the leaves and silk still on, for three to four minutes. It will be hot, so use gloves or a potholder when you remove the corn from the microwave. Cut off about an inch from the stem end. Next, hold onto the silk and top leaves, and shake out the corn. It should come out easily and completely clean. If it doesn't, help it along by squeezing the top and forcing it out. Even if you have to help the corn along, when you remove it from the husk, it will be free of silk.

• **Preventing leftover cake and cookies from getting stale.** Place a slice of bread up against each already-cut-and-exposed side of the cake. Keep the slices in place with toothpicks. The bread will probably get stale, but the cake will be moist and taste fine.

A slice or two of bread in a container of cookies will soften stale cookies.

• **A place for plastic bags.** Plastic bags—the kind you get from the supermarket—can be stuffed into an empty tissue box and kept in your kitchen. A cube Kleenex box will hold about 15. A rectangular—160-tissue size—box will hold about 25 plastic bags.

• **Unwilting vegetables.** When vegetables' cell walls lose moisture, they wilt. Rehydrate them by soaking them in a big bowl of cold water and ice for about 15 minutes. They'll be crisp again.

• **Cutting fresh bread.** The softer the bread, the more difficult it is to cut. Using a warm knife will make it much easier. Warm the knife by dipping it in just-boiled water. Dry the knife, and while it's still warm, slice the bread.

• **Reviving stale rolls.** Place stale rolls in a paper bag, moisten the bag and twist the bag closed. Place the bag in a 300°F oven for a few minutes until the bag is dry. The rolls will seem like just baked.

• **Making better pancakes or waffles.** Fill a ketchup bottle with the batter, and use it for better batter distribution.

• **Softening hard brown sugar.** Put the hardened brown sugar in a microwavable dish, put a moist paper towel on top, and cover the dish with plastic wrap or a microwavable plate. Zap the sugar in the microwave for 20 seconds. If that doesn't do the job, give it another one or two 20-second zappings to have ready-to-use brown sugar.

• **Preventing brown sugar from hardening in the first place.** When you open a new supply of brown sugar, keep two or three marshmallows in the container to prevent the sugar from hardening. When the marshmallows dry up, it's time to use the sugar or replace the marshmallows.

• **Life extension for berries.** What good is buying strawberries on sale if they wind up in the garbage before you've had a chance to finish them? The bacteria on all kinds of berries cause them to rot rather quickly. As soon as you get berries home, bathe them in a bowl of three parts water to one part distilled white vinegar. After about 30 seconds, rinse them in cold water, dry them thoroughly and refrigerate them. The vinegar mixture will kill off the bacteria and give you a few more days to enjoy them. No need to rinse them again before eating—there is no hint of vinegar taste whatsoever.

•**The best pineapple ever.** Twist off the leaves, being careful not to expose the flesh. Then stand the pineapple on a plate upside down, resting it on the surface where the leaves used to be. The idea is to allow the sweetness to be distributed throughout the fruit and not just stay in its lower half. When the entire pineapple turns a light-toasty golden brown, the pineapple is ripe.

•**Natural oven cleaner.** The self-cleaning option on ovens can take its toll—the high temperatures have been known to cause fuses to pop and control panels to burn out. And popular commercial oven cleaners warn of inhaling fumes and possible eye and skin irritation. And then there's the unpleasant residual smell next time you use the oven. Here is a nontoxic do-it-yourself formula from a woman with asthma who refuses to risk using a cleaner that may be detrimental to her health. Blend two cups of baking soda, one cup of distilled white vinegar and one-half cup of liquid dish detergent (Dawn is her choice). Pat a thick coat of the mixture on the entire inside of the oven, including the door. Let it sit for at least 15 minutes, then with a damp rag, microfiber cloth or sponge, wipe the oven clean. If the oven has been neglected for some time, it may take some elbow grease to make it spotless and/or you may have to repeat the process a second time.

Great Kitchen Gadgets— All Under $25

Linda Gassenheimer, an award-winning author of numerous cookbooks, including *Delicious One-Pot Dishes* and *Quick and Easy Chicken.* She also writes the syndicated newspaper column called "Dinner in Minutes." DinnerinMinutes.com

Love the latest kitchen gadgets? Here are some great ones, and all of them are less than $25…

UNDER $10

•**ScoopSaw.** Use this small saw/knife to cut through tough skins on foods such as melons or butternut squash. The scoop has a serrated edge that cleans inside the squash or melon easily. The knife nestles into the scoop for safe and convenient storage. By Chef'n, $9.99.

•**Angry-Mama Microwave Cleaner.** This amusing plastic figure stands about six inches tall with a removable "hair" top. Fill the body to the marked fill lines with vinegar and water. Place in the microwave on high for five minutes. It blows steam from the top of its head. The steam softens splatters and stains for easy wiping. By NewMetro Design, $9.95.

UNDER $25

•**Tong Tools.** This is a combination cooking spoon and fork with multiple uses. Use the spoon for serving and stirring. The fork can be used to lift food, stir pasta and even to whisk sauces.

The cool part: You can attach the tools at the ends of the handles to create tongs to serve anything from noodles to salad. They're safe for nonstick cookware and dishwasher-safe. I use these every day and love them. By Kuhn Rikon, $14.

•**Better Garlic Grater.** This garlic tool uses a back-and-forward motion and protects your fingers! It can grate two to three garlic cloves at a time. Safe for the top dishwasher rack. By Microplane, $14.95.

•**Fast-Prep Kitchen Shears.** These shears are easier to grip than traditional shears and sharper, too. Use them to snip vegetables and herbs—even cooked chicken breast for a salad. The shears come in two sizes—five and seven inches—and are dishwasher-safe. By Fiskars, five-inch, $12.99…seven-inch, $17.99.

•**Combination salad dressing carafe and emulsifier.** The carafe has marked fill lines for vinegar, oil and other ingredients depending on the type of dressing. Add ingredients to the carafe, and the battery-operated mixer emulsifies the dressing in seconds. Store the dressing in the carafe. By Bonjour, $19.99.

•**Ceramic Dual Mill.** This attractive spice mill provides two chambers. It can be used for salt and pepper or other spices. The ceramic grinders will not corrode, and the adjustable dial allows fine-to-coarse grinds. Caps cover both ends of the grinder (salt end and pepper end), which help keep the spices dry in humid conditions. By Kyocera, $24.95.

Keep What in the Freezer? What Ice-Cold Can Do for Shoes, Eggs, More

Joan Wilen and Lydia Wilen, writers and researchers based in New York City who have spent decades collecting household tips and "cures from the cupboard." Their most recent book is *Bottom Line's Treasury of Home Remedies and Natural Cures.* They are authors of the free e-letter *Household Magic Daily Tips*—sign up at BottomLineInc.com.

It is a myth that the life of batteries will be prolonged if they are kept in the freezer or refrigerator. According to the Energizer battery company, "Cold-temperature storage can in fact harm batteries if condensation results in corroded contacts or label or seal damage due to extreme temperature storage."

There are, however, many items—in addition to surprising foods—that can serve you well by being kept in the deep freeze. *Here's what freezing can do...*

•**Stretch leather shoes.** If you have a pair of leather shoes that would be more comfortable if they were just a little bit larger, do this. Place a sturdy plastic freezer bag in each shoe (or double two thin plastic bags). Next, carefully pour water into the bags so that each shoe is completely filled with water. Secure the plastic bags with a twist tie, rubber band or string, making sure that no water will escape. Then to protect the outside of the shoes from getting wet, put each shoe in another plastic bag. Place the shoes in the freezer for 24 hours.

As water freezes, it expands. That expansion is going to stretch the shoes. A day later, when you take the shoes out of the freezer, you will probably have to let them thaw a little before you are able to remove the shoe-shaped, ice-filled bags from your shoes.

A Texas rancher told us that he used this ice procedure on a pair of his cowboy boots and that it worked great.

•**Make eyeliner sharpening more efficient.** If you tend to break off more than you sharpen, put your pencil in the freezer for an hour, then sharpen it. This will result in a good point without wasting chunks of the liner.

•**Get wax off a candleholder.** Place the candleholder in the freezer for an hour or two. The caked-on wax will shrink, and it will be easy to pick off, resulting in a clean candleholder.

Rumor has it that if you want to extend the life of a candle, freeze it overnight before burning it. Not so. Jeff Brown, owner of the Keystone Candle Co., has performed a convincing experiment (watch at YouTube.com/watch?v=uhtowNfdJHk) showing that a frozen candle will not burn longer than a room-temperature taper.

•**Kill worms in vintage wooden objects.** If a flea market purchase—a duck decoy, a bowling pin, salt and pepper shakers—has little pinholes, chances are there is a woodworm infestation. Ask people in the furniture-refinishing business, and they will tell you to keep the wooden object in a plastic bag in the freezer for about two weeks to kill the woodworms and their eggs.

•**Prevent steel wool from rusting.** Once you use a wad of steel wool, place it in a plastic sandwich bag and keep it in the freezer. The steel wool will remain rust-free for weeks.

BETTER WAY...

Use an Onion to Clean Your Grill

All you need to clean a grill is half an onion and a fork (the longer, the better). While the grill is very, very hot, spear the top of the onion (cut horizontally) with the fork and scrub the grill with the cut side to remove the grime.

The Food Republic blog explores the "culture of food" for people who want to eat, drink and live better. FoodRepublic.com

- **Kill dust mites on stuffed toys.** To kill dust mites in that dragged-around and slept-with stuffed toy, put it in a plastic bag and keep it in the freezer for 24 hours once a week.

- **Make panty hose last longer.** Before wearing panty hose for the first time, keep them in the freezer for 24 hours either in the package or a freezer bag—they will run less and last longer.

- **Get gum off a garment.** Place the article of clothing that has gum on it in a plastic bag in the freezer for a few hours. Once the gum is frozen, you can easily pop it off the fabric.

- **Make coffee ice cubes.** Prepare your favorite coffee, and fill an ice cube tray with it. When you want a glass of iced coffee, add a half-dozen of the coffee ice cubes to a cup of coffee. The coffee ice cubes will not dilute the coffee the way regular ice cubes will.

- **Get beer cold in 15 minutes.** If company drops by and the only bottles of beer on hand are at room temperature, simply wrap each bottle or can with a wet paper towel and put it in the freezer. The heat is drawn away from the beer as the water on the towel evaporates. Fifteen minutes later, you will be able to serve nice cold beer.

Caution: Set a timer so you don't forget about the beer in the freezer. The bottle or can could explode.

- **Keep beverages cold when you have a party.** Here is a festive way to keep beverage cans and bottles cold—fill six to 10 colorful balloons with water, making them the size of baseballs, or fill 20 balloons with water, making them the size of golf balls, and then freeze them. When company arrives, put the frozen balloons in a big bowl with the cans and bottles you want to keep cold.

- **Whip cream faster.** Place a metal bowl and a whisk in the freezer for about 10 minutes. As soon as they are out of the freezer, add cream and whatever other ingredients you use and whip it. Because of the chilled bowl and whisk, you will notice a big reduction in the amount of time it takes to get the job done.

- **Make eggs last longer.** If your eggs are about to expire, use this trick many chefs use—freeze egg whites and egg yolks separately in ice cube trays. Once frozen, remove them and transfer them to freezer bags for future use in recipes. This also is a good way to save yolks or whites when you need only one or the other for a recipe.

- **Make a frosty grape snack.** This is one of those things that we thought everyone knew, but we asked around and many people didn't know it. If you didn't, you are in for a refreshing treat. Wash and dry red, black or green grapes, and remove the stems. Some people place the grapes on a baking sheet lined with waxed paper, then freeze them and put the frozen grapes in a freezer bag. But we find that just putting the grapes right into the freezer bag before freezing works just fine. Whenever you want a delicious snack, reach for some frozen grapes. They will stay good for a few months.

- **Turn bananas into guilt-free ice cream.** This also falls into the "everyone must know this by now" category. If you don't already know how to turn bananas into custard or soft ice cream, read on. Peel ripe bananas, slice them into about one-inch chunks and freeze them for at least two hours, until they are frozen solid. Put the frozen pieces in a blender or food processor, and blend until you have a smooth, almost gooey consistency. Scoop it out, and enjoy a guilt-free dessert that is dairy-free and gluten-free and can satisfy the desire for fattening ice cream.

Good-for-You Comfort Food

Laura Cipullo, RD, CDE, a registered dietitian and certified diabetes educator in private practice in New York City. Cipullo is author of *The Diabetes Comfort Food Diet* and is president of the New York chapter of the International Association of Eating Disorders Professionals.

As a health-conscious reader, you probably know that limiting carb intake while increasing fiber and reducing saturated fat is a healthful eating plan to follow. But you're human, and it can be *oh, so hard* to resist carbohydrate-laden, high-calorie comfort foods like creamy mashed potatoes and rich pasta dishes.

Good news: With a few smart tweaks and swaps, you can enjoy even the most decadent-sounding comfort foods without sabotaging your health. *Here's how...**

•**Get the right amount of carbohydrates.** You don't need to eliminate carbs entirely, you just need to eat the right amount, which is probably more than you think.

Research shows that even people with diabetes who eat small, consistent amounts of carbohydrates with every meal or snack as opposed to eating excessive carbs at each meal or eating them once a day have better control of their blood sugar levels and body weight. However, the average woman who has prediabetes or diabetes should moderate carb intake to about 45 grams (g) per meal and men should have no more than about 60 g per meal. (A health-care provider can help adjust amounts based on individual needs.) The allowance is more generous for those who don't have diabetes, but everyone can benefit from sticking to these guidelines.

Some foods with 45 g of carbs: One cup of brown rice...one and a half English muffins. Not too stingy!

•**Fiber is your secret weapon.** Fiber—especially the soluble kind—takes longer to metabolize than other carbs, so it improves blood sugar control and lowers insulin resistance in both people who have diabetes and those who don't. Consistently getting the right amount of fiber can even lessen (or in some instances, eliminate) the need for diabetes medication. The American Diabetes Association recommends that women consume at least 25 g of fiber per day...men should get a minimum of 38 g daily. But aim for 44 g to 50 g a day to reap the health benefits above. Whole grains, beans, fruits and vegetables are all naturally high in fiber.

•**Don't forget healthy fats.** Replacing saturated fats and trans fats with monounsaturated fatty acids (MUFAs), such as olive oil, canola oil, peanut oil, nuts, nut butters and avocado,

*Note: The recipes in this article were developed for people with diabetes, but those who don't have diabetes andpeople with other conditions can benefit as well.

helps lower total and LDL "bad" cholesterol levels, improves the function of blood vessels and benefits insulin levels and blood sugar control.

The following are healthful comfort foods that meet the goals above...

CREAMY MASHED POTATOES

Instead of mashed potatoes loaded with saturated fat from butter, enjoy these mashed potatoes made with yogurt and a surprise ingredient...

What to do: In a large pot, combine 1 pound of peeled (I like to leave the peels on for extra fiber and nutrients) and halved russet (baking) potatoes and 1 small head of cauliflower, cut into florets. Cover with water, bring to a boil, then reduce heat to medium and simmer for 20 minutes, or until the potatoes and cauliflower are easily pierced with a fork. Drain and place in a large bowl with ⅓ cup of vegetable broth and 2 tablespoons of olive oil. Using an electric mixer on medium speed, beat until creamy. Add ½ cup of plain nonfat Greek yogurt and beat until just blended. Try adding garlic or rosemary if you desire. Makes six servings.

Traditional recipe: 250 calories per serving, 5 g saturated fat, 2 g fiber, 39 g carbs.

New recipe above: 132 calories, 1 g saturated fat, 3 g fiber, 19 g carbs.

Why it's good for you: The addition of cauliflower is a sneaky-but-healthy nutrition hack—cauliflower delivers more fiber than potatoes, while cutting the carb content of this dish in half! Plus, a 2014 study in *BMJ* offered further proof that diets high in produce are associated with lower risk for death, particularly cardiovascular mortality. Olive oil is a great source of MUFAs, and the yogurt adds creaminess and even a little protein while curbing carbs.

BROCCOLI PENNE

Instead of white, blood sugar–spiking pasta with high-fat alfredo sauce, have this healthful broccoli pasta dish with mozzarella...

What to do: Cook 6 ounces of multigrain penne pasta in boiling water. Add 2 cups of fresh broccoli florets to the pot during the last two minutes of cooking. Drain the pasta and broccoli, reserving ½ cup of the water. In a large bowl, place the pasta, broccoli, 1 cup of halved grape tomatoes, 6 ounces of fresh, part-skim mozzarella cheese cubed, ¼ cup of pesto sauce and 1 tablespoon of lemon juice. Add the reserved pasta water to the bowl, one tablespoon at a time, stirring gently until the ingredients are combined. Makes four servings.

Tip: Cook the pasta al dente (just until firm). Longer cooking times break down starches, which causes more carbohydrates to be absorbed into your blood, resulting in a faster rise in blood sugar.

Traditional recipe: 800 calories per serving, 30 g saturated fat, 4 g fiber, 69 g carbs.

New recipe above: 341 calories, 5 g saturated fat, 5 g fiber, 34 g carbs.

Why it's good for you: A 2015 study confirmed what we already knew—diets rich in whole grains protect against diabetes, while diets rich in refined carbohydrates like conventional white pasta increase risk. High-fiber broccoli and tomatoes fill you up, which enables you to halve the amount of pasta in this recipe. Flavorful olive oil–based pesto means you can pass on the alfredo sauce—full of artery-clogging saturated fat—and get a dose of MUFAs instead. (*Surprising:* Multigrain pasta contains MUFAs, too.) Ideally, make your own pesto using fresh basil, Parmesan cheese, olive oil, crushed garlic and pine nuts. If you're using store-bought pesto, choose a local brand, which is more likely to have high-quality ingredients and fewer preservatives than a big-box brand. Grilled chicken or trout goes well with this pasta dish.

A Cook's Favorite Simple Salad Dressings

Linda Gassenheimer, an award-winning author of numerous cookbooks, including *Delicious One-Pot Dishes* and *Quick and Easy Chicken*. She also writes the syndicated newspaper column called "Dinner in Minutes." DinnerinMinutes.com

---

I t's easy to make your own salad dressings. *And they're tastier and often cheaper than many store-bought dressings…*

FRENCH VINAIGRETTE BASE

This classic recipe can be the base for many creative dressings. Try using flavored oil or different types of vinegar such as balsamic vinegar or sherry wine vinegar. Or try lemon juice or lime juice instead of vinegar.

2 Tablespoons red wine vinegar
2 rounded teaspoons Dijon mustard
Salt and freshly ground black pepper (about ½ teaspoon each)
6 Tablespoons canola oil or olive oil

Whisk the vinegar and mustard together until well-blended and creamy. Add the salt and pepper. Add half the oil, whisking briskly until well-blended. Add the remaining oil, and continue to whisk until the dressing is thick.

Variations…

Roquefort Dressing: After mixing in the oil, add ½ cup crumbled Roquefort cheese. This is best done in a food processor or blender for a smoother dressing.

Creamy Onion Vinaigrette: Make the basic dressing, and add 2 tablespoons of chopped onion and 1 tablespoon of cream. Mix.

Mixed Herb Dressing: Add ¼ cup of chopped mixed herbs (such as parsley, tarragon, chervil and chives) to the basic dressing.

CHUNKY GREEN DRESSING

This dressing is great as a base for a chunky tuna or chicken salad.

1 cup watercress leaves
1 cup spinach leaves
1 cup parsley leaves
1 cup mayonnaise (or reduced-fat mayo)
1 cup nonfat plain yogurt

Wash the greens, and place them in a bowl. Cover them with boiling water, and let stand five minutes. Drain the greens in a colander, and run cold water over them. Squeeze out the water, and chop the greens in a blender or by hand. Press out any excess moisture. Mix the mayonnaise and yogurt together, then add in the chopped greens.

FRESH TOMATO DRESSING

Juice squeezed from a tomato gives a fresh flavor to the dressing. This goes well on any mixed green salad. It's also good in a shrimp or chicken salad or as a sauce over sliced cold meat.

4 tomatoes
1 cup mayonnaise (or reduced-fat mayo)
1 Tablespoon lime juice
1 Tablespoon warm water

Cut the tomatoes in half, and gently squeeze out the seeds and their juice by hand into a strainer placed over a bowl. Press the seeds in the strainer with the back of a spoon or spatula to extract the juice around the seeds. This should give you about four ounces of juice. Mix the mayonnaise into the strained tomato juice. Add the lime juice and water, and mix well.

LOW-FAT THOUSAND ISLAND

This version of the popular dressing reduces some of the calories by using nonfat yogurt. If you like a little bite, add one tablespoon of chopped onion or grated horseradish and several drops of hot pepper sauce.

½ cup mayonnaise
½ cup nonfat plain yogurt
2 Tablespoons ketchup
2 Tablespoons sweet pickle relish
Salt and freshly ground black pepper

Mix all of the ingredients together.

Tastier Turkey Burgers

Missy Chase Lapine, creator of the Sneaky Chef series of cookbooks on how to hide healthy ingredients in favorite foods. TheSneakyChef.com

Everyone will love these turkey burgers. The secret? My Sneaky Chef Purple Puree of blueberries and spinach. It not only helps make the burgers taste delicious, it also adds a moistness to ground turkey, which often can be dry, and is rich in healthful nutrients. I love these on whole-grain English muffins.

¼ cup Sneaky Chef Purple Puree
   (see recipe right)
2 Tablespoons tomato paste
1 teaspoon Worcestershire sauce
1 teaspoon chili powder
1 teaspoon onion powder

EASY-TO-DO...
One-Minute Quiche

Crack an egg into a microwavable cup or mug, add one tablespoon of milk, one teaspoon of melted butter, a teaspoon of minced fresh herbs (basil, green onions, parsley, etc.) and a pinch of salt and pepper. Whisk.

Toss on top: Four grape tomatoes halved, one-eighth cup of torn bread, one tablespoon of grated cheese. Microwave for 60 seconds or until the quiche is slightly puffed and the eggs are set.

FullThymeStudent.com

½ teaspoon salt and a few turns of freshly ground pepper
½ cup ground oats or flaxseed (ground in a food processor or blender)
1 pound ground turkey

In a mixing bowl, whisk together the Purple Puree, tomato paste, Worcestershire sauce, chili powder, onion powder, salt and pepper. Add in the oats and ground turkey, mixing until combined (it is easiest to mix using your hands). Dampen your hands, and form the mixture into four equal-sized balls, then gently press into patties, about one-half- to three-quarter-inch thick.

Preheat an outdoor grill (or indoor grill pan) to medium-high, and brush or wipe the grill and both sides of the burgers generously with oil.

Grill the burgers for seven to eight minutes on each side until they are cooked through and no longer pink inside (or until the burgers reach an internal temperature of 165°F). Serves four.

SNEAKY CHEF PURPLE PUREE

3 cups raw baby spinach leaves
1½ cups fresh or frozen blueberries, no added syrup or sugar
1 to 2 Tablespoons water

Rinse and place the spinach in the food processor, then pulse a few times. Add the blueberries and one to two tablespoons of water. Puree on high until as smooth as possible. The puree keeps for three days in the refrigerator or three months in the freezer.

The 7 Germiest Spots in Your Home

Charles Peter Gerba, PhD, professor of microbiology and environmental sciences who specializes in virology, parasitology and risk assessment at University of Arizona College of Agriculture and Life Sciences, Tucson. He is coauthor, with Allison Janse, of *The Germ Freak's Guide to Outwitting Colds and Flu.*

Even if you are a germaphobe when you are out in public, you probably relax on your own turf. Don't be fooled—germs are lurking in the average home, and they spread amazingly fast.

In one study, we coated the hands of just one person in a family with *bacteriophage* (a benign surrogate for common gastrointestinal and respiratory viruses). Within eight hours, the hands of every family member had been contaminated, along with things like the refrigerator handle, stove knobs and countertops.

Disease-causing germs, called pathogens, include cold and flu viruses and food-borne bacteria such as *E. coli* and *Salmonella* that can cause dangerous intestinal tract infections. According to the Centers for Disease Control and Prevention (CDC), about 20% of food-poisoning outbreaks are related to food handling in the home.

Here's where germs are most likely to hide in your home…

• **Kitchen sponge.** This is the dirtiest thing in the house. When we tested sponges, we found that 15% tested positive for Salmonella. Sponges often are contaminated with E.coli as well. The more you use the sponge—such as for wiping counters and cleaning the microwave—the farther germs will spread.

My advice: Disinfect your wet sponge by zapping it for 30 seconds in the microwave, running it through a dishwasher cycle or soaking it in a bleach-water solution at least once a week.

• **Cutting boards.** We found that the average cutting board had 200 times more fecal bacteria than toilets. You're safer making a sandwich on a typical toilet seat than on a typical cutting board!

My advice: After cutting meats or uncooked produce, wipe a wooden board *generously* with a sponge that has been soaked in a solution of two tablespoons of bleach to one gallon of water. Let it sit for a few minutes, then wipe off the excess. You can clean plastic cutting boards by running them through the dishwasher. Some cutting boards are impregnated with *triclosan*, an antimicrobial product. But there's no good evidence that it makes a difference.

• **Kitchen towels.** In one recent study, researchers observed 132 individuals preparing meals from raw chicken or ground beef. The participants were frequently seen touching their kitchen towels after handling the raw meats and before washing their hands. When they did wash their hands, they used the contaminated towels to dry them.

My advice: Don't wipe your hands on towels after handling raw meat. Wash your hands first or use paper towels.

• **Bars of soap.** Germs can live quite comfortably in the "slime" on any bar of soap, even antibacterial soap. This can be risky for people with compromised immune systems—the elderly…transplant patients…and those with serious underlying diseases, such as diabetes.

My advice: Use an alcohol-based hand sanitizer, even when you are at home, whenever you would wash your hands (unless your hands are very dirty—then wash them first). People who use a hand sanitizer daily can reduce their risk for infection by 70% to 80%. If you prefer not to use a hand sanitizer, at least switch from bar soaps to liquids.

• **Bathroom towels** are loaded with germs. That's partly because people don't wash their hands thoroughly enough. A scant 16% follow the CDC's advice to lather the fronts and backs of the hands, between the fingers and under the nails, taking a full 20 seconds to do a thorough job.

And people who wash their hands well after "Number 2" often give them just a ritual rinse after urinating because they believe that urine doesn't contain germs. *Not true.* Urine can be loaded with viruses, including *adenoviruses* (which cause colds, sore throats and other

BEWARE...

Germy Desk Danger for Women

In a study, we found that the desks of female workers harbor three to four times more bacteria than men's desks. Women tend to be neater than men, but about 70% kept food at their desks—and it tended to be fresh food that can be contaminated. (Men are more likely to stock their drawers with things such as candy bars.)

It's a good idea to clean desk surfaces with a disinfecting wipe at least a few times a week.

Charles Peter Gerba, PhD, professor of microbiology and environmental sciences , University of Arizona College of Agriculture and Life Sciences, Tucson.

symptoms) and even the virus that causes encephalitis. I'd estimate that up to 70% of the population is excreting viruses in urine at any given time.

Also, every time you flush the toilet with an open lid, bacteria spray as far as six feet into the air around the toilet and can migrate to your towels. And because towels tend to stay moist, they harbor large populations of pathogens. Studies have shown that hand towels can have more E. coli than a toilet bowl after the toilet is flushed.

My advice: Wash bathroom towels every two to three days. Close the toilet lid before you flush. Thoroughly wash your hands or use hand sanitizer after every trip to the bathroom.

• **Phones, remotes, computer keyboards.** When was the last time you wiped down your cell phone, computer keyboard or mouse or TV remote control? When someone in your family has the flu or a cold, about 60% to 80% of household gadgets are probably contaminated with the virus.

Don't assume that germs can't survive on inanimate objects. In fact, they may live longer on your cell phone than on your skin (which has antimicrobial properties). And because we use phones frequently, they're a common source of reinfection.

Example: Suppose that while working in the kitchen, you touch raw chicken that has Salmonella. Your phone rings. When you take the call, the germs will be transferred to your cell phone.

Later, after you have washed your hands, you'll pick up the same germs when you use the phone again.

My advice: If you use your phone after touching raw meat, use a disinfecting wipe to clean your phone immediately after washing your hands. At least once a week, wipe down your devices (including computer keyboards) with an alcohol sanitizer. Do it daily during cold and flu season.

• **Laundry.** Sure, it's dirty, but it's probably even dirtier than you think. The average pair of used underwear contains one-tenth gram of fecal material. When you load clothes into the washer, you could be picking up huge amounts of pathogens if someone who wore them was ill—and there's no guarantee that clothing will be germ-free when the washing cycle is complete. About 95% of households save energy with cold-water settings, which do not kill all germs.

My advice: Wash your clothes in hot water. And wash underwear separately from the other clothes, and after the cycle, run the machine empty, using two cups of bleach, to kill any remaining germs.

18

Living Life

Stress Can Be Good for You: You Just Need the Right Mind-Set...

When it comes to protecting your health, stress is one of your fiercest enemies. It can raise your blood pressure and risk for heart disease...give you headaches and muscle pain...and worsen your diabetes and digestive problems—to name a few of its ill effects. But what if that's only one side of the story?

Recent shift in thinking: There is now compelling evidence that stress can actually *help* you protect your health...make you more effective at work...strengthen your relationships...and propel you toward a more meaningful life.

If that all sounds like an outright fantasy, consider this: In a recent study published in the journal *Health Psychology*, researchers who followed 30,000 Americans for eight years found that risk for death from any cause rose by 43% among participants who had high levels of stress.

But here's the important part—that number applied *only to people who believed that the stress they were experiencing was bad for their health*. Study participants who reported similar levels of stress but did not consider it to be bad for their health had survival rates that were actually *better* than those of people with relatively stress-free lives.

CHECK YOUR MIND-SET

Our highly negative beliefs and expectations regarding stress—our "mind-set"—has been built up over years of cautionary advice about

Kelly McGonigal, PhD, a health psychologist and lecturer at Stanford University in Palo Alto, California. She is also a fitness instructor and meditation teacher and author of *The Upside of Stress* and *The Willpower Instinct*. KellyMcGonigal.com its dire physical and mental health consequences.

What we're now seeing, however, is that this mind-set becomes a self-fulfilling prophecy. Fear of stress—fueled by all those ominous warnings about its negative effects—magnifies your aroused state. You may even try to soothe the discomfort with too much alcohol, cigarettes and/or bad-for-you comfort food. Couple these negative coping mechanisms with the body's hyperaroused state, and you've set the stage for the chronic health problems that are commonly linked to stress.

What works better: To help protect your health, aim for a *positive* mind-set that views stress as a challenge rather than a looming threat.

A NEW WAY OF THINKING

To shift your mind-set about stress, try the exercises below (they may seem simplistic, but they really do make a difference)…

• **Get fired up!** When your palms sweat and you feel the jitters before a demanding situation—say, a presentation at work—tell yourself that you're *excited* rather than stressed. Remind yourself that you're tapping reserves of extra power that will help you think faster and concentrate better.

Helpful: Listen to your favorite "go get 'em" music on your smartphone before an important meeting, difficult negotiation or big presentation.

Good choices: The theme from *Rocky*…the "Ode to Joy" from Beethoven's Ninth…or the theme song from *Chariots of Fire*. Or simply say the phrase "I'm excited" out loud. When anxious participants said this phrase once out loud to the leader of a Harvard study, it helped them perform better under pressure.

• **Help someone out.** Connecting with others can ease our stressful experiences, but going a step further has been shown to actually help protect your health.

Important finding: In a study of 1,000 people, researchers from the University at Buffalo found that highly stressful life events, such as divorce, job loss or the death of a loved one, significantly increased the risk for health problems, such as back pain, diabetes, cancer and heart disease—*except* in people who spent substantial time *helping* friends, neighbors and family. Among those who spent time giving back, there was *no* association between stressful life events and health problems.

This protective effect may be rooted in our biology. The body's stress response not only releases "prepare-to-act" adrenaline, but also oxytocin, the *pro-social* hormone that promotes bonding and affection.

To transform stress from a negative to a positive, stay (or get) involved in community or volunteer projects. I like to call this the "tend-and-befriend" strategy.

Even small gestures count: Open the door for someone carrying packages…and give sincere thanks to a salesperson you normally take for granted.

If your stress is rooted in the fact that many people rely on you or perhaps that you are caring for someone with a serious illness, see below.

• **Look for deeper meaning.** After stressful events, such as an illness that affects you or a loved one, an accident or a work or relationship crisis, part of us struggles to find meaning in what happened. Perhaps stress allowed you to uncover unexpected sources of strength within yourself or other areas of potential personal growth.

With time, if you look hard enough, you may realize that the stressful event helped you find insights about what you can do next time to make things turn out better…learn compassion for the suffering of others…and even increase your appreciation of life itself.

This does *not* mean adopting a "Pollyanna" attitude that requires you to be grateful for losses and calamities. It means accepting the reality of life and asking yourself, whatever the circumstances—*Did I gain anything from this? What have I learned?*

Remembering the good that came from these stressful events will help prepare you for the next ones.

HOW DO YOU DEFINE STRESS?

Instead of viewing stress as a dreaded and harmful physical and/or mental reaction to tough situations, you will feel a greater sense of control if you think of it in more neutral terms—as simply your body's response *when something you care about is at stake.* Try to see that pounding heart or quickened breathing that you're feeling as your body's way of heightening your senses so that you are mentally focused and motivated to do well.

The Best New Thing I Did That You Can Do *Now*!

Lieutenant Raymond E. Foster, a law-enforcement consultant and 24-year veteran of the Los Angeles Police Department, now retired. He also is a former department chair of the Criminal Justice Department at Union Institute University. Police-Lieutenant.com

Steven Lamm, MD, a practicing internist, faculty member at New York University School of Medicine and medical director of the Robert Preston Tisch Center for Men's Health at NYU Langone Medical Center, both in New York City. He is author of *Fighting Fat.* DrSteven Lamm.com

David Sherer, MD, an anesthesiologist and former physician-director of risk management for a major HMO in the metropolitan Washington, DC, area. His most recent book is *The House of Black and White.* DrDavid Sherer.com

Joanne Waldman, director of training for Retirement Options, which certifies retirement coaches, and founder of New Perspective Coaching, a nationwide retirement-planning practice that's located in Chesterfield, Missouri. RetirementOptions.com

Linda Sapadin, PhD, a clinical psychologist and success coach in private practice in Valley Stream, New York. She is author of *How to Beat Procrastination in the Digital Age.* BeatProcrastinationCoach.com

Martha Clare Morris, ScD, professor and director of the Section of Nutrition & Nutritional Epidemiology at Rush University, Chicago. She specializes in dietary and other preventable risk factors in the development of Alzheimer's disease. RushU.Rush.edu

We recently asked a wide range of our *Bottom Line* experts to share one new thing they recently did that went so well that they recommend readers try it…

I BECAME AN UBER DRIVER
Lieutenant Raymond E. Foster

When I was a kid, I wanted to be either a movie usher or a taxi driver. I became a policeman instead, but this year, on a lark, I decided I'd try one of my childhood dream jobs. There aren't many movie ushers anymore, so I signed up to drive for Uber, the ride-share service that lets people use their own vehicles as taxis. I drive only a few hours in the evenings, but I'm enjoying the heck out of it. I've met a lot of interesting people and had some great conversations—sometimes about things I wouldn't get to chat about any other way. One guy spent 30 minutes telling me about how he outruns the police in his souped-up car. In nearly a quarter century on the police force, I never got a suspect to open up to me like that. Every now and then I get a drunk knucklehead passenger, but that's rare. And I net around $20 an hour after paying for gas.

I SLEPT MORE AND LOST WEIGHT
Steven Lamm, MD

Sleeping eight hours a night rather than less helps us function on a higher level in almost every way. We think more clearly, have more energy and manage our time better…and our sex lives improve. It isn't an overstatement to say that our bodies need sleep as much as they need food and water—but while few people would spend their lives chronically hungry or thirsty if they could help it, many spend their lives unnecessarily tired. Until this year, I was one of them. I had been going to bed at 11:30 or midnight and waking up at 7 am. Now I get to bed at 10:30 or 11:00. Within a few weeks of starting this new schedule, I lost the five pounds I'd been trying to lose for years, and I've kept the weight off…and I just feel better!

I RODE A HORSE IN THE MOUNTAINS
David Sherer, MD

I started my eight-mile ride in the small town of Alpine, Wyoming. Our group rode across the Idaho border and up into the Rocky Mountains. It's a very special experience to climb onto a horse and travel up a mountain trail. You don't just see incredible scenery…you see the world from a different perspective. It's a trip back in time—just over 100 years ago, horses and horse-drawn vehicles were how people got around. These days, many Americans haven't ridden a horse since childhood, if at all. It's an experience that is worth seeking out, and it's safe as long as you hire an experienced guide.

I VISITED AN ART MUSEUM
Joanne Waldman

I used to visit museums all the time, but between family and career responsibilities, I somehow managed to go nearly a decade without setting foot in one. This year, with my child off at college, I found that for the first time in a long time I had free time. My husband and I made a date to spend an afternoon at our local Saint Louis Art Museum. It was truly inspiring to stand amid so much beauty and creativity. It made me want to go out and create something myself. Back before I had a child, I used to enjoy photography. Now I'm planning to take that up again.

I SOUGHT OUT JOY
IN THE FACE OF ADVERSITY
Linda Sapadin, PhD

My year did not start off well—I severed a nerve in my left hand in a freak accident. I felt crushed when my doctor told me, "Your hand will never be the same in function or feeling." But rather than wallow in self-pity, I asked myself, *What do I really need to do for myself?* I decided that the answer was to go on a vacation. A month later, I was in Belize, a tiny country in Central America full of friendly faces and spectacular scenery. I have taken four other delightful trips since then, combining business and pleasure when I have the opportunity to do so. For years I have been telling myself that I don't have time for travel, but it turned out that it was just a matter of finding a way to make it happen. Now when I look back on this past year, I don't just think of my accident. I also think of excitement and adventure.

I MADE SURE MY BREAKFAST INCLUDES
A VEGETABLE
Martha Clare Morris, ScD

Vegetables are part of most lunches and dinners, but they often are overlooked at that very important first meal of the day. That's a missed opportunity—vegetables provide necessary nutrients, and most of us are not eating as much of them as we should. Besides, vegetables can be delicious at breakfast. For example, try adding broccoli and mushrooms to your omelet. My favorite vegetable-inclusive breakfast is an egg on toast covered with sautéed spinach and a squirt of lemon juice. Leafy green vegetables such as spinach are rich in folate, vitamin K, lutein, beta-carotene and other nutrients, and they are particularly good for the brain. Studies suggest that consuming leafy greens regularly can significantly slow cognitive decline as we age.

8 Ways to Manage an Impossible Person in Your Life

Mark Goulston, MD, founder/CEO of the Goulston Group, a consulting company that helps business owners think outside of the box. A psychiatrist and an FBI and police hostage negotiation trainer, He has written numerous books including *Just Listen: Discover the Secret to Getting Through to Absolutely Anyone* and *Talking to Crazy: How to Deal with the Irrational and Impossible People in Your Life*. MarkGoulston.com

Most people have to deal regularly with at least one irrational person—someone who routinely acts unreasonably. Whether that person is a raging boss, suspicious neighbor or an emotionally erratic teen, it's hard not to get dragged into feeling crazy ourselves.

The usual way we tend to deal with other people's irrationality is to try to get them to see reason. We use logic to convince them of the wrongness of their points of view. But this strategy frequently makes things worse. Instead of accepting our logic, the other person acts even more irrational, and the situation escalates until both people are acting crazy. This scenario is frustrating, stressful and unproductive.

Trying to argue an irrational person into rationality is pointless because from that person's point of view, his/her behavior is rational. He is in the grip of thinking patterns with roots in the past. His behavior is a response to a perceived threat, and your appeals to reason come across as scolding, condescending and threatening, causing him to cling even harder to the behavior that he views as protecting him from that threat.

Also, the chronically irrational person is more comfortable with extreme behavior than the rest of us. This makes it easy for him to escalate an encounter until the other person loses control.

A better way to deal with crazy-making behavior is the counterintuitive way—lean in to it. Instead of trying to talk the other person out of his world view, empathize with him and act as though that view is real—which it is to that person at that moment. This approach allows him to see you as an ally, not a threat. Though effective, this strategy is difficult. It requires you to stay calm and composed. You need to manage the irrationality that the other person triggers in you. *What to do…*

•**Recognize the pattern.** Most chronically irrational people have a preferred way of operating and over time will drive you into wanting to do something irrational that you'll likely regret.

Examples: Bullying…acting ice-cold…making wild accusations…bursting into tears.

When you can identify someone's habitual brand of irrationality, you are less likely to be blindsided. Instead of reacting automatically, you can be prepared with a calm response.

•**Practice poise.** When confronted with irrationality, repeat to yourself, over and over, *This is an opportunity for poise.*

Think of poise as a mental muscle that gets stronger the more you use it. To strengthen your capacity for poise, practice every day with less extreme challenges. At the beginning of each day, ask yourself, *What are likely to be the most challenging situations I will deal with today?* Make a commitment to demonstrate poise in those situations. Keep in mind that poise is worth developing not just because it makes you more effective with irrational people—it earns you respect from people in all areas of your life and improves your self-respect as well.

•**Remember your mentors.** A good way to access poise under pressure is to call to mind someone who has always cared about you and believed in you. This inner mentor can be living or dead.

Picture that person saying to you, *This is your opportunity for poise. Take advantage of it. You aren't going to shoot from the hip. You can handle this.*

Practice this daily. Picturing one or more inner mentors is comforting and also inspires gratitude. Gratitude acts like a shock absorber and cushions you against your angry reactions to others.

•**Assume innocence.** Adopt the view that other people are *not* setting out to make your life miserable—they are simply struggling to deal with their own problems, however clumsily. Imagine that nothing is going right in the difficult person's life, and remind yourself that his behavior is not really about you—it is his way of displacing his own fear and frustration.

•**Use the "3 strikes and you're calm" technique.** If an encounter escalates and you are about to lose control, this technique will help you regain composure. It is simple enough to remember even under intense stress.

Step 1: Think of the first thing you want to say or do in response to the irrational person—which is usually to defend yourself—and don't do it. Take a breath and exhale.

Step 2: Think of the second thing you want to say or do—often getting even or giving an ultimatum—and don't do that either. Take a breath and exhale.

Step 3: Think of the third thing you want to say or do—which probably has to do with finding a solution. At this point, you have shifted from irrational to rational. Take a breath and exhale.

•**Downshift the discussion.** Once you are poised and calm, say in a quiet, matter-of-fact voice, "Whoa, hold on for a second—what was that about?"

Instead of "whoa," you can say "gee" or "gosh." The key is to use a nonconfrontational tone and to ask with genuine curiosity. You are signaling to the other person that you recognize something is upsetting him and that you are willing to learn more about his world. This usually de-escalates the conversation.

If the other person is still on the attack, remain calm and say, "Whoa, and that too—what was that about?" He may continue to vent, but probably not at you. If you keep demonstrating poise, he will realize that his wild talk isn't working, and you can guide the discussion in a more positive direction.

• **Deepen the conversation with the FUD tool.** FUD stands for Frustrated, Upset and Disappointed. These words invite the person to calm down by talking about the concerns underneath his seemingly irrational behavior.

Start by saying, "You sound frustrated about something. What's that about?" Listen with the intent to understand and empathize—not to talk him out of what he is experiencing. After he has talked about his frustration, say, "I can understand that. You also sound upset. What are you upset about?"

Most individuals who have a hostile or agitated tone will own up to feeling frustrated because that seems less accusatory than telling them they're angry. Then after that, having them talk about what they're upset about helps them to further get things off their chests.

Finally, say, "You sound disappointed. What are you disappointed with?" The word disappointed has an almost magically calming effect. Even irrational people focus on the *what* when asked about being disappointed.

• **Use "mind's eye" language.** After the person has vented, say, "Going forward, in your mind's eye, what can we do to make this better for you?"

This phrasing often helps to shift the person from mindless venting to a positive focus on the future.

Sometimes a person's problems are so ingrained that he can't make the shift. Even then, you can be proud of your own calm response.

Real Help for the 5 Kinds of Procrastinators

Linda Sapadin, PhD, a clinical psychologist and success coach in private practice in Valley Stream, New York. She specializes in helping people overcome self-defeating patterns and is author of *How to Beat Procrastination in the Digital Age.* BeatProcrastinationCoach.com

D o you often put things off? Do you wait until you're up against a deadline before starting a project? If you answered "yes," you're probably one of the estimated 20% of Americans who are chronic procrastinators.

Traditional time-management tips tend not to work for chronic procrastinators. That's because chronic procrastination does not stem from poor time management but instead from one of a number of deeply rooted psychological issues.

Here's a look at five different types of procrastinators and a few steps each can take to overcome his/her problem. (Some procrastinators fit into more than one category.)

THE PERFECTIONIST

Perfectionists tend to work too long on a project in an attempt to achieve perfection—which makes it difficult to get anything done on schedule. Some perfectionists struggle even to begin projects—their need to meet impossibly high standards makes every task seem like an oppressive burden that they would like to avoid. *What to do…*

• **Set time limits for projects, or ask others to do so for you.** Redefine perfection as "the best I can achieve *within this time frame.*"

• **Avoid extremes in your speech and mental self-talk.** Perfectionists tend to think something is either wonderful or horrible. But the vast majority of events actually fall between these extremes. When you catch yourself using extreme terms, replace them with more measured descriptions such as "pretty good" or "pretty bad."

• **Make one deliberate mistake each day.** Choose something that has limited repercussions, forcing yourself to intentionally get it wrong. Watch how little difference this actually makes.

Examples: A perfectionist made her bed with the comforter upside down. This initially filled her with anxiety—but as time passed, she relaxed when she became aware that her husband never even noticed.

Another perfectionist, who was consistently early, decided to arrive 20 minutes late to a social engagement and found it to be a liberating experience.

THE DREAMER

Dreamers have a strong desire to live in the world of ideas…and a strong aversion to completing the real-world steps required to turn these ideas into reality. They are vague in their thinking, hazy with deadlines and often expect fate to intervene and make hard work unnecessary. *What to do…*

• **Develop a detailed to-do list.** Create to-do lists that include not just what you need to do but also time lines and deadlines for each listing.

• **Start turning your dreams into reality.** Dreamers frequently fantasize about a version of reality in which they are far more important or successful than they actually are. Occasional daydreams are fine, but chronically indulging in these reveries can take the place of doing things that could improve your life. If you catch yourself living in a fantasy world, stop. Consider your life as it actually is, then think of a step you could take right now to move toward making your dreams a reality.

• **Change your "I'll try to…" to "I will" or "I am."** With most everyday tasks, there is no trying—either you do it or you don't. When you say you'll "try to," you're just giving yourself the option of opting out of tasks that need to get done.

THE WORRIER

Anxieties about all that could go wrong prevent worriers from moving forward. *What to do…*

• **Remind yourself that not making a decision is a decision.** When your anxieties cause stagnation, say to yourself, *I am choosing to take no action. Is this really the path I want to select?*

• **Take a baby step that does not trigger great fear.** Taking even a very small step forward can be a huge step for a worrier. When action replaces anxiety, the worrier is reminded how wonderful it feels to make progress toward a goal.

• **Replace pessimism with optimism.** Worriers often feel overwhelmed by what they don't know. Hence, every time you think or say, "I don't know…" follow it up with, "But one thing I do know is…" Or when you say, "I can't…" follow it up with, "But one thing I can do is…"

THE CRISIS MAKER

Crisis makers delay working on projects until deadlines loom—they need the adrenaline rush of a deadline to get them moving. They don't consider that this makes life difficult for their colleagues and loved ones…or that it could lead to missed deadlines if a single thing goes wrong. They also don't appreciate that they would do even better work if they focused on projects before their backs were up against a wall. *What to do…*

• **Find motivators other than stress and adrenaline.** Looming deadlines might be an effective motivator for you, but that doesn't mean that they are the only motivator. Reflect on what is truly and deeply meaningful to you. It might be providing for your family…behaving ethically…being viewed as someone people can trust…earning money…earning praise and promotion…or something else entirely. When you catch yourself delaying a responsibility until the last minute, call an alternate motivator to mind and reflect on how starting work immediately serves this cause.

Example: It's important that people you respect view you as someone they can trust. Remind yourself that these people will consider you trustworthy if you fulfill your responsibilities promptly rather than leave them until the last moment.

• **Get your adrenaline rush in your free time.** Competitive games and athletics could fill this need for you.

• **Play "beat the clock" to get tasks done that aren't inherently interesting to you.** Set a timer, and then see if you can create your own personal victory by completing a task in record time.

Example: You might finally create some organization to the mess on your desk by setting your timer for 10 minutes and seeing what you can accomplish in that limited amount of time.

THE DEFIER

Defiers view their responsibilities as impositions on their time forced upon them by unjust systems or authority figures. They might respond to these impositions with direct defiance...or they might indirectly defy by procrastinating, a form of passive-aggressive rebellion. *What to do...*

• **Act, don't react.** When you feel yourself becoming upset about one of your responsibilities, remind yourself that "complain and defy" is the response of an impotent child. "Decide and do" is the approach of a powerful adult. Ask yourself what constructive and cooperative steps you could take to improve the situation, such as suggesting a streamlined way to take care of a task.

• **See yourself as part of a team, not apart from a team.** You're not a victim of a system that is forcing you to complete a task—you're a member of a team that's working together to achieve some larger goal. This team might be your family...your company...or your community. You're much less likely to rebel against a task if you frame it this way in your mind.

• **Mentally review your options.** Reminding yourself that you have options is another good way to contain a rebellious streak and reclaim a sense of control when you feel unfair demands are being imposed upon you. In most situations, when you think about it, you do have options.

Examples: Your wife expects you to take out the garbage, and you don't want to. See if you can trade tasks with your wife or older children.

Or your supervisor expects you to hand in a review of what you have accomplished every week. You find this review takes more time than it is worth. Suggest that a weekly review be changed to a monthly one. Show how much more time-effective that would be.

Say *No* to Family and Friends...and Still Have Them Like You!

Daniel Post Senning, great-great-grandson of etiquette maven Emily Post and coauthor of *Emily Post's Etiquette*, 18th edition. He is also cohost of the *Awesome Etiquette* podcast, which can be found through the Emily Post Institute's website. EmilyPost.com

Your friend asks for a loan. Your cousin asks for a business referral. Your neighbor asks you to donate to a charity. Your coworker asks for your help with a project that shouldn't really be your problem.

It can be very uncomfortable to turn down unwanted requests from people who are close to you—it even can poison a relationship. Some people simply swallow hard and say yes to such requests to avoid these unpleasant consequences.

The trouble is, saying yes to unwanted requests can have unpleasant consequences all their own. It could cost you time or money that you really can't spare or mean that you must do things not in line with your beliefs. Saying yes could lead to similar requests being made in the future. And in the long run, it can damage relationships just as deeply as saying no.

Example: Loaning money to a friend could ruin the relationship if that friend does not pay you back.

Here's how to minimize the risk for hurt feelings or damaged relationships when you must reject a request. Keep in mind that the art of good etiquette is coming up with a response that is not hurtful and doesn't destroy your integrity.

TAKE A LITTLE TIME

A friend, relative or coworker could be especially insulted or embarrassed by a quick rejection—it sends the message that you didn't even consider the request worthy of consideration. Let the person know what your answer is likely to be, but ask for a few minutes, hours or days to consider the request. Stress that you need this time *because of your positive feelings for the person making the request.*

Examples: "I normally say no to requests such as these automatically, but because I consider you a very close friend, I'm going to give your request some thought." Or "I don't think there's any way I'm going to be able to do that, but out of respect to you, I'm going to mull it over. I'll let you know by tomorrow."

If an answer is needed very quickly, still take five to 10 seconds to mull it over before saying no. Use this time to come up with a way to let this person down gently—more on that below.

REJECT CLEARLY BUT KINDLY

People sometimes find it so hard to say no to friends that their nos accidentally come out as maybes or even yeses. When the time comes to give your answer, be clear from the outset that you are saying no.

Examples: Polite but unambiguous opening lines for rejections include, "I'm sorry, I have to say no" or "I just can't do it."

Remind yourself that the person wouldn't have asked if he/she didn't feel close to you—and follow up your clear rejection by expressing *gratitude* for that closeness. Say something along the lines of, "It means a lot to me that our relationship is close enough that you can come to me with this request. I'm really sorry I can't come through for you."

In truth, you probably are not grateful for the request—you actually might be upset with your friend for putting you in an awkward position. But expressing *gratitude* should help your friend get over any embarrassment that he/she might be feeling about the situation, which reduces the odds of long-term damage to the relationship.

Exception: If you reject a friend's request that you make a donation to a charity and/or sign a petition, there is no need to say anything to help this friend overcome embarrassment. People tend to feel good about themselves—not embarrassed—when they make requests on behalf of causes they believe in. Instead say something like, "It's wonderful that you're supporting a good cause…"

GIVE AN EXPLANATION

If possible, provide a brief explanation for the rejection—one that does not reflect neg-atively on the person making the request. *Among the options…*

●**Explain that the request does not fit a system you have in place** or *rules you must follow.* This makes the rejection seem less personal. *Examples…*

• A friend asks you for a business reference. You might say that your employer has a rule barring employees from providing references. (Many companies have this rule.)

• A friend asks to stay with you for a month. You might say that your condo board has a rule against guests staying that long.

• A relative asks for a donation to charity. You might say that you make all of your charitable donations to a small number of nonprofits whose administrative expenses you track closely.

• A friend asks you to add him to your LinkedIn contacts. You might say that you have a policy of adding only people with whom you have worked on multiple occasions.

●**Blame your own limits.** This sends the message that you truly would like to help but can't.

Examples: A friend asks for a loan. If you don't have room in your budget, say so. If you had a bad experience loaning to a friend before, say that.

●**Note that you already have done quite a bit to help.** This way you're not saying no, but rather that your yeses have reached their limit.

Example: You are asked to chair a committee that you already have chaired two years in a row. You could mention the earlier service, then say, "It's time for me to let someone else have his turn."

BRAINSTORM POTENTIAL ALTERNATIVES

Is there a way that you can say no but still provide some form of assistance that you do find palatable? If so, mention this. *Possibilities include…*

●**Offer your time, knowledge or network rather than your money or possessions.**

Examples: A friend asks you to buy cookies to support her child's Girl Scout troop. You could say that you don't eat cookies (or that you already bought cookies from someone else's child), but you would be happy to ask people you know if they are interested. A friend asks to borrow your pickup truck to move a bulky item. You could say that you don't like to loan out your vehicle, but that if the trip is local, you would be willing to do the driving.

•**Offer to help find someone else who can help.**

Example: A neighbor asks for your assistance with a median-strip beautification project. Perhaps you can provide an introduction to someone else in the neighborhood who enjoys gardening.

•**Offer to reevaluate the rejection in the future.**

Example: A friend asks for a donation to his favorite charity. You say no, you already have made your donations for the year—but add that you will include this charity among the group of nonprofits you will consider in future years.

Even if your alternative is not accepted, making the offer sends the message that you do care.

Beware the Hazards of Positive Thinking

Gabriele Oettingen, PhD, professor of psychology at New York University, New York City, and University of Hamburg in Germany. She is author of *Rethinking Positive Thinking: Inside the New Science of Motivation*. WOOPMyLife.org

We are often told to *think positive.* Whether we want to lose weight…quit smoking…negotiate a raise or promotion…achieve great wealth…or even get elected president, we're assured that the key is to ignore self-doubt, banish pessimism and believe that we can do it.

But positive thinking leads to productive action only if we know how to handle it. If we don't, pie-in-the-sky daydreams and unbridled optimism are more likely to lead to

stagnancy than success. For example, a recent study found that people were less likely to make a substantial donation to a charity if they first fantasized that the problem the charity addresses had been solved. Indulging in the positive-thinking fantasy gave their minds the same positive feelings that they would have experienced if they actually had helped solve the problem, robbing them of the drive to take action.

Or consider the upcoming presidential election. Some of the candidates are relentlessly positive about what they could achieve if they are elected—an attitude that whips up crowds and attracts admirers.

The problem: The more an incoming president displays positive thinking, the worse the country seems to do. A 2014 study published in *Psychological Science* examined inaugural addresses from 1933 to 2009 and found that the more idealistic a portrait a president paints, the higher the unemployment rate and the lower the gross domestic product during the ensuing four years. That may be because an overly idealistic president might be more likely to overlook the obstacles…downplay the necessary steps to achieve the economic goals…and pursue risky ventures.

So how do you employ positive thinking as a powerful force? The key is to use it as part of the following four-step strategy, which has been shown to actually increase our odds of taking productive action and achieving a goal…

•**Identify a goal.** Choose something you would like to achieve, whether you call it a "goal" or a "wish." This could be a short-term goal—something you could accomplish today—or a long-term goal that will take much longer. Your goal should be something that you believe you can realistically accomplish but that is somewhat challenging to you. Boil your goal down to a phrase of just three to six words.

Examples: "Book a trip" or "Lose five pounds."

•**Picture the best outcome.** Now imagine what it would be like if your wish came true in the very best possible way. How would you feel? How would your life change?

Let yourself mentally experience this imagined outcome. Revel in it for a few minutes. This helps link the wish to pleasurable feelings in your mind—indulging in fantasies can feel wonderful. Your blood pressure actually might drop, enveloping you in a sense of calm and contentment.

Dreamers tend not to progress beyond this stage, but two crucial steps remain to maximize your odds of making your wish come true.

•**Picture your greatest internal obstacle.** As soon as you stop fantasizing about the best possible outcome of your wish, ask yourself, *What one thing in me is most holding me back from making this wish come true?*

The goal here is to uncover your main internal obstacle, not an external one. If you see an external force as your main hindrance, there's a good chance that the problem will seem insurmountable. If you see something within yourself as the main problem, there's a good chance you will be able to develop a solution.

Example: If your wish is to get a promotion at work, the first obstacle that comes to mind might be, *My boss is a fool who does not appreciate me.* This is not the obstacle you need to identify—a foolish boss is an external problem. Make this obstacle internal by rephrasing it as, *I feel resentment toward my boss that makes it hard for me to earn his respect.*

Your internal obstacle might be instantly obvious, or it might take time to figure out. If it proves elusive, seek it through quiet, private contemplation. Do not ask other people for their input—your odds of understanding and

overcoming the obstacle are much higher if you discover it yourself. If you're not certain whether you have identified the critical internal obstacle, you probably haven't—there's usually a "That's it!" moment of revelation when you have discovered it.

Helpful: People often initially conclude that their main obstacle is, *I don't have time* to pursue the goal. These people may want to dig deeper into why they can't seem to find the time. For example, someone might realize that he/she cannot find time to pursue his wish because he devotes lots of time to helping other people pursue their wishes...and that he does this because he fears not being needed. That fear is a major obstacle. Someone else might realize that he is not finding time for a project because he is afraid of failing.

Boil your obstacle down to three to six words, then spend some time thinking about it. Picture how this obstacle stands in your way, stopping you from reaching your goal.

This reduces the odds that your mind will be satisfied with mere fantasy and helps you do what it takes to make the wish a reality.

Once you have identified and pictured your obstacle, you might realize that you need to modify or even switch your goal because the obstacle is so formidable that you can't overcome it—or the goal is just not worth pursuing.

Example: Your wish is to get up each morning and exercise. Your obstacle is that you feel distracted by everything you have to do during the day. Perhaps it makes sense to change your initial wish to "exercise in the evenings."

•**Develop a plan to overcome your obstacle.** This plan should fit a simple if/then format—*If [obstacle X occurs], then I will [take action Y].*

Example: If I feel insecure when someone questions my proposal, then I will remind myself that I am just as knowledgeable on this topic as anyone.

Developing a plan in advance to overcome your internal obstacle will not just help you overcome this obstacle...it may improve your odds of overcoming any obstacle that appears. The process of obstacle identification and if/

then planning described above trains the mind to look for and get past obstacles, rather than get stopped by them on a nonconscious level.

Helpful: Find a quiet moment each day to identify your goal, your best outcome, your central internal obstacle and your if/then plan. By practicing this procedure every day, you will be much more successful in understanding your wishes and attaining your goals.

The Anxiety Advantage

Kate Sweeney, PhD, an associate professor of psychology at University of California-Riverside, reported by Karen Larson, editor, *Bottom Line Personal*.

I'm a worrier. When I have to wait for the results of a medical test—or some other important news—I agonize over the possibility that things will go wrong. But it turns out that could be a good thing. A study published recently in *Emotion* suggests that worriers are better prepared than nonworriers to cope with bad news when it comes…and we experience greater feelings of joy when the news is good.

But there is a way to reap the benefits of waiting-period anxiety without the unpleasant prolonged anxiety, says Kate Sweeny, PhD, an associate professor of psychology at University of California-Riverside and one of the study's researchers. The trick is to assume the best for most of the waiting period, then brace for the worst just before the verdict is delivered. We receive most of the psychological advantages of anxiety as long as we are anxious in those final moments. But what if there's no clear end date to your waiting period or if you can't ever set aside your worries?

Dr. Sweeny's advice is to select activities that put us in what's known as a "flow state," where the mind is so deeply engaged that we later wonder, *Where did the time go?* That can be solving puzzles, playing chess, painting pictures or getting work done. These activities—not passive things such as watching TV—have the best chance of distracting us from major worries.

When nothing can take our minds off our anxieties, the best option is to prepare for the feared outcome. While waiting for the results of a medical test, for example, investigate treatment options and insurance coverage. One reason we're anxious during waiting periods is that we feel a loss of control. Preparing allows us to partially regain control.

Why Does the Other Line Seem to Move Faster?

David Andrews, author, *Why Does the Other Line Always Move Faster?*

Does it seem like you always choose the slowest-moving line in the grocery store?

You probably don't pick the slowest line as often as you think. More likely you become conscious of the speed of your line only when that speed is exceptionally slow. When you choose a quick line, you're soon out the door with other matters on your mind.

Standing on line is a minor thing, but it makes many people feel surprisingly anxious and powerless. The potential for unease increases when we must choose among multiple lines. Researchers have found that retail customers are happier when there is one line rather than several to choose among—even if this results in a longer wait.

To reduce line anxiety…

• **Distract yourself.** Try to strike up conversations. Or take out your phone, a book or a magazine.

• **Remind yourself how little is really on the line when you are stuck in line.** The typical line will cost you just a few minutes of your life—it only feels like more.

• **Think, I choose to stand in this line.** You likely have options other than standing in line, though they might not be appealing options. For example, you could abandon your shopping cart and take your business elsewhere…or come back later when the line is shorter. Review these options, then choose to remain in line because it makes sense to do so. Reframing a line as a choice can help you regain a sense of control, reducing the feeling of being trapped.

Best Ways to Deal with a Depressed Spouse

Jay Bear, MD, psychiatrist and director of ambulatory services, department of psychiatry, Brigham and Women's Hospital, Boston, reported at LiveScience.com.

If you think your spouse may be depressed, help him/her get a proper diagnosis and treatment—the illness might prevent a depressed person from recognizing that he/she needs help, so express concern and suggest that you tackle the problem together. *Also…*

• **Stay on the same team**—actively work to help your spouse get better…take daily walks, provide rides to doctor's appointments, make sure the spouse takes his/her medication.

• **Try not to get bogged down by resentment**—dealing with a partner's depression can result in angry feelings, especially if you frequently are making excuses for your spouse's social absences, your sex life suffers or household responsibilities shift.

• **Be receptive**—encourage the spouse to talk about what he is feeling, and do not pass judgment.

• **Be patient**—doctors often can help depressed people feel and function better, but it may take some time.

• **Understand that depression usually is an episodic illness**—depressed people experience bad and good periods.

Helpful for spouses of depressed people: Get emotional support from a friend or therapist, and attend couple's therapy when your spouse is feeling better.

Save a Loved One from Suicide

Thomas Joiner, PhD, the Robert O. Lawton Distinguished Professor of Psychology at Florida State University and director of the Laboratory for the Study and Prevention of Suicide-Related Conditions and Behaviors, both in Tallahassee. Dr. Joiner has also been awarded the Guggenheim Fellowship and the Rockefeller Foundation's Bellagio Residency Fellowship and is author of *Why People Die by Suicide* and *Myths About Suicide*.

The instinct to live is hardwired in us. That's why suicidal tendencies can be so difficult—even impossible—to grasp for people who have never felt a desire to die. The more we do know, however, the better

GOOD TO KNOW…

When a Friend Is Suffering…

What *not* to say to a friend who is suffering…

"I know how you feel"—you can't know exactly how someone else is feeling. *"This is God's plan"* can be enraging—"You think God wants me to suffer." *"If you need anything, give me a call"*—rather than putting the burden of effort on a person who already is burdened, ask when you can bring over dinner or help with the laundry.

Andrea Bonior, PhD, licensed clinical psychologist in private practice, Washington, DC, and author of *The Friendship Fix*.

able we are to reach out to people who are at risk of dying by suicide. *To better understand suicide, it's important to know the truth behind several long-standing myths…*

MYTH: Suicide is an act of anger or revenge. Only 10% to 12% of suicides contain an element of anger or revenge. Unfortunately, these tend to draw media attention, painting all suicides with the same brush. In truth, the tendency to die by suicide can most often be attributed to two simultaneously occurring beliefs—the sense that one is a burden…and that one doesn't belong. People considering suicide often think of themselves as a liability for their families, along the lines of *They'd be better off without me.* When accompanied by a lack of belongingness—a sense of loneliness and social alienation—the result can be lethal.

MYTH: Suicide is an easy escape, one that cowards use. Suicide is very difficult to accomplish—only one death occurs for every 20 attempts. Combat soldiers and policemen, who require physical fearlessness in their work, for example, are at high suicide risk. When they experience feelings of alienation and being a burden, their bravery can turn deadly. Physicians and dentists, in particular, are also at high risk—they are so exposed to pain and injury every day that they can become inured to the natural human aversion to taking one's own life.

MYTH: People often die by suicide on a whim. When standing on top of a roof, many people experience a fleeting thought along the lines of *What if I jumped?* When driving a car around a sharp bend, a similar thought might occur—*What if I drove off the road?* It can feel like you had a sudden whim to end it all—but that's not what's happening.

That impulse is called the *high-place phenomenon.* It's considered to be an instinctual safety signal that causes one to pay greater attention and take precautions—for example, to back up from the rooftop. Moments later, though, your slower perceptual system kicks in and misattributes the safety signal as a kind of a death wish. It's nothing of the sort. Our studies have shown that the high-place phenomenon is, in fact, an urge to *live*, not die.

By contrast, taking one's own life is usually preceded by detailed planning and resolve.

MYTH: Unless you're depressed, you're not at risk for suicide. While depression is a significant risk factor for suicide, it is not the only one. Mental disorders such as anorexia nervosa, schizophrenia and borderline personality disorder increase suicide risk. Additional risk factors include stressful life events (such as a death, divorce or job loss), access to firearms and historical factors, including a family history of suicide, previous attempts and childhood abuse. More than one in 10 suicides are related to chronic or terminal illness.

MYTH: Most people who die by suicide leave a note. Seventy-five percent of people who kill themselves don't leave a note or other message for loved ones. Unfortunately, that helps fuel the incorrect notion that the act was impulsive.

To understand why suicide notes are so rare, remember that individuals who are considering suicide are typically in a state of misery and isolation, which makes it very hard to communicate. Those who *do* leave notes tend to provide factual instructions about day-to-day matters rather than an emotional missive.

MYTH: Suicidal behavior tends to peak around the end-of-year holidays. In fact, suicides tend to occur in the spring. That's true around the world. Why? The explanation that I favor comes back to the idea that suicide requires a great deal of resolve and focus. In the spring, all living things—human, animal, even plant—become more energetic. For most people that's a good thing, but a small percentage experience symptoms such as agitation, edginess and trouble sleeping. This clinical state of overarousal, combined with alienation and burdensomeness, is correlated with higher rates of suicides during the spring.

MYTH: There are more suicides in big cities than in rural areas. Not true. People who live in rural counties are 70% more likely to die by suicide than those who live in big, metropolitan areas. The reason may be that rural residents hold more physical occupations, which often go hand-in-hand with a higher level of everyday fearlessness. Another factor may be that they live far from their neighbors, resulting in social isolation. The lack of easy access to doctors and other medical professionals may also contribute.

MYTH: If people want to die by suicide, we can't stop them. A landmark study found that 94% of people who were restrained from jumping off the Golden Gate Bridge in San Francisco were still alive decades later or had died from natural causes. This was true even though they had high-risk characteristics that suggest a determined mind-set—most were men (who are at greater risk than women)… had chosen a highly lethal method (jumping from a high structure)…and were rarely referred to mental health treatment after being restrained (unfortunate but not uncommon). Yet nearly all of them chose to keep on living. This suggests that intervention can save lives.

If you or a loved one is considering suicide or shows suicidal tendencies, there is help available! The suicide hot line 800-273-TALK is a great resource—callers speak with a trained crisis worker who listens to their problems and then provides information on mental health services in the caller's area.

Another good option: Reaching out to a primary care physician who can prescribe medication and/or recommend a mental health professional.

---

5 Toxic Misconceptions About Grief

Alan D. Wolfelt, PhD, CT (certified thanatologist, which indicates an expertise in strategies for coping with death), founder and director of the Center for Loss and Life Transition in Fort Collins, Colorado, and a faculty member in the department of family medicine at the University of Colorado School of Medicine. The recipient of the Association for Death Education and Counseling's "Death Educator" Award, Dr. Wolfelt is author of several books, including *Understanding Your Grief* and *Healing a Spouse's Grieving Heart*. His website is CenterforLoss. com.

---

hen someone you love dies, it's natural to feel the pain of your loss—and to grieve. But too many people try hard *not* to feel the pain. While it's understandable to want to avoid pain, it's a mistake to do so. People who appear to be "doing well" with their grief sometimes develop chronic, low-grade depression, anxiety and/or addiction to alcohol or drugs as they self-treat their emotional pain.

Recent developments: An increasing body of research is now also linking this type of unreconciled grief (meaning an inability to move forward in life without the person who died) to a wide range of *physical* ailments, including fatigue, headache, high blood pressure and heart disease.

For many people, grief is prolonged and unresolved because there are so many misconceptions surrounding it. *Among the most common—and the most dangerous—misconceptions about grief…*

MISCONCEPTION #1: Grief and mourning are the same thing. People tend to use the words "grieving" and "mourning" interchangeably, but they have different meanings.

Grief is the constellation of internal feelings and thoughts you have when someone you love dies. *Mourning* is when you take the grief you have on the inside and express it outside yourself.

Examples of mourning: Talking about the person who died. Crying. Expressing your thoughts and feelings through art or music. Celebrating anniversary dates that held meaning for the person who died.

Many people grieve but don't mourn. When you do not honor a loss by acknowledging it—first to yourself, and then to others—your grief will accumulate. The denied losses then come flowing out in other ways, such as depression and physical problems…all of which compound the pain of your loss.

MISCONCEPTION #2: You should move away from grief, not toward it. Our society does not give people much time to grieve. They're expected to get "back to normal" in short order. People who continue to express grief outwardly are often viewed as weak or self-pitying. The resulting message is, "Shape up and get on with your life."

This attitude leads many people to either grieve in isolation or attempt to run away from their grief through various means, such as overworking or abusing alcohol or drugs. Masking or moving away from your grief creates anxiety, confusion and depression.

What to do: Continually remind yourself that leaning *toward*—not *away*—from the pain will help you heal. To lean toward the pain, when you are feeling bad, stop and allow yourself to feel the emotion by talking to someone or writing about it.

MISCONCEPTION #3: Grief is mainly about the physical loss of the person who died. The death of a loved one creates many *secondary* losses, such as connections to yourself and the world around you.

Examples: You can lose the self ("I feel like a part of me died")…identity (such as your role as a spouse or child)…security (for example, a widow may not feel as safe in her home)…and meaning (when dreams for the future are shattered).

Important: Understanding the range and depth of your personal losses can help you be more *self-compassionate*. This involves showing sensitivity toward yourself for what you're going through.

Physical self-compassion can include eating well, exercising regularly and getting enough sleep.

Emotional self-compassion can include claiming your right to feel a multitude of emotions and the right to talk about your grief.

Mental self-compassion can mean asking yourself two questions on a daily basis that will help you survive the difficult months of grieving and learn to love life again:

1) What do I want? (now that the person you love is gone). Ask yourself what's doable and what you'd like to accomplish today.

2) What is wanted of me? (Who depends on you? What skills and experience can you bring to others?)

Social self-compassion can include finding a grief "buddy"—a friend who has also had a loss—and/or joining a grief support group. To find a group near you, check with local hospices and funeral homes.

Grief forces us to consider what life is about and what greater purpose there might be for our lives. *Spiritual* self-compassion can mean starting each day with a meditation or spending time in nature.

MISCONCEPTION #4: After a loved one dies, the goal should be to "get over" your grief as soon as possible. Grief is not a problem that you can solve or an illness from which you recover. Rather, you become *reconciled* to your grief—you integrate the new reality of moving forward in life without the person who died. With reconciliation comes a renewed sense of energy and confidence, an ability to fully acknowledge the reality of the death and a capacity to become re-involved in the activities of living.

MISCONCEPTION #5: When grief and mourning are fully reconciled, they never come up again. Grief comes in and out like the tide. Sometimes heightened periods of sadness occur even years after the death.

Example: My dad loved Frank Sinatra's music—and I have bursts of grief almost every time I hear Frank's voice.

You will always, for the rest of your life, feel some grief over a loved one's death. It will no longer dominate your life, but it will always be there, in the background, reminding you of the love you had for the person who died. And you needn't think of that as a bad thing.

If you follow the advice in this article but are still struggling with grief, consider seeing a compassionate grief counselor. To find one, consult the Association for Death Education and Counseling (ADEC.org).

19

Business Adviser

How to Succeed as Your Own Boss: Avoid These 6 Mistakes

Many employees dream of saying good-bye to their bosses and becoming self-employed, but those who give it a go often make mistakes that undermine their success. Such mistakes are common because working for oneself—whether the job is freelance writer, consultant, decorator, child-care provider, personal trainer, tax preparer or anything else—involves unique challenges…and because the conventional wisdom about self-employment often is wrong. *Here are six common mistakes to avoid if you want to be your own boss…*

MISTAKE 1: Thinking that a long client list is the secret to success. Self-employed people often are advised to gather as many clients as possible as quickly as possible. That way they won't be devastated if they lose one or two clients. But in many professions, particularly those that sell to other businesses, not to individuals, a long client list is not as reliable a safety net as you might imagine. If all of your clients are in the same sector, which is likely, and there is a recession or sector-wide downturn, many of them might stop supplying work at the same time.

In addition, maintaining a long client list means that you must devote a lot of time to finding and wooing clients—and those are hours that you will not be able to spend doing work that actually pays. Besides, the more clients you have, the greater the odds that scheduling conflicts will cause you to disappoint some of them.

In many professions, a better goal is to cultivate one or two "anchor" clients that you can count on to give you work on a regular basis.

Michelle Goodman, author of *My So-Called Freelance Life*. She is a contributing writer for *Entrepreneur* magazine and has been self-employed since 1992. Anti9to5Guide.com

307

These clients are likely to bring projects to you, saving you the time and trouble of pitching them. And you can build long-term personal relationships with key decision makers and prove your value, reducing the odds that you will be the first expense cut when budgets tighten.

Only after you have anchor clients in place should you focus on lengthening your client list. If possible, do so by finding clients and contacts who are in various sectors or do different types of work.

Example: A plumber who works for contractors on new buildings could develop contacts among commercial real estate owners who need plumbers to do repairs even when new construction is slow.

MISTAKE 2: Overlooking valuable networking opportunities. Most self-employed people understand the importance of networking with potential clients and customers—but many overlook the advantages of also networking with other self-employed people in related fields. Your fellow self-employed pros could send work your way when they are overbooked…when an assignment is not appropriate for them…or when they need to bring in a collaborator with your particular expertise.

Social-media interest groups provide a great forum to do such networking. Search for appropriate groups on Facebook (type relevant words into Facebook's search bar, then click "Groups" on the results page)…LinkedIn Groups (Linked In.com/groups)…or Meetup.com.

Example: A San Francisco–area dog walker who enters "dog walker" into Meetup.com would discover SF Professional Dog Walkers, a group of fellow pros who meet monthly.

MISTAKE 3: Undercharging. Most people set their prices too low when they first become self-employed. If they charge by the hour, for example, they might come up with the hourly rate by taking the amount they earned per week when they worked for someone else and then dividing it by 40—the standard amount of work hours in a week. But that simple math fails to take into account that for the self-employed, many work hours are not billable hours—for example, no one

will pay you for the time you spend pitching potential clients or sending out invoices. The formula also overlooks the fact that self-employed people must pay certain costs out of pocket that previously were covered (at least in part) by their employers, such as health insurance, retirement plan contributions, marketing expenses and office expenses.

Instead of using a formula, network with your contacts to determine how much self-employed people in your field with your level of experience typically charge. Or join social-media groups that attract pros in your field and ask for input about rates.

MISTAKE 4: Getting work but not getting paid. Sometimes getting a client to pay the bill is the most difficult part of a job. Some clients might be slow to pay or might refuse to pay at all.

Before you work with a new client for the first time, enter the client's company name into a search engine along with words such as "unpaid," "bills" or "warning." Proceed with extreme caution if you find warnings from other professionals who struggled to get paid by this client.

If your first assignment from any new client will take more than a week of your time and/or require you to invest in thousands of dollars' worth of supplies, ask to receive a portion of your payment either up front or when certain milestones are met along the way. Be very cautious about accepting major assignments from new clients who balk at this arrangement.

MISTAKE 5: Not knowing what is next. Self-employed people sometimes become so focused on a particular project that they neglect to line up the next job, leading to a work gap. It's perfectly reasonable to build in a few days of cushion between big assignments in case things take longer than expected, but always keep an eye on what's next—even if that means taking a little time away from an important assignment to scout for future work.

Warning: It's particularly important to have assignments lined up well in advance for the summer…and around the winter holidays. Once these arrive, the people who have the authority to give you work might be out of the office on vacation.

MISTAKE 6: Letting office chores slide. A self-employed person typically is his/her own sales department, billing department, benefits department, IT department, office manager and more. All too often, these secondary responsibilities are allowed to slide, and the result can be costly—fail to pay your bills on time, and you might face penalties…fail to focus on inventory, and you might run short of crucial supplies…neglect sales and marketing, and your work could dry up entirely. To avoid this, create a weekly or monthly schedule for recurring office responsibilities.

Alternative: If you do not like or are not good at certain aspects of running your small business, pay someone to handle those tasks for you. Hire a bookkeeper to tackle your invoicing…an accountant to do your taxes…or someone skilled with computers to serve as your on-demand IT department. Find these support professionals though recommendations from other self-employed professionals.

How to Make Money Blogging: A Simple Step-by-Step Guide

Bob Lotich, who has been blogging full time since 2008. His blog, SeedTime.com, receives more than 1.5 million unique visitors each month. He is author of the eBook *How to Make Money Blogging.* EfficientBlogging.com

---

Do you shake your head in wonder at the mistakes you see people making with their homes, lawns or cars? Are you amazed that people are overlooking a wonderful new product, book or TV program?

These days we all can have our opinions heard and share our wisdom with the world. In decades past, only newspaper columnists and their ilk got to have a public platform, but now it's open to anyone who launches a blog—something you can do in a matter of minutes virtually for free, assuming that you own a computer and have Internet access. You don't even need significant computer skills to do this. And writing about an area of profes-sional expertise or personal interest on an Internet blog could earn you income.

A blog isn't likely to make you rich—most take in a few thousand dollars a year or less. But it can be a way to earn a little income doing something you enjoy, and there is a chance that your blog eventually could grow popular enough to provide a real income. One recent survey of women bloggers found that 6% earned more than $60,000 a year.

Here's how to make a blog a moneymaker…

FOCUS YOUR BLOG

Focus your blog on a topic that you know well *and* that interests a large number of potential advertisers. If you see a lot of ads for related products in the press, online or on TV, it's probably a good topic.

Examples: A blog about golf, fashion or personal finance could become profitable because there are lots of companies advertising in these areas. A blog about poetry or philosophy might be emotionally rewarding, but it probably will never be a big moneymaker.

Once you have selected a topic, focus your blog further by targeting a specific niche area, ideally one that seems underserved by current bloggers. For example, a blog I founded called ChristianPF.com (now called SeedTime.com) provides personal finance advice for the Christian community…and the site Tech50Plus.com provides technology advice for the baby boomer generation. But make sure that your niche will be of interest to a fairly large audience—otherwise your blog will have no way to grow. Rather than blog about gardening in Michigan, for example, you might blog about gardening in northern states.

USE WORDPRESS

Use WordPress—a blog-creation and management service—to create your blog. It's easy to use and the industry standard. There is a free version, which you can start with if you choose, but if your goal is to make money from your blog, it is worth paying for a "self-hosted" WordPress blog. Among other advantages, with a self-hosted blog you can sell ad space (more on that below), something you generally are not allowed to do with a blog hosted by basic WordPress. You can set up a self-hosted WordPress blog through services such as HostGator.com and Bluehost.com, typically for around $10 a month.

BUILD A FOLLOWING

In addition to posting articles on your blog at least once a week, visit popular blogs that cover topics related to yours and respond to their blog posts with well-reasoned, noncritical comments. Include your blog address as well as your name when you identify yourself in these comments. After doing this for a while, send e-mails to the people running these blogs and ask to write a guest post on a specific topic on which you are especially well-versed. If they agree (some will, some won't even bother to respond), include a link to your own blog in this post.

Also, offer to write articles on your area of expertise for websites such as Huffington Post or any sites that cover your topic (look for a "contact us" page). Writing for well-read news sites can help readers find your blog—and help establish you as an expert on your topic.

If you have a following on social-media networks such as Twitter, Facebook, LinkedIn and Pinterest, use these to publicize your blog posts.

WRITE STRONG POSTS AND HEADLINES

When you sit down to write blog posts, try to write fairly long, detailed posts—think 1,000 words or more—even if that means you don't write as many posts. There's lots of information on the Internet—what's missing is truly in-depth, reasoned thinking. If you provide that, there's a good chance readers who find you will return again and again.

Don't worry if you cannot write like Shakespeare—just write like you would speak. Most successful bloggers use a conversational tone, though there are exceptions.

If you are not certain what to write, write posts that answer questions asked by your readers.

Helpful: If you don't yet have many readers asking questions, visit sites somewhat comparable to yours and skim the reader comments sections of recent posts—perhaps there are questions that spur ideas but that the author of that blog has not addressed.

GOOD TO KNOW...

It's Not Too Late to Change Careers!

Older workers seeking to change careers report being able to do so 82% of the time—and 90% of those who made this type of change said it was successful.

Most who changed careers successfully relied on skills they already had...unsuccessful people were more likely to report trying to gain new skills. Skills commonly mentioned by workers ages 45 to 65 included problem-solving, interpersonal communication, public communication, reading comprehension, customer service and basic computer skills.

Most successful career changers did not use strategies that usually are claimed to be necessary—77% did not take online classes, 97% did not get a grant or scholarship, 84% did not use formal networking resources such as career fairs and LinkedIn, and 90% did not volunteer in order to become paid employees later.

Survey by American Institute for Economic Research, reported at CBSNews.com.

Create attention-grabbing headlines for your blog posts. If you're not sure what constitutes a compelling headline, scan the news and entertainment website Buzzfeed.com—the master of this.

Examples: Headlines promising a widely desired result in a specific amount of time—"10 Ways to Lose 10 Pounds by Next Week"...or that contradict the conventional wisdom—"Exercise Won't Help You Lose Weight"—often get lots of attention.

After you've written a headline, re-read it to confirm that it contains the keywords that someone searching for the information you are providing is likely to type into a search engine. If your post is about the dangers of reverse mortgages, for example, definitely include the phrase "reverse mortgage" in its title.

Example: "5 Surprising Reverse Mortgage Dangers."

If readers comment negatively on your article, don't become defensive—some negativity is inevitable on the Internet. Instead, try to engage them in a healthy discussion. Blogs tend to be more popular when their authors are accessible.

That said, blog authors have the ability to delete reader comments. Certainly consider removing comments that are offensive or off topic or that include personal attacks on you or other readers.

MONETIZE YOUR BLOG

There are three main ways to profit from a blog…

•**Sell your own product or service.** For example, you might offer hourly consulting, an online seminar or a book about your area of expertise.

Helpful: Books can be inexpensively published through Amazon's CreateSpace (Create Space.com) or e-published through Amazon's Kindle Direct Publishing (KDP.Amazon.com).

•**Earn commissions.** When you write a blog post that mentions a product, you might be able to earn commissions by including a link to a website that sells this product if your readers click the link and buy the item.

Examples: Amazon.com pays commissions that start at about 4% (Affiliate-Program. Amazon.com)…CJ Affiliate (CJ.com) lists other sites that pay commissions.

•**Sell ad space.** Sign up for Google AdSense (Google.com/adsense). Google will find interested advertisers, and you will earn a commission each time one of your readers clicks on one of the ads. How much you might earn per day can vary from a few cents to more than $10, depending on how much advertisers bid.

College Majors That Make the Most Money

The best college majors for high-earning careers are the ones that lead to positions with high starting salaries and strong projected job growth over the next decade.

For example: Software engineering starts at about $61,700…computer science, $61,600… actuarial mathematics starts at $60,800…physics at $57,200…nursing, $56,900…management

information systems, $56,300…civil engineering at $55,100…statistics, $54,900…economics, $51,400…finance, $50,900.

The 10 majors with the most limited career opportunities—and lower earnings potential: Graphic design, education, radio and television, art, music, interior design, drama, animal science, culinary arts, and child and family studies.

Roundup of experts on job growth and earnings potential reported at Kiplinger.com.

Don't Forget a Cover Letter!

Cover letters still are important when job-hunting…

Research the company so that your letter shows that you know what challenges it faces and how you can help meet them. Include three or four important skills that fit what the job description says the company wants. Address the letter to a specific person—find the name of an appropriate individual at the company website or through LinkedIn. Avoid clichés—instead of a general comment such as self-starter, give specific examples of how your self-starting brought success and how it will help the company to which you are applying. Put a header with your name and contact information at the top to make yourself easy to reach.

USNews.com

TAKE NOTE…

Job Search Facts

The average time for a job search is 43 days. Jobs are filled fastest in the hospitality business—36 days. Retail jobs take an average of 40 days to fill…health-care positions, 65 days. Jobs with vice president or director in the title take an average of 76 days.

Data analysis by Jobvite.com, reported at Money.com.

Best Answers to Odd Job-Interview Questions

Michael R. Neece, president and CEO of Interview Mastery, the world's most widely used job-interview-preparation software, Boston. He previously was "Interview Master" for the career website Monster.com and vice president and director of recruiting for companies including Hewlett Packard and Fidelity Investments. InterviewMastery.com

W ho would be the victor in a battle between Spider-Man and Batman? Who would ask such a question? A job interviewer, that's who. More and more job interviewers are asking weird questions like this.

Interviewers realize that job hunters have prepared responses for the common questions such as, "What's your biggest weakness?" So interviewers sometimes ask unexpected questions in hopes of blindsiding applicants and seeing how their minds work under pressure.

Here's a look at some odd interview questions asked by real employers...and smart responses to each.* Even if you don't hear these exact questions, they give you an idea of how to answer similarly odd ones.

●**How lucky are you, and why?** Airbnb asked this question—probably to gauge applicants' attitudes. Upbeat people tend to consider themselves lucky. Employers want to hire upbeat people because their positive attitudes can boost the mood of the whole workplace.

Potential response: "I've been very lucky. Throughout my career I've been fortunate to work with some wonderful people at some wonderful companies. I'm fortunate to have a loving family and supportive friends..."

●**How many quarters would you need to reach the height of the Empire State Building?** JetBlue asked this question to determine how applicants think through difficult analytical problems. What assumptions do they make? Do they see that the question has multiple interpretations?

*The odd interview questions in this article were collected by employer-analysis and career-guidance company Glassdoor (Glassdoor.com), except as noted.

Potential response: "I will have to make some assumptions to answer. First, I'll assume that we're talking about stacking quarters one on top of another, not standing them on their ends...and not using quarters to pay for a trip up to the building's observation deck. I'll also assume that the quarters can be piled in a single stack without toppling over. Given these assumptions, I'll need to know the thickness of a quarter and the height of the Empire State Building. I could obtain precise information online, of course, but I'll assume you don't want me to do that. I know that the Empire State Building is around 100 stories tall and a roll of 40 quarters is around three inches long. Do you want me to keep going and give you an actual numerical estimate?"

Similar interview questions....

●How many people flew out of Chicago last year?

●How many square feet of pizza are eaten in the US each year?

●How many cows are in Australia?

The idea here is to test analytical problem-solving ability—you don't need to come up with the answer, just how you would get to the answer.

●**What would you do if you were the one survivor in a plane crash?** Airbnb asked this to find out how well applicants establish priorities under pressure.

Potential response: "First, I'd assess the immediate dangers. Is the plane sinking in

---

BETTER WAYS...

Avoid These Interview Mistakes

Interview mistakes and what to do instead...

Failing to explain your previous work clearly—show what benefits you provided to your previous company and prove that you can explain complex subjects. *Showing off*—answer questions respectfully, without seeming to brag. *Failing to answer questions*—ask for clarification if you do not understand a question, but do not bluster or talk around it. *Acting like a robot*—having no passion about work you've done is a turnoff for employers.

BusinessInsider.com

---

water? Is it on fire? How badly am I hurt? You can't respond intelligently without some understanding of what the situation is. Second, I would confirm that I truly was the only survivor—someone might be injured and in need of my help. Once I have myself—and any other survivors—clear of immediate danger, I'd consider whether help is likely to reach me soon. If not, my next priority might be finding shelter or water to drink."

Other similar questions…

• If you were asked to unload a 747 full of jelly beans, what would you do?

• It's Thursday, and we're staffing you on a project in Canada on Monday. Your flight and hotel are booked…your visa is ready. What are the top five things you do before you leave?

• You are a head chef at a restaurant, and your team has been chosen to be on the Iron Chef America TV show. How do you prepare your team and beat the competition?

Interviewers are interested in how you would set priorities under pressure—what would you do first and why?

• **On a scale of one to 10, rate me as an interviewer.** Kraft Foods interviewers didn't ask this question because they wanted to know how they were doing—they did so to test candidates' ability to communicate their opinions. Obviously you do not want to disparage your interviewer—but answering "10" makes you look like someone who evades difficult conversations.

Potential response: "I'd say you've done very well. The questions you've asked thus far have given me an opportunity to show that I could make a contribution to your company. I hope I've done just as well with my answers. There are topics that we have not yet covered, such as my background with [mention a skill that you would like to discuss], but I am sure there's a good chance you will get to them before the end of the interview."

• **Describe the color yellow to somebody who's blind.** Spirit Airlines asked this question to test candidates' creativity…and also to test their ability to understand other people's perspectives. Some candidates no doubt leapt to the conclusion that a blind person would

have no experience with colors, but that is not necessarily so.

Potential response: "First, I'd want to know if the person has always been blind. If not, I'd ask what he or she remembers about colors and start from there. If he has always been blind, I would describe yellow using senses other than sight. I'd say yellow is warm, like the sun on your skin on a pleasant day."

Other similar questions…

• If you were a pizza deliveryman, how would you benefit from scissors?

• A penguin walks through that door right now wearing a sombrero. What does he say, and why is he here?

Interviewers look for creative answers that show you can look at the world through another perspective.

• **Who would win a fight between Spider-Man and Batman?** A Stanford University interviewer asked this to evaluate candidates' ability to make decisions without having all the information.

Potential response: "It depends on a number of factors. What weapons and tools does each have? Batman, in particular, seems to depend on his gadgets. And where is this fight taking place? If it's on top of a tall building, Spider-Man would have a big advantage. If we assume that they each have their usual equipment and the battleground is neutral, I'd choose…"

Then choose one of the superheroes—it does not matter which. Defend your choice using whatever knowledge you have about these characters. In the real world, people often must make decisions based on imperfect information. Failing to choose a superhero would make you appear indecisive.

• **If you were a Muppet, which Muppet would you be?** An interviewer at a cybersecurity company asked my wife this question during a job interview. He was trying to get a sense of how she—and other candidates—saw themselves. What was most important was not which Muppets they chose, but how well they linked the choices to positive workplace traits. But candidates can score bonus points on questions such as this one by coming up with creative responses. My wife picked a Muppet that the interviewer had not previously even considered a Muppet...and she got the job.

Her response: "Yoda. He is intelligent, patient, thoughtful and willing to share his knowledge." Other candidates likely named Muppets on *The Muppet Show*—but those Muppets are goofy, not the image job hunters hope to project. Yoda, a Muppet created for the *Star Wars* movies, has a far more positive image.

Other similar questions...

- If you were a box of cereal, what would you be and why?
- If you were a new crayon, what color would you be and why?
- If there were a movie about your life, who would play you and why?

The interviewer is looking for creative responses that give insight into who you are and that show your positive view of the world.

What You *Must* Bring to Your Next Interview

B e sure to bring a "marketing tool kit" to job interviews. Have one hand free to shake hands, and use the other to carry a folder or briefcase with information about you. This will show that you are prepared for the interview. The items should be self-explanatory so that you can leave them behind. Introduce them naturally during the interview.

Include paperwork that the prospective employer requires...copies of your résumé...your reference list, with contact information...examples of your past work...recommendation letters from previous supervisors...printouts of LinkedIn recommendations...and a competency comparison—a simple table showing what the prospective employer is seeking through the job posting and how you meet the specific requirements.

Roundup of experts on job interviews, reported at USNews.com.

Key Questions to Ask Before Taking a Job

W hat personalities do well here? This tells you whether you would be a good fit. *What are the personal or professional development opportunities?* The answer shows how much the company values its employees. *What is the typical career path for this position?* Knowing that there is one is important if you hope to stay with the company and advance within it. *What is the company culture like?* Find out how the firm regards work/life balance and what a typical workday looks like. *Do you have a bonus program?* Get details on all forms of pay, including salary, bonuses and equity. *Why do you like working here?* Let the interviewer tell you his/her view. *What values are important to the company?* Be sure that they are in line with yours.

Roundup of experts on job interviewing, reported at MarketWatch.com.

Interesting Finding...

T he average US worker would have to work 127.7 years to make one year of the average CEO's pay. The average CEO pay was $6.4 million in 2014 at the 3,000 largest US companies—up from $5.5 million in 2013. The average wage for all Americans was $43,041 in 2013 (latest data available).

MarketWatch.com

Job Perks Worth Negotiating For...

A dditional vacation time...the option to telecommute one or two days a week... parental leave if you plan to start or enlarge a family...flexible hours...membership in a professional organization or useful club—such as an airline club if your job requires you to travel a lot…working on a project that you're interested in…or a change of title.

DailyWorth.com

Love Your Job Again— When All You Want to Do Is Quit

Kerry Hannon, jobs expert for AARP and a columnist for *The New York Times* and PBS's *Next Avenue*. She is author of *Love Your Job: The New Rules for Career Happiness.* KerryHannon.com

Dream of quitting your job? You're not alone. A recent report by the Conference Board, a research group, found that less than 50% of workers are satisfied with their jobs.

Trouble is, changing jobs can be a major challenge, particularly for people over age 50—employers tend to prefer younger workers despite age-discrimination laws. And there's

WHAT TO DO…

4 Steps to a Higher Salary

Four keys to getting a much higher salary…

• **Go into the salary negotiation only after doing lots of research**—know the average salary for your position, and be ready to discuss the company's and department's recent profits.

• **Prove that you, personally, are worth additional money**—document, in numbers, what you have done to make or save the company far more than what you are paid.

• **Imagine that you are negotiating on behalf of someone else**—this can make it easier to be forceful and emphatic if you tend to be shy when asking for more money.

• **After making your request, sit quietly and confidently without saying anything more**—put a fair number on the table, and wait for your manager to respond.

Roundup of experts on salary negotiations, reported at Finance.Yahoo.com.

no guarantee that your new job will be more satisfying than your old one. Often the best solution is to find a way to enjoy your current job more. *Eight ways to do that…*

• **Learn something new.** There's a good chance boredom is at the heart of the problem if you're feeling dissatisfied with a job you've held for years. One way to beat workplace boredom is to volunteer to tackle new projects or take on new roles for your employer.

Examples: Participate in an employer-sponsored training program to learn a new job skill. Volunteer to help out in a different department.

Even learning something unrelated to your job during your free time could help overcome workplace boredom. People tend to feel more satisfied with all aspects of their lives when they are learning—even aspects of their lives that are not directly related to the topic they are learning about.

Examples: Take a public-speaking class at a community college. Enroll in a creative-writing workshop. Sign up for an acting workshop or improvisational comedy. All of these activities will translate to enhanced creativity and communication in the workplace—and boost your happiness, too.

• **Focus on your employer's mission.** People who believe their employers make a positive contribution to the world tend to be more satisfied in their work. You don't have to take a job with a charity to accomplish this…you just have to hear positive feedback from people who use and enjoy your company's products or services.

Example: Visit your company's social-media web pages, and read the comments posted by customers, focusing on the compliments.

• **Declutter your work area.** People tend to be happier and calmer when they are in tidy spaces. Decluttering an office also tends to be a task that can be easily achieved within a short time—perhaps a few hours—allowing you to mentally chalk up a workplace accomplishment when you need one.

• **Connect with colleagues.** People who like the people they work with also tend to like their work. That is no coincidence—forming

315

positive connections with colleagues makes work seem more meaningful and the workplace seem more pleasant, in general.

If you do not get along especially well with the coworkers you currently know, make connections with other people in your company. Not only might you meet some people you like, you might form some useful professional contacts in the process.

Examples: Ask people from other departments to join you for coffee or lunch. Volunteer for charity projects sponsored by your employer. Join the company softball team or bowling league.

•**Come up with a positive response to your negative internal mantra.** Each time you catch yourself feeling unhappy at work, jot down what you're thinking. Develop an upbeat response, and train yourself to think it whenever you feel unhappy about work.

Example: Some workers in their 50s, 60s and older are dogged by the thought, *My sector is changing, and I'm too old to learn anything new.* They could counter this thought with, *I have decades of experience responding to change. I've always managed to remain productive before, so I certainly can now.*

Also: Spend as much time as possible around coworkers who have positive attitudes and as little as possible around complainers—other people's attitudes rub off on us. Meanwhile, laugh and smile as much as possible in the workplace, and cut out your own complaining—your upbeat attitude could help improve the overall mood for everyone.

•**Glory in workplace successes—even when they aren't yours.** People who are dissatisfied at work often feel, *There's just no winning here.* They are less likely to feel this way if they celebrate the accomplishments of their colleagues as well as their own.

Example: When a coworker receives a raise, promotion or praise from the boss, don't think, *That should have been me.* Instead, think, *Look at that—it is possible to succeed here.*

•**Stop asking, Why does my boss have it in for me?**...and start asking, How can I make my boss's life better? Sometimes when people aren't happy with their jobs, the main source of their displeasure is a poor relationship with their direct supervisor.

The secret to improving a strained relationship with a boss is coming to terms with the fact that this relationship is not about you—it's about your boss. Whether you like it or not, your job is to make it easier for your boss to do his/her job. Your boss's job is to make it easier for his boss to do his job—not to make your job more pleasant for you.

To be happy at work, you need to come to terms with these facts. If you can answer, *What can I do to make my boss look good to his boss?* (or *What can I do to help my boss earn more money?*), then you have uncovered the secret to a better relationship with your boss. If you don't know the answer, come right out and ask your boss, "What can I do to make your life better?"

•**Remind yourself that you have the power to quit.** Feeling powerless is a common cause of worker dissatisfaction. Remind yourself periodically that even if you don't have much power in your current position, you always have the power to quit and do something else—you simply choose not to exercise that power for now.

In the meantime, take steps to improve your ability to get a good job, such as obtaining training and certification in in-demand skills. Even if you never change jobs, this should help you feel more in control of your career.

Walking Meetings Are Better Than Standing Ones

While standing meetings in general are shorter than sit-down ones but still may include overdone PowerPoint presentations, distracting chitchat and frequent checking of smartphones. Walking meetings—used by executives at Facebook, Twitter and elsewhere—

are better for brainstorming and encouraging creativity.

Best: Cover only one topic per meeting to keep it short and reduce the need for note-taking. Send an advance note to participants to set the agenda and explain the meeting's intended outcome. Plan a route in advance— walking near a park or another quiet place is best. Include only two or three people in a walking meeting, although more can be added as people gain experience with the format. Do not use walking meetings to introduce complex concepts that require visual support.

Roundup of experts on corporate meetings, reported at BBC.com.

That's a Great Idea!

Bryan Mattimore, cofounder of The Growth Engine Company, an innovation agency, Norwalk, Connecticut, and author of *21 Days to a Big Idea*, reported by Karen Larson, editor, *Bottom Line Personal.*

I magine that you had to come up with an idea for a new invention…in 30 seconds… while standing in front of 200 people. Could you do it? It sounds like a nightmare come true—not a recipe for creativity. But when Bryan Mattimore, president of the consulting agency The Growth Engine Company, put 15 librarians in this seemingly impossible spot, all 15 came up with solid ideas—such as socks that glow in the dark so matching pairs can be identified in early-morning bedrooms… and a bathroom pencil for jotting down ideas on shower walls that can be wiped away easily later.

The secret? Mattimore, author of *21 Days to a Big Idea,* gave each librarian a pair of cards listing some concrete nouns—words such as lamp, phone, pencil, sock and window. One of the cards also included adjectives—words such as elastic, illuminated and reversible. He instructed the librarians to choose one word from each card and combine them into a possible new product, a creative-thinking strategy known as the "and technique."

To try the "and technique," jot down a list of nouns relevant to your professional field or area of interest. Then jot down some adjectives that represent potentially desirable product features or qualities, too, such as illuminated…reversible…micro…and smart. Then combine a noun with a noun or an adjective with a noun, writing down any combinations that sound like possible new products.

Mattimore once used the "and technique" with his family at dinner, and his young daughters came up with an idea for a new smartphone app. Just don't ask Mattimore what that app does—his daughters' kitchen-table product idea is currently in development.

Time-Management Tips

For much better time management at the office…

Do the most important or difficult task first. Doing hard jobs early reduces the chance that you will have to stay late to finish them. Track your activities—you may be spending more time on an activity than you thought. Set limits for things that take up more time than you want them to. Decide how often you need to check e-mail, and shut it down the rest of the time so that you are not distracted. *And:* Mute smartphone alerts.

Roundup of experts on time management, reported at Time.com/money.com.

Get What You Want! Lessons from Top Negotiators

G. Richard Shell, a professor at University of Pennsylvania's Wharton School of Business, chairperson of Wharton's legal studies and business ethics department and academic director for that school's executive negotiation workshop and strategic persuasion workshop. He is author of several books about negotiating, including *Bargaining for Advantage: Negotiation Strategies for Reasonable People* and *The Art of Woo: Using Strategic Persuasion to Sell Your Ideas.* GRichardShell.com

Donald Trump has always tried to intimidate and crush his counterparts in negotiations. Sister Mary Scullion, an influential advocate for the homeless, searches for solutions that allow everyone to win. Their negotiating styles could hardly be more different—yet both are extremely successful.

We asked business school professor G. Richard Shell, an expert on the topic of negotiations, to identify some of the most notable negotiators from modern times…lay out the lessons that can be learned from each…and explain how our readers can use these lessons to be successful in their own dealings…

DONALD TRUMP:
THE FIERCE COMPETITOR

Trump is an expert at finding and exploiting the most vulnerable weak spots of his opponents. He understands that the ability to make someone else's life worse can be a powerful bargaining chip in negotiations.

Example: For weeks, he refused to rule out the possibility of running for president as an Independent if he didn't win the Republican primary. Trump said his use of that leverage was aimed at forcing the Republican Party to treat him "fairly."

How you can use Trump's negotiating technique: First, be honest with yourself about whether you, like Trump, are cut out to make thinly veiled threats, use people's weaknesses against them and create enemies. If not, don't try this—you'll find it stressful and unpleasant, and it might backfire.

If this strategy does fit your personality, don't just ask yourself, *What do I want?* before negotiations. Also consider, *What power do I have to make my opponent's situation worse?*

If the person on the other side of the negotiating table has an archrival, you might threaten to work with that rival, for example. If he/she is working under a tight deadline, you could delay closing the deal. If he is very busy or impatient, you could make the negotiations extremely detailed and time-consuming. Whatever way you inflict pain or the threat of pain, use that to try to get a better deal than was originally offered in exchange for backing off this tactic.

SISTER MARY SCULLION:
THE PROBLEM SOLVER

Sister Mary, a Catholic nun, has devoted her life to helping the homeless of Philadelphia, where she is executive director of Project HOME. Her efforts have been so successful that in 2009, *Time* magazine included her on its list of the world's 100 most influential people.

Her success in negotiating for the homeless is rooted in the fact that she does not simply try to win people over to her cause—she seeks solutions that align the interests of people who have the power to help the homeless with the interests of the homeless.

Examples: When Sister Mary wants a politician to support a project, she explains how it will get homeless people off the streets of that politician's district, helping him politically. When she wants a real estate developer to build low-cost housing, she makes sure the project will produce a profit for that developer.

For one recent fund-raiser, Sister Mary found homeless people who had artistic ability, gave them art supplies, then arranged an exhibition of their work. The homeless didn't

---

EASY-TO-DO…

Don't Let E-Mail Embarrass You

If you are writing an e-mail about a sensitive subject, be sure to add the recipient's e-mail address after you are done composing your message. This will ensure that if you accidentally hit "send" while writing, you won't send off an unfinished—and potentially embarrassing—e-mail.

From Life Hacks by Keith Bradford.

just receive a handout…they got a start as professional artists. The donors didn't just give money…they bought paintings they could hang on their walls.

How you can use Sister Mary's negotiating technique: Before any negotiation, ask yourself what are all the things that the other party in the negotiation needs or wants, and think about how you can help him get these things. In doing so, look beyond the obvious. For example, in negotiating with a potential buyer of your home, the price may be only one factor. Your flexibility in timing your move, your willingness to accept unusual financing, etc., may be equally important. Once you've figured out an arrangement that will help the other party in ways beyond the obvious, present your idea not as a request but as a solution that will benefit everyone.

WARREN BUFFETT: THE PARAGON OF PREPARATION AND PATIENCE

Warren Buffett, whose fortune was made in buying and, to a lesser extent, managing companies, never enters any negotiation until he has a deep understanding of the business that is the subject of the negotiation…the alternatives available to him…and the sector that the business is in. Nor will he negotiate unless he believes that the timing is in his favor—if a company he likes seems overvalued, he waits.

When Buffett finally does enter negotiations, he makes a fair offer, not a low-ball offer. His offers are so fair, in fact, that at least initially, he sometimes is criticized by analysts for being too generous. But Buffett is not being generous—paying a little extra is part of his long-term strategy. It increases the odds that the executives of the company he is seeking to acquire will be enthusiastic about the sale and about working for him…and it telegraphs the message to people who enter future negotiations with Buffett that he will offer them a fair deal, increasing the chance that they, in turn, will accept his terms.

How you can use Buffett's negotiating technique: Gain as much knowledge as possible prior to a negotiation. For example, do not try to buy a new car until you have first researched precisely which car and options you want and the price other buyers are pay-

ing for this vehicle. Patiently wait to negotiate until the other side is most likely to offer you a good deal—with new cars, for example, that's typically near the end of a model year and near the end of a calendar month. Then make a reasonable offer that allows both sides to walk away happy.

ANNA WINTOUR: THE CONNECTOR

Anna Wintour, the infamously demanding *Vogue* magazine editor in chief who inspired the Meryl Streep role in the film *The Devil Wears Prada,* has positioned herself as the hub at the center of the wheel of the fashion industry. She knows virtually everyone of importance in fashion, whether it is designers, celebrities, advertisers or publishing executives. Her connections give her tremendous power in negotiations. She can leverage them by bringing people together…or by threatening to shut people out of the industry if they displease her. Her power is so great that her advocacy can be the deciding factor in the choice of a designer at a fashion house.

How you can use Wintour's negotiating technique: Build as broad a network as possible. Get to know people throughout your company and industry, as well as your community. Find out what really matters to these people and what challenges they face. Then look for opportunities to help these people form useful connections with other people you know. Those people later might be in a position to help you. Encourage people to come to you when they encounter problems. When someone treats you poorly, let everyone in your network know about it—if enough people react negatively, this could serve as a warning to others not to cross you.

BILL CLINTON: THE CHARMER

Former president Bill Clinton uses his considerable personal magnetism as a negotiating tool. It is said that his opponents, knowing his reputation, sometimes refuse to meet with him face-to-face for fear that he will charm them into agreeing to something that isn't in their best interests.

How you can use Clinton's negotiating technique: You can't learn this sort of charm—you either have it or you don't. If you are fortunate enough to have it, understand that your power of personal magnetism is strongest when you are face-to-face and diminishes with time and distance. Push people to sign on the dotted line right away, before they have a chance to reconsider. (Conversely, if you are negotiating with a charmer—someone you find yourself liking immensely despite yourself—sleep on any deal before finalizing it.)

RONALD REAGAN: THE MAN OF PRINCIPLE

President Ronald Reagan was a man with deeply held beliefs, and he refused to compromise those beliefs during negotiations. Reagan strongly believed in the importance of standing up to Communism, for example, so rather than try to smooth over differences between the US and the Soviet Union, he stood at the gate between East and West Berlin and exhorted Soviet leader Mikhail Gorbachev to "tear down this wall."

Refusing to compromise might seem like a terrible negotiating tactic, but it actually can be quite effective when used properly. If people believe you truly cannot be moved off of a position, they often will back down.

How you can use Reagan's negotiating technique: First, identify which of your beliefs are your core beliefs—the ones on which you are unwilling to budge. There cannot be many of these—if you have more than one or two, people will see you as unreasonable,

not principled, and refuse to deal with you at all. Communicate very clearly that you will not waiver on these core beliefs. Explain why they are so central to who you are. Perhaps compromising in these areas would run counter to your ethical compass or religious beliefs. Perhaps you gave your word to a now-deceased loved one. Then offer to brainstorm with your negotiation opponent about how you can find common ground without your having to give ground on this issue.

10 Ways to Get Noticed: A PR Master Shares His Secrets

Robert L. Dilenschneider, founder of The Dilenschneider Group, a corporate strategic consulting and public relations firm based in New York City. He is author of *50 Plus! Critical Career Decisions for the Rest of Your Life.* Dilenschneider.com

Large companies pay public relations firms to promote their brands. These firms do this through a variety of strategies, such as crafting the organization's essential message into concise, memorable language…reaching out to the media and the target audiences to repeatedly deliver the message…and getting third parties to publicly praise the company. Unfortunately, many small companies and entrepreneurs cannot afford such services, and few, if any, job seekers and employees can pay professionals to spread the word about their skills.

Good news: Armed with the following 10 commandments of PR, you can handle your own publicity…

1. Make your message as clear as possible—even if that means sacrificing detail. It's tempting to elaborate on everything you can do each time you run an ad or meet someone who seems interested. Don't. People are more likely to remember what you say if you hone it down to a concise message.

If you're not sure what constitutes a clear message, look for a Procter & Gamble ad—

this consumer-products company is masterful with messages. Charmin toilet paper's slogan, "Please, don't squeeze the Charmin," speaks to softness. Bounty paper towels are dubbed, "The Quicker Picker Upper," emphasizing absorbency.

Examples: Your message might be, "I'm the guy who figures out the really tough engineering problems," or "I'm the woman who knows how to motivate sales teams," or "We're the local plumbing company you can trust."

2. Provide examples that support your message. Examples don't just help make your point…they also help your audience remember it. People tend to recall stories long after they have forgotten facts and figures.

Example: If your message is, "I'm the consultant who's always there when he's needed," share a story about helping a client on Christmas Day.

3. Consider your audience. As you hone your message, remember that your goal isn't to come up with something that will resonate with everyone or even with people like you—it's to come up with something that will sway the very specific group of people who could potentially become your clients or customers. Think about what *these* people want and what they will understand. Solicit input from allies you have among this group. Otherwise your message might miss the mark.

Example: A young professor at an Ivy League university appeared to be on a professional fast track. He spoke at international conferences, published articles in prestigious journals and was beloved by his students—yet he was not granted tenure. It turned out that the other professors in his department, the people who made the career-breaking tenure decision, did not want to work with a star who would outshine them. To reach this audience, the professor should have been sending the message, "I'm a team player who will help with the department's thankless tasks," not "I'm a star"—at least until he had tenure.

4. Repeat your message—constantly. By tomorrow most people will have forgotten what you told them today. Say it again—in a fresh way, if possible.

Example: Monitor the news for events that are related to your business or message, then repeat your message in terms of how it fits in with these events.

5. Establish yourself as an expert on something. Choose a specific topic within your sector that you know very well, then spread the word that you are the person to trust on this topic. Do not worry that this will pigeonhole you—it's better to be considered the expert on one specific thing than a generalist who is never the top choice for anything.

Start a blog or newsletter focused on your area of expertise. Send press releases to media members who cover this topic.

Examples: Promote yourself as "Nebraska's Ice Dam Expert" or "Washington County's expert on tax law."

6. Keep control of your message. There might come a time when someone attempts to wrest control of your message away from you. A company competing with yours might spread negative rumors about you. A colleague who disagrees with your strategy—or who is competing with you for a promotion—might interrupt with difficult questions when you make presentations. A dissatisfied customer might leave negative reviews on social-media sites.

BETTER WAYS…

No More Eyestrain at Work

Four ways to prevent tired eyes when at work…

Dim your computer screen to match the brightness level of your room. Sit slightly to the left of the center of the monitor—this allows your gaze to be more naturally centered when reading left-aligned text. Raise or lower your chair until your eye level aligns with the top of the monitor so that you can gaze comfortably at the center of your screen (we naturally look downward by about 10° to 15°). Increase the font size of what you are reading—a 12-point font works well for most people. Take frequent breaks by blinking your eyes, going for a walk or focusing your eyes on something other than your computer screen.

GoodHousekeeping.com

Among the ways to maintain control of your message when challenged…

• Provide direct but calm responses. Do not get drawn into heated arguments—if you do that, the only message people will remember will be your temper.

• Spread your message in writing, rather than verbally, as much as possible. Send an e-mail. Circulate a memo. Write an article for a local paper. Words in print are more difficult for opponents to distort.

• Repeat your message…more than ever. When two contrary viewpoints are being presented, people tend to put more stock in the one they hear more often.

7. Motivate third parties to spread your message. Having someone else sing your praises is always more effective than doing so yourself. The best way to accomplish this is to treat your clients and anyone else you come into contact with as well as you feasibly can. Give people more than they are expecting—even just a little more—and they will extol you to their acquaintances.

Example: Automaker Tesla recently updated the software of certain cars it already had sold to include a new "Autopilot" feature. Tesla owner and talk show host Stephen Colbert spent more than five minutes on his show talking about how much he loves his Tesla, citing this "Autopilot" update in particular.

8. Expand your network. Be visible wherever your potential clients or customers are likely to be, including trade shows, professional meetings, community gatherings and/or social-media sites. Do not be heavy-handed pushing your message or selling yourself in these places…just strive to be known to everyone and nice to everyone. People who know and like you are much more likely to work with you.

9. Follow up—quickly. A single interaction often is not enough to create a new client or contact. When you make a positive connection, come up with an excuse to reach out to this person a second time within a day or two. Send an e-mail to say how much you enjoyed the initial conversation, and ask if there is any additional information you can provide.

Or send an article that covers the topic you discussed, with a note saying, "I thought this might be of interest." Don't put it off or you may miss an opportunity.

Example: I met an interior decorator at a dinner party and told her she would be perfect for a couple I knew who had just bought a huge new home. But she didn't follow up with me until months later, by which point the couple had hired a different decorator.

10. Strive to be the person *doing* the scrutinizing for the media, not the person *under* scrutiny. Many people believe that the best publicity comes when the media does a story about their company. But when a journalist does a story about a person or company, he/she generally tries to dig up the bad as well as the good to give the story "balance." It is better to be the expert that the media turns to when something needs to be scrutinized.

Example: If a newspaper profiles a criminal defense attorney, it likely will mention cases he lost, as well as those he won, muddying his image among readers. If that attorney instead tells reporters who cover the local courthouse that he would be happy to share his insight about trials, he is likely to be presented positively, as the voice of wisdom.

The Two-Hour Stand-Up Challenge

New British guidelines advise office workers to be on their feet for at least two hours during the typical eight-hour workday.

How to do this: Adjustable desks for sitting and standing…standing-based work projects…and walking breaks.

Why: Sitting for prolonged periods increases risk for heart disease, diabetes and cancer.

Caution: Too much standing may lead to low-back, knee and foot pain, so be sure to alternate sitting and standing.

John P. Buckley, PhD, professor of applied exercise science, University of Chester, UK.

20

Don't Get Fooled

Cyber-Crooks Could Crack Your Nest Egg: How to Protect Your Financial Accounts

High-tech thieves are trying to crack your nest egg. An incredible 88% of brokerages and 74% of investment advisory firms say that they have been targets of cyber attacks, in most cases involving malware or fraudulent e-mails, according to a recent SEC report.

In many of the attacks involving fraudulent e-mails, the financial firms were tricked into transferring to scammers amounts ranging from $5,000 to $75,000.

There are no laws that require investment firms to compensate investors for cyber-theft losses, although in many cases the companies do. However, if a high-tech thief manages to transfer your life savings to his own offshore account, that money might be gone for good—even if it is your investment firm's lax security that allows the crime to happen.

Investment companies are working to beef up their security. A recent survey by the consulting firm PricewaterhouseCoopers found that US financial services companies are rapidly increasing their cyber-security spending. Citigroup now spends more than $300 million per year. JPMorgan Chase plans to double its spending from $250 million to $500 million over the next five years, following a 2014 data breach that put 76 million JPMorgan customers at risk and a 2013 incident in which pre-paid cards were accessed by hackers.

Gary Miliefsky, founder and CEO of SnoopWall, a counter-intelligence technology company. He is a member of the advisory board of the Center for the Study of Counter-Terrorism and Cyber Crime, based at Norwich University in Vermont. He previously served as editor of *Cyber Defense Magazine* and advised the US Department of Homeland Security's National Infrastructure Advisory Council. SnoopWall.com

But while financial companies are spending huge amounts on cyber-security technology and staff, successful attacks remain common. *Here's why the firms remain vulnerable and what you can do to protect your money...*

THE FLAWS THAT REMAIN

Two of the biggest vulnerabilities...

•**Investment company employees fall for the same identity-theft tricks that trip up individuals.** Investment companies warn their customers to be wary about clicking on links in e-mails or opening attached files—the e-mails might be from cyber-criminals trying to steal account information. However, employees at those companies sometimes fall for the same scam, accidentally giving cyber-criminals access to computers containing customer information.

•**Account information is not always encrypted.** If you ask an investment company whether it encrypts customer data, it likely will assure you that it does, then tell you about "128-bit Secure Sockets Layer (SSL)" encryption or something similar. But this means only that *digital communications* between your computer and the company are encrypted. Most companies don't encrypt account information when it is stored on the company's hard drives or used internally...or confirm that it is encrypted when it is shared with corporate partners or vendors.

If investment firms would practice end-to-end encryption, it wouldn't be such a big deal when hackers break into their systems—the hackers would not be able to read the encrypted files.

Why don't investment companies do this? Because end-to-end encryption is not only expensive, it also makes life more difficult for executives and employees. And even though end-to-end encryption can be useful, companies that use it often make mistakes that expose account information long enough for lurking hackers to pounce.

HOW TO EVALUATE SECURITY

The daunting reality is that no investment firm or investment account is completely safe from cyber-criminals—but some are safer than others. Here's how to tell whether your investment companies are doing everything possible to protect your assets and how to decide which of the security options they offer are worth the trouble...

•**Can you get an extra security code sent to your phone?** Roughly half of large financial companies now offer *two-factor authentication*. If you opt to get this protection, your investment firm will text a onetime-use code to your cell phone (or give you a key-fob-size "token" that displays a code) each time you try to log in. You must enter this code on the company's website to access your account. This greatly improves account security—cyber-criminals are unlikely to have access to your phone (or token) even if they get their hands on your account information.

Among the firms that offer it: Bank of America, Charles Schwab, E*Trade, Fidelity, Goldman Sachs, Merrill Edge, T. Rowe Price, USAA, Vanguard.

Firms that don't: Capital One ShareBuilder, Scottrade, TD Ameritrade.

Helpful: If you want the security of two-factor authentication without having to check a phone or token for a code each time you log in, find out whether the company offers the option of requiring authentication only when logging into the account from a computer other than the one you normally use, as many firms do.

•**Is there a history of hacks?** If your investment firm has had customer accounts breached repeatedly in recent years, it could be a sign that its cyber defenses are especially weak. If it has suffered any major breach in the past 12 months, it still might be in disaster-recovery mode—it can take a full year for a company to figure out exactly what happened and to confirm that hackers are 100% flushed from its systems.

The Privacy Rights Clearinghouse maintains an online database of known data breaches. At PrivacyRights.org, click "Data Breaches timeline since 2005," then enter the financial company's name into the box labeled "Search the entire database for a company or organization by name."

Examples: Schwab and Scottrade both had breaches in the past 12 months.

•**Will the company make good on cyber-theft losses?** If investment companies cannot protect their customers from online criminals, they should at least repay any money that is stolen. An increasing number now offer on-line security guarantees that promise to do this, although these guarantees usually have limitations.

Examples: Ameriprise, Fidelity and TD Ameritrade promise to cover losses that occur "through no fault of your own." Scottrade and

Vanguard customers must follow a checklist of security procedures, such as using up-to-date security software, to remain eligible for reimbursement guarantees. Charles Schwab and E*Trade impose relatively few restrictions. Schwab asks customers to safeguard account-access information and to report unauthorized transactions as quickly as possible, while E*Trade asks them just to not share user IDs and passwords and to review statements and report unauthorized trades promptly. American Funds, Franklin Templeton, Pimco and T. Rowe Price do not currently have written cyber-security guarantees (though they still might compensate investors for cyber-crime losses if the customer is not to blame).

If you can't find a cyber-theft guarantee on a financial company's website, type the company's name and the words "online security guarantee" or "online fraud policy" into a search engine...or call the company's customer service department.

Helpful: See whether the company has cyber-theft insurance to compensate customers if there are large-scale losses.

BEWARE...

Why Your Fingerprint Won't Protect Your Accounts

Biometric security confirms your identity by scanning some characteristic of your body—such as your fingerprints, irises or the shape of your face—or by listening to your vocal patterns. Recent iPhones and iPads and some other devices already include fingerprint scanners, and a few investment companies have launched biometric-security programs—Vanguard offers voice verification, for example. Facial or iris scanners would use the cameras built into computers. *There are problems, however...*

•**The bad guys can beat biometrics.** Biometric technology is improving, but for now, the face, iris and fingerprint scanners sometimes can be fooled with photos. Voice scanners can be fooled with voice recordings.

•**Biometric systems can be frustrating to use.** A finicky biometric system might deny you access to your own account if, for instance, you have a cold that distorts your voice.

•**Some biometrics need additional hardware.** Most of today's computers and smartphones do not include fingerprint readers, for example.

•**You can't change your biometric data if it's stolen.** If an investment company uses biometric security, it must store your biometric data in its computers. If that computer is hacked, the crooks might get their hands on details about your fingerprints, face, eyes or voice that they could use to invade accounts.

Gary Miliefsky, founder and CEO, SnoopWall, a counter-intelligence technology company. SnoopWall.com

Your Most Important Computer Questions Answered

Michael B. Cole, owner of Magic Computer Consulting in New York City. He has worked for tech giants Microsoft and Apple, providing support to corporate executives and consumers. MagicComputerConsulting.com

---

We use computers all the time, but many of us still know surprisingly little about them. *Here are answers to the five questions I'm asked most often as a computer consultant...*

•**I've read about Hillary Clinton's e-mail security problems. Where is my e-mail kept?** When you send an e-mail, a copy is sent to the e-mail server belonging to your e-mail service provider (Google, Microsoft, etc.). That server maintains a copy of all the e-mails you send or receive until you choose to delete them.

Your service provider also sends a copy to the service provider of the person to whom you sent the e-mail. It waits on that server until that person opens his e-mail program on his computer and receives a copy of your message. A copy of the recipient's e-mail also remains on his service provider's server until it is deleted. When any other e-mail program is used on any additional device (laptop, smartphone, tablet) with the same e-mail account, it also receives a copy of the e-mail.

All of this amounts to a minimum of four copies for every e-mail successfully sent and received. One person can never delete all four copies. You do not have access to the recipient's computer or server and cannot delete those copies. And deleted e-mails can sometimes be retrieved.

●**Should I delete "cookies"?** As you navigate among websites, your Internet browser (Internet Explorer, Safari, Google Chrome, Firefox, etc.) will receive very small files that collect browsing data. These are cookies. They usually don't contain personally identifiable data, such as your name, but they can contain information about your browsing session at a particular website, storing information about which articles you read, what items you browsed for on a shopping website and which ads you have clicked on. A cookie also may save your geographic location and even the name of your Internet service provider and what model computer you are using. It is safe to assume that all major commercial websites are using cookies.

As to whether you should get rid of cookies or not, many websites either prohibit or limit your visiting if cookies are blocked, so you can't really get very far without them. Some people prefer to frequently delete their cookies. Since a cookie will automatically be created again when you visit a website, this is not a permanent solution.

There are two types of cookies that your browser identifies—cookies from the website you are visiting…and third-party cookies. Third-party cookies usually are advertiser-related and often are shared among websites that use a common Internet advertising service. Most third-party cookies can be blocked with an Internet browser setting. Doing so does not in any way restrict your ability to surf the web.

To block third-party cookies, find your browser's settings for "Privacy" that let you control how cookies are controlled. On Windows computers, look in your Internet browser (Internet Explorer, Safari, Google Chrome, Firefox, etc.) for a menu item called "Options" or "Internet Options." On a Mac, look in your Internet browser for a menu item labeled "Preferences."

●**What do I need to do to be safe while downloading programs from the Internet?** Here are three excellent rules from Brian Krebs, a former reporter for *The Washington Post* who writes a blog called *Krebs on Security* that focuses on computer security…

Rule 1: If you didn't go looking for it, don't install it! This minimizes the danger of a malicious program taking over functions in your computer. Of course, sometimes even a program you have actually requested will include an additional "payload" containing an additional program that you did not request. Sometimes, when you choose to download a new program, you are notified about the additional program so that you may "opt out."

Rule 2: If you installed it, update it. Any program that you obtain, even free ones, may have problems that get fixed later with a subsequent update. Updates are necessary to keep your programs and computer functioning properly. (Also see the next question.)

Rule 3: If you no longer need it, remove it. Unused programs have been proven to slow down computer performance and create conflicts with other software. Even if you downloaded a program just to try it but haven't used it since, you should think about removing it.

●**I keep getting pop-up messages about specific updates.** Should I follow the prompts and do the updates? Usually, yes. The majority of the software we use requires maintenance and updating. Despite testing, some problems are not discovered until hundreds of thousands of people already are using them. (That's one reason some people are wary about getting brand-new software when it's first released.)

Software companies provide free updates because it's one way to significantly reduce problems and improve the user experience. Often updates are created to provide enhanced protection against known security vulnerabilities. Even though your own experience may be fine, it still is recommended to receive and install updates.

Expect regular updates not only for your operating system but also for specific software products such as *Java, Adobe Flash* and *Adobe Reader.* These popular, free programs are frequent targets of criminals and must be updated to be safe.

Sometimes you may encounter fraudulent messages regarding updates. If you are unsure about any particular update request, it is best to ignore it rather than granting it permission to be installed. Sometimes you can tell if it's fraudulent from spelling or grammar errors, inaccurate program or company names, or even incorrect logos or other graphics. If you're still unsure, you can go to the company's website to see if the version you have is still current.

●**What are the questions I should ask a support technician before letting that person perform any work on my computer?** Since I believe that "first do no harm" should apply when solving any computer problem, it is important that you ask these four questions—in the described sequence—before you let anyone take action on your computer…

Question 1: Would you restate my problem? It is very important that the technician has thoroughly assessed both the symptom of your problem and your specific environment (including specific computer model and software versions). For example, a fix that might be good for Windows 10 may cause harm when used on Windows 7.

Question 2: What action do you plan to take? The techie should be able to clearly and competently describe his intentions before proceeding. You may need to ask for a more understandable, jargon-free explanation.

Question 3: Is your proposed fix designed to address my specific problem? This minimizes the prospect of a hasty selection from a limited number of known fixes. There even is a possibility that the symptoms of your problem are unique and require the assistance of a more skilled technician.

Question 4: Have you ever done this before? While it may not completely disqualify your technician, it is not ideal to let him practice on your system.

If you stick to these questions, the answers should give you a good feel for the technician's ability to get the job done…or not.

Hack-Proof Your Apps

Kim Komando, who has been providing technology tips for more than 20 years. She hosts *The Kim Komando Show,* a weekly national radio program, and she writes a technology column for *USA Today.* Komando.com

Did you know that your smartphone and tablet can be infected with viruses and malware—just like desktop and laptop computers? This typically happens when you download a *malicious* app.

Once it is on your device, hackers can steal sensitive material such as account details, passwords and photos. They can cause your operating system to crash, rendering your device useless. They even can hijack your contacts list and send spam texts to your friends, family and associates.

How to protect your devices…

●**Get apps only from official websites.** The official Apple iOS and Android app stores each offer more than a million apps to choose from. They do an excellent job of scrutinizing new apps and quickly weeding out malicious or infected ones. Nonofficial sites that offer unique apps or free versions of popular paid apps often have low security standards, and some may even be fronts for hacker groups. This is especially true for Android, which is installed on more than half of all mobile devices in the US. Unlike iOS, Android has an "open" operating system—smartphone and tablet manufacturers can alter the software to work on their devices. These altered systems can be more susceptible to hackers.

Helpful: If you have an Android device, make sure you don't accidentally install unofficial apps. Go to the Settings menu, tap "Security," then uncheck the "Unknown Sources" option. Also, avoid clicking on any link to an app that you receive in a text or an e-mail.

•**Install an antivirus/malware app.** The Apple and Android app stores offer *Lookout* and other antivirus apps for free.

Scam Alert: Fake Windows 10 Upgrades

Avoid opening links in your e-mail promising a free copy of Microsoft's new operating system, Windows 10. Although the e-mail appears legitimate, clicking on the link actually downloads malicious software that locks you out of the files on your computer, then forces you to make a ransom payment to the sender to regain access.

The only ways you should download the upgrade: Click on the Windows 10 icon that appears in the notification area of your task bar in Windows 7, 8 and 8.1...or get the software directly from *Microsoft.com.*

Max Eddy, a software analyst focusing on digital security for PCMag.com.

Scammers Target Online Daters

Barbara Sluppick, founder of RomanceScams.org, a support group for victims of dating scams.

Scams targeting people who use online dating websites and social-media sites are on the rise—and very profitable for the scammers. In the second half of 2014 alone, online dating scammers robbed Americans of an estimated $82 million. Both men and women are targeted—and frequently the victims are seniors.

Scammers might ask victims for financial support during a fabricated emergency...or for help with travel costs for a visit that eventually will be canceled...or to deposit a check for

them and send them the cash (the check will bounce).

Five red flags that your "date" may be a scammer...

•**He/she claims to be an American who is temporarily abroad.** In one common variation, the scammer claims to be in the military and temporarily deployed overseas. A scammer wants his/her victims to believe that the scammer's permanent residence is close to the victim's so that the victim can imagine a life together. But most scammers actually are based in foreign countries—western Africa is the most common location.

•**You notice strange quirks in language.** These scammers often speak and write English very well, but they might not be familiar with expressions that are common in the US. One woman noted that her "American" beau seemed confused by the expression "See you later, alligator."

•**His/her photo matches someone else's.** Scammers pass off other people's photos as their own. Load any pictures you have of this person into both TinEye.com and Google Image Search (Images.Google.com, then click the camera icon in the search bar). It's a very bad

---

GOOD TO KNOW...

The Top 10 Most Dangerous Names to Search Online

Searching for popular names plus terms such as "download" or "MP4" often leads to sites filled with spyware, adware and viruses.

10 most dangerous names to search: Comedian Jimmy Kimmel was most dangerous, followed by DJ Armin van Buuren, singer and actress Ciara, rapper Flo Rida, musicians/singers Bruce Springsteen, Blake Shelton, Britney Spears and Jon Bon Jovi, comedian Chelsea Handler and singer Christina Aguilera.

Self-defense: Get celebrity information from trusted websites...use antivirus software, and keep it updated...do not give out your personal information...do not download software, music or videos from unknown sites...and do not open e-mail attachments from unknown sources.

Consumer Reports. ConsumerReports.org

sign if these sites find these images elsewhere on the Internet with someone else's name on them.

• **Video chats never work properly.** Perhaps the sound works but not the picture when you try to video chat with your new love interest...or perhaps the picture works but not the sound.

• **You are asked for money and/or to engage in unusual banking activities.** If someone you have never met in person is asking for these things, you almost certainly are being scammed.

How Instagram Scam Lures Naïve Victims

In this con, the victim sees an Instagram account featuring photos of people holding large amounts of cash—with a description of how easy it is to make money with only a small initial investment. The victim is told to text or instant-message the account holder for details. People who do are asked for an initial investment of several hundred dollars or more—or sometimes they are asked to send their debit card and account PIN to a specified address so that a check can be deposited into their account. The come-on is a complete fraud—Instagram accounts making the offering are quickly deleted after someone sends money or a debit card, and the thieves make off with the money or clean out the victim's account.

Fraud.org, a project from the National Consumers League.

Crowdfund Scams

Andrew Dix, cofounder and CEO of Crowdfund Insider, which covers alternative finance. Crowdfund Insider.com

Crowdfund websites such as Kickstarter. com and Indiegogo.com connect projects in need of funding, such as inventions and charitable causes, with people willing to provide financing. But some of the projects are scams. The US Federal Trade Commission recently settled a fraud case against a would-be board game developer who, it claimed, spent much of the $122,000 he raised on Kickstarter on personal expenses. Earlier this year, a woman in Iowa received probation after she raised money to pay for cancer treatments for her healthy young daughter.

Before sending money...

• **Read the comments section.** The major crowdfund websites let site visitors leave comments. If there's something suspicious, there's a chance that someone else will have called attention to it.

Also: The Reddit web page Shitty Kickstarters (Reddit.com/r/shittykickstarters) serves as a forum for red flags. My website, Crowdfund Insider.com, covers potential scams, too.

• **Make sure plenty of other backers believe in the project.** If a project has lots of support, that means lots of other people have decided it seems legitimate.

• **Explore the background of the person behind the project.** Can you find legitimate-looking social-media pages for him/her? Does his track record include relevant experience? Has he launched other successful crowdfund campaigns in the past?

• **Be careful with Indiegogo projects involving the development of high-tech hardware.** Claims of forthcoming technology can be hard to prove. Indiegogo does not require a working prototype for these projects. The other best-known crowdfunding site, Kickstarter, does require a working protoype.

• **See if similar products are already available elsewhere in the world.** Occasionally someone takes a product already on sale, typically in Asia, and posts it on a crowdfund site as if it were a brand-new project he is trying to develop. Enter relevant keywords into search engines to see if similar products exist.

"IRS" Phone Scam

Phone scammers are increasingly posing as IRS collection agents. The scammers accuse people of failing to respond to numerous IRS notices. If the victim has caller-ID, the call will appear to come from the IRS. The scammers then say that the only way to avoid massive penalties—or even jail time—is to make a payment immediately with a credit or debit card. The actual IRS never requests credit or debit card information over the phone.

Steven J. Weisman, Esq., an attorney based in Waltham, Massachusetts, and founder of the scam-information website Scamicide.com.

Beware Smartphone-Camera Spies

A pair of identity thieves used their smartphone cameras to record the Social Security numbers of about 1,000 Walmart customers who were providing these numbers to cash checks. The thieves positioned themselves to one side and slightly behind these customers.

When providing private data in a public place: Use your body, hand or a book or magazine to shield the information.

Steven J. Weisman, Esq., an attorney based in Waltham, Massachusetts, and founder of the scam-information website Scamicide.com.

New Credit Card Scam: Stealing Security Codes

Curtis Arnold, founder of the news and review websites CardRatings.com and BestPrepaidDebitCards.com. He is author of How You Can Profit from Credit Cards.

The three- or four-digit security codes printed on credit and debit cards are meant to protect you from criminals who want to charge purchases to your account. But criminals—who already have their hands on

millions of stolen card account numbers—are tricking cardholders into revealing the codes as well.

The scam works like this: You receive a phone call from someone who claims to work in your card issuer's fraud-prevention department. The caller reads your credit card account number to you and says that suspicious transactions have been identified on the account, then asks you to confirm whether you made a particular purchase. When you say you did not, the caller tells you not to worry because a new account number will be issued and you won't be responsible for any fraudulent charges. But first you have to provide the security code to prove that the card still is in your possession. If it is not, you might be responsible for some of the fraudulent charges, the caller claims.

Even savvy consumers fall for this scam because the caller already knows the card account number, making it easier to convince you that it is the card issuer calling.

What to do: If a caller claims to be from your card issuer's fraud-prevention department, ask for the caller's name and/or employee ID, hang up, then call the 800-number on the back of your card and ask to speak to the fraud-prevention department or that particular employee. If the call was not from the card issuer, explain that your account number

---

TAKE NOTE...

Popular Purchases Using Stolen Credit Cards

The most popular attempted purchases using stolen or compromised credit cards...

Rolex watch...Louis Vuitton handbag...diamond engagement ring...MacBook Air...smartwatch...vouchers for iTunes...World of Warcraft gold...pizza...and luxury hotel rooms. Scammers also are attempting to purchase business services, such as logo and website design, and search engine optimization services meant to facilitate large-scale scamming.

Sampling of nearly three million attempted fraudulent transactions by sales-fraud detection company Forter, reported at MarketWatch.com.

likely has been stolen. The issuer will give you a new card with a new number.

Mystery-Shopping Scam

Being a mystery shopper entails shopping at a store and reporting on the experience. Scammers have used e-mail and regular mail to promote nonexistent mystery-shopping jobs for a long time. Now some scammers are taking to LinkedIn. They pose as members of IntelliShop, a legitimate mystery-shopping company. Unlike legitimate mystery-shopper assignments, they ask victims to pay up-front to get a job—but the job does not exist. Or they ask a victim to cash a large check written by the scammers, use some of the money to shop at specified stores, keep part of the remainder and wire the rest back to the supposed agency. The scammer keeps the wired money. The check eventually bounces, and the victim must make good on it.

Self-defense: If you want to become a mystery shopper, visit MSPA.org, the website of MSPA North America, which is the trade association for mystery-shopper companies. The site provides a list of legitimate firms you can contact.

Kiplinger.com

Do-It-Yourself Home Security Systems

Ry Crist, an associate editor for *CNET,* a consumer-electronics website. Crist specializes in smart and automated home electronics products and systems. CNET. com

---

About 20% of homes in the US have professionally installed and monitored security systems. These services, with maintenance and monitoring fees that add up to several hundred dollars a year, are beyond the budgets of many people. Also, many exist-ing homes would require custom installation and wiring.

But a different type of home security has been catching on—do-it-yourself (DIY) systems that have no contracts and, in most but not all cases, no additional fees beyond the cost of the equipment and no professional monitoring. Instead of requiring wires in the walls, DIY systems typically use the existing Wi-Fi network in your home…wireless door and window sensors…an app on your smartphone or tablet to control the system…and optional wireless cameras. You can install, customize and monitor these systems yourself.

DIY systems aren't right for everyone, especially if you don't want to figure out where to put sensors and/or you are unwilling to sacrifice the added security of professional outside monitors to contact authorities when you are away or under threat. But for home owners willing to do without that extra layer of security, DIY systems can provide some peace of mind without a lot of the extra cost.

HOW IT WORKS

The centerpiece of a DIY home security system typically is a base station that connects to your home's Wi-Fi router. The base station usually contains a built-in, very loud 110-decibel alarm and communicates with various sensors, including motion detectors for rooms and contact sensors for doors and windows, all of which can be attached with double-sided tape. The wireless motion-detecting video cameras that also can be used in these systems tend to get a lot of attention—there's a certain gee-whiz factor using your smartphone or tablet to see what's going on in your living room from anywhere in the world—but video cameras are not as important as the other components for actually deterring break-ins.

With most DIY systems, you choose whether to receive a text message, an automated phone call or both whenever a sensor or video camera is triggered. Many also can be controlled manually with a wireless keypad that you affix near an entranceway and/or with a key-chain remote.

Drawback: Most DIY systems depend on the Wi-Fi network in your home, so they might not fully function if you lose electrical power unless they have a battery backup.

A basic, entry-level DIY system starts at about $200,* while an elaborate system with lots of additional sensors and cameras can run several thousand dollars. A comparable entry-level professional home security service for a small house typically charges a $99 installation fee and a $40 monthly monitoring fee with a mandatory 36-month contract (that is a savings of $1,340 with the average DIY system).

WHAT TO BUY

There are more than two dozen companies offering DIY home security systems, ranging from well-known brands to start-ups. *Consider these three factors when you choose…*

• **Price.** Most DIY systems are cheaper than a professional home security service when you consider that with DIY, you might not have any outside monitoring to pay for. But there is a wide range of how much you can spend.

• **Size of your house.** For a small apartment, a very limited DIY system with base station and contact sensor on the front door may be enough. A large house may require a system that's easy and affordable to expand and offers you options such as range extenders that strengthen Wi-Fi signals to reach rooms far from the router.

• **Type of protection you need.** Most systems offer a basic security package and let you customize it to your needs by adding additional sensors, sirens, cameras and remotes. But you may want a system that also offers additional types of protection beyond break-ins. For example, some systems have carbon monoxide sensors and flood sensors. Others have key-chain remotes that elderly parents can carry around in the house to alert you via smartphone if they have an emergency.

My favorite DIY systems now…

• **iSmartAlarm**—best very basic, inexpensive system. The starter package comes with a base station, two door/window sensors, a motion sensor and two key-chain remotes. It took me just 15 minutes to open the box and get the system up and running.

Cost: $199.

*Prices subject to change.

Note: The starter package does not include a camera, but you can buy one for an additional $150. iSmartAlarm.com

• **Piper Pro**—best for home owners who want a system that provides more flexibility and greater potential coverage. You get a base station with a Piper NV night-vision video camera and your choice of three other items (for example, you can choose door/window sensors or smart plugs that plug into existing electrical outlets and allow you to automate lights and appliances and turn them on and off remotely).

Cost: $349.99. GetPiper.com

• **Iris by Lowe's**—best for a larger house or if you want home automation as well as security. To use Iris for security and/or home automation, you'll need to buy the Smart Hub—the brains of the system—and then add on what you want. The basic home security package comes with a motion detector, two door/window sensors and an alarm keypad. What sets Iris apart is the wealth of affordable options—more than 60 add-on devices for security and home automation, including a programmable thermostat ($99)…smart plugs ($31.49)…and an electric water heater controller ($59.99).

Cost: $59 for the hub…$99 for the basic security package. An optional $10/month plan gives you more advanced controls and lets you have up to six people notified when an alert is triggered. IrisByLowes.com

• **SimpliSafe**—best if you do not want to monitor the security system yourself but want low monitoring costs. This is a hybrid DIY/professional offering with no contract. You install the system, but it is professionally monitored, so when an alarm is triggered, the system makes a cellular phone call to a dispatcher. The Economy package consists of a base station, a wireless keypad, three door/window sensors, one motion sensor and a key-chain remote. Extra sensors are available, and there is a battery backup for the base station and a cellular backup in case the power goes out.

Cost: $259.95 for equipment plus a $14.99 to $24.99/month fee, depending on the options you want. SimpliSafe.com

Home Security System Scams

Steven J. Weisman, Esq., attorney and senior lecturer in the department of law, tax and financial planning at Bentley University in Waltham, Massachusetts. He is founder of the scam-information website Scamicide.com and author of *The Truth About Avoiding Scams*.

A home security system monitored by a security company is supposed to increase your safety and protect your property—but scammers and burglars have worked up some ways to turn these systems to their advantage and victimize home owners who have them.

How scams like this work: You receive a call from what you think is your security company saying that there's a problem with your system that must be fixed...or that your system is due for a free upgrade. Soon a technician appears at your door.

This technician might have a shirt or an ID tag that identifies him/her as an employee of the security company. (In some versions, there is no initial phone call—a technician simply arrives unexpectedly. A legitimate home security company will not do this.)

But this technician actually is a criminal who learned which security company you use from the sign posted on your lawn or in your window. If you give him access to your security system, he might case your home to see if it is worth burglarizing and then disable your security system (or get you to divulge your security code) so that he can safely break in later. He also might say that he needs to schedule a follow-up visit, then try to get you to say when you will be unavailable so that he knows when it is safe to break in.

A variation: Rather than burglarize your home, the fake security technician might ask you to sign some paperwork that he says is routine but that actually locks you into an expensive, long-term contract with a different and untrustworthy provider.

What to do: If someone calls or shows up at your home claiming to represent your security system company, call the company using a phone number that you know to be authentic to confirm this person's identity before letting him in. If you're told this person is not with the company, refuse him entry and, if possible, jot down his license plate number and give this to the police.

If possible, swap lawn signs with a friend who uses a different security company—that way, if a scammer tries to pull this on you by phone or with a surprise visit, he will claim to work for the wrong company, immediately exposing his ruse.

How to Pack Your Digital "Go Bag"

Joseph C. Kvedar, MD, vice president of Connected Health, Partners HealthCare, a Boston-based organization that uses information technology, including mobile phones, apps and remote monitoring, to help healthcare providers and patients manage chronic conditions and improve health and wellness. A professor at Harvard Medical School, he is also author of *The Internet of Healthy Things*. In 2013, Dr. Kvedar launched the website Wellocracy.com, which provides impartial information on new personal "self-health" technologies.

We all know to keep water, ready-to-eat food and similar basic necessities packed in an emergency supply kit—aka a "go bag"—in case a natural disaster or some other crisis forces us to leave home at a moment's notice.

But these days, smartphones as well as other digital devices such as tablets offer several new options to help you and your loved ones stay safe. So-called "disaster apps" (short for "applications"—software programs that can be downloaded to mobile devices) are game changers in the way that people can now find vital information, connect with one another and respond during a disaster.

PREPARE TO PREPARE

It's important to remember that smartphones still need to be charged to operate during a crisis, so it is wise to keep a small cell phone charger with you at all times—inexpensive ones (less than $10) can be found at electronics stores, discount stores and even drugstores.

GOOD TO KNOW...

In Case of Emergency

In Case of Emergency (ICE) and flashlight apps reside on most mobile devices and do not require Wi-Fi or cell service to operate. If you don't have a cell phone that will allow you to use an ICE app, be sure to create an emergency contact card that you carry with you at all times in your wallet or purse.

For a downloadable contact card that you can print out, go to: FEMA.gov/media-library/assets/documents/108887.

Joseph C. Kvedar, MD, vice president, Connected Health, Partners HeathCare, Boston.

Good to know: Data demands for text messages are smaller, so texts may go through even if networks are overloaded during a disaster and cell phone calls can't be made.

5 PREPAREDNESS APPs

To stay safe, take some time—before you need them—to download the apps that are most appropriate for your family. Below are five excellent disaster apps that are free of charge and can be used on both Apple and Android phones and devices...

For convenience: Put several apps into a folder (named "disaster" or something similar).

The following apps require Wi-Fi or cell service...

•**American Red Cross** (at RedCross.org/mobile-apps/emergency-app) is a good all-in-one app that offers 35 different alerts for severe weather (including hurricanes, winter storms and earthquakes) and a map to open Red Cross shelters. You receive text alerts whenever severe weather is predicted. With this app, you can monitor these conditions in your own area plus the locations of your loved ones.

Great feature: With "Family Safe," you can use this app to tell loved ones that an alert has been issued in their area and check to be sure they are safe.

•**Winter Survival Kit** (go to ag.NDSU.edu/extension/apps/winter-survival-kit). Created by North Dakota State University, this app will help you find your location if you are stranded in severe winter weather, call 911 and notify your friends and family.

Great feature: The app's "gas calculator" estimates how long you can run your engine on your remaining fuel. The app also reminds you every 30 minutes to periodically turn off your engine to check your exhaust pipe for snow buildup—a crucial step in avoiding deadly carbon monoxide poisoning.

•**Outbreaks Near Me by HealthMap** (at HealthMap.org/outbreaksnearme). This app shows all the current disease outbreaks in your community, including up-to-date tallies of flu cases in your area.

Great feature: You can set the app to alert you via text whenever an outbreak is occurring in your area.

•**ReUnite** (log on to lpf.nlm.nih.gov/People Locator-ReUnite) allows the public to report missing and/or found people after a large-scale disaster.

Great feature: This app allows you to upload photos and a physical description of a missing loved one to help disaster relief personnel find that person after an emergency.

•**Federal Emergency Management Agency** (FEMA.gov/mobile-app) gives tips on what to do before, during and after more than 20 types of disasters, as well as the locations of open shelters and disaster recovery centers in your area, which offer crucial services during floods, earthquakes and other natural disasters.

Great feature: This app's "Disaster Reporter" allows you to upload photos of damage and recovery efforts in your area.

Index